Pact's Multicultural BookSource

An Opinionated Guide to Books that Reflect, Open, and Address Issues for:

adoptive families
blended families
families of color
foster families
interracial families
gay or lesbian families
kinship adoption
multiracial families
single-parent families
families with special-needs kids
transracial families

Pact
An Adoption Alliance

Second Edition

Cover design by Gail Steinberg and Beth Hall

Text design by Gail Steinberg and Beth Hall

Printed in the United States of America

information exploration affirmation

1700 Montgomery Street, Suite 111
San Francisco, CA 94111
415-221-6857 (voice)
510-482-2089 (fax)
800-750-7590 (birth parent line)
www.pactadopt.org(website)
info@pactadopt.org (email)

Dedicated to Matthew and Elijah Weller

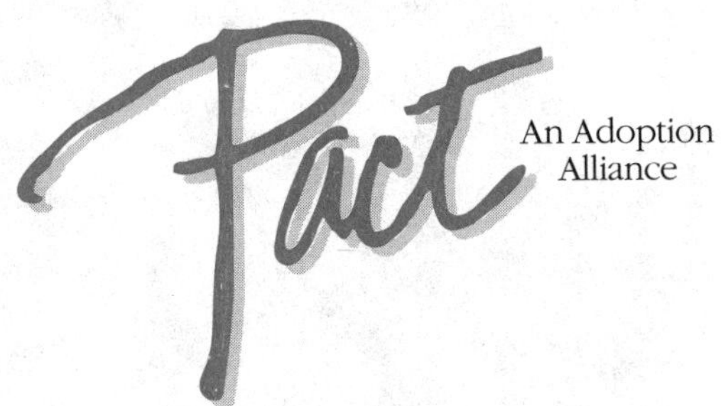

Pact Partners

The second edition of Pact's BookSource, represents Pact's continuing commitment to our mission of providing resources, information and support to adoptive families of children of color. As is true so often in the nonprofit world, producing this catalogue would have been impossible were it not for the extraordinary efforts, donations and sponsorship of many individuals and corporations. On behalf of the children and all who love and care for them, we offer our deepest appreciation to those who have contributed to this important effort.

This reference guide has been made possible through the generous financial support of Target Stores and Mervyn's California, family-oriented companies serving as good neighbors to their communities. Their innovative partnerships with local community leaders like Pact reflect their joint commitment to improving the quality of life for all families — and particularly for children. Nordstrom, Inc., another outstanding corporate neighbor, provided additional funding at a critical moment in the production of this edition. On behalf of the children of our communities, we wish to acknowledge the essential contributions of these important corporate citizens.

Once again we offer special thanks to the Outrageous Foundation for their significant, consistent and uncommonly generous dedication to Pact's work.

We wish to thank the Junior League of Oakland-East Bay for a grant made by their enabling funds program, without which this second edition could not have been completed. As community sponsors who stepped in at a challenging moment, their generous support enabled the project to bridge a particularly difficult gap.

Pact's BookSource has also been made possible through the generous financial support of Banc of America Securities, a full-service brokerage and investment bank with offices in San Francisco. Their timely corporate commitment helped enable this edition of the BookSource.

Our thanks also to Frank and Susan Dunlevy, and to their children, for their valuable help in shepherding this project through its early stages.

Our enormous thanks go to Rebecca Weller, for her extraordinary commitment to excellence and for the many hours she has dedicated to the editing of this book. Without her meticulous regard for the catalogue's myriad details and her thoughtful attention to content, we could not have produced a work of this scope.

Jeff Stranger of The Print Connection has shown a level of dedication to this project that has made an enormous difference. We are very grateful for his efforts.

The first edition of this reference guide was produced under Federal Grant #90-C0-093, Administration of Children, Youth and Families. This second edition rests on the foundation of the initial effort, enabling us to include new publications, update pertinent information and expand our reach

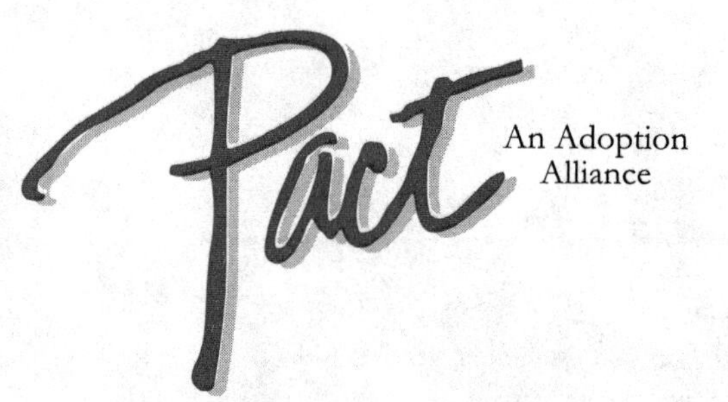
Pact
An Adoption
Alliance

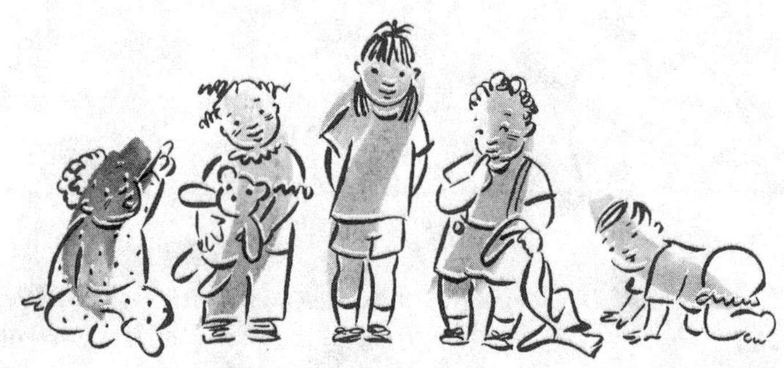

Contents

Why Reading Matters

James is an African American six-year-old with white parents who rarely asks questions about having been adopted. Recently, he and his mother read Two Birthdays for Beth *(Gay Lynn Cronin, Perspective Press). Though in the past James had never spoken explicitly about his feelings on adoption, he had heard his parents talk about it with his sister; it was a familiar family topic.*

"I wonder why Beth isn't sure she likes having two birthdays?" asked his mother.

"She wishes she just came out of her mommy's tummy. Blah, blah, blah," James said. "She doesn't always want to talk about it."

"Does she feel sad?" mom asked.

"Yes, and sorta mad," said James. "Sometimes she gets mad at herself but she tries not to, 'cause she didn't do anything wrong. Her other parents loved her. So do her real mom and dad." (To James, "real parents" means his adoptive parents.)

His mom told him she could understand why Beth felt sort of mad and sad and that she thought it was OK to feel that way. They continued reading, and when they had finished the book, James got up and spent ten minutes searching his room for his copy of Love You Forever *(Robert Munsch, Firefly Press). Mom and James cuddled up in their favorite reading chair, finding particular pleasure in the comfort of the story's refrain: "I love you forever, I like you for always. As long as I'm living, My baby you'll be."*

By attributing his own feelings to a fictional character, James found a way to address some of his deepest concerns. He is certainly not alone is discovering that books can provide a means of expression when direct communication feels too threatening. It is sometimes surprising to discover that both the universal and the unique can be found in just about every human situation, aspects that differentiate it from any other experience and elements that link it to the essentially human. In reading books reflecting the world's great variety of lives, ideas, attitudes, beliefs, histories, all readers (young and old) discover that within the great differences, there are tremendous commonalities.

Just as most of us are gratified to discover characters who resemble us, whether in appearance or attitude or background or circumstance, many adopted kids of color love books that include encounter characters who resemble them in obvious and subtle ways. Such books are hard to find in ordinary bookstores. Sure, in February you might find a bookstore display celebrating Black History Month and a table offering a dozen books with African American characters; in the "Parenting" section you'll find a few books about adoption mixed into the selections on breastfeeding and baby names. But to be relegated to limited sections and "special" occasions both marginalizes race and adoption and reflects only a token sampling of the wonderful array available for those who embrace these issues at the center of our lives.

For children like James, whose lives don't fit the fantasized "Ozzie and Harriet" stereotype (and whose really does?), finding stories whose characters resemble themselves can be an exhilarating and transformative event. So it is, too, for parents and other adults touched directly by issues of adoption and race. To stumble upon a description and analysis of attachment disorder, for example, can be a "Eureka!" moment for a parent struggling to understand a newly-adopted toddler. And not only can books parallel our experience; they can lead us to worlds otherwise unknown, offering us insight into unfamiliar ways, introducing us to new points of view. By exposing our children to the endless varieties of human relationships, we teach them not only about accepting others but about accepting themselves as well. So, in seeking books for your family, please consider those stories that differ from your family's experiences — of adoption history, cultural and racial identities, and family life — as well as ones that echo and reflect it.

Reading can change our hearts and minds, intrigue and challenge us, make us laugh at ourselves. We hope Pact's BookSource will help you fill your homes with the diversity, wonder, and beauty of books.

Pact An Adoption Alliance

How To Use PACT'S BookSource

Classifying books into appropriate age levels for children is an inexact science. Each child is unique. Our recommendations are rough guidelines only, for children's interests don't always depend on their ages: Imari, at four years old, immerses herself in one book's bright pictures, while her ten-year-old brother Elijah reads over her shoulder, intrigued by the story of a big brother's adjustment to the adoption of a younger sibling. But to serve as a rough guide, Pact's BookSource is organized into general categories: books for infants and toddlers; preschoolers and early school-age; school-agers; teens and young adults; and adults. Our catalogue is further organized by three topics: adoption, racial issues, and family life. And "for all ages" offers books whose appeal defies categorization.

This reference guide, containing annotated listings of approximately 1,200 English-language (and sometimes bilingual) books, is designed to provide access to the world's wonders and to increase awareness of and pride in diverse identities. For readers dissatisfied with the limited guides and catalogues otherwise available, we hope Pact's BookSource will be your principal source for current, concise and informative referrals to the widest possible range of books related even implicitly to adoption and multicultural issues. For each book, we include a wealth of information to maximize the catalogue's utility — not just the usual suspects like title, author, illustrator, publisher, date of publication, number of pages, price and ISBN identification number, but additional tools to make your search fruitful and discerning: a synopsis or summary of contents; excerpts from published reviews; awards received; "who should read" guide; age level; a list of relevant keywords; and Pact's own rating of the book.

"Books are the food of youth," wrote Cicero. And the best nourishment comes from the best books. But how do you know which books will help a transracially-adopted teenage girl to appreciate herself as not just unusual but extraordinary? Or enable you to breeze past the merely adequate books to find just the right story to inspire an early-reader's love of adventure and loyalty? Or help a little one cut her teeth (literally and figuratively!) on sturdy rhyming board books celebrating children who happen to share her curly hair and chocolate skin? So be forewarned: our reviews are opinionated. In compiling this exhaustive catalogue, our goal has been to serve as a kind of radar screen, helping you to locate books reflecting your interests and to filter the ordinary from the compelling, the "must-haves" from those that are (in our informed and opinionated opinion) a waste of trees. In order to be as helpful as possible, we have even included some books we hate, enabling you to make the most informed selections. We are most impressed by books that deal with complicated issues like race and adoption without being either sugary or heavy-handed. We are also suckers for original thought, inspired use of language, accurate information, glorious illustrations, and beautiful presentations (high-quality papers, strong graphics). With just a few exceptions for those we could not review prior to publication, every book has been read and rated by one of our reviewers. Your feedback and comments are always welcome.

Note: About 3% of the books are currently unrated. A blank "rating" box does not suggest that we dislike the book, but only that we have not yet had a chance to review it ourselves.

This is how the Pact Rating Scale works:

@@@@ We Love This Book!
@@@ Excellent
@@ O k
@ Lackluster
✶ Read at your own risk

Books For The Youngest Among Us

"For your most important twenty minutes today... read with a child."
—Rosemary Wells, American Booksellers for Children

Reading aloud offers you and your child a private world of exploration, conversation and love. These sturdy board books offer multicultural representations, bright illustrations and a minimum of text, making them perfect for babies and toddlers.

Here are some ideas to help you make reading time more fun:

- Start with simple books; very young children enjoy clear, bright illustrations;
- Vary your voice to represent different characters or to dramatize the visual narrative;
- Follow the words with your finger to help demonstrate the relation of story to words;
- Talk about the pictures, but don't stay on one page too long;
- If your child finds it hard to sit still, try using your own words to tell the story;
- Talk about the story after reading it;
- Make reading a time to cuddle and relax. Let your child tell you when to turn the page.

Rating

BABY BORN

A multicultural lift-the-flap book celebrating babies.

Hooray for wonder-full watercolors! This sturdy lift-the-flap book celebrates babies of all heritages, following them from birth, through the seasons, to that joyful first birthday. Each experience contains a surprise under every flap. "An adorable lift-the-flap book that works," writes Kirkus Reviews; Smithsonian named it one of their "Notable books for children."

Keywords

Multicultural

Age Range,

Preschool, early school-age

Author: Anastasia Suen

Author: Chih-Wei Chang

ISBN# 1-880000954 *Date Published,* 1998 *Price,* $ 6.95

Publisher, Lee & Low Books *Pages,* 20

Rating

BABY DANCE

"Dance, little baby/Move to and fro Coo and crow, baby/There you go.'

From Kirkus Reviews: "An African American father croons to his baby daughter while engaging in a spontaneous and steadily more exuberant dance. A boisterous romp."

Keywords

African American, Board Book

Age Range,

Baby

Author: Ann Taylor

ISBN# 694012068 *Date Published,* 1999 *Price,* $ 5.95

Publisher, Harper Collins *Pages,*

BABY FACES

Though babies can't talk, their faces show us how they feel.

A padded board book, sure to capture the attention of the youngest among us who love to look at other babies. Multicultural photographs of babies' faces.

Keywords

Board Book, Multicultural

Age Range,

Baby

Editor: DK Publications

ISBN# 789436507 *Date Published,* 1998 *Price,* $ 4.95

Publisher, DK Pub Merchandise *Pages,* 10

BABY SAYS

Sometimes, big brother likes playing with baby, but sometimes he doesn't.

Our goal in seeking books for the very youngest among us is to find those that positively reflect children of diverse heritages. In *Baby Says*, the reader follows two African American brothers at play. Baby is so young that he can speak only a few words, but in his repertoire are many tricks to get his big brother's attention. As with all of John Steptoe's books, this one has great illustrations. *Baby Says* is a sturdy board book that will withstand the demands of a baby's eager "reading."

Keywords

Family Life, Diversity, Multiracial, African American, Black Identity, Multicultural

Age Range,

Baby

Illustrator: John Steptoe

John Steptoe, a two-time Caldecott Honor Book recipient, is the author of *Jumping Mouse; Baby Says; Creativity; Mufaro's Beautiful Daughter* and *Stevie.*

ISBN# 0-688-11855-0 *Date Published,* *Price,* $ 3.95

Publisher, Morrow *Pages,* 32

BABY'S COLORS

Rating 

A vibrantly illustrated baby board book!

Help your little ones learn colors as they follow along with you. *Baby's Colors* is part of a collection of sturdy board books from Golden Books. It makes a fine companion to *Peekaboo Baby*. The illustrations are warm, clear, and bright, inviting and filled with realistic detail. You and your children will enjoy the rich illustrations of African American characters. There is a minimum of text, but even the youngest reader will enjoy the book's explicit and implicit messages about colors: that the world is filled with colorful objects, and that children of color are significant members of that world.

Keywords

African American, Board Book, Family Life, Black Identity

Age Range:

Baby

Author: Naomi MacMillan

ISBN# 307128733 *Date Published:* *Price:* $ 4.95

Publisher: Golden *Pages:* 32

BIG FRIEND, LITTLE FRIEND

Rating 

Little friend and big friend sure know how to have fun!

Two friends make their way through the familiar activities that make up a baby's day. Greenfield and Gilchrist are two of our most talented creators of books for young children and *Big Friend, Little Friend* is a most winning combination of talents. The illustrations are charming; the pages made of sturdy cardboard.

Keywords

Board Book, African American, Multicultural

Age Range:

Baby

Author: Eloise Greenfield

Illustrator: Jan S. Gilchrist

Eloise Greenfield is the author of *Nathaniel Talking; Big Friend, Little Friend* and many more.

ISBN# 863162045 *Date Published:* 1991 *Price:* $ 5.95

Publisher: Black Butterfly *Pages:*

CLAP HANDS

A board book for babies, with multiracial illustrations.

Another of the appealing simple rhyming texts for the littlest; all the babies are adorable and they happen to be of many races. Helen Oxenbury is known for her delight/full illustrations of very young children and, like her others, *Clap Hands* offers a clear, bright, pick-me-up-and-tickle-me message that children and adults can enjoy together. There is a touch of whimsy to Oxenbury books that will appeal both to your child and to you. *Clap Hands* is a sturdy board book, designed to withstand whatever adventures your child may take it on.

Keywords

Board Book, Multicultural, Multiracial, Family Life

Age Range:

Baby

Author-Illustrator: Helen Oxenbury

Helen Oxenbury is a great favorite for her delightfully illustrated multicultural books for very young children.

ISBN# 689819846 *Date Published:* 1987 *Price:* $ 6.99

Publisher: Macmillan *Pages:* 10

EAT, BABIES, EAT!

A must-have baby board book!

What great games babies can play! They can find their ears and eyes and toes, too. Best of all, when babies find their mouths, they can have a treat! Angela Medearis has created a truly fun-filled little book about babies that you and your little one will both enjoy. The infants in the illustrations are of many races, all darling, and all positive reflections of children from a variety of racial and ethnic backgrounds. What is nicest about this book is the diversity of the children reflected and the balance of images of children of all different races.

Keywords

Board Book, Multiracial, Multicultural, Family Life, Diversity

Age Range:

Baby

Author: Angela Medearis

Angela Medearis is the author of *Eat, Babies, Eat!; Too Much Talk,* and more.

ISBN# 1-56402-257-9 *Date Published:* *Price:* $ 4.95

Publisher: Candlewick *Pages:*

FACES

Happy, sad, angry and more. Faces of children expressing their feelings.

Cute illustrations and a multiracial approach do not make up for the fact that the only child with brown skin is used to illustrate an "angry" face, and that the "brave" child is blond with light skin. Though Jan Piénknowski is a prolific and successful author of books for young children, we think she and her editors missed the negative connotations implicit in the illustrations for this book. Believing as we do in the destructive power of all such messages, however subtle and unintended, we do not recommend this book.

Keywords

Board Book, Multiracial, Core Issues (Feelings)

Age Range.

Baby

Author: Jan Piénknowski

Nikki Grimes is the author of *Baby's Bedtime, Meet Danitra Brown, Something On My Mind,* and *Wild Wild Hair.* Tom Feelings is the illustrator of *Something On My Mind.*

ISBN# 67172846 — Date Published. 1990 — Price. $ 2.95

Publisher. Little Simon — Pages. 24

Rating

HELEN OXENBURY'S 4 BABY BOARD BOOKS

Oxenbury's books present images of children of all different races.

The fun in Oxenbury's books comes because each page of delightful multicultural illustrations presents an active image with a simple phrase that children can imitate. Made of sturdy cardboard for little fingers.

Keywords

Board Book, Family Life, Multicultural, Multiracial

Age Range.

Baby

Author-Illustrator: Helen Oxenbury

Helen Oxenbury is a great favorite for her delightfully illustrated multicultural books for very young children.

ISBN# 689806086 — Date Published. 1996 — Price. $ 8.99

Publisher. Little Simon — Pages.

HERE ARE MY HANDS

Head, fingers, knees and toes; eyes and ears and mouth and nose...

Here is a book for little ones learning to describe themselves that invites creative and spontaneous responses. Bright colors, clear illustrations, and a sturdy board book format.

Keywords

Multicultural, Board Book

Age Range.

Baby

Author: John Archambault

Illustrator: Ted Rand

ISBN# 805059113 — Date Published. 1998 — Price. $ 6.95

Publisher. Henry Holt — Pages. 26

I LOVE YOU SUN, I LOVE YOU MOON

A head start for baby on the beauty of the world.

"I love you earth, and you love me." A board book celebrating nature for the youngest, depicting multicultural characters in charming illustrations. Books in Print writes, "DePaola's familiar, charming illustrations of chubby, round-faced children carry this book, which teaches an appreciation for the natural world. The text is the epitome of simplicity. Each page proclaims affection for some element of nature, 'I love you, flower,' 'I love you, stars,' etc. ending with. 'And you love me.' The bright artwork populated by multiethnic youngsters conveys the environmental message."

Keywords

Board Book, Diversity, Multicultural, Multiracial

Age Range.

Baby

Author: Karen Pandell

Illustrator: Tomie DePaola

Tom Feelings is the illustrator of *Something On My Mina* and *To Be A Slave.*

ISBN# 0-399-22628-1 — Date Published. 1994 — Price. $ 5.95

Publisher. Putnam's Sons — Pages. 18

Rating

I'M SPECIAL, I'M ME

You're special in your own way – like your favorite characters from The Puzzle Place.

A parade of favorite characters from *The Puzzle Place,* an award-winning public TV show, tell toddlers what they like and what makes them special. This is an especially small board book that can be managed by very small hands or tucked into baby-sized pockets. The cartoon-like illustrations are clear and bright in bold primary colors, and there is a minimum of text. With images of children with a variety of skin colors and physical features, this book conveys a positive message about racial diversity and self-esteem.

Keywords

Board Book, Self-Esteem

Age Range:

Baby

Author: Ken Skalski

ISBN# 0-448-41298-5 *Date Published:* 1996 *Price:* $ 4.50

Publisher: Putnam Pub Group *Pages:* 16

Rating

IF I WERE A BUNNY, OR A PANDA, OR A...

Your child's photograph illustrates this charming story!

A great concept book for babies. What better self-esteem builder for your child than his or her own picture made central throughout? Once you paste in your child's picture on the page provided in the back of this book, your child's face will illustrate every single page! Though the text is simple, the fabulous illustrations make this simple book amusing and novel. It is constructed of heavy laminated cardboard, perfect for little hands to carry around. We love this book and are very sure every member of your family, particularly your child, will love it, too.

Keywords

Board Book, Self-Esteem

Age Range:

Baby

Author: Deborah Bennett D'Andrea

Illustrator: Michael B. Ayers

ISBN# 1-878338-00-5 *Date Published:* 1989 *Price:* $ 5.99

Publisher: Picture Me Books *Pages:* 12

LET'S PRETEND (A JUMP AT THE SUN BOARD BOOK)

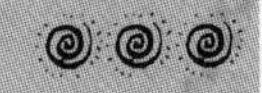

Have fun! The sky's the limit. Have a jump at the sun.

Let's Pretend follows a delightful three-year-old girl in imaginative play: having fun running a store, baking a cake, driving a car, and acting like a grown-up. Great illustrations enliven this sturdy board book for babies and toddlers. It's a nice addition that the child depicted just happens to have brown skin.

Keywords

Board Book, African American, Family Life

Age Range:

Baby

Author: Dessie Moore

ISBN# 694005916 *Date Published:* 1994 *Price:* $ 5.95

Publisher: Harper Collins *Pages:* 10

MAMA BIRD, BABY BIRD

A reassuring board book about mamas and children.

Joshua and sister find a nest of baby birds and watch the mother bird feed and love the birds, just as the children's own mother does for them. This book's simple but significant message is that parents take care of their children, keeping them safe from harm. Angela Johnson's drawings are realistic and wonderfully detailed, using warm, clear colors and depicting simple scenes. The text is short and easy to understand, making in total a wholly affirmative story about family life for toddlers. The positive reflections of African American children make this book especially appealing.

Keywords

Board Book, Mothers, Family Life, African American

Age Range:

Baby

Author: Angela Johnson

Angela Johnson is the author of *Mama Bird, Baby Bird; The Aunt In Our House; Julius, The Leaving Morning; Gone From Home; Heaven;* and more.

ISBN# 0-531-06848-X *Date Published:* 1994 *Price:* $ 4.95

Publisher: Orchard *Pages:* 12

Rating

MAMA, DO YOU LOVE ME?

An Inuit daughter search for the limit of her mother's love in board book format.

A well-loved favorite, now available in a board book edition. This imaginative and reassuring story set in Alaska tells about unconditional love, presenting a model for terrific parenting. Horn Book calls it "A beautiful combination of a rich culture and a universal theme."

Keywords

Board Book, Core Issues (Feelings)

Age Range,

Baby

Author: Barbara M. Joosse

Illustrator: Barbara Lavalee

ISBN# 811821315 Date Published, 1998 Price, $ 6.95

Publisher, Chronicle Books Pages, 24

Rating

MAX'S BATH

Ruby gives her brother Max two baths, but he winds up dirtier than ever.

This "first book" features Rosemary Wells's irrepressible bunny Max. Max is a well-loved character, the star of his very own series of funny stories which have only recently been reissued. In *Max's Bath*, the more Max bathes, the dirtier he gets! Boat! he exclaims as his cup of sherbet slowly sinks in the tub. After two baths and one shower, he's finally clean. This wonderful story presenting realistic characters is funny — and babies love to chew on it (nontoxic, of course).

Keywords

Board Book

Age Range,

Baby

Author: Rosemary Wells

Rosemary Wells is the author of *Read To Your Bunny; Max's Bath; Max's Bedtime; Max's Toys;"Max's Ride;* and *Max's Breakfast.'*

ISBN# 803722664 Date Published, 1998 Price, $ 5.99

Publisher, Dial Pages, 12

MAYBE MY BABY

A parent imagines the variety of possibilities that lie ahead for these lively toddlers.

A love poem from parent to child, this board book is illustrated in a way that babies love — with funny photos of other babies of various races and cultures.

Keywords

Diversity, Family Life, Multiracial, Multicultural

Age Range,

Baby

Author: Irene O'Book

Paula Hibble

ISBN# 694008729 Date Published, 1997 Price, $ 5.95

Publisher, Harper Row Pages, 14

MY HAIR IS BEAUTIFUL... BECAUSE IT IS MINE!

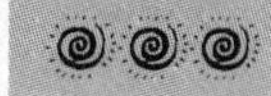

A wonderful, sturdy board book for babies about beautiful African American hair.

Realistic drawings and positive text highlight a variety of African American children as they describe their hair textures and styles in this book for the youngest among us. Paula DeJoie says she wrote this book because she felt it was an intolerable omission when she discovered that there was nothing in print to affirm the beautiful hair and skin of her own Black children. For the sake of all children of color, we are so glad she created this book and its companion, *My Skin Is Brown,* both of which emphasize cultural pride and individual value.

Keywords

African American, Hair, Board Book, Self-Esteem, Racial/Ethnic Identity, Black Identity

Age Range,

Baby

Author-Illustrator: Paula DeJoie

Paula DeJoie is the author/ illustrator of *My Skin Is Brown* and *My Hair Is Beautiful.* She lives in northern California.

ISBN# 0-86316-219-3 Date Published, 1996 Price, $ 5.95

Publisher, Black Butterfly Children's Books Pages, 10

Rating

MY SKIN IS BROWN

An easy -to-hold board book that celebrates the skin tones of African American children.

Words and pictures celebrate the brown skin tones of African American children. Whether deep and dark like chocolate, creamy brown like toffee, or spicy brown like cinnamon, each shade suggests a positive association and promotes viewing all shades of Black as beautiful. In the same genre as *Color Me Proud* and *All The Colors of the Earth,* this delightful little book does a wonderful job of presenting a range of colors to the very youngest children, all with esteem-building connotations. A sturdy, cardboard, easy to hold board book for the very youngest readers.

Keywords

Board Book, African American, Racial/Ethnic Identity, Self Esteem, Board Book, Black Identity

Age Range:

Baby

Editor: Jan Colbert

Jan Colbert wrote *My Skin Is Brown. Dear Dr. King* was edited by Jan Colbert and Ann McMillan Harms with photographs by Ernest C. Withers and Roy Cajero.

ISBN# 0-86316-239-8 *Date Published:* 1996 *Price:* $ 5.95

Publisher: Black Butterfly *Pages:* 12

Rating

PEEKABOO BABY!

A board book about how Baby loves to play peekaboo. Can you play, too?

Its clear, warm–toned illustrations and minimal text lend appeal to this story of an African American baby boy and all the ways he learns to play peekaboo. It is a companion to *Baby's Colors*, also a sturdy board book, which are made to last of nontoxic cardboard construction. The drawings are realistic and well-detailed and the text conveys the simple pleasures of first learning how to play with another person. The game of "peekaboo" is known the world over, and this book reinforces the universality of this human behavior.

Keywords

Board Book, African American, Black Identity, Games and Activities

Age Range:

Baby

Author: Ray Simmons

ISBN# 307128717 *Date Published:* 1996 *Price:* $ 4.00

Publisher: Golden *Pages:* 18

PRETTY BROWN FACE

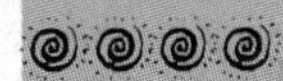

Celebrating beautiful babies!

A delightful book celebrating the beauty and delight of warm brown skin. Companion book to *Shake, Shake, Shake* and *Watch Me Dance.*

Keywords

African American, Self-Esteem, Black Identity

Age Range:

Baby

Illustrator: J. Brian Pinkney

Illustrator: Andrea Pinkney

J. Brian Pinkney is the award-winning illustrator of *Shake Shake Shake; Watch Me Dance; Happy Birthday, Dr. Martin Luther King; Max Found Two Sticks;* and *Mirandy & Brother Wind.*

ISBN# 152006435 *Date Published:* 1997 *Price:* $ 4.95

Publisher: Whitman *Pages:* 14

RAINBOW IS OUR FACE

Positive reflections for the youngest among us.

Two-year-old Chelsea and her older sister spend the day painting rainbows and then have a dream about rainbows in the night. A positive picture of family life, one in which the girls just happen to be African American.

Keywords

African American, Board Book

Age Range:

Baby

Author: Laura Pegram

ISBN# 863162177 *Date Published:* 1995 *Price:* $ 8.95

Publisher: Black Butterfly *Pages:* 12

Rating

RUNAWAY BUNNY

Since its publication in 1942, The Runaway Bunny *has never been out of print.*

A young bunny decides to run away: "'If you run away,' said his mother, 'I will run after you. For you are my little bunny.'" And so begins a must-have story for every child who has ever tested — or might ever test — a parent's love. Margaret Wise Brown believed that the best children's books speak about the world through images near to their experience. The repetitive, predictable text in *The Runaway Bunny* encourages young children to follow along, giving voice to the lines. In each of the colored drawings, little bunny is hidden somewhere, so readers have to find him. A great board book, also available in Spanish and in book-and-cassette boxed editions.

Keywords

Board Book, Core Issues (Feelings), Family Life

Age Range:

Baby

Author: Margaret Wise Brown

Illustrator: Clement Hurd

Margaret Wise Brown is the author of *Goodnight Moon; Baby Animals*; and more.

ISBN# 61074292 Date Published: 1999 Price: $ 7.95

Publisher: HarperCollins Pages:

Rating

SHAKE, SHAKE, SHAKE

Explore the joy of movement!

A baby boy discovers a popular African percussion instrument, the shekere. Companion book to *Pretty Brown Face* and *Watch Me Dance.*

Keywords

African American, Music and Dance, Black Identity

Age Range:

Baby

Illustrator: J. Brian Pinkney

Illustrator: Andrea Pinkney

J. Brian Pinkney is the award-winning illustrator of *Shake Shake Shake; Watch Me Dance; Happy Birthday, Dr. Martin Luther King; Max Found Two Sticks*; and *Mirandy & Brother Wind.*

ISBN# 015200632X Date Published: 1997 Price: $ 4.95

Publisher: Harcourt Brace Pages:

WALKING WITH GOD BOARD BOOKS: YES I CAN

Traditional religious teachings in a photo-filled board book.

Heidi Bratton, an award-winning photojournalist, gently introduces and celebrates traditional family values and religious teachings. *Yes I Can* is a translation of the Ten Commandments.

Keywords

Multicultural, Multiracial, Religion, Christianity

Age Range:

Baby

Author: Heidi Bratton

ISBN# 809166399 Date Published: 1997 Price: $ 5.95

Publisher: Paul Pages: 14

WATCH ME DANCE

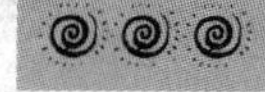

Come dance!

A young girl entertains her brother by clapping her hands and stomping her feet. A companion book to *Shake, Shake, Shake* and *Pretty Brown Face.*

Keywords

African American, Music and Dance, Black Identity, Sibling Issues

Age Range:

Baby

Illustrator: J. Brian Pinkney

Illustrator: Andrea Pinkney

J. Brian Pinkney is the award-winning illustrator of *Shake Shake Shake; Watch Me Dance; Happy Birthday, Dr. Martin Luther King; Max Found Two Sticks*; and *Mirandy & Brother Wind.*

ISBN# 152006311 Date Published: 1997 Price: $ 4.95

Publisher: Whitman Pages:

WAVE GOOD-BYE

Rating

"Wave your elbows, wave your toes. Wave your tongue and wave your nose."

Put on your favorite music and push the chairs back to make a big space. The fun begins when your little ones find their own ways to wave their elbows, eyes, ears, knees, bellies, lips,backsides, chins, and more. A get-up-and-join-in story, even more fun if parents wave, too.

Keywords

Multicultural, Multiracial, Games and Activities, Music and Dance

Age Range:

Preschool, early school-age

Author: Rob Reid

ISBN# 188000030X *Date Published:* 1996 *Price:* $ 14.95

Publisher: Lee & Low Books *Pages:*

WELCOMING BABIES

Rating

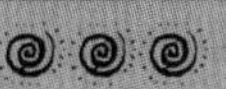

A look at the diverse ways people around the globe treasure new life.

A celebration of life and diversity. As you and your little one explore ways of welcoming babies from all over the world, you can share stories about your own traditions and cultures. This is a nice introduction to the idea that a family's rituals, small and large, help define each family as unique. For families first connected through adoption, respecting and developing family traditions can be particularly meaningful, for rituals can affirm the understanding that families belong together not because of how they look or came to be family, but for what they do. Endearing illustrations.

Keywords

Cultural History, Holidays and Celebrations, Diversity, Birthdays

Age Range:

Baby

Author: Margy Burns Knight

Illustrator: Anne Sibley O'Brien

Margy Burns Knight also wrote *Welcoming Babies* and *Talking Walls*, illustrated by Anne Sibley O'Brien.

ISBN# 884481246 *Date Published:* 1994 *Price:* $ 7.95

Publisher: Tilbury *Pages:* 40

YOU ARE MY PERFECT BABY

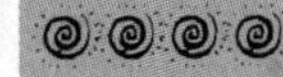

A very appealing new book for the youngest

In the kind of verse that makes your heart swell up and your eyes get teary, National Book Award winner Joyce Carol Thomas celebrates all that's precious about a new baby. Bennett's warm-toned, realistic illustrations interpret each line of verse with love and care.

Keywords

Multicultural, Board Book, African American

Age Range:

Baby

Author: Joyce Carol Thomas

Illustrator: Nneka Bennett

Joyce Carol Thomas is the author of *Brown Honey in Broomwheat Tea* and *I Have Heard of a Land.*

ISBN# 694010960 *Date Published:* 1999 *Price:* $ 5.95

Publisher: Harper Row *Pages:* 12

Preschoolers & Early School-age

Children in this age group are always busy and always thinking. In the preschool and early-elementary years, the ability to imagine is essential to a child's mental development. Exposure to books, to their narrative and pictures, to an adult's enthusiasm for reading, is an important element of future success; books encourage and promote the use of imagination. In developing these selections, we've sought books that are bright and funny, helping to catch and stimulate young children's eager interest and intense curiosity. When reading aloud together, give your child the chance to ask plenty of questions — sometimes children will want to take the story in a totally new and intriguing direction. Be flexible and go with their lead. Pleasure is the key to a lifelong love of reading.

For these pre-readers and early-readers, we've sought to offer a broad and diverse collection of books which can be enjoyed by all children while being particularly significant to adopted children and children of color, who often find themselves excluded from representation in much of traditional children's literature. Stories involving adoption, non-traditional family life and racial identity — whether explicitly expressed or merely symbolically suggestive — reflect an underlying appreciation of cultural differences and similarities. In our collection, you'll find many stories flowing from the deep pool of folk literature; in making our selections from folk tales, we've tended to choose those traditional stories — or new versions of old favorites — which reflect a rich cultural heritage, in which women and girls as well as men and boys take the lead, and in which differences are recognized and celebrated rather than ignored or minimized. One key to terminology: in "picture books," the story unfolds in pictures as well as words; "I-Can-Read" books for beginning readers use a controlled vocabulary with many familiar words that children can sound out.

Rating

ABBY

A fun picture book about plain old sibling rivalry and family love.

"WHY SHE ALWAYS gotta CRY LIKE THAT? ... she THINKS YOU DON'T LIKE HER... OKAY, GIRL, I LIKE YOU." Kevin was born into the family; Abby was adopted. Abby annoys Kevin but he loves her anyway. A fun picture book about plain old sibling rivalry and family love. Most children can easily identify with the problems of the main characters. One of the few books about sibling rivalry in families built by adoption that also reflect families of color. A Pact bestseller, *Abby* has become a classic because of its down to earth appeal.

Keywords

Adoption, African American, Family Life, Sibling Issues, Blended Family, Black Identity

Age Range,

Preschool, early school-age

Author: Jeanette Caines

Illustrator: Steven Kellogg

ISBN# 0-06-443049-9 Date Published, 1984 Price, $4.95

Publisher, HarperCollins Pages, 32

Rating

ADOPTED AND LOVED FOREVER

An ultra-positive Christian view of adoption.

Supposedly a young child's description of what it means to be adopted, emphasizing that parents of adopted children choose them, love them, and will never leave them, but the text sounds nothing like a child's thoughts. Full of the pabulum that some parents hope their adopted children believe about growing up adopted, it is informed by no sense of realism. Children hardly ever talk like the nameless child in this story, and the sugary sweetness may seem coercive or unattainable to a real child. Illustrations show Caucasian parents with an Asian adopted daughter.

Keywords

Adoption, Christianity

Age Range,

Preschool, early school-age

Author: Anita Dellinger

Illustrator: Patricia Mattozi

ISBN# 570041678 Date Published, 1987 Price, $5.99

Publisher, Concordia Pages, 22

ADOPTED LIKE ME

Is it okay to be adopted? Ask Ben.

Ben is a curious polar bear who was adopted at birth. He feels different from everyone because of how he came to be a member of his family. Then he make a new friend who was adopted, too. Sweet, full-color illustrations reach out to engage the reader in this reassuring and supportive story. Jeffrey LaCure's personal experience as a person who grew up adopted makes this sensitive story feel authentic and well considered. A proven favorite of young children, this book has become a Pact bestseller.

Keywords

Adoption, Family Life, Friendship, Core Issues (Feelings)

Age Range,

Preschool, early school-age

Illustrated by Author: Jeffrey R. LaCure

ISBN# 963571702 Date Published, 1993 Price, $9.95

Publisher, Adoption Advocate Pages, 24

ADOPTION IS FOR ALWAYS

Celia, age 5, has many adoption questions.

This little book presents important information about adoption in a way that a young child can understand. "But...I want you and Mommy to be my ONLY mommy and daddy!" cries Celia, who comes to know not only why her birth mother entrusted her to her parents, but also that her adoptive parents will be hers for always. Nice illustrations. Books in Print: "Celia is just beginning to understand the significance of the word adoption. Although her parents deal with her questions with honesty and love, she wonders if she was given up because she was bad. Would her birth mother take her away from her adoptive parents? One of the best titles about adoption available for young children."

Keywords

Adoption, Attachment, Core Issues (Feelings), Self-Esteem, Adopted Child, Triad Issues

Age Range,

Preschool, early school-age

Author: Linda Walvoord Girard

Linda Walvoord Girard is the author of *Adoption is for Always* and *We Adopted You, Benjamin Koo.*

ISBN# 0-8075-0187-5 Date Published, 1991 Price, $4.95

Publisher, Whitman Pages, 32

Rating

ADOPTION STORIES FOR YOUNG CHILDREN

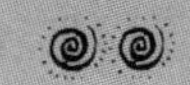

"Adoption is spelled l-o-v-e."

A picture book about 5-year-old Ryan, who knows a lot of people who are part of the adoption triad. Shows kids how often adoption touches people's lives in a variety of ways, but the story is not particularly engaging and does not easily hold a young reader's attention.

Keywords

Adoption, Core Issues (Feelings), Triad Issues

Age Range:

Preschool, early school-age

Author: Randall B. Hicks

Photographer: William W. Rockey

ISBN# 0-9631638-2-5 Date Published: 1994 Price: $ 8.95

Publisher: Wordslinger Pages: 56

Rating

ALL ABOUT ME

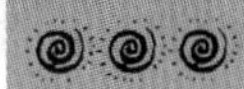

Your child is invited to write, draw and color in this washable book.

All About Me was written to provide opportunities for parents and children to have open, frank and meaningful conversations about being adopted. Illustrated with wonderful, colorful art produced by adopted children, it encourages children to participate in the story by "filling in the blanks." The large format is easy for young fingers to handle and it's washable, so the fun can happen over and over again! Spiral bound.

Keywords

Adopted Child, Adoption

Age Range:

Preschool, early school-age

Author: Lynn Burwash

Author: Cie McMullin

Lynn Burwash and Cie McMullin are adoptive mothers.

ISBN# 966885805 Date Published: 1998 Price: $ 10.95

Publisher: Self-published Pages: 11

ALL BABIES

Great for younger kids who need a hands-on activity when talking about adoption.

A coloring book about adoption that starts with the child's birth, *All Babies* contains easy-to-color pictures and simple text. The main message is, "All babies need to know they are wanted very much, just like you are." This inexpensive coloring book is very traditional in feeling and in its own way provides a reassuring format for adopted children, putting the focus on the strength of the parent's love for the child and the similarities among the experiences of children who join their families through adoption.

Keywords

Adoption, Games and Activities, Diversity

Age Range:

Preschool, early school-age

Author: Maureen Connelley

Illustrator: Loretta Vecchio

Maureen Connelley is the author of *All Babies* and *Given In Love.*

ISBN# 1-56123-0634 Date Published: 1994 Price: $ 1.00

Publisher: Centering Corp. Pages: 16

ALL KINDS OF FAMILIES

Kids can create their own definitions of family based on their own experiences.

A family is always part of you — a special part of your life. This book talks about family from a social, experiential point of view. It delivers the message that family is determined by YOU and those who surround you — how you act and feel together — and isn't dependent on biology or physical matching. Embraces adoptive, transracial, traditional, alternative, and divorced families in a lucid, supportive style. Pictures show all races and different kinds of family constellations.

Keywords

Multiracial, Family Life, Self-Esteem, Diversity, Transracial Adoption

Age Range:

Preschool, early school-age

Author: Norma Simon

Author: Carolyn Rubin

Illustrator: Joe Lasker

Norma Simon is the author of *All Kinds of Families, Why Am I Different,* and *I Am NOT a Crybaby*

ISBN# 0-8075-0282-0 R Date Published: 1976 Price: $ 14.95

Publisher: Whitman Pages: 40

Rating

ALLISON

An Asian child finds out she has been adopted.

When Allison tries on the red kimono her grandmother has sent her, she is suddenly aware that she resembles her favorite doll more than she does her mother and father. When her parents explain that she is adopted, Allison's doll becomes her only solace — until she finds a stray cat in the garden and learns the true meaning of adoption and parental love.

Keywords

Adoption, Asian American, Family Life, Fiction, Japanese American

Age Range.

Preschool, early school-age

Illustrator: Allen Say

Allen Say is the author/illustrator of *Allison; How My Parents Learned to Eat; Emma's Rug; Stranger In The Mirror; Boy of the Three Year Nap; Grandfather's Journey* and more.

ISBN# 039585895X Date Published. 1997 Price. $ 17.00
Publisher. Houghton Mifflin Pages. 32

Rating

AN MEI'S STRANGE AND WONDROUS JOURNEY

The story of a baby girl's adoption from China, told in her own voice.

Kirkus Reviews: "An Mei remembers her mother leaving her on the steps of an orphanage, then stealing away into the windy night. While she makes peace with her new family, she can still hear 'the sound the wind had made against the buttons of my mother's coat when she left me on the steps.' Children will wonder how An Mei can recall the events of her first days so clearly, while adults will only question why such a conceit was used to tell her story. The core of the story is very affecting, but the piece lumbers under the weight of the sentiments and the overripe imagery."

Keywords

Asian, Chinese American, Adoption, International Adoption, Grief and Loss, Core Issues (Feelings)

Age Range.

Preschool, early school-age

Author: Stephan Molnar-Felton

ISBN# 78924770 Date Published. 1998 Price. $ 15.95
Publisher. DK Ink Pages. 32

BEAR

How a bear cub makes a new life after being separated from mama.

A young bear awakens to find that his mother is gone and he is all alone. Driven by fear and hunger, he must confront an unfriendly wilderness and meet the challenge of surviving on his own. The Caldecott Award-winning illustrator of *Owl Moon* brilliantly depicts the drama of the animal world in this tale of courage, self-determination, and personal victory. Full color.

Keywords

Adoption, Self-Esteem, Orphan, Core Issues (Feelings)

Age Range.

Preschool, early school-age

Author: John Schoenherr

ISBN# 0698-11376-4 Date Published. Price. $ 5.95
Publisher. Paper Star Pages.

BEGINNINGS

Parents and children discuss how their families came to be.

No two adoption journeys are exactly alike. In this book, five different stories are told through the eyes of the child. Expresses the gratitude parents feel about being able to parent.

Keywords

Adoption, Family Life

Age Range.

Preschool, early school-age

Author: Virginia Kroll

Virginia Kroll is the author of *Beginnings, Hats Off To Hair, Masai and I*, and more.

ISBN# 807506028 Date Published. Price. $ 14.95
Publisher. Whitman Pages.

Rating

BLESSING FROM ABOVE, A

A book that can be individualized for each adopted child.

The author believes that every adoption is a divine transaction. "Every adoption is a blessing from above — for the parents, for the child, for the birthmother."

Keywords

Adopted Child, Adoption, Spiritual Meanings, Christian

Age Range:

Preschool, early school-age

Author: Patti Henderson

Author: Liz Edge

Patti Henderson is the mother of two adopted sons. Liz Edge is an adopted person.

ISBN# 307102165 | Date Published: | Price: $ 9.95

Publisher: Golden | Pages: 32

Rating

BRAVE HORACE

Horace is back and he won't be scared!

Since your child probably has a soft spot for Horace the leopard, this new tale provides a great opportunity to talk about why it's a good idea to talk about feelings and not keep them to yourself. Horace is both thrilled and terrified that he has been invited to a monster movie party — but he can't tell anyone how scared he is. He pretends to be brave but it doesn't really help. Only when he finds out that his friend Fred is even more frightened than he is does Horace figure out how to rescue both his friend and himself.

Keywords

Adopted Child, Core Issues (Feelings), Friendship, Self-Esteem

Age Range:

Preschool, early school-age

Author: Holly Keller

Holly Keller is the author of *Horace* and *Brave Horace*.

ISBN# 688154077 | Date Published: 1998 | Price: $ 15.00

Publisher: Greenwillow | Pages: 32

CAROLYN'S STORY

The story of Carolyn, adopted from Honduras.

Sometimes it's okay to be different and other times Carolyn just wants to be like everyone else. Accompanied by photographs of Carolyn's early years, and written in Carolyn's first-person voice, it reflects a common experience in adoption: As her father explains in a prefatory note, "On one hand, [Carolyn]'s proud to be adopted, because it's different.... On the other side, Carolyn just wants to fit in — to be like everyone else." Includes a glossary of common adoption terms and adoption resources.

Keywords

Adoption, Latino/a, Girl Power, Self-Esteem, Racial/Ethnic Identity

Age Range:

Preschool, early school-age

Author: Perry Schwartz

ISBN# 0-8225-2580-1 | Date Published: 1996 | Price: $ 22.27

Publisher: Lerner | Pages: 40

CHICKEN THAT COULD SWIM, THE

Huh? How can a chicken swim?

Great confusion reigns in the garden of the Man Who Loves Birds when he allows Silky the chicken to hatch a duck egg — and the new duckling wishes to join his brothers and sisters in the pond. A story about parenthood as something more than a birth right.

Keywords

Core Issues (Feelings), Family Life, Parenting, Adoption

Age Range:

Preschool, early school-age

Author: Paul Adshead

ISBN# 859533468 | Date Published: 1990 | Price: $ 6.99

Publisher: Child's Play | Pages:

Rating

CHRISTOPHER CHANGES HIS NAME

A lighthearted story with a simple message about being different.

Tired of having an ordinary name, Christopher decides to change his — until he realizes that he's special just the way he is. A good story to stimulate conversation with your child about feelings of being different. Why does Christopher want to be different? What's good about it? What's not so good about it? What made Christopher change his mind? Christopher just happens to have brown skin.

Keywords

Adopted Child, Racial/Ethnic Identity, Diversity, Core Issues (Feelings), Names, Self-Esteem

Age Range:

Preschool, early school-age

Author: Itah Sadu

Itah Sadu is the author of *Christopher, Please Clean Up Your Room.*

ISBN# 1552092143 *Date Published:* 1998 *Price:* $ 5.95
Publisher: Fire Fly *Pages:* 32

Rating

CLEO AND THE COYOTE

Everyone wants to belong.

Cleo is a stray dog from the city who has an adventure with a coyote on the desert in this poignant story about wanting to be loved and to belong to someone. This is another example of a good book that, although it never mentions the word "adoption," nonetheless addresses some of the core emotions of adoption. It's the kind of book that can help children identify their feelings through exploring the losses and challenges others face. The children in the illustrations have features that make them appear Latino or Native American. A Children's Choice for 1997 book for the International Reading Association and the Children's Book Council highlighting kids' favorite books.

Keywords

Family Life, Core Issues (Feelings), Native American, Latino/a, Grief and Loss

Age Range:

Preschool, early school-age

Author: Elizabeth Levy, III

ISBN# 6024271 *Date Published:* 1997 *Price:* $ 14.95
Publisher: HarperCollins *Pages:* 32

CORA AND THE ELEPHANTS

Cora, a child who was adopted by African elephants, searches for her roots.

Growing up with her adoptive family of elephants, young Cora eats fruits from the trees of Africa, swims in the local watering hole, and otherwise enjoys her life —except when she tries to remember how she got there.

Keywords

Adoption, Core Issues (Feelings), Transracial Adoption, Triad Issues

Age Range:

Preschool, early school-age

Author: Lissa Rovetch

Illustrator: Martha Weston

ISBN# 014054481X *Date Published:* 1997 *Price:* $ 4.99
Publisher: Puffin *Pages:* 32

DAVID'S FATHER

David's father ate 26 snails, 3 octopuses and 16 bricks with chocolate sauce.

When David moved to the neighborhood, Julie was afraid of David's father because he was a giant. David, who was adopted, is not a giant and looks like a regular kid. When Julie got to know David's father, she found out he was very nice after all, but still kind of scary. "You think he is scary?" asks David. "Wait till you meet my grandmother." A hilarious story written from the point of view of the adopted child who has to explain to the world about his very strange parents. Every adopted child should have this book!

Keywords

Transracial Adoption, International Adoption, Adoption, Fathers, Family Life

Age Range:

Preschool, early school-age

Author: Robert Munsch

ISBN# 0-920236-64-2 *Date Published:* 1983 *Price:* $ 4.95
Publisher: Firefly *Pages:* 32

Rating

DAY WE MET YOU, THE

Share The Day We Met You with your adopted child."

Adopted children and their parents will want to celebrate that important day — the first homecoming — with this lovely and affirming book. Written for parents to read aloud, its details offer opportunities to reaffirm the details of this important homecoming. Affectionate and personal, it creates a mood that's just right. The New York Times says, "Its success is in mood rather than substance. Flowers in the baby's room, wind chimes in the window are comforting and reassuring."

Keywords

Adoption, Core Issues (Feelings)

Age Range:

Preschool, early school-age

Author-Illustrator: Phoebe Koehler

This is Phoebe Koehler's first picture book, and was inspired by friends who have adopted children.

ISBN# THIS ONE! *Date Published:* 1990 *Price:* $ 5.99

Publisher: Macmillan *Pages:* 42

Rating

DID MY FIRST MOTHER LOVE ME?

A book that articulates an essential question in every adopted child's heart and mind.

Morgan knows her adoptive mother and father love her, but she wonders about her birth parents. Did they love her too? At the end of the book, there is a nice discussion for adults about how to talk about adoption with children. Books in Print writes, "When Morgan asks, 'Did my first mother love me?' her mother reads the letter her birth mother wrote to her. It relates the wish to give her child a safe and happy life, but acknowledges sadly that this is not possible [for her to do herself]. The adoptive family's openness and love are evident." A Pact bestseller.

Keywords

Adoption, Mothers, Birth Parent, Core Issues (Feelings), Triad Issues, Grief and Loss

Age Range:

Preschool, early school-age

Author: Kathryn M. Miller

Illustrator: Jamie Moffett

Kathryn M. Miller is the author of *Did My First Mother Love Me?* and *Do I Have A Daddy?*

ISBN# 0-930934-84-9 *Date Publisshed:* 1994 *Price:* $ 5.95

Publisher: Morning Glory *Pages:* 48

DOUNIA

Dounia joins her family through international adoption.

This author thinks a good book should touch you and that its memory should linger in your mind. *Dounia*, about a girl who joins her family through international adoption, manages to do both. Dounia and her new family do not look alike. The story gives words to the fears and uncertainty a young child feels in a new environment. The last line says it all: "Dounia would like to give her a kiss too. But she doesn't dare. Tomorrow she is sure that she will dare...."

Keywords

Adoption, International Adoption, Core Issues (Feelings), Attachment

Age Range:

Preschool, early school-age

Author: Natacha Karvoskaia

ISBN# 0-916291-58-8 *Date Published:* 1995 *Price:* $ 13.95

Publisher: Kane-Miller *Pages:* 32

FAMILY FOR JAMIE, A

A picture book about why parents want to adopt.

This author wants adopted kids to know why their parents wanted to adopt them. This is not an engaging work, and better versions are available to address this important topic.

Keywords

Adoption, Transracial Adoption, International Adoption, Family Life

Age Range:

Preschool, early school-age

Author: Suzanne Bloom

ISBN# 517574926 *Date Published:* *Price:* $ 13.00

Publisher: Roundhouse *Pages:*

Rating

FAMILY TREE

This book was not available for review in time for publication in this edition of the BookSource. If you would like updated information, please call Pact at 415 221-6957.

Keywords

Adoption, Transracial Adoption, Family Life, Fiction

Age Range,

Preschool, early school-age

Author: Pierre Coran

Illustrator: Marie-Jose Sacre

ISBN# *Date Published,* 1999 *Price,* $ 15.95
Publisher, Carolrhoda books *Pages,* 32

Rating

FOREVER FAMILY, A

Eight-year-old Jennifer Jordan-Wong is adopted after living as a foster child.

This is the story of eight-year-old Jennifer Jordan-Wong, a child who has lived in a foster home, was placed into adoption by her birth parents and then was legally adopted. This true story tells about Jennifer's experiences with foster parents, social workers, and getting used to the new life she leads with her adoptive family.

Keywords

Adoption, Foster Child, Family Life, Foster Care, Core Issues (Feelings), Adopted Child

Age Range,

Preschool, early school-age

Author: Roslyn Banish

ISBN# 0-06-446116-5 *Date Published,* 1992 *Price,* $ 5.95
Publisher, HarperCollins *Pages,*

FOSTER BABY

A straightforward way to explain why foster children need a family for awhile

Foster Baby explains in simple terms that a foster child needs care, hugs, attention, love, routine, and more while he is being cared for by another family. The expressive watercolor illustrations reflect a lively foster family of Native Indian heritage caring for a Native baby. Father and mother share parenting in a balanced way and siblings issues are realistically portrayed. The graphics are particularly captivating and pull you right in to the clear prose.

Keywords

Family Life, Foster Child, Foster Parent, Native American, Core Issues (Feelings)

Age Range,

Preschool, early school-age

Author: Rhian Brynjolson

ISBN# 921827547 *Date Published,* 1996 *Price,* $ 10.00
Publisher, Pemmican *Pages,* 36

GOING HOME

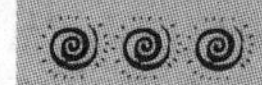

A family trip "back home" to Mexico is different for American-raised kids.

Though this beautiful book does not directly invoke adoption, it is a classic adoption core-issue story, asking what it means to feel "at home" in two places, and familiar with strangers. Three Mexican American children return with their parents for a visit with their extended family in Mexico; while there, the children are introduced to the ordinary but unfamiliar. With love heaped on them by relatives they'd never met, they realize that being in the place called "back home" is something special. In this home that is not home, the children come to understand both their parents' joy at returning and their parents' original urge to leave Mexico for the opportunities America offered.

Keywords

Cultural History, Latino/a, Mexican, Mexican American, Core Issues (Feelings)

Age Range,

Preschool, early school-age

Author: Eve Bunting

Illustrator: David Diaz

Eve Bunting is the author of *Going Home, Smoky Night,* and many more.

ISBN# 0-06-4453509-1 *Date Published,* 1996 *Price,* $ 5.95
Publisher, HarperCollins *Pages,* 36

Rating

GOOSE

Baby goose is adopted by a family of woodchucks who don't know she can fly.

Adopted by woodchucks at birth, a baby goose never feels she truly belongs until she discovers on her own that she can fly.

Keywords

Adoption, Core Issues (Feelings), Transracial Adoption, International Adoption

Age Range:

Preschool, early school-age

Author: Molly Bang

Author of *Ten, Nine, Eight; The Grey Lady and the Strawberry Snatcher'; The Paper Crane* and more.

ISBN# 59089005 Date Published: 1996 Price: $ 10.95

Publisher: Blue Sky Pages: 32

Rating

HAPPY ADOPTION DAY

Hip, hip, hooray, it's Happy Adoption Day!

This bright, cheerful book shows the joy and love of new parents as they watch their child grow and as they mark each year with an Adoption Day celebration. Musical notation of the song is included, so you and your child can sing along with the rousing chorus.

Keywords

Adoption, Holidays and Celebrations, Family Life

Age Range:

Preschool, early school-age

Author: John McCutcheon

John McCutcheon is an accomplished singer, songwriter and musician. He has had two Grammy nominations and had won two Children's Album of the Year Awards.

ISBN# 0-316-55455-3 Date Published: Price: $ 15.95

Publisher: Little, Brown Pages:

HORACE

This is a very popular picture book...an adoption bestseller!

Horace looks different from his mom and dad but comes to realize they belong together for reasons more important than appearance. This classic story has been a favorite of adopted children since its first publication.

Keywords

Adoption, Family Life, Core Issues (Feelings), Multiracial

Age Range:

Preschool, early school-age

Author: Holly Keller

Holly Keller is the author of *Horace* and *Brave Horace.*

ISBN# 688118445 Date Published: 1997 Price: $ 4.95

Publisher: Mulberry Pages: 32

HOW I WAS ADOPTED

An overly simple view of adoption.

Sometimes things that look too good to be true are indeed just unrealistic and saccharine. Books in Print writes, "Samantha is smiling in all the illustrations. Her parents are always smiling. The pictures she draws are of smiling people. The author says to encourage children's feelings — both positive and negative — but no negative feelings are mentioned, or even hinted at in the book. This title will not encourage open sharing and could even be harmful to adopted children by reinforcing the idea that they have to be cheerful, no matter what. It holds the parents to an unreal standard, too. Betty Lifton's *Tell Me a Real Adoption Story* includes the birth mother as a person with feelings, not just a uterus."

Keywords

Adoption, Adopted Child, Adoptive Parent, Birth Parent, Triad Issues

Age Range:

Preschool, early school-age

Author: Joanna Cole

ISBN# 688119298 Date Published: 1995 Price: $ 16.00

Publisher: Morrow Pages: 48

Rating

JAMAICA AND BRIANNA

A real story about friendship and teasing.

Jamaica hates having to wear her brother's hand-me-down boots, especially when her friend Brianna teases her about wearing boys' boots. When Jamaica gets to buy her own new pair, she chooses tan cowboy boots and tells Brianna that "her" pink fuzzy boots are ugly. Watercolor paintings show the snowy outdoors, the crowd at the bus stop, the warm interiors of Jamaica's home, the cheerful bustle of the shoe store, and the busy school coat room, where the quarrel is resolved and the boots are lined up together. Jamaica is African American, Brianna is Asian American, the setting is suburban, and kids everywhere will recognize friendship's challenges and rewards.

Keywords

African American, Asian American, Friendship, Race Relations, Multicultural, Black Identity

Age Range:

Preschool, early school-age

Author: Juanita Havill

Illustrator: Anne Sibley O'Brien

ISBN# 395644895 Date Published: 1993 Price: $ 5.95

Publisher: Houghton Mifflin Pages:

Rating

KOALA FOR KATIE, A

Katie is playing adoption. How well does she understand?

Katie, an adopted child, is playing "adoption" with her toy koala bear. This is a promising idea for a story book examining adoption, but unfortunately, it doesn't go beyond the most superficial level. The book doesn't explore the feelings motivating the game. What are Katie's questions? How does she relate the way she joined her family to what she knows about how other children in her world joined theirs? What does she wonder about her birth parents? Though this book was no doubt intended to reduce a child's sense of isolation by creating an adopted character, it doesn't bring us any closer to understanding Katie's views.

Keywords

Adoption

Age Range:

Preschool, early school-age

Author: Jonathan London

Cynthia Jabar

Jonathan London is the author of *A Koala for Katie* and *The Lion Who Had Asthma.*

ISBN# 807542105 Date Published: 1997 Price: $ 4.95

Publisher: Whitman Pages: 24

LEVI: THE SMARTEST BOY IN THE WORLD

Levi's not too crazy about his new stepfather.

From the publisher: "Levi knows what he loves and what he hates. He loves baseball, but he hates spinach. And he's not too crazy about his new stepfather, David, either, until David helps Levi see that new experiences can be just as much fun as familiar ones."

Keywords

Adopted Child, Adoption, Blended Family, Family Life

Age Range:

Preschool, early school-age

Author: Jeane Heimberger Candido

Jeane Heimberger Candido has published an adult novel about the civil war entitled *The Redemption of Corporal Nolan Giles.* This is her first book for children.

ISBN# 1886383340 Date Published: 1998 Price: $ 10.00

Publisher: Pride Publications Pages: 30

LITTLE GREEN GOOSE, THE

Single fatherhood through adoption.

What makes a family belong together? Father goose so much wants to raise a baby that he adopts and hatches an egg but the baby turns out to be an emerald green dragon! Oooh, the talk that starts around the barnyard! Who would have thought his friends could be so insensitive, making fun of his little green goose like that? But don't worry. When all is said and done, the underlying message rises to the surface: love, not biology, is what makes a family belong together.

Keywords

Family Life, Fathers, Single Parent Families, Adopted Child, Transracial Adoption

Age Range:

Preschool, early school-age

Author: Adele Sanson

Author: J. Alison James

ISBN# 735810710 Date Published: 1999 Price: $ 15.95

Publisher: Pages: 32

LOOK WHO'S ADOPTED

Rating 

A child's look at famous people who joined their families through adoption.

Wendell Rabbit is a turtle adopted by a family of rabbits. As the narrator of this book, he introduces children to a list of famous people who share three things: Each one joined his or her family through adoption; each one grew up to make important contributions to our world; and each one learned to take responsibility for his or her own actions. From the back cover: "Wendel may be a turtle, but he lives with a family of rabbits. You share something very special with Wendel and some of Wendel's friends. Do you know what it is? Wendel would like you to meet these friends and show you the interesting and fun things that they do."

Keywords
Adoption, Role Models, Self-Esteem, Adopted Adult, Adopted Child, Core Issues (Feelings)

Age Range:
Preschool, early school-age

Author: Michael S. Taheri
James F. Orr

ISBN# 1879201216 Date Published: 1997 Price: $ 8.95
Publisher: J&E Publishing Pages: 32

LUCY'S FEET

Rating 

Helpful to blended families with both birth and adopted children.

This funny and serious book offers Lucy's "less than proper" feelings about her adoption as compared with her brother's entrance into the family by birth: Who is she like? Is she lovable? Does she really belong? How come baby brother Elliot came from inside her mother and she did not? Appealing.

Keywords
Adoption, Family Life, Sibling Issues, Girl Power, Core Issues (Feelings)

Age Range:
Preschool, early school-age

Author: Stephanie Stein

ISBN# 944934056 Date Published: Price: $ 14.00
Publisher: Perspectives Pages: 32

MAGIC TREE, THE

A folk tale from Nigeria

Mbi, an orphan boy, is constantly asked to "do this," and "do that" by his many unkind relatives — until a special fruit tree grows, just for him! E.B. Lewis' appealing, lifelike illustrations of Mbi, a strong African child, and his relatives add interest to a story that should appeal to any child who has been adopted or is growing up in foster care.

Keywords
Adopted Child, Africa, Family Life, Folk tales and Legends

Age Range:
Preschool, early school-age

Author: T. Echewa Obinkaram
Illustrator: E.B. Lewis

ISBN# 688162312 Date Published: 1999 Price: $ 16.00
Publisher: Morrow Pages:

MAMA ONE, MAMA TWO

How Maudie went to live with Mama Two in a "for awhile home."

Mama One got too sad to take care of her daughter Maudie, though nobody knew why. She needed help and Tom, a social worker, took Mama One to a place where she could find out what made her sad. Tom told Maudie that it wasn't her fault. It wasn't anyone's fault. Then Tom took Maudie to a "for awhile home" and she met Katherine, her Mama Two. A clear and touching story about a young child's feelings when she has to go into foster care while she worries about her mother.

Keywords
Core Issues (Feelings), Foster Child, Mothers, Grief and Loss, Depression

Age Range:
Preschool, early school-age

Author: Patricia MacLachlan
Illustrator: Ruth Bornstein

Patricia MacLachlan won the 1986 Newbery Medal for *Sarah, Plain and Tall.*

ISBN# 60240822 Date Published: 1987 Price: $ 15.89
Publisher: HarperCollins Pages:

Rating

MOTHER FOR CHOCO, A

Choco wished he had a mother, but who could his mother be? Ah hai

A Mother for Choco and *Are You My Mother?* by P.D. Eastman illustrate how similar stories can have differing effects on children's self esteem! Both are designed to address fear of abandonment. The Eastman story is resolved when the steam shovel lifts the bird back into his nest, where his look-alike mother awaits him and all is well. The Kasza story ends with Mrs. Bear acknowledging that she will perform the parenting needs he is missing — fun, love, nurture, protection. The word adoption is never once used in this story,but its message is that people who don't look alike can form healthy, loving families.

Keywords

Adoption, Mothers, Family Life, Multicultural

Age Range.

Preschool, early school-age

Author: Keiko Kasza

ISBN# 0-698-11364-0 *Date Published.* 1992 *Price.* $ 5.99

Publisher. Paper Star *Pages.* 32

Rating

MR. ROGERS — LET'S TALK ABOUT IT: ADOPTION

Reassuring answers to common questions young children have about adoption.

Discusses what it means to be part of a family and tackles some feelings adopted children may have. A fine resource for little ones. The main message is that belonging in a family comes from being loved. Fred Rogers opens the door for adoptive families to safely talk about their good and not-so-good feelings in a book that reinforces family unity.

Keywords

Adoption, Adopted Child, Family Life, Core Issues (Feelings)

Age Range.

Preschool, early school-age

Author: Fred Rogers

Mr. Rogers is host of the popular children's TV show.

ISBN# 698116259 *Date Published.* 1998 *Price.* $ 5.99

Publisher. Putnam-Paperstar *Pages.* 32

MY ANGEL GOES HOME

A Heavenly Tale of Adoption

"Why was I adopted?" "Because God wanted you to be exactly who you are and he wants us to be your parents." This book — which we do not recommend — tells the story of how the Great Guardian Angel preps kids for birth in this world. She shows Amy how she'll reach her parents courtesy of a birth lady who acts as God's messenger to deliver her safely to those whom he wants to raise her. Lathrop writes that babies given up for adoption are delivered to the parents they were meant to have as part of a spiritual plan. Unfortunately, in her rendition of that plan the birth parents are reduced to messengers while the adoptive parents have been chosen by God to raise the child.

Keywords

Adopted Child, Spiritual Meanings, Core Issues (Feelings)

Age Range.

Preschool, early school-age

Author: Kathleen Lathrop

Kathleen Lathrop is the author of *Adoption: A Reference Handbook* and *My Angel Goes Home.*

ISBN# 964212803 *Date Published.* 1997 *Price.* $ 17.95

Publisher. Diotima Press *Pages.*

MY DADDY

Will my daddy come back?

As the boy in *My Daddy* watches his father leave and eagerly awaits his return, his anxiety and fear are transformed into comfort, security, and finally a joyful reunion. Lyrical lines and imaginative illustrations combine to illuminate the larger-than-life love of a child for his father. Though this book is not about adoption and the characters are white, the central theme of the book — separation and reconnection — is sure to touch the deeper feelings of children who have been adopted, providing an excellent opportunity to talk about the issue without invoking the child's particular history.

Keywords

Adopted Child, Core Issues (Feelings), Family Life, Fathers, Grief and Loss

Age Range.

Preschool, early school-age

Author: Susan Paradis

ISBN# 1886910308 *Date Published.* *Price.* $ 15.95

Publisher. Front Street/Publishers Group West *Pages.*

Rating

MY REAL FAMILY

When her parents adopt Blanche, Sarah thinks they don't care about her anymore.

Sarah, convinced that she is adopted, runs away from the Bear Family Theater to find her "real parents." Though offering adopted children confirmation that they're not "the only one," this book falls short of engaging them or helping them to fully identify with the characters. Both the characters and the unemotional story line seem too pat; there are no characters of color; and the conclusion seems too good to be true.

Keywords

Adoption, Core Issues (Feelings), Family Life, Sibling Issues

Age Range:

Preschool, early school-age

Author: Emily Arnold McCully

Emily Arnold McCully has illustrated more than 100 books for children and won the 1993 Caldecott Medal. She lives in New York.

ISBN# 152776982 *Date Published:* 1994 *Price:* $ 14.00
Publisher: Harcourt Brace *Pages:* 32

Rating

MY SPECIAL FAMILY

Open adoption workbook for children.

This large-size, simply-formatted book offers lots of fill-in-the-blank questions and spaces for pictures and mementos. Though this book fills a needed gap in the memory book category, it lacks visual appeal and does not compare well to the many more engaging books available for this age range. This book is out of print, but if you place an order we may be able to find you a used copy within 2-6 months. We will notify you and request your approval of the price and condition. We will also notify you if we are unable to locate this title within six months.

Keywords

Open Adoption, Family Life, Adoption, Memory Book

Age Range:

Preschool, early school-age

Author: Kathleen Silber

Author: Debra Marks Parelskin

Kathleen Silber is the co-author of *Children of Open Adoption* and a pioneer and spokesperson for open adoption.

ISBN# 0-9640009-1-1 *Date Published:* 1993 *Price:* $ 12.95
Publisher: OPAP *Pages:*

OLIVER

How would Oliver's life be different if he had not been adopted?

Oliver learns that all people imagine other lives they might be living and that what he is feeling is normal.

Keywords

Adoption, Core Issues (Feelings), Adopted Child

Age Range:

Preschool, early school-age

Author: Lois Wickstrom

ISBN# 0-9611872-5-5 *Date Published:* *Price:* $ 14.95
Publisher: Our Child Press *Pages:*

ON THE DAY YOU WERE BORN

Incredible things happen when a baby is born.

Sometimes children who have been adopted think they have not been born. This beautifully illustrated picture book provides a wonderful springboard to talk about the day your child entered the world. A bestseller.

Keywords

Family Life, Adoption, Birthdays, Core Issues (Feelings)

Age Range:

Preschool, early school-age

Author-Illustrator: Debra Frasier

ISBN# 0-15-257995-8 *Date Published:* *Price:* $ 16.00
Publisher: Harcourt *Pages:* 32

Rating

ONE WONDERFUL YOU

"You are unique because you are a wonderful blend of both your families.'

From the text: "You are who you are because of all the wonderful things you were born with (from your birth family) and because of all the great stuff your adoptive family gave you." This straightforward, clear and entertaining book talks in language kids can understand about genetics, heritage and what adoption really means. The simple message reinforces basic information in an appealing way. Multicultural cartoon-like illustrations add appeal to the direct but humor-filled message. Strongly recommended.

Keywords

Adoption, Birth Parent, Self-Esteem, Family Life, Adopted Child, Triad Issues

Age Range,

Preschool, early school-age

Author: Francie Portnoy

ISBN# 965405119 *Date Published,* 1997 *Price,* $ 9.95

Publisher, Children's Home of N.C. *Pages,* 48

Rating

OVER THE MOON: AN ADOPTION STORY

"Forever and always we will be your mommy and daddy....'

Once upon a time a teeny-tiny baby was born. At the same time, a man and a woman had a dream. They saw the baby in a basket surrounded by beautiful flowers and they knew it was the child they had been longing for. In this story, reminiscent of Jamie Lee Curtis' *Tell Me Again About the Night I Was Born* and Robert Munsch's *Love You Forever*, a mom and dad fly to a faraway place to adopt their baby. Bright, exuberant illustrations tell the story of how one family came together with the lively appeal of Guatemalan folk art. The child has brown skin and looks Central American. The message is reassuring, the illustrations are delightful and the text is happy.

Keywords

Adoption, International Adoption, Guatemalan, Core Issues (Feelings), Latino/a

Age Range,

Preschool, early school-age

Author: Karen Katz

ISBN# 805050132 *Date Published,* 1997 *Price,* $ 15.95

Publisher, Henry Holt *Pages,* 32

PABLO'S TREE

A story about Pablo and his grandpa, in a family built by adoption.

"Este árbol; es para mi nieto. This tree is for my grandson." With simple text and bright cut-paper art, grampa's special relationship with Pablo comes alive in a family built by adoption. Great look at a Latino family.

Keywords

Adoption, Latino/a, Mexican American, Mexican, Intergenerational, Bilingual

Age Range,

Preschool, early school-age

Author: Pat Mora

Pat Mora is a poet and the author of *Pablo's Tree* and *The Desert Is My Mother/El Desierto Es Mi Madre.* She lives in Santa Fe, NM.

ISBN# 0-02-7674010 *Date Published,* 1994 *Price,* $ 16.00

Publisher, MacMillan *Pages,*

PINKY & REX & THE NEW BABY

When Rex's family adopts a new baby boy, Pinky and Rex feel left out.

This paperback reprint of a classic story about adoption will be particularly interesting for adopted children when new siblings join the family.

Keywords

Sibling Issues, Adopted Child, Adoption, Girl Power

Age Range,

Preschool, early school-age

Author: James Howe

Author: Melissa Sweet

ISBN# 068982548X *Date Published,* 1999 *Price,* $ 3.00

Publisher, Aladdin *Pages,* 48

PLAIN NOODLES

Rating 

Captain and Sophia Figg take care of a bunch of new babies.

Captain and Sophia Figg tend a lighthouse alone on an island. As her children have grown up and moved away, Sofia misses having babies about. So when a rowboat full of irresistible babies miraculously appears, Sofia is delighted. What ensues is delightful mayhem as Sofia feeds and diapers her charges and wonders where she'll find another diaper. This silly story provides an interesting opportunity to talk with your child about what she understands about why you adopted her and how it was during your first days together as a family. Where do plain noodles fit into your life?

Keywords

Adopted Child, Mothers, Adopted Child, Core Issues (Feelings)

Age Range:

Preschool, early school-age

Author: Betty Waterton

Illustrator: Joanne Fitzgerald

ISBN# 888991320 Date Published: 1997 Price: $ 5.95

Publisher: Greenwood Publishing Pages: 32

RAISING SWEETNESS

Rating 

The sheriff is raising eight orphans he rescued.

"Long as I got a biscuit, they got half." The big-hearted sheriff is a saint, a character embodying all the stereotypes of the "goodly" adoptive parent. Books that reflect some of the myths about adoptive families and birth parents can best be used as a starting point for interesting conversation between adoptive parents and their kids, providing an opportunity to point out and name some of the stereotypes that fuel adoptism.

Keywords

Adoption, Adoptive Parent, Foster Care

Age Range:

Preschool, early school-age

Author: Diane Stanley

Author: G. Brian Karas

ISBN# 399232257 Date Published: 1999 Price: $ 15.99

Publisher: Putnam-Paperstar Pages: 32

REAL SISTERS

"Everyone should understand this because it's true," says one 8-year-old reviewer.

Claire is adopted and Black. Jenny is born to the family and white. When kids tease Claire, she thinks of many things — both good and bad — that she and Jenny do together and knows in her heart that they are real sisters. Nice illustrations.

Keywords

Adoption, Sibling Issues, Family Life, Transracial Adoption, International Adoption, Self-Esteem

Age Range:

Preschool, early school-age

Author: Susan Wright

Illustrator: Bo-Kim Louie

ISBN# 0-921-556-42-X Date Published: 1994 Price: $ 5.95

Publisher: Ragweed "Press Pages: 24

ROMULUS AND REMUS

Two baby boys are raised by mother wolf with her cubs.

In this sweetened version of the Latin legend, Romulus and Remus grow up to found a city where people of all races and backgrounds come to live. This book can be used to stimulate conversation about telling the truth about hard things, making it particularly interesting for adoptive families. But Horn Book writes, "In this oversimplified and ultimately misleading story, Romulus does not kill Remus; instead, Remus goes away to hunt with the wolves."

Keywords

Adopted Child, Self-Esteem, Folk tales and Legends, History, Orphan, Foster Child

Age Range:

Preschool, early school-age

Author: Anne Rockwell

ISBN# 689812906 Date Published: 1997 Price: $ 3.99

Publisher: Aladdin Pages: 40

Rating

SEEDS OF LOVE

For brothers and sisters awaiting a new sibling through international adoption.

A much-needed book about how it feels to be a big kid and be separated from mom and dad when they go to pick up your new baby. Even though she has fun with her grandma, Carly misses her parents. Every day, she puts a sticker on the calendar to show they will be home one day sooner; every day, she waters her seeds. When the sprouts come up, she knows her parents and baby sister will be coming home from China soon.

Keywords

Sibling Issues, Adoption, Core Issues (Feelings), International Adoption

Age Range:

Preschool, early school-age

Author: Mary E. Petertyl

Illustrator: Jill Chambers

ISBN# 0-9655753-1-4 Date Published: Price: $ 15.95
Publisher: Folio One Pages: 32

Rating

SPECIAL KIND OF LOVE, A

There are many ways to say I love you.

A father loves his son deeply but has trouble telling him so. Instead, he makes wonderful things for his son from boxes — an airplane, a big castle, a go-cart built for two. In the tradition of *Mama, Do You Love Me?*, this heartwarming story offers a testimonial to the strength of parental love, and an affirmation that communication comes in many forms.

Keywords

Family Life, Fiction, Fathers, Core Issues (Feelings)

Age Range:

Preschool, early school-age

Author: Stephen Michael King

ISBN# 0-590-67681-4 Date Published: 1993 Price: $ 15.95
Publisher: Scholastic Pages:

STELLALUNA

Adopted children and birth parents especially adore this book.

Because it addresses the baby bat's desire for reunion with her bat family, some adoptive parents have a difficult time with it, but we think it offers useful opportunities for conversation. A young bat falls into a bird's nest and is raised like a bird until she is reunited with her bat family. When she's finally reunited with her mother and the other bats, she learns that the differences between bats and bird are much less significant than her newfound friendship. A great book to stimulate adoption talk. Reading Rainbow and ABBY award winner. A Pact bestseller. Also available as a popup book which comes with a hanging mobile.

Keywords

Adoption, Core Issues (Feelings), Family Life, Parenting, Diversity

Age Range:

Preschool, early school-age

Author: Janell Cannon

ISBN# 152802177 Date Published: Price: $ 16.00
Publisher: Harcourt Brace Pages:

STEPHANIE'S PONYTAIL

Stephanie wants so much to be different that she's willing to shave her head.

Stephanie wants to be different. Every day, she comes to school with a hairdo more outrageous than the day before. And each time, the copycats fix their hair to look just like hers — until the day she promises to shave her head. This is a story about the importance of individuality and standing up for independent thought, an effort that is sometimes challenging for adopted children and children being raised across racial lines, since such children, so often feeling "different," may generally try to be the same as their peers.

Keywords

Core Issues (Feelings), Girl Power

Age Range:

Preschool, early school-age

Author: Robert Munsch

ISBN# 1550374842 Date Published: Price: $ 5.95
Publisher: Fire Fly Pages: 32

Rating

STEVIE

A foster child story.

The story of young African American boy who resents a younger child who temporarily lives with them, and then regrets his loss.

Keywords

Foster Child, Foster Care, Family Life, Sibling Issues, Core Issues (Feelings)

Age Range:

Preschool, early school-age

Illustrator: John Steptoe

John Steptoe, a two-time Caldecott Honor Book recipient, is the author of *Jumping Mouse; Baby Says; Creativity; Mufaro's Beautiful Daughter* and *Stevie.*

ISBN# 64434427 Date Published: 1996 Price: $ 5.95
Publisher: HarperCollins Pages: 32

Rating

TALL BOY'S JOURNEY

How will Kim Moon Young learn to fit in? The journey from Korea for adoption.

Kim Moon Young comes to the United States from Korea when he is eight. He is surrounded by strangers who speak a language he cannot understand and who do very strange and unusual things. This story of how he begins to feel more comfortable in his new home is a good place to start the conversation about what it must feel like to be internationally adopted.

Keywords

Adoption, Transracial Adoption, International Adoption, Korean American

Age Range:

Preschool, early school-age

Author: Joanna H. Kraus

ISBN# 876146167 Date Published: 1992 Price: $ 5.95
Publisher: Carolrhoda books Pages: 48

TELL ME A REAL ADOPTION STORY

If there is an essential "how it happened" book for adopted children, this is it.

Finally! A book where the child's need to know is honored, the birth family is authentic and honest talk between parent and child is valued. A mother's recounting of a traditional "and they lived happily ever after" leaves her daughter unsatisfied. "'It was all make-believe. Tell me a real adoption story.'" And so mom does, beginning with one set of parents hoping for a baby and a young woman who "'said she loved you very much. And would never forget you.'" A wonderful picture of a baby falling from the sky demonstrates the absurdity of adoption stories that do not include birth parents. Especially nice is to change the details of the story to fit your child's history.

Keywords

Adoption, Adopted Child, Birth Parent, Triad Issues, Adoptive Parent, Core Issues (Feelings)

Age Range:

Preschool, early school-age

Author: Betty Jean Lifton

Illustrator: Claire A. Nivola

Betty Jean Lifton is a therapist in private practice and the author of *Tell Me A Real Adoption Story*, *Journey of the Adopted Self*, and *Lost and Found.*

ISBN# 0-679-80629-6 Date Published: 1993 Price: $ 13.00
Publisher: Alfred A. Knopf Pages: 32

TELL ME AGAIN ABOUT THE NIGHT I WAS BORN

Add the details of your child's own arrival to this charming story.

A heartwarming story with real-life details your child can connect to — about how the phone rang in the middle of the night and the scream you let out when they said I was born; how Grandma and Grampa slept through it like logs; how the airplane had no movies and no peanuts; how you couldn't grow a baby in your tummy; how you went to the hospital and felt very small; how tiny and perfect I was; about how I didn't like my first diaper change — and all those lively memories of specificity and love. In a significant oversight, however, little mention is made of the birth parents' place in the event of a child's birth.

Keywords

Adoption, Adopted Child, Birthdays, Core Issues (Feelings), Family Life

Age Range:

Preschool, early school-age

Author: Jamie Lee Curtis

Illustrator: Laura Cornell

Jamie Lee Curtis is an actor and photographer. She is also the author of *When I Was Little: A Four-Year Old's Memoir of Her Youth.*

ISBN# 0-06-024528-X Date Published: 1996 Price: $ 14.95
Publisher: HarperCollins Pages: 32

Rating

THROUGH MOON AND STARS AND NIGHT SKIES

A story about being adopted internationally.

Designed to be reassuring, this book may not be realistic enough to hold a child's attention. A little boy is scared as he must fly for a day and a night through blue skies and clouds and stars before he comes to a place he can call home... with his new adopted family. The poetic feel of the language seems directed more to the comfort of the adults involved in an adoption plan, particularly the adoptive parents, than the child's honest feelings. This may not appeal to children whose personal experience and memories of the fear, losses, and confusion that come with the territory of being transplanted from one country to another do not match the positive tone set by the child in this book.

Keywords

Adoption, International Adoption, Boy Focus, Adopted Child, Core Issues (Feelings), Grief and Loss

Age Range.

Preschool, early school-age

Author: Ann Turner

ISBN# 64433080 Date Published. 1992 Price. $ 5.95

Publisher. Trophy Press Pages. 32

Rating

TWICE UPON-A-TIME: BORN AND ADOPTED

Sometimes adopted children don't understand that they were first born.

This book sets the record straight with easy-to-understand text and simple pen and ink illustrations; its pages have something of the feel of a coloring book, which may make this a good hands-on opportunity for a child to record the details of his or her own beginnings.

Keywords

Adoption, Birthdays, Core Issues (Feelings)

Age Range.

Preschool, early school-age

Author: Eleanor Patterson

Illustrator: Barbara Ernst Prey

ISBN# 960743219 Date Published. 1987 Price. $ 5.95

Publisher. EP Press Pages. 46

TWO BIRTHDAYS FOR BETH

Addresses the confusion about being born to one family and adopted into another.

In this charming book, which has a fresh appeal, Beth's adoption day celebration is coming and she imagines a party and presents, exactly like a second birthday. When she finds out Mom hasn't planned what she's hoping for, she's disappointed and confused. Why not? This reassuring story is the only one we know of to address this common question and is enjoyed by adopted children. Beth and Mom just happen to be African American, and Mom is a single parent, helping her daughter sort out her mixed-up feelings about birth and adoption.

Keywords

Adoption, African American, Family Life, Holidays and Celebrations, Birthdays, Single Parent Families

Age Range.

Preschool, early school-age

Author: Gay Lynn Cronin

ISBN# 944934137 Date Published. Price. $ 14.00

Publisher. Perspectives Pages.

TWO LOVES FOR SELENA

Addresses the question, "Why didn't my first family keep me?"

A man plants Selena, a seed, in a flower pot, but when she grows too big for the pot and becomes sick, he doesn't know how to care for her. Then Bern comes along and replants her in a garden where she flourishes, a happy transplant.

Keywords

Adoption, Birth Parent, Core Issues (Feelings), Triad Issues

Age Range.

Preschool, early school-age

Author: Laurie Tanner

Illustrator: Wendy Avner

ISBN# 1-56123-061-8 Date Published. 1993 Price. $ 2.95

Publisher. Centering Corp. Pages. 24

Rating

WE ADOPTED YOU, BENJAMIN KOO

A very positive and strong affirmation of interracial and international adoption.

3eing from Korea didn't matter until Benjamin noticed he lidn't look like mom and dad. He had lots of questions then nd didn't like the answers. This warm and reassuring story xplains how he comes to understand what makes a real amily.

Keywords

Adoption, International Adoption, Korean American, Transracial Adoption, Family Life, Core Issues (Feelings)

Age Range:

Preschool, early school-age

Author: Linda Walvoord Girard

Linda Walvoord Girard is the author of *Adoption is for Always* and *We Adopted You, Benjamin Koo.*

ISBN# 0-8075-8695-1 | Date Published: | Price: $ 5.95

Publisher: Whitman | Pages:

Rating

WHEN JOEL COMES HOME

Welcoming a new baby.

Joel and his adoptive parents are coming home for the first time, so their friends go to meet them at the airport, in this story told from the view of the small child who gets to be the first one to hold Joel. This book's charming illustrations illuminate a wonderful celebration of the feeling of family and friends welcoming a new member to the family.

Keywords

Adoption, International Adoption, Asian American, Sibling Issues

Age Range:

Preschool, early school-age

Author: Susi G. Fowler

ISBN# 688110649 | Date Published: 1993 | Price: $ 9.00

Publisher: Greenwillow | Pages: 24

WHEN YOU WERE BORN IN CHINA

A very touching memory book for children adopted from China.

In this honest and sensitive book, Sara Dorow manages to convey clear messages about why children are placed for adoption and about the people who provide interim care for the children while they are waiting for their permanent families. Respectful text explains why adoption plans are made for Chinese daughters. Includes mention of China's policies regarding population control and the cultural desire to parent a son. This is a wonderful book, whose text is warm and reassuring even when dealing with complex issues. Includes over 100 photographs of children and families.

Keywords

Adoption, Chinese American, International Adoption, Cultural History, Foster Child, China

Age Range:

Preschool, early school-age

Author: Sara Dorrow

ISBN# 0-963847 2-1-X | Date Published: | Price: $ 16.00

Publisher: Yeong & Yong | Pages: 42

WHEN YOU WERE BORN IN KOREA

A memory book for children adopted from Korea.

This book includes over fifty photos and respectful text covering why adoption plans are made in Korea and introducing the notion of interim care providers and orphanages. This excellent book belongs in the home of every family with a child adopted from Korea.

Keywords

Adoption, International Adoption, Cultural History, Korean American, Korean

Age Range:

Preschool, early school-age

Author: Brian Boyd

ISBN# 0-963847 2-01 | Date Published: 1993 | Price: $ 16.00

Publisher: Yeong & Yong | Pages: 44

Rating

WHY SO SAD, BROWN RABBIT

A "where's my mother" story with a twist.

Three little ducklings are sure they've found their mother — and she's a male brown rabbit. He's always been eager to have children so he could teach them rabbit games and is happy to fill the role — if only they'd stop calling him Mama. This story provides another opportunity to talk about what makes a family belong together and is especially fun for single parent families led by fathers.

Keywords

Fathers, Adoption, Family Life, Core Issues (Feelings), Parenting, Single Parent Families

Age Range.

Preschool, early school-age

Author: Sheridan Cain

Illustrator: Jo Kelly

ISBN# 525459634 Date Published. 1998 Price. $ 14.99
Publisher. Dutton Pages. 32

Rating

WHY WAS I ADOPTED?

A wide variety of questions kids frequently ask about adoption.

Despite this book's popularity, its attitudes toward race, birth parents and the adopted child's own feelings makes it unacceptable. When mentioning the fact that birth parents can be very young, for example, it coercively and pejoratively demands, "Who'd want to be brought up by a couple of other children?" (and illustrates the wish's apparent absurdity by depicting a young child reading "Hamlet" while the confused birth parents are reading a comic book). It emphasizes that an child is "chosen" and that adoptive parents (as opposed to birth parents?) "really love children," with the patronizing conclusion, "pretty nice of them, isn't it?" Finally, the sole depiction of a person of color is a truly offensive caricature of Blackness.

Keywords

Adoption, Adoptive Parent, Adopted Child

Age Range.

Preschool, early school-age

Author: Carole Livingston

Illustrator: Arthur Robins

ISBN# 0-8184-0400-0 Date Published. 1996 Price. $ 9.95
Publisher. Carol Publishing Group Pages. 46

ZACHARY'S NEW HOME

A validating story for foster and adopted children

A story for foster and adoptive kids about a kitten who is upset because he has to move from his first family to a foster family and then to an adoptive family. He thinks no one loves him; sometimes he feels angry, though he doesn't know why. He runs away to find his first mother's home even though she used to hurt him, but he feels better when he gets back to his foster/adoptive parents, who keep him safe and who love him even when he isn't happy.

Keywords

Adoption, Foster Child, International Adoption, Core Issues (Feelings), Foster Care, Family Life

Age Range.

Preschool, early school-age

Author: Paul Blomquist

ISBN# 945354274 Date Published. 1990 Price. $ 8.95
Publisher. Magination Pages. 32

ZILLA SASPARILLA AND THE MUD BABY

Adoptism for the very young.

Much to her surprise, when Zilla Sasparilla retrieves a shoe which has become stuck in the mud of the river, she also pulls out a baby, whom she takes home, cleans up (as his skin turns from brown to white), and raises...all the time worrying that she will lose him back to the nasty muddy river. This book claims to be about the love between parent and child after adoption, but the underlying message is about the new parent's fear of and disdain for the child's origins (birth parents). A book full of adoptism and racial put-downs, not recommended except as an opportunity to talk with your child about negative attitudes about adoption and race.

Keywords

Adoption, Racism

Age Range.

Preschool, early school-age

Author: Judith Gorog

Illustrator: Amanda Harvey

ISBN# 1564022951 Date Published. 1996 Price. $ 14.99
Publisher. Candlewick Pages. 32

AN ANGEL JUST LIKE ME

Rating

A new book from the author of Amazing Grace.

An original Christmas story from the award-winning author of *Amazing Grace*. Tyler's family needs a new Christmas tree angel, but the only angels Tyler can find have blond hair. Searching for a new angel for his family's tree — one that looks like him — has become his special project. But it's not until Christmas day that Tyler discovers that angels, like people, come in all different colors.

Keywords

African American, Race Relations, Self-Esteem, Black Identity, Holidays and Celebrations

Age Range:

Preschool, early school-age

Author: Mary Hoffman

Mary Hoffman is the author of *Amazing Grace* and *An Angel Just Like Me.*

ISBN# 803722656 Date Published: 1997 Price: $ 14.99

Publisher: Dial Pages: 32

ASHANTI TO ZULU: AFRICAN TRADITIONS

Rating

An ABC of African culture.

Ashanti to Zulu. This ABC of African culture covers a broad range of African traditions, from talking drums to the weaving of kente cloth. Authenticity of details is represented through the incredible illustrations and the spirited text. This is a gorgeous introduction to the tribes of Africa! A Caldecott Medal-winner, it was illustrated by Leo and Diane Dillon who created the art for *The People Could Fly* by Virginia Hamilton. A hardcover version of this book is also available by special order.

Keywords

Africa, Cultural History, Racial/Ethnic Identity, Self-Esteem, Black Identity

Age Range:

Preschool, early school-age

Author: Margaret Musgrove

Illustrator: Leo Dillon

Illustrator: Diane Dillon

ISBN# 0-14-054604-9 Date Published: 1977 Price: $ 4.99

Publisher: Puffin Pied Piper Pages: 32

AUNT HARRIET'S UNDERGROUND RAILROAD

Too much all at once.

Books in Print: "Cassie and Be Be, the young protagonists of Ringgold's *Tar Beach*, take a fantastical flight. They encounter a remnant of the Underground Railroad whose conductor is Harriet Tubman. Rambunctious Be Be boards the train, leaving his worried sister to follow behind with only directions from 'Aunt Harriet' and the kindness of strangers to guide her.... Cassie, Be Be and Harriet resonate with pride and energy, but their spirits can't help this work take flight."

Keywords

African American, Cultural History, Girl Power, Racial/Ethnic Identity, Black Identity, US History

Age Range:

Preschool, early school-age

Author-Illustrator: Faith Ringgold

Faith Ringgold is also the author of *Dinner At Aunt Connie's House* and *Bonjour Lonnie.*

ISBN# 0-517-88543-3 Date Published: 1993 Price: $ 6.95

Publisher: Dragonfly, Crown Pages: 32

BANZA, THE

A folk tale from Haiti.

The Banza is one of the few folk tales from Haiti available in paperback for young readers. This story is retold with delight and the illustrations are filled with whimsy and the power to inspire — a fun book for all ages. Publisher's Weekly says, "A banza is a little banjo and this one has magical powers! Wolkstein's airy, humorous version of this Haitian folk tale will add laurels to her status as a folklorist." While children from Haitian backgrounds may delight to see this story, it is equally important for children of all backgrounds to make the acquaintance of the stories and traditions of a variety of cultures.

Keywords

Folk tales and Legends, Haiti

Age Range:

Preschool, early school-age

Author: Diane Wolkstein

Illustrator: Marc Brown

ISBN# 140546057 Date Published: 1984 Price: $ 4.99

Publisher: Puffin Pages:

Rating

BARBER'S CUTTING EDGE, THE

The first book about hair for African American boys! Hooray.

The story of how a young boy's trip to the barbershop turns into a fun lesson about the secret to success. Mr. Bigalow's cutting edge includes "all the definitions from elementary to college." There are many books about African American hair care for girls but this is the only one we know of especially for boys. The illustrations are realistic in style and the story will hold the interest of young children. Most important, The *Barber's Cutting Edge* will acquaint children with what happens in the barber's chair and prepare them for their first visits.

Keywords

Hair, African American, Self-Esteem, Racial/Ethnic Identity, Black Identity, Boy Focus

Age Range:

Preschool, early school-age

Author: Gwendolyn Barrie-Laven

ISBN# 0-89239-127-8 Date Published: Price: $ 14.95

Publisher: Children's Book Pages:

Rating

BAT BOY AND HIS VIOLIN, THE

A great story for both baseball fans and music lovers.

More than anything, Reginald loves playing Tchaikovsky and Mozart on his violin. But his father needs a bat boy, not a "fiddler." Learning how to be a bat boy takes up all his practice time for his violin so Reginald must practice his music during spare moments on the field. The players are inspired by his music and go on to face the Monarchs, "the best colored team there is," with new spirit. Reginald's heartfelt passion for music and ability to share it with the team teaches his father that there is more than one way to find acceptance. The Horn Book calls the illustrations by E.B. Lewis "arrestingly beautiful." The book's characters are African American.

Keywords

African American, Boy Focus, Black Identity, Music and Dance, Sports, Self-Esteem

Age Range:

Preschool, early school-age

Author: Curtis Gavin

Illustrator: E. B. Lewis

ISBN# 0-689-80099-1 Date Published: 1998 Price: $ 16.00

Publisher: Simon & Schuster Pages: 32

BIG BOY

When Oli gets his wish to be big, he finds big problems and responsibilities.

From American Library Association: "Set in contemporary East Africa, Oli is tired of being the little one, tucked in bed with a story. He wants to be as big as his brother; no, he wants to be bigger than everyone. He sneaks out into the woods, and a magical Tunuka-zawadi bird grants him his wish. He sneezes, and elephants stampede. He jumps into the sea and causes a tidal wave. Of course, he wakes up in the woods in his mama's arms, and his loving family takes him home to bed. Less glossy than the art in Mollel's *Orphan Boy*, the stunning pictures here have a strong sense of contemporary East Africa."

Keywords

Africa, Self-Esteem, Family Life, Black Identity

Age Range:

Preschool, early school-age

Author: Tololwa M. Mollel

Tololwa M. Mollel is author of *Orphan Boy, Big Boy*, *The Princess Who Lost Her Hair* and more.

ISBN# 395845157 Date Published: 1997 Price: $ 5.95

Publisher: Clarion Pages: 27

BLACK COWBOY, WILD HORSES: A TRUE STORY

Love and respect for the unique talents of cowboys of color.

Though hardly ever mentioned, one of every three cowboys who helped tame the West was either Mexican or Black. This is the true story of Black cowboy, Bob Lemmons, a former slave "who could make the horses think he was one of them — because he was." A hero with uncanny tracking abilities, he trails a herd of mustangs and tames the wild horses. Pinkney's dramatic watercolors add the look of the Texas plains to the story and capture the energy of all the pretty horses as they gallop across sweeping, double-page spreads.

Keywords

African American, Role Models, Self-Esteem, History, US History

Age Range:

Preschool, early school-age

Author: Julius Lester

Illustrator: J. Brian Pinkney

Julius Lester is the author of *To Be A Slave; Sam* and the *Tigers; From Slave Ship To Freedom Road; What A Truly Cool World; Black Cowboy; Wild Horses*, and more.

ISBN# 803717881 Date Published: 1998 Price: $ 20.95

Publisher: Dial Pages: 40

Rating

BLACK SNOWMAN, THE

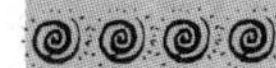

"I hate being black!" Jacob says. A book for anyone who struggles with identity.

Mama tells Jacob his thoughts are nonsense, but it takes the special power of a beautiful, brightly- woven cloth with a rich African history, along with an amazing Black snowman, to change his outlook and enable him to become proud. Don't miss this book! Books in Print says, "Mendez's message is be proud of yourself and your ancestry. Due to the complexity of the story, this book is suitable for an older audience than most picture books. The artist reinforces the snowman's message to Jacob, that there is dark beauty all around him, if he would only look for it."

Keywords

African American, Core Issues (Feelings), Racial/Ethnic Identity, Self-Esteem, Black Identity

Age Range:

Preschool, early school-age

Author: Phil Mendez

Illustrator: Carole Byard

ISBN# 0-590-44873-0 *Date Published:* 1989 *Price:* $ 5.99

Publisher: Scholastic *Pages:* 48

Rating

BRIGHT EYES, BROWN SKIN

These happy kids are playful, cooperative, curious and full-speed-ahead.

Olivia, Jordan, Ethan and Alexa all have "bright eyes, brown skin... warm as toast and all tucked in." They are happy kids who are playful, cooperative, curious and full-speed-ahead. This paperback picture book is very appealing to young children, offering a recite-along rhyme which encourages a game to affirm each child's own physical characteristics. The range of skin tones illustrated by the realistic images encourage children to respect diversity within their race and affirms the beauty of all brown skin, be it light tan or deep mahogany. Children are aware of skin tone differences as early as three or four years of age, and this book creates positive reflections for children of African American heritage.

Keywords

African American, Self-Esteem, Racial/Ethnic Identity, Black Identity, Diversity

Age Range:

Preschool, early school-age

Author: Cheryl Willis Hudson

Author: Bernette G. Ford

Cheryl Willis Hudson is the author of *Bright Eyes, Brown Skin* , *The Many Colors of Mother Goose* and *The Kids' Book of Wisdom*

ISBN# 0-940975-23-8 *Date Published:* 1990 *Price:* $ 6.95

Publisher: Just Us Books *Pages:* 24

BRINGING THE RAIN TO KAPITI PLAIN

A Reading Rainbow book by a Caldecott Award- winning writer.

The rhythmic "add-on" story of an African boy who eventually brings much-needed rain to Kapiti Plain. Each page adds a new verse to the story. A fun to read aloud interactive book which encourages repeating and chanting along. Think of this book as a terrific introduction to the African tradition of oral history and group participation. Beatriz Vidal's wonderful drawings of African landscapes and people enhance this story but *Bringing the Rain to Kapiti Plain* is a story book, not a picture book. The words themselves convey the story which can be fully understood and enjoyed without the pictures.

Keywords

African American, Folk tales and Legends, Poetry, Black Identity

Age Range:

Preschool, early school-age

Author: Verna Aardema

Illustrator: Beatriz Vidal

Verna Aardema is the author of *Borreguita and the Coyote, Bringing The Rain To Kapiti Plain*, and *Why Mosquitoes Buzz In People's Ears.*

ISBN# 0-14-054616-2 *Date Published:* 1992 *Price:* $ 5.99

Publisher: Puffin *Pages:* 32

BROTHERS OF THE KNIGHT

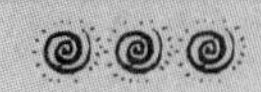

This is the first picture book by popular producer, choreographer and dancer Debbie Allen.

A hip retelling of the folk tale of the twelve dancing princesses by actress-producer Debbie Allen. Reverend Knight can't figure out why his twelve sons' hightops are "worn to threads, messed up, torn up, stinky, dirty, tacky, jacked up" each and every morning when the boys claim to have been asleep all night. Then the housekeeper discovers the boys' nightly trips to a swinging dance hall. They fear their father's disapproval, but he turns out to have a dancing past himself. Nelson's exuberant images capture the spirit, enriching the appeal to all children and particular for African American children will identify with the characters.

Keywords

African American

Age Range:

Preschool, early school-age

Author: Debbie Allen

Illustrator: Kadir Nelson

Debbie Allen is an award-winning dancer and entertainer. Kadir Nelson lives in San Diego.

ISBN# 803724888 *Date Published:* 1999 *Price:* $ 15.99

Publisher: Dial *Pages:* 40

Rating

BROWN LIKE ME

A picture book

This is a new release. We were not able to review it in time for publication but wanted to let you know of its availability. For updated information call 415-221-6957.

Keywords

African American

Age Range:

Preschool, early school-age

Author: Noelle Lamperti

ISBN# 1892281031 *Date Published:* 1999 *Price:* $ 12.95

Publisher: New Victoria *Pages:* 32

Rating

BUS RIDE, THE

How one child can make a difference.

This book has an introduction by Rosa Parks.

Keywords

Black Identity, Race Relations, Racism, Core Issues (Feelings), Cultural History, Fiction

Age Range:

Preschool, early school-age

Author: William Miller

Illustrator: John Ward

William Miller is the author of *Frederick Douglass; Richard Wright and the Library Card; Zora Hurston and the Chinaberry Tree; The Bus Ride;* and *House by the River.*

ISBN# 80000601 *Date Published:* 1998 *Price:* $ 15.95

Publisher: Lee & Low Books *Pages:* 32

COLOR ME PROUD

A favorite. Recommended by many Pact families.

African Americans who have made a difference are featured in this coloring book and name puzzle, an activity book that teaches pride in heritage.

Keywords

African American, Cultural History, Self-Esteem, Racial/Ethnic Identity, Black Identity, Biography

Age Range:

Preschool, early school-age

Author: Deborah Easton

ISBN# 188582100X *Date Published:* 1994 *Price:* $ 5.95

Publisher: Identity Toys *Pages:*

COLORS AROUND ME

Why are some people dark and some light:

This book explains that the skin of Black people encompasses a wide range of different shades and that all them are beautiful. Skin colors are compared to food colors. Highly recommended by Pact parents. Recommended by Darlene Powell Hopson and Derek S. Hopson, authors of *Different and Wonderful* and *Raising the Rainbow Generation.*

Keywords

African American, Black Identity, Diversity

Age Range:

Preschool, early school-age

Author: Vivian Church

ISBN# 0-910030-15-4 *Date Published:* 1971 *Price:* $ 6.95

Publisher: Afro Am Publishing "Co. *Pages:* 28

Rating

DARK DAY, LIGHT NIGHT

'Manda needs cheering up: Aunt Ruby makes her list the things she likes.

Angry with the whole world before her aunt challenges her to think about the things she likes, young Manda finds her bad mood fading in the face of sunshine, music, and the cream-colored cat that visits her window. Kirkus Reviews called it "An exceptionally warm vignette. This simple story, told in a colloquial first-person present tense, is seamlessly written; 'Manda's restored well-being feels authentic. The tenderly expressive portraits show African Americans in slightly old-fashioned surroundings."

Keywords

African American, Family Life, Core Issues (Feelings), Black Identity

Age Range:

Preschool, early school-age

Author: Jan Carr

Illustrator: James E. Ransome

ISBN# 078681201X" *Date Published:* 1997 *Price:* $ 4.95

Publisher: Disney Press *Pages:* 32

Rating

DAY OF DELIGHT

What are Black Jews like? A Jewish Sabbath in Ethiopia.

The Ethiopian Jews represent a way of life that is quickly vanishing. This evocative picture book, with vivid prose and striking illustrations, provides a memorable look at a unique culture. One of the few books to address this topic. Black Jewish children will recognize themselves in this book, and all children will be able to appreciate the pleasures of discovering familiar human desires in an unfamiliar setting.

Keywords

Judaism, Cultural History, African American, Holidays and Celebrations, Black Identity

Age Range:

Preschool, early school-age

Author: Maxine Rose Schur

Illustrator: J. Brian Pinkney

J. Brian Pinkney is the award winning illustrator of *Shake Shake Shake; Watch Me Dance; Happy Birthday, Dr. Martin Luther King; Max Found Two Sticks;* and *Mirandy & Brother Wind.*

ISBN# 803714130 *Date Published:* 1994 *Price:* $ 15.99

Publisher: Dial *Pages:*

EMEKA'S GIFT

Traditions and customs of the Igala tribe of southern Nigeria.

From Booklist: "Photographs taken in a village in southern Nigeria illustrate a warm hearted counting story. On the way to visit his grandmother, Emeka sees people and objects in groups numbering from 2 to 10. There is a nice balance between difference and sameness here: children play games in familiar ways, even when the games aren't familiar, and, refreshingly, the emphasis is on the artifacts of daily life rather than museum pieces."

Keywords

Africa, Family Life, Cultural History, Intergenerational

Age Range:

Preschool, early school-age

Author: Ifeoma Onyefulu

ISBN# 140565000 *Date Published:* 1999 *Price:* $ 5.99

Publisher: Puffin *Pages:* 24

FOLLOW THE DRINKING GOURD

Black Americans portrayed as followers, rather than as leaders.

A story of how slaves followed the stars, rivers and trees to freedom. Told in terms that young children can comprehend, this book offers a good way to introduce talk about the history of slavery. However, the text emphasizes the role played by white people in the Black flight to freedom. Black people are shown being dependent on the elements and on whites. Rather than making their own decisions, the Black characters seem fearful and dependent, looking to the heroic (and white) Joe for directions.

Keywords

African American, Folk tales and Legends, Black Identity, US History

Age Range:

Preschool, early school-age

Author-Illustrator: Jeanette Winter

Jeanette Winter is the author and illustrator of many books for children, including *Cowboy Charlie, Diego,* and *Shaker Boy.*

ISBN# 0-679-81997-5 *Date Published:* *Price:* $ 6.99

Publisher: Knopf *Pages:* 48

FORTUNE TELLERS, THE

Rating: ◎◎◎◎

Original folk tale recounting how a poor, unhappy, hardworking carpenter becomes a fortuneteller.

Lloyd Alexander's very funny story of a carpenter in the West African country of Cameroon visiting — and then becoming — the village fortuneteller is brought to life with some of Caldecott Medalist Trina Schart's most memorable artwork. Boston Globe-Horn Book Award. New York Times Best Illustrated Book of the year. School Library Journal Best Book of the Year.

Keywords

Folk tales and Legends, Africa, Cameroon, Boy Focus, Self-Esteem

Age Range,

Preschool, early school-age

Author: Lloyd Alexander

Illustrator: Trinan Schart Hyman

ISBN# 1405652338 *Date Published,* 1997 *Price,* $ 5.99

Publisher, Puffin *Pages,* 32

FREDERICK DOUGLASS

Rating: ◎◎◎

The African American abolitionist who discovered the meaning of freedom.

This story projects a clear and positive perspective for young people in general and offers a role model that African American children will identity with. Douglass is portrayed as a well-rounded character developing a clear sense of self as he helps the community. Publishers Weekly writes, "The success of this penetrating book lies in Miller's ability to convincingly convey Douglass' thoughts and feelings during his formative years as a plantation slave; and in Miller's focus on the limited — and pivotal — period of youth. The result is a searing, personal story that is easily absorbed by young readers."

Keywords

African American, Self-Esteem, Racial/Ethnic Identity, Role Models, Biography, Black Identity

Age Range,

Preschool, early school-age

Author: William Miller

Illustrator: Cedric Lucas

William Miller is the author of *Frederick Douglass; Richard Wright and the Library Card; Zora Hurston and the Chinaberry Tree; The Bus Ride;* and *House by the River.*

ISBN# 18800000423 *Date Published,* 1996 *Price,* $ 5.95

Publisher, Lee & Low Books *Pages,* 32

FROG WHO WANTED TO BE A STAR, THE

Rating: ◎◎◎◎

A message book (You can do It!) delivered with wit, humor, and fun.

The Frog who wanted to be a singer is one of the stories most often requested when Linda Goss performs. Frog is feeling mighty bad, mighty sad, and mighty frustrated. What happens as he sets out to solve his problem surprises everyone, including Frog himself. This story projects a clear and positive perspective for young people in general and a role model that African American children will identity with. Frog is portrayed as a well-rounded character progressing toward self-realization and the development of success.

Keywords

Self-Esteem, African American, Black Identity

Age Range,

Preschool, early school-age

Author: Linda Goss

Linda Goss is the author of *The Frog Who Wanted To Be A Star* and *Jump Up and Say.*

ISBN# 0-531-06895-1 *Date Published,* *Price,* $ 16.95

Publisher, Orchard *Pages,*

GLORIOUS ANGELS, A CELEBRATION OF CHILDREN

Rating: ◎◎◎

A companion volume to Brown Angels, *a collection of poems and photographs of children.*

Walter Dean Myers once again uses antique photographs of children, this time from all over the world. "When we celebrate these children," he says, "we celebrate ourselves." His book Brown Angels is very popular with Pact families. This one should have as least as broad an appeal.

Keywords

Diversity, Multicultural, Multiracial, Self-Esteem, Racial/Ethnic Identity, Poetry

Age Range,

Preschool, early school-age

Author: Walter Dean Myers

Walter Dean Myers is the author of *One More River To Cross; Brown Angels; Me, Mop,* and the *Moondance Kid s, Slam, Malcolm X, Hoops,* and many more.

ISBN# 64467260 *Date Published,* 1997 *Price,* $ 6.95

Publisher, HarperCollins *Pages,* 48

Rating

GOLDEN BEAR

A special tribute to a special relationship and to a youngster's fertile imagination.

Whether rocking in the rocking chair, making a snowman together, or playing pirates in the tub, *Golden Bear* is the perfect companion for a young child. This truly sweet book, with its intensely colored chalk illustrations, will be enjoyed by all children, especially those who identify with the African American little boy. A special book to read over and over. A Pact bestseller.

Keywords

Core Issues (Feelings), African American, Black Identity, Friendship

Age Range:

Preschool, early school-age

Author: Ruth Young

ISBN# 0-050959-3 Date Published: Price: $ 4.99
Publisher: Puffin Pages: 32

Rating

GRANDPA, IS EVERYTHING BLACK BAD?

An African American boy appreciates his dark skin by learning about his heritage.

Montsho is worried. On his long list of things that seem scary, bad, or sad, everything is black. Does that mean everything black is bad? Since he has black skin, does that make him bad too? The first half of this book covers his list: being scared of the dark, black widow spiders, witches, black sheep, getting a black eye, bad guys on TV. Through his wise words, his Grandpa inspires his imagination with visions of his proud heritage, and his magical African drum lets Montsho hear the beauty of his ancestry for himself. This is a book for children of all races, to help them perceive and question society's interpretations of the colors black and white. Presents a great opportunity for discussion.

Keywords

Africa, African American, Antiracist Strategies, Black Identity, Racial/Ethnic Identity, Cultural History

Age Range:

Preschool, early school-age

Author: Sandy Lynne Holman

ISBN# 964465507 Date Published: 1998 Price: $ 18.95
Publisher: Culture Coop Pages: 32

GREAT AFRICAN AMERICAN ATHLETES

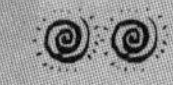

African American athletes to color.

Drawings of contemporary heroes to color, paint, or just enjoy as is. This collection of heroes projects a clear and positive perspective for young people in general, while comprising a group of role models that that can be appreciated by children in general while offering strong role models to African American children in particular.

Keywords

Biography, African American, Cultural History, Black Identity, Sports, Role Models

Age Range:

Preschool, early school-age

Author-Illustrator: Taylor Ogden

ISBN# 048629319X Date Published: 1996 Price: $ 2.95
Publisher: Dover Pages:

HAPPY BIRTHDAY, MARTIN LUTHER KING

Martin Luther King, Jr.'s story, told in words that very young children will understand.

Books in Print: "The author's brief narrative outlines the leader's civil rights accomplishments that kids are most likely to understand — those that enabled African Americans and whites to sit together in buses, drink from the same water fountains and attend the same schools. Marzollo's language is equally accessible: 'His dream was that people everywhere would learn to live together without being mean to one another.'"

Keywords

Race Relations, Self-Esteem, Black Identity, Biography, Birthdays, Role Models

Age Range:

Preschool, early school-age

Author: Jean Marzollo

Illustrator: J. Brian Pinkney

J. Brian Pinkney is the award-winning illustrator of *Shake Shake Shake; Watch Me Dance; Max Found Two Sticks*; and *Mirandy & Brother Wind.*

ISBN# 0-671-87523-X Date Published: 1993 Price: $ 3.95
Publisher: Scholastic Pages: 32

Rating

HAPPY TO BE NAPPY

Nappy hair is great!

Acclaimed African-American author and poet bell hooks joins forces with illustrator Chris Rashchka to celebrate the joy and beauty of "nappy hair" in an exuberant, rhythmic, read-aloud book.

Keywords

African American, Hair

Age Range:

Preschool, early school-age

Author: bell hooks

Illustrator: Chris Raschka

ISBN# 786804270 Date Published: 1999 Price: $ 14.99

Publisher: Hyperion Pages: 32

Rating

I LOVE MY HAIR

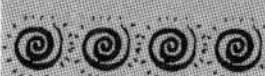

African American hair is a crown of glory.

Kenyana, a young African American girl, doesn't feel very lucky about her hair until her Mama shows her the many wonderful ways she can style it. Soon she is filled with pride over its versatility and finds ample reasons to love her hair. Appealing illustrations.

Keywords

Hair, Self-Esteem, African American, Black Identity

Age Range:

Preschool, early school-age

Author: Natasha Tarpley

Illustrator: E. B. Lewis

Natasha Tarpley is the author of *I Love My Hair* and *Testimony.*

ISBN# 316522759 Date Published: 1998 Price: $ 14.95

Publisher: Little Brown Pages: 32

IN THE TIME OF DRUMS

Mentu retells the legend of a slave rebellion.

"Based on the Gullah legend of a slave rebellion at Ibo's Landing in the Sea Islands, this stirring picture book tells the story from the point of view of an African American child. Mentu is island born and has never known Africa, but his beloved grandmother, Twi, is an Ibo conjure woman who remembers the times before. Unlike many who work in the fields, 'harvesting what they could not keep,' she is not broken by slavery. She teaches Mentu the old stories and songs and her secrets. Then one hot, breathless day, a slave ship arrives with a whole village of Ibo from Benin...." — Booklist.

Keywords

African American, History, Racism, Race Relations

Age Range:

Preschool, early school-age

Author: Kim L. Siegelson

Illustrator: J. Brian Pinkney

ISBN# 078680436X Date Published: 1999 Price: $ 15.99

Publisher: Jump At The Sun Pages: 32

IT TAKES A VILLAGE

A picture book by a former Peace Corps worker, set in Benin, West Africa.

From Booklist: "Yemi is proud that she's to take care of her little brother, Kokou, while their mother is busy selling mangoes. When he wanders off, Yemi searches everywhere for him, but in fact, everyone in the village has taken special care of him, just as Yemi's mother always knew they would. The title comes from the African proverb, 'It takes a village to raise a child.'" Kirkus Reviews writes, "The author's deep-felt, attractively designed illustrations include many details of the marketplace and underline its warm, neighborly atmosphere. A nicely shaped and unusually likable story."

Keywords

Africa, Sibling Issues, Family Life, Core Issues (Feelings), Extended Family

Age Range:

Preschool, early school-age

Author: Jane Cowen Fletcher

ISBN# 590465732 Date Published: 1994 Price: $ 15.95

Publisher: Scholastic Pages:

JUNETEENTH JAMBOREE

Rating 

What is Juneteenth?

Cassandra and her family have moved to her parents' hometown in Texas, but it doesn't feel like home to Cassandra until she experiences Juneteenth, a Texas-born tradition celebrating the end of slavery. Joining her parents in the community celebration, Cassie learns about the day when slaves in Texas learned they were free, some two years after the Emancipation Proclamation, while she wonders why the news took so long to reach them. One of the few books to address Juneteenth celebrations, *Juneteenth Jamboree* projects positive images children will enjoy.

Keywords

African American, Self-Esteem, Race Relations, Racism, US History, Holidays and Celebrations

Age Range:

Preschool, early school-age

Author: Carole Boston Weatherford

Illustrator: Yvonne Buchanan

ISBN# 1880000180 Date Published: Price: $ 15.95

Publisher: Lee & Low Books Pages:

KENTE COLORS

Rating 

Vivid paintings and rhymes introducing us to kente cloth and its weavers.

Vivid, colorful paintings illustrate this simple rhyming text offering an introduction to kente cloth and its weavers. The oversize scale and bright, detailed, realistic paintings offer an engaging account of the colors and meanings of kente cloth and of the culture of the Ewe weavers.

Keywords

Africa, Cultural History, Racial/Ethnic Identity, Black Identity

Age Range:

Preschool, early school-age

Author: Deborah Newton Chocolate

Illustrator: John Ward

ISBN# 0-8027-8388-0 Date Published: 1996 Price: $ 6.95

Publisher: Walker and Co. Pages: 32

KOFI AND HIS MAGIC

Kofi lives in Bonwire, West Africa where kente cloth is woven.

Maya Angelou shares a slice of the daily life of Kofi, a child from the West African town of Bonwire, known for its weaving of beautiful kente cloth. This book is the second in a series about children's lives around the world, following *My Painted House, My Yellow Chicken.* As with its predecessor, its photographs are breathtaking; Courtney-Clarke has an extraordinary ability to capture the spirit and individuality of people and to reveal the beauty that is found among ordinary details of their lives. A wonderful evocation of a traditional African way of life.

Keywords

Self-Esteem, Racial/Ethnic Identity, African American, Cultural History, Black Identity, Africa

Age Range:

Preschool, early school-age

Author: Maya Angelou

Illustrator: Margaret Courtney-Clarke

Maya Angelou is a world-famous author. Her works include *Kofi and His Magic; My Painted House, My Friendly Chicken and Me;* and *Life Doesn't Frighten Me.*

ISBN# 0-517-70453-6 Date Published: 1996 Price: $ 17.00

Publisher: Clarkson Potter Pages: 48

LET'S GET THE RHYTHM OF THE BAND

The title says it all.

In a small package, this book accomplishes a lot. Cut paper drawings offer a multitude of African and African American cultural images; efficient and accessible narratives introduce various eras of the music's cultural history (The African Source; Folk Music, etc.); the accompanying scores and musical games allow for play-along and sing-along opportunities; and inset mini-histories illuminate central musical figures (Mahalia Jackson, Bessie Smith, The Supremes). The accompanying cassette offers wonderful versions introduced by brief narrative histories.

Keywords

African American, Cassette, Cultural History, Music and Dance, Black Identity

Age Range:

Preschool, early school-age

Author: Cheryl Warren Mattox

Illustrator: Varnette P. Honeywood

Cheryl Warren Mattox is the editor of *Let's Get the Rhythm of the Band* and *Shake it to the One You Love The Best.*

ISBN# 0-938971-97-2 Date Published: 1993 Price: $ 9.95

Publisher: JTG of Nashville Pages: 64

Rating

MARKITA

A story about feelings regarding skin tones for children.

For Markita Jackson, being the darkest member of a light-skinned family means being slighted in many littleways. Pleasant stories about beautiful flowers in a colorful human bouquet offer little comfort to a young girl who never feels as special as her fair-skinned cousins.

Keywords

African American, Multiracial, Race Relations, Black Identity, Racism, Family Life

Age Range.

Preschool, early school-age

Author: Alissa Nash

Illustrator: Debby London

ISBN# 091354339X Date Published. 1997 Price. $ 7.95
Publisher. African American Pages. 36

Rating

MARY HAD A LITTLE LAMB

A new twist on an old favorite, this time with African American characters.

Children have delighted in the story of Mary and her pet lamb for more than 150 years. What happens when Mary's lamb follows her to school one day? Now this special friendship, time and place come to life in the rich patterns, colors and textures of distinctive fabric relief collages, creating a stunning picture book full of details and childlike whimsy. Illustrated by photographs, in this version Mary is an African American child.

Keywords

African American, Folk tales and Legends, Black Identity, Self-Esteem, Poetry

Age Range.

Preschool, early school-age

Author: Bruce McMillan

ISBN# 590437747 Date Published. 1992 Price. $ 4.95
Publisher. Scholastic Pages. 32

MASAI AND I

What would Linda's life be like if she were Masai

One day in school, Linda learns about the proud people of East Africa called the Masai. She feels a sense of kinship and begins to wonder what her world would be like if she were Masai. Would she know her neighbors? Would she have pets or play in the plains with giraffes and ostriches and zebras? Would her family be different?

Keywords

Africa, Cultural History, Core Issues (Feelings), Folk tales and Legends, Black Identity, Self-Esteem

Age Range.

Preschool, early school-age

Author: Virginia Kroll

Virginia Kroll is the author of *Beginnings, Hats Off To Hair, Masai and I,* and more.

ISBN# 0-689-80454-7 Date Published. 1997 Price. $ 5.99
Publisher. Aladdin Pages. 32

MAX FOUND TWO STICKS

Max changes what starts out to be a ho-hum day into an exciting one.

One day when Max doesn't feel too much like talking to anybody, he finds two sticks that make a perfect pair of drumsticks. Soon he is beating out a rhythm on anything he can find, from his thigh to a bucket to a large garbage can. Suddenly a marching band comes around Max's corner and the most wonderful thing happens. Wonderful full-color illustrations depict main characters who just happen to be African American.

Keywords

African American, Boy Focus, Music and Dance, Black Identity

Age Range.

Preschool, early school-age

Illustrator: J. Brian Pinkney

J. Brian Pinkney is the award-winning illustrator of *Shake Shake Shake; Watch Me Dance; Happy Birthday, Dr. Martin Luther King; Max Found Two Sticks;* and *Mirandy & Brother Wind.*

ISBN# 068981593X Date Published. 1997 Price. $ 5.99
Publisher. Aladdin Pages. 32

MEET DANITRA BROWN

Rating 

Poems about the "most splendiferous girl in town."

Zuri Jackson wants readers to meet her friend, Danitra Brown. In thirteen rhymes, Zuri narrates an unforgettable portrait of the many ways in which friends bring out the best in each other.

Keywords

African American, Friendship, Black Identity, Poetry

Age Range:

Preschool, early school-age

Author: Nikki Grimes

Nikki Grimes is the author of *Baby's Bedtime, Meet Danitra Brown, Something On My Mind,* and *Wild Wild Hair.* Tom Feelings is the illustrator of *Something On My Mind.*

ISBN# 688154719 Date Published: 1997 Price: $ 4.95

Publisher: Mulberry Pages: 32

MINTY

Rating

A Story of Young Harriet Tubman. A Caldecott Medal winner.

From Booklist: "Set on the Maryland plantation where Harriet Tubman ("Minty") was raised as a slave, this fictionalized story dramatizes what daily life was like for her as a child. Schroeder's words are clear and strong and Pinkney's realistic portraits are powerful. As in *John Henry*, the dappled double-page landscapes connect the strong child hero to the might of the natural world. Minty's mother tells her to 'pat the lion,' but her father knows she means to run away, and several idyllic paintings show him teaching her to read the night sky, swim in the river and survive in the woods."

Keywords

African American, History, Cultural History

Age Range:

Preschool, early school-age

Author: Alan Schroeder

Illustrator: J. Brian Pinkney

Alan Schroeder is the author of *Satchmo's Blues; Minty;* and more.

ISBN# 803718888 Date Published: 1996 Price: $ 16.99

Publisher: Dial Pages:

MIRANDY AND BROTHER WIND

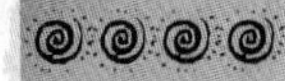

A Caldecott Honor book about a proud young girl.

How do you catch the wind? This engaging tale dances with spirit and good humor, and its rich, eye-catching watercolors of the rural South make it a rare, rewarding picture book to be read and enjoyed again and again. A great depiction of African American life and lore. "Everyone says that if Mirandy captures the Wind he will do her bidding, but nobody seems to know how to capture him." —Books in Print. Coretta Scott King Award Winner.

Keywords

African American, Self-Esteem, Folk tales and Legends, Girl Power, Black Identity

Age Range:

Preschool, early school-age

Author: Patricia McKissack

Illustrator: J. Brian Pinkney

J. Brian Pinkney is the award-winning illustrator of *Shake Shake Shake; Watch Me Dance; Happy Birthday, Dr. Martin Luther King; Max Found Two Sticks;* and *Mirandy & Brother Wind.*

ISBN# 0-679-88333-9 Date Published: 1996 Price: $ 6.99

Publisher: Random House Pages:

MORE THAN ANYTHING ELSE

"More than anything else," nine-year-old Booker T. Washington wanted to learn to read.

Booker T. Washington must leave the cabin before dawn to work in the salt works, returning home after dark. Learning to read seems unlikely. After seeing a man reading to a crowd, Booker tells his mama his dream of reading and she hands him a book. His story then takes a thrilling turn. Books in Print: "Throughout the narrative, Booker glows with his desire to read, and the inspiring tone of the language predicts a bright future. Soentpiet's watercolors perfectly match the emotional level of the text. Booker lifting a heavy shovel of salt, practicing his letters by candlelight, his shining face after writing his name; these images help the words create a moving, inspirational story."

Keywords

Self-Esteem, Black Identity, African American, Cultural History, Biography, Role Models

Age Range:

Preschool, early school-age

Author: Marie Bradby

Illustrator: Chris K. Soentpiet

ISBN# 0-531-09464-2 Date Published: 1995 Price: $ 15.95

Publisher: Orchard Pages: 32

Rating

MOTHER CROCODILE

Senegalese folk tale about the history of Africa.

Just because Mother Crocodile once snapped at him when he teased her, Golo-the-Monkey tells the other animals that she's crazy. He even tells the little crocodiles, her children, who believe him. Sadly, when disaster comes to the young crocodiles' tranquil river, it is almost too late to heed Mother Crocodile's warnings. Coretta Scott King Award winner.

Keywords

Folk tales and Legends, Self-Esteem, Africa, Black Identity

Age Range:

Preschool, early school-age

Author: Rosa Guy

ISBN# 440410061 Date Published: Price: $ 4.99

Publisher: Bantam Pages:

Rating

MUFARO'S BEAUTIFUL DAUGHTER

A classic African tale, similar to – but different from – the traditional Cinderella.

Zimbabwean folk tale of pride going before a fall. Two sisters, spiteful Manyara and considerate Nyasha, compete for the young king who is searching for a bride. Illustrations, which will fill the heart of every Black girl, glow with John Steptoe's vision of the land and people of his ancestors. A Coretta Scott King Award winner.

Keywords

Africa, Girl Power, Folk tales and Legends, Black Identity

Age Range:

Preschool, early school-age

Illustrator: John Steptoe

John Steptoe, a two-time Caldecott Honor Book recipient, is the author of *Jumping Mouse; Baby Says; Creativity; Mufaro's Beautiful Daughter* and *Stevie.*

ISBN# 688040454 Date Published: 1987 Price: $ 16.00

Publisher: Lothrop Pages:

MY PAINTED HOUSE, MY FRIENDLY CHICKEN

A beautiful book from cover to cover.

One of America's favorite poets joins a respected photojournalist to introduce a girl named Thandi, her best friend (a chicken) and her painted village among the Ndebele people of South Africa. The extraordinary photographs, bright and intensely colorful, make this book a feast for the eyes and offer moments of extreme beauty among the lives and ways of the Ndebele people. A treasure.

Keywords

Africa, Cultural History, African American, Black Identity, Self-Esteem, Role Models

Age Range:

Preschool, early school-age

Author: Maya Angelou

Illustrator: Margaret Courtney-Clarke

Maya Angelou is a world-famous author. Her works include *Kofi and His Magic; My Painted House, My Friendly Chicken and Me;* and *Life Doesn't Frighten Me.*

ISBN# 0-517-59667-9 Date Published: 1994 Price: $ 6.99

Publisher: Clarkson Potter Pages: 42

NAPPY HAIR

Brenda has the nappiest hair in the whole family – and the most wonderful.

In a unique and vibrant picture book that uses the African American call-and-response tradition, a family talks back and forth about adorable Brenda's hair. The family delights in poking gentle fun with their hilarious descriptions, all the time discovering the inherent beauty and value of Brenda's hair.

Keywords

Hair, African American, Black Identity

Age Range:

Preschool, early school-age

Author: Carolivia Herron

ISBN# 0-679-87937-4 Date Published: 1997 Price: $ 6.99

Publisher: Knopf Pages: 32

NOBODY OWNS THE SKY

Rating: @@@@

The story of Bessie Coleman, the first licensed Black aviator in the world.

Born over a century ago, Bessie Coleman spent her days in the cotton fields, but she always wanted to fly. Miraculously, she went on to become the first licensed African American aviator in the world. Now Reeve Lindbergh, the daughter of Anne Morrow Lindbergh, another pioneering aviator, honors the memory of Bessie Coleman with a poem that sings of her life and her astonishing accomplishment. Lindbergh wrote this book because "Bessie was an incredibly brave person who was hardly noticed, while my parents got so much publicity that it was difficult for them to live their normal lives. I saw a crazy imbalance and wanted to set things right." Full color.

Keywords

Adoption, Self-Esteem, Biography, Role Models, Girl Power

Age Range:

Preschool, early school-age

Author: Reeve Lindbergh

Reeve Lindbergh, the author of *Where is the Sun*, is the daughter of Charles Lindbergh and Anne Morrow Lindbergh.

ISBN# 763603619 | Date Published: 1998 | Price: $ 5.99

Publisher: Candlewick | Pages: 32

PALM TREES

Rating: @@@

Many girls will identify with this entertaining, not-so-hair-raising story.

On a hot summer's day, an African American girl and her friend have to untangle a challenge to their friendship. This story shows how the heroine discovers a new appreciation of herself and of her glorious hair. Books in Print: "A story of independence and friendship set in an African American community. After her mother leaves for work, Millie sits down in front of the mirror to fix her unruly hair. Patiently struggling with the comb, she neatly ties up two pony tails. She dresses and walks outside, feeling very grown up, but her happy mood is destroyed when her friend Renee says, 'You've got palm trees on your head.'"

Keywords

Friendship, Hair, African American, Self-Esteem, Black Identity, Race Relations

Age Range:

Preschool, early school-age

Author-Illustrator: Nancy Cote

ISBN# 0-02-724760-0 | Date Published: 1993 | Price: $ 14.95

Publisher: Four Winds Press | Pages: 40

PICTURE BOOK OF JACKIE ROBINSON, A

Rating: @@@

A portrait of the first African American player in the major baseball league.

Horn Book: "When Jackie Robinson joined the Brooklyn Dodgers in 1947, there were no other African Americans playing in the major leagues. The thoughtful, brief portrait illuminates the courage and character of an American hero. Appealing watercolors complement the simple text." And Kirkus Reviews says, "Adler's biography tells how a courageous man and outstanding athlete desegregated major league baseball. Easily read and educational."

Keywords

Biography, African American, Cultural History, Role Models, Sports, Black Identity

Age Range:

Preschool, early school-age

Author: David A. Adler

Illustrator: Robert Casilla

David A. Adler is author of *A Picture Book of Eleanor Roosevelt* and *Hilde and Eli.*

ISBN# 823413047 | Date Published: 1994 | Price: $ 6.95

Publisher: Holiday House | Pages:

PRINCESS WHO LOST HER HAIR, THE

Rating: @@

An Akamba (African) legend.

When a proud and vain princess loses her hair — her most prized possession — a beggar boy helps her to learn the meaning of generosity and brings an end to the drought that has plagued the kingdom of the haughty princess. Books in Print writes, "A vain princess whose refusal to give even a strand of her beautiful hair to a bird building a nest costs her her hair and her kingdom its livelihood. As famine descends upon the land, Muoma, a beggar boy, sets off to find the bird. For sharing his last food, water, and strength with an ant, a flower, and a mouse, respectively, he is rewarded, and he subsequently helps and marries the humbled princess. The interdependence of all living things figures strongly here."

Keywords

Folk tales and Legends, Africa, Hair, Black Identity, Friendship

Age Range:

Preschool, early school-age

Author: Tololwa M. Mollel

Author: Charles Reasoner

Tololwa M. Mollel is author of *Orphan Boy, Big Boy*, *The Princess Who Lost Her Hair* and more.

ISBN# 081672816X | Date Published: 1993 | Price: $ 3.95

Publisher: Troll | Pages: 32

RAISING DRAGONS

Rating

The adventures of Hank the dragon and "Cupcake," the African American child who raises him.

Booklist says that "the focus here is on the strong, smart, devoted little girl, who is willing to work hard to give substance to what most people think is strictly make-believe. A book that pushes children to look beyond the obvious." Kirkus Reviews calls it "a fresh and cheery tall tale, told in an appropriately matter-of-fact tone." Children love this story.

Keywords

African American, Family Life

Age Range.

Preschool, early school-age

Author: Jerdine Nolan

Illustrator: Elise Primavera

ISBN# 152012885 | Date Published. 1998 | Price. $ 16.00

Publisher. Harcourt Brace | Pages. 40

RICHARD WRIGHT AND THE LIBRARY CARD

Rating

A poignant childhood turning point for one of this country's most brilliant writers.

This is a true story of this important Black American author and his determination to borrow books from the public library that turned him away because of his color. As a young Black man in the segregated South of the 1920s, Wright was motivated and sustained by his love of reading; with a co-worker's help, Wright's love of language and his unwavering perseverance come together to make his dream a reality. An inspirational story for children of all backgrounds, this book relates a turning point in the life of a man who became one of this country's most brilliant writers, the author of *Native Son* and *Black Boy*.

Keywords

African American, Racial/Ethnic Identity, Role Models, Self-Esteem, Biography, Black Identity

Age Range.

Preschool, early school-age

Author: William Miller

Illustrator: Gregory Christie

William Miller is the author of *Frederick Douglass; Richard Wright and the Library Card; Zora Hurston and the Chinaberry Tree; The Bus Ride;* and *House by the River.*

ISBN# 1880000881 | Date Published. 1997 | Price. $ 6.95

Publisher. Lee & Low Books | Pages. 32

SATCHMO'S BLUES

What was Louis Armstrong like as a child?

It's a pleasure to be in his company on the steamy streets of New Orleans as Louis Armstrong grows up determined to make his own amazing version of the music that surrounds him. The New York Times Book Review says that it "stands very successfully on its own as a touching story about a small boy's passionate determination to achieve his goal." "The incredible drive that carried Armstrong from poverty to worldwide fame is shown clearly in young Louis's single-minded pursuit of a dream, and therein lies the book's message and its appeal." —Kirkus Reviews

Keywords

African American, Music and Dance, Role Models, Biography

Age Range.

Preschool, early school-age

Author: Alan Schroeder

Author: Floyd Cooper

Alan Schroeder is the author of Satchmo's Blues; Minty; and more.

ISBN# 440414725 | Date Published. 1999 | Price. $ 5.99

Publisher. Yearling Books | Pages. 32

SKY SASH SO BLUE

Susannah's blue sash is an emblem of hope and enduring love in a slave family.

History is brought alive by this story of a slave family's efforts to create a wedding celebration even when they're denied even the simplest elements of the ceremony — a wedding dress and a preacher. Susannah's sister is marrying a free Black man in a secret wedding; her family, who are slaves, manage to gather enough bits of cloth to make her an "all-over" dress. The award-winning artist Benny Andrews here makes his debut as a picture book illustrator. His illustrations, using a technique of painted fabric collages, render this story powerful and beautiful.

Keywords

Black Identity, Core Issues (Feelings), Cultural History, Family Life, Self-Esteem, Girl Power

Age Range.

Preschool, early school-age

Author: Libby Hawthorn

Illustrator: Benny Andrews

Libby Hawthorn has written many books for children both in her native Australia and in the United States.

ISBN# 689810903 | Date Published. 1998 | Price. $ 16.00

Publisher. Simon & Schuster | Pages. 32

TEAMMATES

Rating

Describes the racial preiudice experienced by Jackie Robinson when he joined the Brooklyn Dodgers.

This book offers an account of Jackie Robinson's difficulties in becoming the first Black player in Major League baseball and relates the acceptance and support he received from his white teammate, Pee Wee Reese. Books in Print says, "Golenbock has taken a single moment of baseball history, set it in its social context, and created a simple and moving tribute to courage and brotherhood." Received the Redbook Children's Picture book Award. A Parent's magazine "Best Kids' Books of 90" selection; an NCSS-CBC Notable Children's Trade Book in the Field of Social Studies.

Keywords

Race Relations, Self-Esteem, Biography, Sports, Friendship, Role Models

Age Range:

Preschool, early school-age

Author: Peter Golenbock

Illustrator: Paul Bacon

ISBN# 0-15-284286-1 Date Published: 1992 Price: $ 6.95

Publisher: Harcourt Brace Pages: 32

TO BE A DRUM

Rating

"Long before time, on the continent of Africa; the rhythm of the earth beat."

Evelyn Coleman invites readers to join the present and the past — to listen and to become a drum. An appealing story reflecting the history and spirit of African people. Engaging illustrations add much to the text. A Smithsonian Magazine Notable Book for Children for 1996.

Keywords

African American, Cultural History, Music and Dance, Self-Esteem, Racial/Ethnic Identity, Black Identity

Age Range:

Preschool, early school-age

Author: Evelyn Coleman

Illustrator: Aminah Brenda Robinson

Evelyn Coleman is the author of *To Be A Drum* and *White Socks Only.*

ISBN# 807580066 Date Published: 1996 Price: $ 16.95

Publisher: Whitman Pages: 32

TOO MUCH TALK

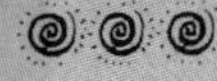

A fun tale everyone will enjoy.

A traditional West African folk tale about a talking yam, the fish that says that yams can talk and the weaver whose cloth has something to say on the matter. Great illustrations.

Keywords

Folk tales and Legends, African American, Black Identity, Africa

Age Range:

Preschool, early school-age

Author: Angela Medearis

Angela Medearis is the author of *Eat, Babies, Eat!; Too Much Talk,* and more.

ISBN# 1-56402-323-0 Date Published: Price: $ 5.99

Publisher: Candlewick Pages:

WHAT A TRULY COOL WORLD

A funny, irreverent, and contemporary view of creation.

In a reinvention of Zora Neale Hurston's African American tale, Lester and Cepeda have fun "playing with God" because He might get lonely if we take Him too seriously. God is humanized, in this story: he wears house slippers, has a wife named Irene and a secretary named Bruce, and works with Shaniqua, "the angel in charge of everybody's business." A "truly cool" and purely playful account. From Kirkus Reviews: "The language is winning: Bruce greets his boss with 'Yo! What's up, Deity?' Cepeda's paintings carry the warmth: Bruce wears strap-on wings and has a computer of Everything That Is Going to Be; God's chair is a bright red recliner."

Keywords

African American, Folk tales and Legends, Spiritual Meanings

Age Range:

Preschool, early school-age

Author: Julius Lester

Author: Joseph Cepeda

Julius Lester is the author of *To Be A Slave; Sam and the Tigers; From Slave Ship To Freedom Road; What A Truly Cool World; Black Cowboy; Wild Horses,* and more.

ISBN# 590864688 Date Published: 1999 Price: $ 15.95

Publisher: Scholastic Pages: 40

Rating

WHEN JOE LOUIS WON THE TITLE

Jo worries that people will laugh at her unusual name.

Jo was born the night Joe Lewis won the title and her grandpa, John Henry, met her grandma. Jo's grandfather helps her feel better about herself when he tells her the story of why she is named for the heavyweight boxing champion Joe Louis. Vivid, full-color illustrations add greatly to this story that combines family history with American history and Black pride.

Keywords

Self-Esteem, Racial/Ethnic Identity, African American, Girl Power, Black Identity

Age Range.

Preschool, early school-age

Author: Belinda Rochelle

ISBN# 0-395-81657-2 Date Published. Price. $ 5.95
Publisher. Houghton Mifflin Pages.

Rating

WHITE SOCKS ONLY

Grandma's story shows a strong Black community, not often depicted in children's literature.

Grandma tells a story of walking into town alone in Mississippi on a hot day: she had never before gone alone. There was a "Whites Only" sign on a nearby fountain, but that didn't bother this child — after all, she was wearing her clean white socks. Evelyn Coleman combines memories of her Southern childhood with magical realism to create a story that resonates with power. Tyrone Geter's full-color illustrations convey great feeling and emotion.

Keywords

Race Relations, Racism, African American, Cultural History, Girl Power, Black Identity

Age Range.

Preschool, early school-age

Author: Evelyn Coleman

Illustrator: Tyrone Geter

Evelyn Coleman is the author of *To Be A Drum* and *White Socks Only.*

ISBN# 080758956X Date Published. 1996 Price. $ 6.95
Publisher. Whitman Pages.

WHY THE SUN AND MOON LIVE IN THE SKY

An African folk tale.

This is the simple tale of the Sun, the Moon, and the Water and how they came to be where they are. Illustrations by Blair Lent capture a true feeling of Africa. Caldecott Honor book. Books in Print says, "Striking primitive illustrations aid in the retelling of this African folk tale about the consequences of an overwhelming visit from Water and his people."

Keywords

Africa, Folk tales and Legends, Black Identity

Age Range.

Preschool, early school-age

Author: Elphinstone Dayrell

Illustrator: Blair Lent

ISBN# 0-395-53963-3 Date Published. 1990 Price. $ 6.95
Publisher. Houghton Mifflin Pages. 32

WILD WILD HAIR

Tisa hides when it's time to comb and braid her hair. Then what happens.

Tisa hates Mondays because that's when she gets her long, thick, wild hair combed and braided, so she hides. But once Tisa's hair is done, she loves it so much her mother can hardly tear her away from the mirror.

Keywords

Hair, African American, Self-Esteem, Black Identity

Age Range.

Preschool, early school-age

Author: Nikki Grimes

Nikki Grimes is the author of *Baby's Bedtime, Meet Danitra Brown, Something On My Mind,* and *Wild Wild Hair.* Tom Feelings is the illustrator of *Something On My Mind.*

ISBN# 0-590-26590-3 Date Published. 1997 Price. $ 3.99
Publisher. Houghton Mifflin Pages.

Rating

Rating

A IS FOR ASIA

An alphabetical introduction to the diverse people, land, and cultures of the world's largest continent.

From Booklist: "From A for Asia to Z for Zen, the alphabet arrangement provides an introduction to the geography, culture, holidays, traditions, and animals of the area that is home to more than one-half of the world's population. The paragraph for each letter describes as well as names its letter. Heo's brightly detailed illustrations pick up the extraordinary diversity of the huge area with a wide range of folk-art styles, from delicate batik craft in Indonesia to camel riders racing in Saudi Arabia. The word for each letter is written in an Asian language; for example, 'lotus' is in Hindu, 'monsoon' is in Urdu."

Keywords

Asian, China, Japanese , Korean , India, Arab

Age Range:

Preschool, early school-age

Author: Cynthia Chin-Lee

Illustrator: Yumi Heo

Cynthia Chin-Lee is the author of *Almond Cookies and Dragon Well Tea,* and *A is for Asia.*

ISBN# 531300110 *Date Published:* 1997 *Price:* $ 15.95

Publisher: Orchard *Pages:* 32

AEKYUNG'S DREAM

Aekyung's Dream should be helpful to kids trying to adjust to change.

This book will sensitize others to the issues of moving from one culture and family to another. Bilingual in English and Korean. Books In Print says, "Aekyung is a shy Korean girl experiencing great difficulty in adjusting to America. Ultimately, she realizes that the birds sing in the languages of all people. This charming tale is told with a naive simplicity that touches the heart, and although all of the trappings are Korean, the experiences belong to any child in any alien land. The text itself is hand-lettered and lovely, adding a finishing homey touch to this poignant and highly original story. Aekyung's Dream is a gem."

Keywords

Korean American, Bilingual, Self-Esteem, Girl Power, Core Issues (Feelings), International Adoption

Age Range:

Preschool, early school-age

Author: Min Pack

ISBN# 0-8239-042-5 *Date Published:* 1992 *Price:* $ 18.95

Publisher: Children's Book Press *Pages:* 24

ANIMALS OF THE CHINESE ZODIAC

Follow the animals of ancient China on their journey to visit the Buddha.

Kirkus Reviews: "Yet another book taking on the story behind the Chinese Zodiac; there have been at least eight since 1991, among them *Clara Yen's Why Rat Comes First, Demi's The Dragon's Tale and Other Animal Fables of the Chinese Zodiac* and *Ed Young's Cat and Rat.* Explosions of color result in pages that are predominantly red and yellow, reminiscent of Chinese fireworks."

Keywords

Asian, Chinese, Cultural History, Folk tales and Legends, China

Age Range:

Preschool, early school-age

Author: Susan Whitfield

Illustrator: Philippa-Alys Browne

Susan Whitfield is a historian of China.

ISBN# 1566562368 *Date Published:* 1997 *Price:* $ 16.00

Publisher: Kane Miller *Pages:* 40

AT THE BEACH

"Everything works together to create a flawless picture book." – Publishers Weekly, starred review

Xiao Ming and his mother go to the beach. Sketching in the sand, she teaches him how to make Mandarin Chinese words by drawing comparisons between the character and the object it resembles: "See, it looks like a person walking." Young readers can learn ten Chinese characters in this wonderfully innovative picture book illustrated with intricate cut-paper collages. The illustrations feature multicultural beachcombers.

Keywords

Asian American, Chinese American, Language, Chinese

Age Range:

Preschool, early school-age

Author-Illustrator: Huy Voun Lee

ISBN# 805058222 *Date Published:* 1998 *Price:* $ 6.95

Publisher: Henry Holt *Pages:* 32

Rating

BOY OF THE THREE-YEAR NAP, THE

A poor Japanese woman maneuvers events to change the lazy habits of her son

Taro is lazy as can be but he gets his comeuppance in this funny folk tale when his wise mother uses to her advantage — and against his — his own trick for avoiding work. Winner of the Caldecott Honor Medal and the Boston Globe-Horn Book Award, and selected as an ALA Notable Children's Book. Japanese-style illustrations.

Keywords

Folk tales and Legends, Japanese

Age Range:

Preschool, early school-age

Author-Illustrator: Allen Say

Allen Say is the author/illustrator of *Allison; How My Parents Learned to Eat; Emma's Rug; Stranger In The Mirror; Boy of the Three Year Nap; Grandfather's Journey* and more.

ISBN# 039566957X *Date Published:* 1993 *Price:* $ 6.95

Publisher: Houghton Mifflin *Pages:* 32

Rating

C IS FOR CHINA

An A-B-C photo book of China.

An alphabetical and photographic journey through China, depicting its people, customs, history, religion, and beliefs. Recommended for the home library of every child born in China.

Keywords

Asian, Chinese, Asia, International Adoption, Racial/Ethnic Identity, China

Age Range:

Preschool, early school-age

Author: Sungwan So

ISBN# 038239786X *Date Published:* 1998 *Price:* $ 6.95

Publisher: Silver Burdett Press *Pages:* 32

CHERRY TREE, THE

A story from India.

A little girl in Northern India plants a cherry seed and cares for the cherry tree through its difficult life. She is rewarded by the sight of its first pink blossom against the landscape and the pleasure of nurturing life which depends on her to survive. This book touches on a core issue of adoption — thriving in a new environment which is not one's native habitat — and offers a springboard to conversation about the commitment of the nurturer to support life, growth, and the establishment of deep roots in a new home. "Abounds with quiet wisdom and life," says Publisher's Weekly.

Keywords

Adoption, Core Issues (Feelings), India, Girl Power, Parenting

Age Range:

Preschool, early school-age

Author: Ruskin Bond

Illustrator: Allan Eitzen

ISBN# 1563976218 *Date Published:* 1996 *Price:* $ 7.95

Publisher: Boyds Mill Press *Pages:* 32

CHI-HOON, A KOREAN GIRL

What would my life be like if I were growing up in Korea today?

Try on life in Korea, through the pages of the diary of an eight-year-old girl growing up in Seoul. Vivid full-color photographs and easy to read text draw a clear picture of an individual girl as well as her culture. Chi-Hoon wishes she hadn't been born in the year of the pig; she'd like to rename it the year of the koala bear. The diary she is required to keep for school reveals a girl who tries hard to be a dutiful daughter and wants badly to win the weekly school prize, but who's not always as docile or as high-achieving as she'd like to be.

Keywords

Cultural History, Korean, Racial/Ethnic Identity, Self-Esteem, Girl Power

Age Range:

Preschool, early school-age

Author: Patricia McMahon

ISBN# 1563977206 *Date Published:* 1993 *Price:* $ 9.95

Publisher: Boyds Mill Press *Pages:* 48

Rating

CHINA: FROM THE TRUE BOOKS SERIES

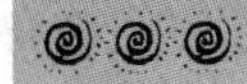

A visit to China for young children.

An engaging visit with the people, the history, and the natural landscapes of China, packed with facts and full-color photos. Referrals to books, organizations and websites about China are included.

Keywords

Asia, China

Age Range:

Preschool, early school-age

Author: Ann Heinrichs

ISBN# 516261657 *Date Published:* 1997 *Price:* $ 6.95

Publisher: Children's Press *Pages:*

Rating

CHINATOWN

A young boy and his grandmother celebrate the rich environment of Chinatown.

In this tribute to his own childhood in Chinatown, William Low melds a spare, evocative text with richly descriptive art, a combination that lends a feeling of immediacy to every page. Herbal shops, outdoor markets, and a tai chi chuan class in the park are among the many sights a young boy sees when taking a walk with his grandmother. An exciting book for children adopted from China.

Keywords

Asian American, Chinese American, Cultural History, Racial/Ethnic Identity, Self-Esteem

Age Range:

Preschool, early school-age

Author: William Low

ISBN# 885042148 *Date Published:* 1997 *Price:* $ 15.95

Publisher: Holt *Pages:* 32

CHINESE EYES

How does a child cope with racism?

The Korean American child in this story encounters racial prejudice for the first time when she is told she has "Chinese eyes." She doesn't know what it means, but she knows it was meant to hurt. A good book to foster discussion with kids.

Keywords

Racism, Self-Esteem, Asian American, Christianity, Korean American, Racial/Ethnic Identity

Age Range:

Preschool, early school-age

Author: Marjorie Waybill

Author: Pauline Cutrell

ISBN# 836117387 *Date Published:* 1981 *Price:* $ 14.95

Publisher: Herald Press *Pages:* 32

CHINESE MIRROR

Amusing retelling of a Korean folk tale.

Retelling of a traditional Korean tale in which a mirror brought from China causes confusion within a family — each member who looks in it sees a different stranger. This funny story evokes larger truths layered beneath than the engaging plot. As is true of the wonderful Indian folk tale *The Blind Men and The Elephant*, this story refreshes our recognition of important truths: that life is not limited just to what we think we know and that when we open ourselves to new possibilities, there are whole universes of new knowledge to discover. Korean children will take pride in this delightful story from their rich cultural tradition, while all children will appreciate the story's message.

Keywords

Folk tales and Legends, Asian, Diversity, Korean

Age Range:

Preschool, early school-age

Author: Mirra Ginsburg

ISBN# 152175083 *Date Published:* 1987 *Price:* $ 6.00

Publisher: Voyager *Pages:* 32

Rating

CHINESE MOTHER GOOSE RHYMES

Forty rhymes, riddles, lullabies and games.

Includes a diversity of selections including lady bugs, kites, and bumps on the head. The illustrations are terrific — powerful and richly colored. A must-have for children adopted from China and fun for children of any racial or ethnic heritage. When children are little, it is of great importance that they have books in their lives that positively reflect children like themselves. They also need access to books that help them understand people who are different from themselves. Ed Young, the illustrator, has also illustrated *Lon Po Po*. His work has tremendous appeal.

Keywords

Chinese American, Folk tales and Legends, Poetry, Asian

Age Range.

Preschool, early school-age

Author: Ed Young

Author: Robert Wyndham

Ed Young is the author/illustrator of *Chinese Mother Goose Rhymes; Lon po po; Mouse Match;* and *Voices of the Heart.*

ISBN# 399217185 Date Published. 1989 Price. $ 7.95

Publisher. Putnam-Paperstar Pages. 48

Rating

CLEVERSTICKS

No one else but Ling Sung knows how to use chopsticks.

Ling Sung doesn't like school. All the other kids seem to be good at something. Terry can tie his shoes; Mangit can print her name.... Then one day Ling Sung discovers he can do something, too — a "cleverstick" trick that his whole class wants to try.

Keywords

Self-Esteem, Racial/Ethnic Identity, Diversity, Asian, Chinese American

Age Range.

Preschool, early school-age

Author: Bernard Ashley

ISBN# 0-517-88332-5 Date Published. Price. $ 5.99

Publisher. Crown Pages.

DANCING DRAGON, THE

A Chinese New Year Celebration.

Ba-Boom! go the drums. Pop! go the firecrackers. As you read about the New Year's celebration, this book physically unfolds to reveal the five-foot-long dancing Chinese dragon!

Keywords

Asian, Racial/Ethnic Identity, Self-Esteem, Chinese American

Age Range.

Preschool, early school-age

Author: Marcia Vaughan

Marcia Vaughn has written over 65 children's books. Her story *Wombat Stew* won the Honor Award in the 1995 Storytelling World Awards.

ISBN# 1572551348 Date Published. Price. $ 5.95

Publisher. Mondo Pages.

DAY OF AHMED'S SECRET

A young boy in Cairo carries a special secret all throughout his day.

Ahmed's secret is set in Cairo. He delivers butane gas to customers all over the city of Cairo during the day, keeping his secret safe inside himself. All day long, as he maneuvers his donkey cart through the streets crowded with cars and camels, down alleys filled with merchants' stalls, and past buildings a thousand years old, he thinks about the secret, which he will tell only to his family. ALA Notable book. School Library Journal Best Book of the Year.

Keywords

Arab, Cultural History, Family Life

Age Range.

Preschool, early school-age

Author: Florence Perry Heide

Author: Judith Heide Gilliland

Illustrator: Ted Lewin

ISBN# 0-688-14023-8 Date Published. Price. $ 4.95

Publisher. Morrow Pages.

Rating

EMPEROR AND THE KITE, THE

How Princess Djeow Seow uses her wit to prove her true worth to her father.

Djeow Seow, the Emperor's tiniest daughter, is always forgotten by her family as she spends her days flying a kite made from paper and sticks. When her father is taken prisoner, only Djeow Seow's courage, and a little help from her kite, can save him. Traditional Asian cut-paper illustrations embellish this sensitive tale of love and loyalty. Winner of the Caldecott Honor award.

Keywords

Family Life, Fathers, Folk tales and Legends, Girl Power, Chinese, Self-Esteem

Age Range:

Preschool, early school-age

Author: Jane Yolen

Jane Yolen is the award-winning author of more than 100 books including *Girl Who Loved The Wind* and has been called "America's Hans Christian Anderson."

ISBN# 0698116445 Date Published: 1998 Price: $ 5.95

Publisher: Putnam-Paperstar Pages: 32

Rating

ER-LANG AND THE SUNS

A Tale from China

China's seven suns are shining endlessly and the people are suffering from the blinding light and burning heat. Er-Lang unselfishly and ingeniously saves his people by creating the very first night. The playful illustrations draw children to this easy-to-follow story.

Keywords

China, Folk tales and Legends

Age Range:

Preschool, early school-age

Author: Tony Guo

Author: Euphene Cheung

Author: Karl Edwards

ISBN# 1879531216 Date Published: 1995 Price: $ 4.95

Publisher: Mondo Pages: 24

EVERYONE KNOWS WHAT A DRAGON LOOKS LIKE

Another engaging folk tale from China.

The story of how a boy saves his city through his unselfish kindness to an old man and becomes the only person to know what a dragon really looks like. Funny, with great illustrations.

Keywords

Chinese, Folk tales and Legends

Age Range:

Preschool, early school-age

Author: Jay Williams

Illustrator: Mercer Mayer

ISBN# 002045600X Date Published: 1991 Price: $ 6.95

Publisher: Macmillan Pages:

FAVORITE FAIRY TALES TOLD IN INDIA

Indian folk tales filled with lions and tigers and alligators, kings, and jackals.

Selected from stories first collected over a hundred years ago. Includes The Valiant Chattee-maker; The Little Jackals; The Cat and the Parrot; The Blind Man, the Deaf Man and the Donkey; The Alligator and the Jackal; Sir Buzz; The Banyan Deer and more.

Keywords

Folk tales and Legends, India, Cultural History

Age Range:

Preschool, early school-age

Author: Virginia Haviland

Retold by Virginia Haviland

ISBN# 0-688-12600-6 Date Published: Price: $ 4.95

Publisher: Morrow Pages:

Rating

GOLDEN SLIPPER

A Vietnamese Cinderella legend.

The story of a young girl who meets her dream prince with the assistance of her animal friends. This is a popular legend about a time when a few powerful families ruled over Vietnam and poor girls dreamed of prosperous lives with the reigning princes. Very similar to the popular Western Cinderella tale.

Keywords

Folk tales and Legends, Vietnam

Age Range:

Preschool, early school-age

Author: Darrel Lum

ISBN# 816734062 Date Published: Price: $ 3.95

Publisher: Troll Pages: 32

Rating

GRANDFATHER'S JOURNEY

A subtle story about loving two countries and longing for one's home in both.

Winner of the 1994 Caldecott Medal, this is a story about immigration and acculturation. Grandfather and the boy return to Japan with the dream of coming home again — only to find they feel like outsiders. "The funny thing is, the moment I am in one country, I am homesick for the other," observes Say near the end of this poignant account of three generations of his family's moves between Japan and the US. Wonderful for any child who has ever faced loss or who has an interest in family origins. Beautiful illustrations.

Keywords

Asian American, Chinese American, China, Intergenerational, Racial/Ethnic Identity, Multicultural

Age Range:

Preschool, early school-age

Author-Illustrator: Allen Say

Allen Say is the author/illustrator of *Allison; How My Parents Learned to Eat; Emma's Rug; Stranger In The Mirror; Boy of the Three Year Nap; Grandfather's Journey* and more.

ISBN# 395570352 Date Published: 1999 Price:

Publisher: Houghton Mifflin Pages: 32

HOW MY PARENTS LEARNED TO EAT

A fun Reading Rainbow selection about crossing cultural lines.

John was a blond American sailor, stationed in Japan during W.W.II. He falls in love with Aiko, a Japanese school girl. In this story, they have never shared a meal and worry in silence that their cultural limitations might wreck their romance. But after she learns to use a fork and he masters chopsticks, they get married.

Keywords

Multicultural, Parenting, Asian, Biography, Japanese American, Asian American

Age Range:

Preschool, early school-age

Author: Ina R. Friedman

ISBN# 395442354 Date Published: 1987 Price: $ 4.95

Publisher: Houghton Mifflin Pages: 24

KOREAN CINDERELLA, THE

A beautiful retelling of a story found in almost every culture.

In the land of Korea,where magical creatures are as common as cabbages, lives a child named Pear Blossom. She is as lovely as the the pear tree planted in celebration of her birth, but she is mistreated by her jealous stepmother, Omoni, who forces her to cook and clean until midnight and demands she complete three tasks no human could ever do alone. With help from magical animals, Pear Blossom becomes a nobleman's wife.

Keywords

Folk tales and Legends, Asian, Korean, Asian American

Age Range:

Preschool, early school-age

Author: Shirley Climo

Shirley Climo has researched many versions of the Cinderella story around the world. Her works include *King Of the Birds, T.J.'s Ghost, A Month of Seven Days* and *Someone Saw A Spider.*

ISBN# 0-06-020432-X Date Published: Price: $ 5.95

Publisher: HarperCollins Pages:

Rating

LAST DRAGON, THE

How Peter learns about his Chinese heritage.

From Booklist: "Although this story features a little boy, its main character is really a Chinese American community. Peter is not happy about spending his summer in Chinatown with his great-aunt. But his feelings change when he spots an old, 10-man dragon in a shop window. The watercolor illustrations are full of details unique to Chinatown." But Horn Book writes, "The theme of community pride is appealing, but the plot is lengthy and the characters unconvincing. Realistic watercolors skillfully portray the busy neighborhood."

Keywords

Boy Focus, Chinese American, Chinese, Intergenerational

Age Range:

Preschool, early school-age

Author: Susan Miho Nunes

Illustrator: Chris K. Soentpiet

ISBN# 395845173 Date Published: 1997 Price: $ 5.95

Publisher: Clarion Pages: 32

Rating

LITTLE OH

A Pinocchio-like story sure to capture readers' hearts.

From Kirkus Reviews: "Little Oh, an origami girl created by a lonely Japanese woman, is lost. She is chased by a hungry dog, floated down a foaming cataract, and flown home by a friendly crane. A motherless boy finds her, and when he and his father return her to her mother, the paper girl miraculously becomes a human child, the man and woman fall in love and marry, and Little Oh's family is complete. LaMarche demonstrates his extraordinary ability to portray emotions in the human face, and his soft mixed-media paintings are filled with details of exceptional beauty. A flawless work."

Keywords

Folk tales and Legends, Family Life, Japanese American

Age Range:

Preschool, early school-age

Author: Laura Krauss Melmed

Illustrator: Jim Lamarche

Laura Krauss Melmed is the author of *The Rainbabies.*

ISBN# 688142087 Date Published: 1997 Price: $ 16.00

Publisher: Lothrop Pages: 32

LON PO PO

A Red-Riding-Hood story from China.

Winner of the 1990 Caldecott Medal, this book offers powerful and richly colored illustrations. Books in Print said, "Like ancient Oriental paintings, the illustrations are frequently grouped in panels. Juxtaposition of abstract and realistic representations, the complicated play of color and shadow, and the depth of the artist's vision all help transform this simple fairy tale into an extraordinary and powerful book."

Keywords

Folk tales and Legends, Asian, Chinese American, Chinese

Age Range:

Preschool, early school-age

Author: Ed Young

Ed Young is the author/illustrator of *Chinese Mother Goose Rhymes; Lon po po; Mouse Match;* and *Voices of the Heart.*

ISBN# 0-698-11382-9 Date Published: 1990 Price: $ 5.95

Publisher: Putnam-Paperstar Pages: 32

LOTUS SEED, THE

A story about the continuity of family and culture after significant disruption.

A young Vietnamese girl saves a lotus seed and carries it with her everywhere, in order to remember a brave emperor and the homeland that she has had to flee. This is a beautifully illustrated book, highly recommended.

Keywords

Asian, Racial/Ethnic Identity, Family Life, Vietnam, Girl Power, Core Issues (Feelings)

Age Range:

Preschool, early school-age

Author: Sherry Garland

Sherry Garland is the author of *Song of The Buffalo Boy* and *The Lotus Seed.*

ISBN# 0-15-249465-0 Date Published: Price: $ 6.00

Publisher: Harcourt Brace Pages: 32

MAGIC AMBER

Rating

A Korean legend.

An old rice farmer and his wife are repaid for their generosity and kindness. The antiquity of this tale is enhanced by the vividly colored, charming illustrations. Children of Korean heritage will take pride in this uplifting story which comes from their culture, while children from other backgrounds will gain new understanding of some of the values inherent to traditional Korean family life. To expand their world, we must introduce all our children to the rich contributions of the many peoples of the earth, contributions that stretch back over time and still meet our needs today.

Keywords

Folk tales and Legends, Korean

Age Range,

Preschool, early school-age

Author: Charles Reasoner

ISBN# 816734089 Date Published, 1994 Price, $ 3.95

Publisher, Troll Pages, 32

MIN-YO AND THE MOON DRAGON

Rating

How Min-Yo changes the night sky forever.

In a small village in China, people notice that the moon appears to be falling from the sky. Min-Yo climbs the cobweb staircase between the earth and moon to ask the moon dragon for help. Kirkus Reviews says: "The story (Hillman's first) is smoothly told and its details are appealing, though it seems a bit empty — a fable without a moral. Acceptable, but hardly essential."

Keywords

Chinese, Folk tales and Legends, Asian

Age Range,

Preschool, early school-age

Author: Elizabeth Hillman

Illustrator: John Wallner

ISBN# 015200985X Date Published, 1996 Price, $ 5.00

Publisher, Voyager Pages,

MING LO MOVES THE MOUNTAIN

Why Ming Lo and his wife would rather move the mountain than move themselves.

Ming Lo and his wife live beside a big mountain which causes them no end of trouble. "Husband," says Ming Lo's wife, "you must move the mountain so that we may enjoy our home in peace." But how can a man as small as Ming Lo move something as big as a mountain? Maybe the village wise man will know.

Keywords

Chinese, Family Life, Folk tales and Legends

Age Range,

Preschool, early school-age

Author: Arnold Lobel

Arnold Lobel is the author of *Ming Lo Moves Mountains, Frog and Toad Are Friends* and many more.

ISBN# 688006116 Date Published, Price, $ 4.95

Publisher, Morrow Pages, 32

MOUSE MATCH

"To find an answer they had not only to look but also to see."

Caldecott Medalist Ed Young offers a gorgeous retelling of an ancient Chinese tale of a father mouse who travels to the end of the earth in search of the perfect husband for his wonderful daughter. How could he have known his journey would lead him back home? From Kirkus Reviews: "The most unusual aspect of the story is its accordion format: A strip of heavy, coated cardboard has been folded into the picture-book format. Every turn of a fold brings readers to a discernible spread, but every spread blends into the next."

Keywords

China, Folk tales and Legends

Age Range,

Preschool, early school-age

Author-Illustrator: Ed Young

Ed Young is the author/illustrator of *Chinese Mother Goose Rhymes; Lon po po; Mouse Match;* and *Voices of the Heart.*

ISBN# 152014535 Date Published, 1997 Price, $ 20.00

Publisher, Harcourt Brace Pages, 52

Rating

NIM AND THE WAR EFFORT

What was it like to be a Chinese American during World War Two?

A Chinese American schoolgirl, Nim proves to her classmates that she can be true to both her country and her heritage when she collects the most paper for a war-effort paper drive during World War II. Culturally and historically authentic details contribute to the overall effect, such as the special flag pin worn by Chinese Americans so they would not be identified as "the enemy," the Japanese. Quiet and understated, this story is based on Lee's experiences growing up in San Francisco's Chinatown during the war years.

Keywords

Chinese American, Race Relations, Racism, Racial/Ethnic Identity, US History, Intergenerational

Age Range:

Preschool, early school-age

Author: Milly Lee

ISBN# 374355231 *Date Published:* 1997 *Price:* $ 16.00

Publisher: Farrar-Strauss *Pages:* 40

Rating

NINE-IN-ONE, GRR! GRR!

Award-winning Hmong/Laotian story, a culture under-represented in children's literature.

This book's rhythmic text and appealing, brightly-colored pictures make it a good choice for preschool story hours. ALA Notable book. Books in Print says, "A tiger journeys to the god Shao to find out if she will have cubs. Shao replies she will have nine cubs a year — if she can remember his words. As she has a poor memory, she creates a chant to recite for the journey home, 'Nine-in-one Grr- Grr.' The Eu bird overhears her and asks Shao to change what he said, for 'Soon there will be nothing but tigers in the land.' But this cannot be done, so the bird flies back to the tiger, distracts her, and substitutes his own 'one-in-nine,' meaning one cub born in nine years.

Keywords

Asian, Folk tales and Legends, Hmong/Laotian, Girl Power

Age Range:

Preschool, early school-age

Author-Illustrator: Nancy Hom

ISBN# 0-89239-110-3 *Date Published:* 1992 *Price:* $ 6.95

Publisher: Children's Book *Pages:* 32

ONE SMALL GIRL

Do all Asian Americans look alike?

Although warned not to touch anything, Jennifer finds a way to amuse herself by fooling a lady who thinks all Asian Americans look alike.

Keywords

Asian American, Race Relations, Chinese American, Girl Power

Age Range:

Preschool, early school-age

Author: Jennifer Chan

ISBN# 1879965054 *Date Published:* 1993 *Price:* $ 12.95

Publisher: Polychrome *Pages:* 32

OUR BABY FROM CHINA

An American couple goes to China to adopt a baby.

A photo essay of one couple's travel to China to adopt baby Ariela. Emotionally evocative color photos and simple text allow the reader a glimpse into the world of international adoption and Chinese culture. As the adoptive parents meet and bring their new baby home to America, one can't help but feel their joy. A perfect book for adoptive parents who have transformed their lives, and their child's life, through Chinese international adoption.

Keywords

Adoption, Asian, Chinese American, Chinese, International Adoption, Racial/Ethnic Identity

Age Range:

Preschool, early school-age

Author: Nancy D'Antonio

ISBN# 0-8075-6162-2 *Date Published:* 1996 *Price:* $ 13.95

Publisher: Whitman *Pages:* 24

Rating

RED EGGS AND DRAGON BOATS

Discover why everyone eats fish for Chinese New Year's.

A book about favorite festivals celebrated by Chinese people throughout the world: Chinese Lunar New Year, Clear Brightness Festival, Full-Month Red Egg and Ginger Party, Dragon Boat Festival, and Moon Festival. Includes stories, traditions, and recipes. This book is essential for families of Chinese-born children.

Keywords

Asian, Chinese American, Racial/Ethnic Identity, Festivals, Asian American

Age Range,

Preschool, early school-age

Author: Carol Stepanchuk

Carol Stepanchuk is a folklorist with a long-standing interest in Chinese festivals and popular culture. She is the author of *Mooncakes* and *Hungry Ghosts: Festivals of China*.

ISBN# 1881896080 *Date Published,* *Price,* $ 16.95

Publisher, Pacific View Press *Pages,*

Rating

ROCKABYE CROCODILE

A folk tale from the Philippines.

Two elderly boars live next door to one another in the jungle. Annabel is cheerful and kind. Nettie is mean and selfish. When sweet Annabel receives gifts from a mother crocodile after she has been kind, mean Nettie tries to copy her friend. But she acts in a mean and selfish way and receives terrible gifts. Nettie learns her lesson, however, and they all live happily ever after.

Keywords

Filipino American, Family Life, Folk tales and Legends, Friendship

Age Range,

Preschool, early school-age

Author: Jose Aruego

ISBN# 0-688-12333-3 *Date Published,* *Price,* $ 4.95

Publisher, Morrow *Pages,*

SAM AND THE LUCKY MONEY

How Sam discovers that sometimes the best gifts come from the heart.

Sam is finally old enough to spend the lucky money his grandparents have given him for Chinese New Year's Day in Chinatown, but he is disappointed because he does not have enough to buy the basketball he really wants. Yet when he decides to give his money to a man who has no shoes so that the man can buy some socks, he learned he was the lucky one. Storytime, PBS, rates it a "Story Pick," Bank Street College says it has "outstanding merit," and Books in Print writes, "The illustrations masterfully combine Chinatown's exotic setting with the universal emotions of childhood through expressive portraits of the characters."

Keywords

Core Issues (Feelings), Asian American, Self-Esteem, Chinese American, Festivals, Holidays and Celebrations

Age Range,

Preschool, early school-age

Author: Karen Chinn

Illustrator: Cornelius VanWright

Illustrator: Ying Hwa Hu

Karen Chinn lives in New York City. This is her first picture book.

ISBN# 1880000539 *Date Published,* 1995 *Price,* $ 6.95

Publisher, Lee & Low Books *Pages,* 32

SEVENTH SISTER

A Chinese legend about the Goddess of weaving.

A lonely shepherd is saddened when the maiden he loves must leave him and return to help her sisters weave the tapestry of the night sky.

Keywords

Asian, Self-Esteem, Folk tales and Legends, Chinese

Age Range,

Preschool, early school-age

Author: Cindy Chang

Author: Charles Reasoner

Retold by Cindy Chang

ISBN# 0-8167-3412-7 *Date Published,* *Price,* $ 3.95

Publisher, Troll *Pages,*

Rating

SILENT LOTUS

The inspiring story of how a mute child found a way to communicate.

A beautiful young girl in Cambodia is born deaf and cannot speak. What she can do, however, is dance. She is so graceful and beautiful that she is chosen by the king and queen to become a court dancer. Dance becomes her language and she becomes the most popular dancer in her country. Vibrant watercolors and drawings based on the 12th-century bas-reliefs on the Cambodian temples of Angkor Wat bring added realism to this gentle tale of the thousand-year-old tradition of the Khmer court ballet. Full color throughout.

Keywords

China, Self-Esteem, Special Needs, Friendship, Asian, Language

Age Range:

Preschool, early school-age

Author: Jeannie Lee

Jeannie Lee is the author of *Silent Lotus* and *The Song of Mu-Lan.*

ISBN# 0-374-46646-7 Date Published: 1994 Price: $ 4.95
Publisher: Farrar-Strauss Pages:

Rating

SIM CHUNG AND THE RIVER DRAGON

A Korean folk tale.

Sim Chung is willing to sacrifice herself to help her father be able to see again — she will even dare to enter the underwater kingdom of the fierce river dragon. This beloved Korean folk tale about a brave and beautiful young girl is perfect for the early independent reader.

Keywords

Folk tales and Legends, Korean, Self-Esteem

Age Range:

Preschool, early school-age

Author: Ellen Schechter

Illustrator: June Otani

ISBN# 553371096 Date Published: 1993 Price: $ 3.99
Publisher: Bantam Pages:

SOMETIMES MOON

Another lovely book from the creators of The Squiggle!

Selene sees the changing Moon as thin and silver like Grandpapa's boat, sometimes as a half circle like Mama's knitting basket, and sometimes round and chubby like the baby's cheeks. Pierr Morgan's delightful illustrations reflect Asian images.

Keywords

Asian, Family Life

Age Range:

Preschool, early school-age

Author: Carola Lexus Schaefer

Illustrator: Pierr Morgan

Carola Lexus Schaefer is the author of *The Squiggle* and *Sometimes Moon.*

ISBN# 517709805 Date Published: 1999 Price: $ 17.00
Publisher: Crown Pages: 40

SQUIGGLE, THE

The pleasures of imagination: what can you do with a line?

Something akin to the wonderful Harold and the Purple Crayon is at work here — but with text as well, and incidentally offering Chinese cultural references. As the children go off with their teacher to the park, walking "in a bunched-up, slow, tight, straight line," the last little one sees a length of string, which becomes, in these engaging marker and gouache illustrations, a Chinese dragon and the Great Wall of China and a rising full moon, among other things; by the end, all the children together form "a squiggle of a line."

Keywords

Asian American, Chinese American, Multicultural

Age Range:

Preschool, early school-age

Author: Carola Lexus Schaefer

Illustrator: Pierr Morgan

Carola Lexus Schaefer is the author of *The Squiggle* and *Sometimes Moon.*

ISBN# 0-517-70047-6 Date Published: 1996 Price: $ 6.99
Publisher: Crown Pages: 32

Rating

TASTY BABY BELLY BUTTONS

Uh oh! The monster's coming. Hide your belly button.

Urikohime, a brave girl born from a melon, battles the monstrous giant, who steal babies to eat their tasty belly buttons, in this scary adventure enhanced by Meilso So's clever watercolors. An author's note explains the origin of this story in Japanese folklore. School Library Journal, Starred Review: "Some people may quake at the idea of giants kidnapping babies so they can eat their belly buttons, but these things happen in Japanese folklore. Throughout the narrative, Sierra incorporates descriptive sound words traditionally used in Japanese storytelling to draw readers into the action and uses just the right combination of droll and dramatic elements."

Keywords

Asian, Japanese, Japanese American, Folk tales and Legends

Age Range.

Preschool, early school-age

Author: Judy Sierra

Illustrator: Meilo So

ISBN# 679893695 | Date Published. 1999 | Price. $ 17.00
Publisher. Knopf | Pages. 40

Rating

TOO MANY SUNS

"Long ago, when dragons were young, ten suns lived at the edge of the world..."

Midwest Book Review writes, "Julie Lawson has deftly woven threads of Chinese mythology into a rich tapestry of her own making. How 'Youngest Brother' manages to save one sun to light the world is a compelling tale for all ages. The lavish, full-color illustrations by Martin Springett add extra sparkle to the brilliance of *Too Many Suns*. The illustrations alone are reasons to own this book."

Keywords

China, Folk tales and Legends

Age Range.

Preschool, early school-age

Author: Julie Lawson

Author: Martin Springett

Julie Lawson is the author of *Too Many Suns* and *Turns on a Dime*.

ISBN# 077372897X | Date Published. 1997 | Price. $ 18.95
Publisher. Stoddart Kids | Pages. 32

UMBRELLA

A Caldecott Honor Book about independence.

A three-year-old Asian girl receives an umbrella for her birthday. She cannot wait to use it. When it finally does rain, she discovers a new independence as she walks without holding her Dad's hand the whole way. A fun book that happens to offer Asian characters.

Keywords

Asian, Self-Esteem

Age Range.

Preschool, early school-age

Author: Yashima Taro

ISBN# 0-14-050240-5 | Date Published. | Price. $ 4.99
Publisher. Puffin | Pages.

WAY OF THE CIRCLE

A tale from China.

In this tale of wisdom of ancient China, young Sun Lo learns about the value of showing love and kindness to others.

Keywords

Folk tales and Legends, Asian, Self-Esteem, Chinese

Age Range.

Preschool, early school-age

Author: James Vollbracht

Illustrator: Chris Foleen

ISBN# 0-915166-76-3 | Date Published. 1993 | Price. $ 6.95
Publisher. Impact | Pages. 48

Rating

WE CAME FROM VIETNAM

The efforts of a Vietnamese refugee family to adjust to life in Chicago.

The history of the Nguyen family in Vietnam: how they left their home with only the clothes they wore, made their way to the United States, and settled into life in the Uptown area of Chicago, IL.

Keywords

Race Relations, Racial/Ethnic Identity, Racism, Vietnamese, Vietnamese American, Family Life

Age Range:

Preschool, early school-age

Author: Muriel Stanek

ISBN# 0-8075-8699-4 *Date Published:* 1985 *Price:* $ 12.00

Publisher: Whitman *Pages:* 46

Rating

WHY RAT COMES FIRST

Understanding the Chinese zodiac

"Once upon a time" and "Long ago and far away" tales are a great way to introduce children to the spirit of a culture. Yen's retelling of this Chinese folk tale is a warm look at the Chinese zodiac that will promote positive understanding for young people in general and cultural pride that Chinese children will understand as specific to them. A good story for reading aloud, Hideo Yoshida's charming illustrations enhance the text in a delightful ribbon of color as small figures tumble off the boundaries of the pages and make you want to grab them close.

Keywords

Asian, Chinese, Folk tales and Legends, China

Age Range:

Preschool, early school-age

Author: Clara Yen

Illustrator: Hideo Yoshida

ISBN# 892390727 *Date Published:* 1997 *Price:* $ 14.95

Publisher: Children's Book *Pages:* 32

WHY THE PINÅ HAS A HUNDRED EYES

Filipino legends, each one about the origins of a local fruit.

Where did the mango get its shape? Why does a guava have a crown? Did angels really use their fingerprints to make the brown markings on a lansome? Vivid text and soft delicate drawings leave no doubt as to why this book won the 1994 National Book Award for Children's Literature, Manila Critics Circle.

Keywords

Filipino American, Folk tales and Legends, Cultural History

Age Range:

Preschool, early school-age

Author: Neni Romana-Cruz

Illustrator: Felix M. Miguel

ISBN# 971-630-026-3 *Date Published:* 1995 *Price:* $ 11.95

Publisher: Paperworks *Pages:*

YEH-SHEN, CINDERELLA FROM CHINA

A Chinese version of Cinderella.

Yeh-Shen, a beautiful girl, is left in the care of her wicked stepmother, who treats her badly day after day. Finally the festival comes. With an interesting twist, this version differs from the European Cinderella story — so you have to read the book to find out if Yeh-Shen finds her way to the prince. The story is believed to be at least 1000 years older than the oldest known Western version.

Keywords

Asian, Chinese, Folk tales and Legends

Age Range:

Preschool, early school-age

Author: Ai-Ling Louie

Retold by Ai-Ling Louie

ISBN# 039920900X *Date Published:* *Price:* $ 5.95

Publisher: Putnam-Paperstar *Pages:* 32

Rating

ABUELA

Rosalba's imagination is flying high. We wish we could have an adventure with her.

Flying around Manhattan, somersaulting in midair, and resting in the sky on a chair-shaped cloud, Rosalba and her grandmother, her abuela, are having a grand adventure. How do they manage this exhilarating travel? — on Rosalba's marvelous imagination. Kirkus Reviews writes, "Since 'Abuela' speaks 'mostly Spanish,' Rosalba mentions many Spanish words. Though the story line is slight, the relationship glows with affection; the Spanish vocabulary is well integrated and clear in context. Kleven's illustrations — jewel-like collages of sparkling images and patterns, crammed with intriguing details — effectively transmit Rosalba's joy in her narrative."

Keywords

Family Life, Latino/a, Bilingual

Age Range.

Preschool, early school-age

Author: Arthur Dorros

ISBN# 1405622657 *Date Published.* 1997 *Price.* $ 4.99
Publisher. Puffin *Pages.* 40

Rating

ABUELA'S WEAVE

Guatemalan artisans, Abuela and her granddaughter Esperanza, weave from the heart.

"Pull back hard," old Abuela said. "Make it jolt, so the threads stay close, like family." The family counts on sales of tapestries at the Fiesta de Pueblos but they are afraid there will be no buyers since more and more machine-made weavings are for sale. Fabric-like borders on each page add authenticity and color to this appealing story. Infused with history and family tradition, this story should be enjoyed many times over. Richly detailed pictures. The San Francisco Chronicle: "Young Latinos will see their own family's reverence for abuelitas (grandmothers) validated in a story in which the old and familiar clearly triumph over the 'new and improved.'" 1993 Parents' Choice award.

Keywords

Cultural History, Family Life, Self-Esteem, Guatemalan, Holidays and Celebrations

Age Range.

Preschool, early school-age

Author: Omar Castaneda

Illustrator: Enrique O. Sanchez

ISBN# 1-880000-20-2 *Date Published.* 1993 *Price.* $ 6.95
Publisher. Lee & Low Books *Pages.*

ADVENTURES OF CONNIE AND DIEGO, THE

Las Aventuras De Connie Y Diego

"Once upon a time" tales are a great way to introduce children to ways of coping with feeling different. This contemporary legend about Mexican American twins who are truly multicolored provides a great jump start to conversations to help you understand your child's understanding of identity issues and belonging. Bilingual in English/Spanish, this book is not just for Latino children; the Los Angeles Times called it magical and bold as an Aztec tapestry, pointing out that the book highlights how the twins "discover that color isn't as important as character."

Keywords

Latino/a, Mexican American, Multicultural, Bilingual

Age Range.

Preschool, early school-age

Author: Maria Garcia

Illustrator: Malaquias Montoya

Translator: Alma Flor Ada

ISBN# 892391243 *Date Published.* 1994 *Price.* $ 6.95
Publisher. Children's Book *Pages.* 22

AMELIA'S ROAD

"A quietly courageous child making the best of a difficult necessity."

This story of the importance of home will strike a chord with children who find themselves having to cope with moving. Amelia, a child of migrant farm workers, is weary of wandering with the seasons and longs for a home with a fine yard and shade tree. Features richly-colored, folk art-inspired illustrations.

Keywords

Family Life, Latino/a, Core Issues (Feelings)

Age Range.

Preschool, early school-age

Author: Linda Jacobs Altman

Illustrator: Enrique O. Sanchez

ISBN# 188000027X *Date Published.* 1995 *Price.* $ 6.95
Publisher. Lee & Low Books *Pages.*

Rating

AMIGO MEANS FRIEND

How Jose and George make friends across cultural lines.

When Jose and George first met, they did not share a common language. Each thought that the other talked strangely, and their lack of shared language kept them separate. After time, as each learned to say something in the other's language, they saw that they could become friends in spite of their different cultural backgrounds. This book, designed for beginning readers, takes a positive approach to the differences that can sometimes divide young children, portraying them instead as strong foundations for rich and satisfying relationships.

Keywords

Race Relations, Latino/a, Friendship

Age Range:

Preschool, early school-age

Author: Louise Everett

Illustrator: Sandy Rabinowitz

ISBN# 816710015 Date Published: 1987 Price: $ 1.95

Publisher: Troll Pages:

Rating

ANGEL'S KITE/LA ESTRELLA DE ANGEL

How Angel finds what has been lost.

Ever since the church bell disappeared in Angel's beloved town, life just hasn't been the same. This is the bilingual (English/Spanish) story of how Angel, a young kite maker, mysteriously brings back the missing bell by creating a special kite bearing an intricately detailed drawing of the town. — Huh? And exactly how did this come about? Unfortunately, the story line does not clear up the confusion likely to arise for most young readers, but the collage illustrations are appealing and bilingual books are in short supply.

Keywords

Bilingual, Mexican

Age Range:

Preschool, early school-age

Author: Alberto Blanco

Illustrator: Rodolfo Morales

Translator: Dan Bellm

Alberto Blanco is one of Mexico's most notable poets. He wrote *Desert Mermaid* and *Angel's Kite/La Estrella De Angel.*

ISBN# 892391561 Date Published: 1994 Price: $ 6.95

Publisher: Children's Book Pages: 32

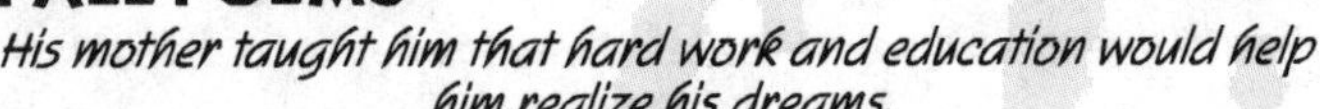

ANGELS RIDE BIKES AND OTHER FALL POEMS

His mother taught him that hard work and education would help him realize his dreams.

Francisco Alarcon says that in Los Angeles in the autumn, mariachis play like angels, angels ride bikes, and the earth dances the cha-cha. His mother taught him that hard work and education would help him realize his dreams; in this English/Spanish collection of poems, he honors his family and celebrates the memorable moments of his childhood: when the ice cream man came, the first day of school, going to the street market, and more. Maya Christina Gonzalez' exuberant images enhance the text.

Keywords

Bilingual, Mexican American, Latino/a, Poetry, Racial/Ethnic Identity

Age Range:

Preschool, early school-age

Author: Francisco X. Alarcon

Illustrator: Maya Christina Gonzalez

Francisco X. Alarcon is an award-winning poet. He directs the Spanish for Native Speakers Program at the University of CA, Davis.

ISBN# 089239160X Date Published: 1999 Price: $ 15.95

Publisher: Children's Book Pages: 32

ARROZ CON LECHE

Popular songs and rhymes from Latin America

A wonderful collection of beloved Latin American songs, games, and rhymes, with text in both Spanish and English, complemented by beautiful watercolor illustrations of Latin American land- and cityscapes.

Keywords

Latino/a, Mexican, Central America, Argentina, Bilingual, Music

Age Range:

Preschool, early school-age

Editor: Lulu Delacre

ISBN# 590418866 Date Published: 1999 Price: $ 4.95

Publisher: Scholastic Pages:

Rating

BIG BUSHY MUSTACHE

Cinco de Mayo is a family affair.

It's almost Cinco de Mayo, and Ricky's class is going to put on a play. As his costume, Ricky picks a big, bushy mustache, just like his dad's. Although he's supposed to leave it in school, he wears the mustache home and loses it. Lucky for him, his Mama and Papi have a plan. The next morning his Mama hands him a new big, bushy mustache — fresh from the smiling face of his clean-shaven Papi! With humor and tenderness, Soto evokes a warm celebration of both the beloved tradition of Cinco de Mayo and the strong bonds of love between father and son.

Keywords

Latino/a, Family Life, Mexican American

Age Range:

Preschool, early school-age

Author: Gary Soto

Illustrator: Joseph Cepeda

Gary Soto is an acclaimed poet and fiction writer. He is the author of *Living Up The Street; Jesse; Nerdlandia, Chato's Kitchen* and *Baseball in April.*

ISBN# 679880305 Date Published: 1998 Price: $ 17.00

Publisher: Pages: 32

Rating

BIRTHDAY SWAP, THE

A Mexican American girl looks for the perfect birthday gift for her sister.

It's the day before her older sister's birthday, and five-year-old Lori is determined to find her own gift to give. Little does Lori know that the best, most perfect gifts sometimes come to us when we least expect them. In this warmhearted tale about the joys of giving and receiving, Loretta Lopez celebrates family love and togetherness. Fun, colorful illustrations.

Keywords

Family Life, Latino/a, Holidays and Celebrations, Sibling Issues, Mexican American

Age Range:

Preschool, early school-age

Author: Loretta Lopez

ISBN# 1880000474 Date Published: 1997 Price: $ 15.95

Publisher: Lee & Low Books Pages: 32

BORN IN THE GRAVY

Spanish and English interweave. Wonderful illustrations.

Margarita is more comfortable with English than Papa is. During a trip to the soda shop for ice cream, Papa hears all about Margarita's first day at kindergarten: from her new friends, to the fire truck that rescued the principal from a tree, to the first graders who teased her.

Keywords

Bilingual, Latino/a, Family Life

Age Range:

Preschool, early school-age

Author: Denys Cazet

ISBN# 531070964 Date Published: 1997 Price: $ 5.95

Publisher: Orchard Pages: 24

BORREGUITA AND THE COYOTE

A book that should be on every child's shelf.

The combination of wonderful pictures, a Spanish text, and the notion that a wily Borreguita (sheep) can outsmart the coyote captures children's hearts and minds. A favorite picture book that has stood the test of time.

Keywords

Bilingual, Latino/a, Self-Esteem, Multicultural

Age Range:

Preschool, early school-age

Author: Verna Aardema

Illustrator: Peter Mathers

Verna Aardema is the author of *Borreguita and the Coyote, Bringing The Rain To Kapiti Plain,* and *Why Mosquitoes Buzz In People's Ears.*

ISBN# 679889361 Date Published: 1991 Price: $ 6.99

Publisher: Random House Pages: 32

Rating

CHATO'S KITCHEN

Cool cool Chato, the barrio cat, is outsmarted by a family of mice.

Chato, the coolest cat in East L.A., and his buddy, Novio Boy, prepare to serve up a feast for their new next door neighbors in the barrio, a family of "ratoncitos," little mice. Chato prepares fajitas, frijoles, salsa, and enchiladas, although planning all along that his guests will be the main course. But the mice bring along their own guest, Chorizo, the toughest dog in the barrio. An ALA Notable Book. A fun to read story with plenty of spice and no sugarcoating.

Keywords

Latino/a, Food

Age Range:

Preschool, early school-age

Author: Gary Soto

Illustrator: Susan Guevara

Gary Soto is an acclaimed poet and fiction writer. He is the author of *Living Up The Street; Jesse; Nerdlandia, Chato's Kitchen* and *Baseball in April.*

ISBN# 399226583 Date Published: 1995 Price: $ 5.95
Publisher: Putnam-Paperstar Pages: 31

Rating

DIEGO

Outstanding illustrated biography for very young children.

The life story of a great Mexican muralist Diego Rivera, 1886-1957, is made accessible for the youngest among us. Using bold colors in his vibrant paintings, Diego drew on every surface that crossed his path. The graphic explorations of his childhood encourage young reader-artists to join in the fun as Diego draws out his love for his country. Among other issues, it introduces political oppression and the notion of the afterlife. The NY Times Illustrated Children's Book Award. A Reading Rainbow book.

Keywords

Racial/Ethnic Identity, Latino/a, Bilingual

Age Range:

Preschool, early school-age

Author: M. J. Abadie

Illustrator: Jonah Winter

M. J. Abadie is the author of *Multicultural Baby Names* and *Diego.*

ISBN# 067985617X Date Published: 1994 Price: $ 5.99
Publisher: Knopf Pages: 34

DIEZ DEDITOS

10 Little Fingers & Other Play Rhymes and Action Songs from Latin America

Booklist writes, "Lively finger rhymes and exuberant songs. Ample opportunities to get kids clapping, giggling, wiggling, tickling, and more." Kirkus Reviews says: "A nifty compilation of songs and finger rhymes, some of them original, some recalled from Orozco's Mexican childhood, and some collected during tours in Latin America and Spain." And Horn Book adds, "Every entry includes well-translated bilingual lyrics, a music score for piano and guitar, easy-to-follow pictographs, and a brief text — only in English — explaining the movements and, in some cases, the origins of the song."

Keywords

Mexican, Mexican American, Music and Dance, Latino/a, Bilingual, Games and Activities

Age Range:

Preschool, early school-age

Translator: Jose-Luis Orozco

Author: Elisa Kleven

ISBN# 525457364 Date Published: 1997 Price: $ 18.99
Publisher: Dutton Pages: 48

FAMILY PICTURES/CUADROS DE FAMILIA

School Library Journal calls this "An inspired celebration of American cultural diversity....

Carmen Lomas Garza is considered one of the major Mexican American painters in this country. Family Pictures, Carmen's loving story of her childhood in a traditional Latino community in South Texas, shows everyday activities that remain vivid in memory: picking oranges for her grandmother, making tamales with the entire family, swimming in the Gulf of Mexico. The sum of the details creates a rich and important bank of information about Mexican American life today. Wonderful illustrations. Bilingual in English and Spanish.

Keywords

Mexican American, Latino/a, Bilingual, Family Life, Extended Family

Age Range:

Preschool, early school-age

Author: Carmen Lewis Garza

Carmen Lomas Garza is a renowned American painter and graphic artist. Garza lives in San Francisco, CA.

ISBN# 0-89239-108-1 Date Published: 1996 Price: $ 6.95
Publisher: Children's Book Pages: 32

Rating

FIESTA FIREWORKS (1-2)

Enjoy the sparkling spirit of a Mexican festival as you learn about the culture.

From Booklist: "In Tultepec, a Mexican town noted for its fireworks, Caren helps prepare for a fiesta honoring San Juan de Dios. The festival includes a parade, an amusement park, and towers of fireworks. The book's large format gives plenty of space for Ancona's clear, full-color photos. Readers who have little idea of life in Mexico will learn as much from the pictures as from the words, which clearly describe preparations for the festival. Spanish words used in the text are usually defined in parentheses at first use, italicized wherever they appear, and also defined in a glossary."

Keywords

Mexico, Mexican, Festivals, Bilingual

Age Range:

Preschool, early school-age

Author/Illustrator: George Ancona

George Ancona is the author of *Powwow; Let's Dance; Fiesta Fireworks; The Piñata Maker; Fiesta USA: Being Adopted* and more.

ISBN# 688148174 Date Published: 1998 Price: $ 16.00
Publisher: Lothrop Pages: 32

Rating

FROM THE BELLYBUTTON OF THE MOON

Del Imbligo de la Luna

A collection of 22 English and Spanish poems about Alarcon's childhood travels with his family to Mexico to visit his grandma and other relatives. The poems are brought to life by Gonzalez' happy, tropical-colored images. As Kirkus Reviews describes: "Each poem sits near its twin, and it's fun, even for non-Spanish speakers, to compare the two versions and learn the words. Most are simple and celebratory: the sound of a dog's bark in the two languages; a favorite cow named Mariposa; the joys of an aunt's breakfast. His grandmother taught him that Mexico is Aztec for bellybutton of the moon."

Keywords

Mexican American, Mexico, Latino/a, Bilingual, Poetry

Age Range:

Preschool, early school-age

Author: Francisco X Alarcøn

Illustrator: Maya Christina Gonzalez

Francisco X. Alarcon is an award-winning poet. He directs the Spanish for Native Speakers Program at the University of CA, Davis.

ISBN# 892391537 Date Published: 1998 Price: $ 15.95
Publisher: Children's Book Pages:

GET SET! SWIM!

How a Latina girl learns about teamwork and family pride at her first swim meet.

"Jessenia's team is behind, but she manages to win her last match. Jessenia's story is juxtaposed against the memories Mami has of her home in Puerto Rico. The well-executed artwork is strong in both design and color. A good choice for those looking for books in which a Latino family is center stage," says Booklist. But Kirkus Reviews writes, "The story never gives testimony to Jessenia's joy in swimming, or to her being part of the team. The half-stated ideas may not be enough to compel children through the pages."

Keywords

Puerto Rico, Latino/a, Family Life, Friendship, Core Issues (Feelings)

Age Range:

Preschool, early school-age

Author: Jeannine Atkins

Author: Hector Viveros Lee

Jeannine Atkins is the author of *Get Set! Swim!, Aani* and the *Tree Huggers,* and more.

ISBN# 1880000660 Date Published: 1998 Price: $ 15.95
Publisher: Lee & Low Books Pages: 32

GOLD COIN, THE

Determined to steal old Dona Josefa's gold coin, Juan follows her around the countryside.

Alma Flor Ada is a renowned storyteller whose first language is Spanish. This original story, translated from the Spanish, has the feel of a folk tale.

Keywords

Cambodia, Latino/a, Fiction, Boy Focus

Age Range:

Preschool, early school-age

Author: Alma Flor Ada

Alma Flor Ada is author of *Gathering The Sun; My Name is Maria Isabel; Lizard and the Sun; The Gold Coin* and many other important books about Latino heritage.

ISBN# 689717938 Date Published: 1994 Price: $ 5.95
Publisher: Aladdin Pages:

Rating

GRACIAS, THE THANKSGIVING TURKEY

Gracias, El Pavo De Thanksgiving

In this warm holiday story, a young Puerto Rican boy saves the life of his pet turkey with help from his close-knit New York City family and neighborhood; beginning Spanish vocabulary is woven into the text.

Keywords

Bilingual, Puerto Rico, Family Life, Food

Age Range:

Preschool, early school-age

Author: Joy Cowley

Illustrator: Joseph Cepeda

ISBN# 590399640 *Date Published:* 1998 *Price:* $ 5.99

Publisher: Scholastic *Pages:* 32

Rating

GRANDCHILDREN OF THE INCAS, THE

The ancient Incas lives, and the lives of their modern descendants.

Children of Peru and Bolivia explore how their lives are influenced by the history of their Inca ancestors whose descendants live in Colombia, Ecuador, Peru, Bolivia, Chile and Argentina.

Keywords

South America, Peru, Cultural History, Latino/a

Age Range:

Preschool, early school-age

Author: Matti Pitkanen

ISBN# 876145667 *Date Published:* 1992 *Price:* $ 6.95

Publisher: First Ave. Editions *Pages:*

HAIRS PELITOS

Descriptions of the many types of hair in one girl's family.

This jewel-like vignette from Sandra Cisneros's best-selling *The House on Mango Street* shows, through simple, intimate portraits, the diversity among us. "This exuberant bilingual picture book, with eye-catching artwork, is an affectionate picture of familial love and a cozy bedtime book." —The Horn Book. A Parenting Magazine Best Children's Book of the Year.

Keywords

Latino/a, Hair, Bilingual, Mexican American

Age Range:

Preschool, early school-age

Author: Sandra Cisneros

Illustrator: Terry Ybanaz

Sandra Cisneros is the award winning Mexican American author of *The House on Mango Street* and *Hair Pelitos.*

ISBN# 679890076 *Date Published:* 1997 *Price:* $ 6.99

Publisher: Dragonfly Books, Random House *Pages:* 32

I HAD A HIPPOPOTAMUS

A Mexican American boy takes a delightful trip with a box of animal crackers.

What would you do with a hippopotamus? Or a kangaroo? Or a coyote? Come take an imaginary journey with a box of animal crackers. Focuses on the joys of sharing and the warmth of family. "A winning spin on the notion that 'tis better to give than to receive," says Publisher's Weekly.

Keywords

Family Life, Latino/a, Mexican American

Age Range:

Preschool, early school-age

Author: Hector Viveros Lee

ISBN# 1-880000-28-8 *Date Published:* 1997 *Price:* $ 6.95

Publisher: Lee & Low Books *Pages:* 32

Rating

IN MY FAMILY

En mi familia

Carmen Lomas Garza is considered one of the major Mexican American painters in this country. In My Family is the eagerly awaited follow-up to her best-selling Family Pictures, Carmen's loving story of her childhood in a traditional Latino community in South Texas. Once again, the sum of the authentic details creates a rich and important bank of information about Mexican American life today. Wonderful illustrations. Bilingual in English and Spanish.

Keywords

Mexican American, Latino/a, Bilingual, Family Life, Extended Family, Biography

Age Range

Preschool, early school-age

Author: Carmen Lewis Garza

Carmen Lomas Garza is a renowned American painter and graphic artist. Garza lives in San Francisco, CA.

ISBN# 892391383 Date Published 1998 Price $ 15.95

Publisher Children's Book Pages 32

Rating

JOSEFINA

A counting book inspired by Mexican folk artist Josefina Aguilar.

Josefina, a Mexican artist, works in soft clay. Her story includes her Mama and Papa in heaven, eight mourners, and the strength that comes from her conviction that "life goes on." The wonderful illustrations in the style of Mexican folk art could tell the story on their own.

Keywords

Self-Esteem, Latino/a, Role Models, Mexican, Biography

Age Range

Preschool, early school-age

Author-Illustrator: Jeanette Winter

Jeanette Winter is the author and illustrator of many books for children, including *Cowboy Charlie, Diego*, and *Shaker Boy*.

ISBN# 0-15-201091-2 Date Published Price $ 15.00

Publisher Harcourt Brace Pages 36

JUAN BOBO

Juan Bobo belongs to all Puerto Ricans.

Getting water from the stream and taking care of the family pig challenge a legendary Puerto Rican noodlehead in this bright Caribbean "I can read book," which offers four funny tales with controlled vocabulary in English and Spanish.

Keywords

Folk tales and Legends, Latino/a, Bilingual

Age Range

Preschool, early school-age

Author: Carmen T. Bernier-Grand

Illustrator: Ernesto R. Nieves

ISBN# 0-06-444185-7 Date Published 1995 Price $ 3.75

Publisher HarperCollins Pages 64

LIZARD AND THE SUN, THE; LA LAGARTIJA Y EL SOL

A folk tale in English and Spanish (Picture Yearling Book)

Once, a long, long time ago, the sun disappeared from the sky. Everything was dark. All the animals went to search for the sun, but the sun was nowhere to be found. All the animals gave up, except for the lizard. Finally, one day she discovered the sun fast asleep. Then the emperor organized a great feast, with the finest dancers and musicians, so the sun would wake up and never fall asleep again. Since that day, all lizards love to lie in the sun, to remember the day when one of their own brought light and warmth back to the world. In English and Spanish

Keywords

Bilingual, Mexican, Folk tales and Legends

Age Range

Preschool, early school-age

Author: Alma Flor Ada

Illustrator: Felipe Davalos

Alma Flor Ada is author of *Gathering The Sun; My Name is Maria Isabel; Lizard and the Sun; The Gold Coin* and many other important books about Latino heritage.

ISBN# 440415314 Date Published 1999 Price $ 6.99

Publisher Yearling Books Pages 48

MAGIC DOGS OF THE VOLCANOES

Rating

Los Perros Magicos De Los Volcanes

Once upon a time, magic dogs called cadejos lived on the volcanoes of El Salvador and protected the villagers from harm. When wicked lead soldiers threatened to attack, two ancient volcanoes helped the cadejos. This contemporary folk tale is based on a traditional Salvadoran story and is an engaging introduction to this country and its culture. Bilingual in English and Spanish. Vibrant illustrations.

Keywords

Bilingual, Latino/a, El Salvador, Folk tales and Legends

Age Range:

Preschool, early school-age

Author: Manlio Argueta

Illustrator: Elly Simmons

Translator: Stacey Ross

ISBN# 892391294 Date Published: 1995 Price: $ 6.95

Publisher: Children's Book Pages: 32

MARIO'S MAYAN JOURNEY

Rating

A young boy's view of ancient Mayan culture.

Mario awoke with a start; when he went outside, two Mayan children were waiting for him. Together they visit ancient ruins in the jungles of the Yucatan Peninsula. Was it a dream? A fun story for any child interested in Latino history and culture.

Keywords

Latino/a, Central America, Cultural History, History

Age Range:

Preschool, early school-age

Author: Michelle McCunney

ISBN# 1572552034 Date Published: 1997 Price: $ 4.95

Publisher: Mondo Pages:

MOST BEAUTIFUL PLACE IN THE WORLD, THE

A young Guatemalan boy triumphs over poverty and abandonment to find love and self-respect.

Seven-year-old Juan, who lives in Guatemala, is abandoned by both his father and his mother. By reaching out, he is able to find love. Be prepared! His birth parents are presented as completely uncaring and without compassion for him. This story is difficult. Though Juan is a survivor, his birth parents are dealt with as stereotypes — unloving and unkind. Children who have been adopted may take a great interest in talking about Juan's situation.

Keywords

Adopted Child, Grief and Loss, Family Life

Age Range:

Preschool, early school-age

Author: Ann Cameron

ISBN# 394804244 Date Published: Price: $ 3.99

Publisher: Random House Pages:

MY FIRST BOOK OF PROVERBS

Mi Primer Libro De Dichos

An English/Spanish collection of 27 popular Mexican American dichos, or proverbs. Each dicho evokes the wisdom, humor, optimism, or joy that are the foundation of Latino cultures. Exuberant, bursting with color illustrations by contemporary folk-artists do the words proud. This collection is not just for Latino children, but will be appreciated by everyone who enjoys understanding how humans are unique and how we are similar.

Keywords

Latino/a, Bilingual, Proverbs

Age Range:

Preschool, early school-age

Author: Ralfka Gonzalez

Author: Ana Ruiz

ISBN# 892391340 Date Published: 1995 Price: $ 15.95

Publisher: Children's Book Pages:

Rating

MY HOUSE/MI CASA

"Creatively designed introduction to a second language... attractive and useful." —Kirkus Reviews

Captioned illustrations with Spanish and English texts describe things found in a house. Think of this book as an introduction to Spanish for young English-speaking children. The bright and cheerful pictures and clear text bring a sense of fun this laundry list of words for things found in and about one's house. This book will certainly have greatest appeal to any child interested in being able to speak Spanish. And for children of Latino heritage, in particular, being able to understand and speak the language is an important key to feeling comfortable with the Latino community. We encourage parents to start from the beginning in assisting the child to become fluent in both English and Spanish.

Keywords

Bilingual, Latino/a, Self-Esteem, Language

Age Range,

Preschool, early school-age

Author: Rebecca Emberley

ISBN# 316234486 Date Published, 1993 Price, $ 5.95

Publisher, Little Brown Pages, 32

Rating

PEPITA TALKS TWICE

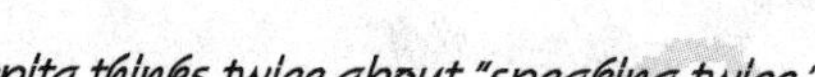

Pepita thinks twice about "speaking twice.'

When Pepita decides to speak only one language, English, she discovers the benefits of being bilingual. This bilingual book deals with a fairly complex set of feelings that may be more in keeping with the development of an older child than Pepita. Unfortunately, the picture book format will turn off older children for whom the story may have more resonance. Nevertheless, the book's simple and appealing text addresses an issue we have not seen covered anyplace else, and will prove useful to any child struggling with identity issues as reflected in language.

Keywords

Bilingual, Latino/a, Language, Racial/Ethnic Identity, Multicultural

Age Range,

Preschool, early school-age

Author: Ofelia Dumas Lachtman

Illustrator: Alex Pardo DeLange

ISBN# 1558850775" Date Published, 1995 Price, $ 14.95

Publisher, Arte Publico Press Pages, 28

RACE OF TOAD AND DEER, THE

This fast-moving Guatemalan folk tale would surely have Aesop nodding with approval.

Toad shouldn't have a chance of winning against Deer. After all, Deer's legs are swifter than the wind, or so he boasts. With his slow and steady little hops, Toad can't possibly keep pace. Or can he? Toad is a lot more clever than Deer —and he has friends in all the right places. Books in Print says, "In this Guatemalan variation on the tortoise-and-hare fable, the laurels go not to virtuous persistence but to crafty footwork."

Keywords

Folk tales and Legends, Latino/a, Guatemalan

Age Range,

Preschool, early school-age

Author: Pat Mora

Illustrator: Maya I. Brooks

Pat Mora is a poet and the author of *Pablo's Tree* and *The Desert Is My Mother/El Desierto Es Mi Madre. She lives in Santa Fe, NM.*

ISBN# 0-531-09477-4 Date Published, 1995 Price, $ 14.95

Publisher, Orchard Pages, 32

SATURDAY SANCOCHO

Tradition! Maria and her grandparents find a way even when challenges make preparations seem impossible.

"Every Saturday Maria looks forward to making chicken sancocho with her grandparents; but one day there is nothing in the house except eggs. How will they have their classic dish? A visit to the market holds the key to new discoveries in this fine ethnic story." Midwest Book Review. Publishers Weekly say "Torres's text bounces with make-a-deal energy.... A recipe for sancocho prepared throughout Center and South America rounds off the tale."

Keywords

Latino/a, Intergenerational

Age Range,

Preschool, early school-age

Author-Illustrator: Leyla Torres

Leyla Torres is the author of *Liliana's Grandmothers*, *Saturday Sancocho*, and *Subway Sparrow.*

ISBN# 374464510 Date Published, 1999 Price, $ 5.95

Publisher, Farrar-Strauss Pages, 32

Rating

SLEEPING BREAD

The fable-like quality and the unusual cultural context have plenty of appeal.

"Once upon a time, in the sleepy little village of San Pedro, a bakery shop opened onto the square. It was called Panaderia el Milagro, which means 'Miracle Bakery,' and a miracle did happen there. This is the story." And so begins the story of a baker who was kind to a beggar and a town which was not. In the end, the beggar saves the town's festival and becomes their patron saint. Recommended by the Center for Children's Books.

Keywords

Folk tales and Legends, Latino/a, Self-Esteem, Mexican, Guatemalan

Age Range:

Preschool, early school-age

Author: Stefan Czernecki

ISBN# 1-56282-519-4 Date Published: 1991 Price: $ 4.95

Publisher: Hyperion Pages: 40

Rating

SNAPSHOTS FROM THE WEDDING

This is a wedding you won't want to miss.

Maya, the flower girl with pitted black olives on each of her fingers, is our guide to a Mexican American wedding, unique yet universal. She makes sure we don't miss any good parts: the groom's arm is in a cast (he broke it playing softball); the alter boy's dirty sneakers show under his dress; Maya dances with her papi, standing on his feet; Isabel's eyes are shiny because she is the bride. What a splendid time! A myriad of culturally authentic details create a rich picture and Garcia's illustrations, 3D photographs of Sculpy clay figures set against pale pink lace perfectly preserve our memories. An inspired collaboration.

Keywords

Latino/a, Mexican American, Family Life, Holidays and Celebrations

Age Range:

Preschool, early school-age

Author: Gary Soto

Illustrator: Stephanie Garcia

Gary Soto is an acclaimed poet and fiction writer. He is the author of *Living Up The Street; Jesse; Nerdlandia, Chato's Kitchen* and *Baseball in April.*

ISBN# 698117522 Date Published: 1998 Price: $ 5.99

Publisher: Paper Star Pages: 32

THREE GOLDEN ORANGES, THE

Once upon a time, long ago and far away....

Kirkus Reviews writes, "Ada reworks the traditional story of Blancaflor, taking swipes at greed, vanity, and the practice of arranged marriages in the process. Some well-traveled types help make the points: older brothers full of themselves and not above treachery; the innocent, well-intentioned youngest brother; a wise older woman; and a young woman in dire circumstances, with the moral fiber to endure.... Ada invests her lengthy retelling with a quiet musicality that softens the predictability of the narrative. Meanwhile, the Spanish countryside comes blazingly alive under the bold illustrations of Cartwright's stylized, utterly transporting artwork."

Keywords

Folk tales and Legends, Latino/a

Age Range:

Preschool, early school-age

Author: Alma Flor Ada

Alma Flor Ada is author of *Gathering The Sun; My Name is Maria Isabel; Lizard and the Sun; The Gold Coin* and many other important books about Latino heritage.

ISBN# 689807759 Date Published: 1999 Price: $ 16.00

Publisher: Athenaeum Pages: 32

TOO MANY TAMALES

How a close-knit contemporary Latino family finds a way to solve a problem.

While helping cook tamales, a young girl tries on her mother's ring, later realizing that it is missing. It must be in the tamales — and the only way to find out is to eat all of them.

Keywords

Family Life, Latino/a, Mexican American, Girl Power, Food

Age Range:

Preschool, early school-age

Author: Gary Soto

Gary Soto is an acclaimed poet and fiction writer. He is the author of *Living Up The Street; Jesse; Nerdlandia, Chato's Kitchen* and *Baseball in April.*

ISBN# 0-399-22146-8 Date Published: Price: $ 5.99

Publisher: Putnam's Pages:

Rating

TORTILLA FACTORY, THE

A tribute to Mexican workers; homage to life, from seed to plant to tortilla.

We feel that the simple text of this slightly boring rendition may not hold the child's interest, but other reviewers feel differently: Horn Book writes, "The text traces the journey of corn from harvest and grinding to the tortilla factory. By concentrating on hands rather than on the faces of the workers, the oil-on-linen paintings demonstrate respect for the ethic of hard work and hold broad, universal appeal. Readers will embrace the book for its clear emphasis on the simple beauty found in the cycles of life for plants and human beings. Also available in Spanish."

Keywords

Cultural History, Latino/a, Mexican American

Age Range.

Preschool, early school-age

Author: Gary Paulsen

Ruth Wright Paulson

Gary Paulsen is the author of Sarny: A Life Remembered, The Tortilla Factory and more.

ISBN# 152016988 Date Published. 1998 Price. $ 7.00
Publisher. Voyager Pages. 32

Rating

TORTILLITAS PARA MAMA

Nursery Rhymes in English and Spanish

A classic collection of nursery rhymes, each in both English and Spanish, collected from the Spanish community in the Americas, many with instructions for accompanying finger plays or other activities. Barbara Cooney's illustrations of Latino/a children and families are delightful reason enough to own this book.

Keywords

Latino/a, Bilingual

Age Range.

Preschool, early school-age

Author: Margot C. Greigo

Author: Barbara Cooney

ISBN# 805002855 Date Published. 1987 Price. $ 5.95
Publisher. Holt Pages. 32

UNCLE NACHO'S HAT

Uncle Nacho is lovable but unable to change. Adapted from a Nicaraguan folk tale.

Nacho is attached to his old hat. Even when his niece Ambrosia gives him a new one, he's pleased but skeptical. Finally, he realizes it's time to push himself to change his style. This uplifting story about adapting to change is brimming with comedy and color and will both encourage discussion and delight the children. Bilingual: English and Spanish.

Keywords

Folk tales and Legends, Latino/a, Bilingual, Nicaragua

Age Range.

Preschool, early school-age

Author: Harriet Rohmer

Harriet Rohmer is the founding director of Children's Book Press, a nonprofit publisher.

ISBN# 0-89239-112-X Date Published. Price. $ 6.95
Publisher. Children's Book Press Pages.

WE ARE A RAINBOW/SOMOS UN ARCO IRIS

We are all different. We are all the same.

Despite its good intentions, this Spanish/English book about the world's commonalities falls short of engaging young readers. Its goal is to help young readers begin building cultural bridges of common human understanding through simple comparisons of culture from breakfast foods to legends, but the lightweight text is generalizing instead of specific. Instead of offering concrete details children can identify with, it makes vague and banal statements about the need to get along, like "When we do not understand each other, we feel bad." Though the young narrator talks about feeling like an outsider after moving to the United States from a Spanish-speaking country, the book lacks emotional impact.

Keywords

Multicultural, Latino/a, Bilingual

Age Range.

Preschool, early school-age

Author: Nancy M. Tabor

Illustrator: Judi Kurjian

ISBN# 0-88106-417-3 Date Published. 1995 Price. $ 6.95
Publisher. Charlesbridge Pages. 32

WHERE FIREFLIES DANCE

Rating

Ahi, Donde Bailan Las Luciernagas

Culturally authentic details create a mosaic of Mexican culture. Writing in Spanish and English from a place "where (her) imagination and memory blend," Corpi intertwines proud and affectionate memories of her Mexican with the legend of the revolutionary Juan Sebastian — the legend that convinced her we each must find our own destiny. Reisberg's witty graphics shine like the sun at midday. Her drawing of a patterned bus in neon bright colors bound for "El Mundo" (the world) is a vivid image of the colorful journey we each must take to find our own destiny in the world.

Keywords

Bilingual, Mexico, Family Life, Latino/a

Age Range:

Preschool, early school-age

Author: Lucha Corpi

Illustrator: Mira Reisberg

ISBN# 892391456 *Date Published:* 1997 *Price:* $ 15.95

Publisher: Children's Press *Pages:* 32

WHY THERE IS NO ARGUING IN HEAVEN

Rating 

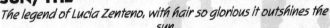

A tale of the beginning of the world illustrated with Mayan images throughout.

Through this ancient Mayan myth of the creation of the world, Deborah Norse Lattimore conveys the wisdom, vitality, and earthy humor of the people whose ancestors told this story and who still live today in Guatemala and parts of Mexico.

Keywords

Guatemalan, Latino/a, Folk tales and Legends, Spiritual Meanings

Age Range:

Preschool, early school-age

Author: Deborah Norse Lattimore

ISBN# 0-07-23717-1 *Date Published:* *Price:* $ 16.00

Publisher: HarperCollins *Pages:*

WOMAN WHO OUTSHONE THE SUN, THE

The legend of Lucia Zenteno, with hair so glorious it outshines the sun.

The river is so taken with Lucia that it jumps into her hair each day. Each day she returns the river to its bed by combing out the water, fish and otters. After the villagers' meanness towards her, however, she leaves their village, carrying their precious river in her hair. After they learn their lesson, Lucia returns the river to the villagers. Bilingual in Spanish and English. Books in Print: "Both the Spanish and English read gracefully. An excellent discussion starter, dealing as it does with issues of the differences between people and respect for nature, the book has a natural place in multicultural and environmental units." Parenting Magazine Award: Outstanding Children's Book of 1991.

Keywords

Bilingual, Latino/a, Folk tales and Legends, Hair, Cultural History

Age Range:

Preschool, early school-age

Author: Alejandro C. Martinez

ISBN# 0-89239-101-4 *Date Published:* 1991 *Price:* $ 6.95

Publisher: Children's Book *Pages:* 32

Rating

BLACK IS BROWN IS TAN

This poetry about biracial identity has been a favorite for over thirty years.

This collection of poems about biracial identity, presented in an accessible, conversational voice, have stood the test of time and serve as a good springboard for discussing racial heritage with children. This series projects a clear and positive perspective for young people in general, standing up for an "I'm okay" attitude that will likely feel supportive to multiracial children. The poems express the voice of a well-rounded character who values helping the community while progressing toward self-realization. One of the few books of poetry to address this topic.

Keywords

Racial/Ethnic Identity, Multiracial Identity, Poetry

Age Range.

Preschool, early school-age

Poet: Arnold Adoff

Arnold Adoff, the winner of the 1988 NCTE Award for Excellence in Poetry for Children, is the author of over 30 books.

ISBN# 0-06-443269-6 *Date Published.* 1973 *Price.* $ 3.95
Publisher. Harper Row *Pages.*

Rating

BLACK LIKE KYRA, WHITE LIKE ME

A book to help your child recognize racism.

When a Black family moves to an all-White neighborhood, the White adults behave rudely and children's friendships break up. Horn Book points out that "this story opens in a patronizing and stereotypical manner with the assumption that only a White neighborhood is a safe place in which to live. The overall stance regarding prejudice is a positive one, but it is marred with mixed and unrealistic messages. Also, the book's format is dull and uninteresting." If your child does bring this book home, you can use it as an example of issues to consider carefully and teach your child to recognize the author's bias. Being able to identify "isms" is strengthening for all kids.

Keywords

African American, Race Relations, Racism

Age Range.

Preschool, early school-age

Author: Judith Vigna

Illustrator: Kathleen Tucker

ISBN# 807507784 *Date Published.* 1992 *Price.* $ 14.95
Publisher. Concept Books *Pages.*

BLACK, WHITE, JUST RIGHT!

An upbeat picture book for biracial children or children in transracial adoptions.

When cultures and colors combine, a daughter reflects on having inherited the best of both worlds. Although as one of the few books for children of biracial heritage, *Black, White, Just Right* is interesting just because of its topic, we would have wished for a more realistic or authentic portrayal of a child's understanding of the complexity of biracial heritage. Instead, this book offers a somewhat simplistic and saccharine portrait that seems almost preachy. Nevertheless, it presents a positive message about biracial heritage, so though it is not the book we might have wished, it is better than nothing.

Keywords

Multiracial Identity, Transracial Adoption, Racial/Ethnic Identity, Self-Esteem

Age Range.

Preschool, early school-age

Author: Marguerite W. Davol

ISBN# 807507857 *Date Published.* *Price.* $ 14.95
Publisher. Whitman *Pages.*

CREATIVITY

People "mixing up together" makes things fun.

In Steptoe's posthumously-published story, Charles doesn't get it when "this new dude walks in"" to Mr. Cohen's classroom and speaks in Spanish. Though Hector is dark-skinned like Charles, who is African American, Charles speaks English. But by learning about the history of Puerto Rico, Charles comes to see that he and Hector are connected and that everyone in the classroom "is the result of different people mixing up together." Helping his new friend to learn English gives him the idea that languages can mix, too, and that riffing on the English language can be "creative." Lewis' realistic watercolors reflect a contemporary urban environment in this fun read for kids.

Keywords

Friendship, Race Relations, Puerto Rico, Multiracial Identity

Age Range.

Preschool, early school-age

Author-Illustrator: John Steptoe

Illustrator: E.B. Lewis

John Steptoe, a two-time Caldecott Honor Book recipient, is the author of *Jumping Mouse; Baby Says; Creativity; Mufaro's Beautiful Daughter* and *Stevie.*

ISBN# 395687063 *Date Published.* 1997 *Price.* $ 15.95
Publisher. Clarion *Pages.* 32

Rating

HOW MY FAMILY LIVES IN AMERICA

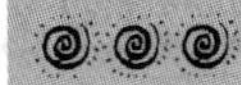

Three children – an African American, a Hispanic American, and an Asian American – describe their families.

Sanu invites friends over to eat tiebou dienn and to "hear stories about when his mom and dad were little in Senegal and in Baltimore"; Eric, whose mother was born in New York City and his father in Puerto Rico, enjoys both baseball and arroz con pollo y habichuelas with his family; Taiwanese Chin Lan ("My name in America is April") has sesame noodles in school and pizza for dinner. Their first-person stories reflect their pride in their dual heritages, as well as their place as full members of mainstream US culture.

Keywords

Multiracial Identity, African American, Puerto Rico, Racial/Ethnic Identity, Cultural History, Diversity

Age Range:

Preschool, early school-age

Author: Susan Kuklin

ISBN# 689822219 *Date Published:* 1992 *Price:* $ 5.99

Publisher: Aladdin *Pages:* 40

Rating

LESS THAN HALF, MORE THAN WHOLE

For children who struggle with the question, "Where do I belong?"

What does it mean to come from multicultural heritage? Tony is less than half Native American and part Anglo. Growing up in a largely Native American environment, he wonders where he belongs. His search for an answer finally ends when his grandfather helps him to understand that he is not "less than half" but rather "more than whole." The message of love, acceptance, and belonging is handled realistically without exaggerated sentimentality. A very positive book.

Keywords

Multiracial Identity, Native American, Transracial Adoption, International Adoption, Racial/Ethnic Identity

Age Range:

Preschool, early school-age

Author: Kathleen Lacapa

Author: Michael Lacapa

Kathleen and Michael Lacapa work with school-age children in and around the White Mountain Apache Reservation in Arizona.

ISBN# 873585925 *Date Published:* 1994 *Price:* $ 7.95

Publisher: Northland *Pages:* 40

LET'S CALL HIM LAU-WILI-WILI-HUMU-HUMU-NUKUNUKU-NUKUNUKU-APUAA-OIOI.

What shall we name the baby?

When a trigger fish and a butterfly fish marry and have a fish child, an argument erupts over what to name it. The happy resolution in this Hawaiian tale speaks to multiethnic families. A very funny and appealing paperback picture book.

Keywords

Asian, Race Relations, Multiracial Identity, Racial/Ethnic Identity, Hawaii

Age Range:

Preschool, early school-age

Author: Tim Myers

ISBN# 1-880188-66-X *Date Published:* 1993 *Price:* $ 5.95

Publisher: Bess press *Pages:* 24

LET'S DANCE!

Dancing is a way of celebrating all around the world.

Colorful and festive photographs capture the flash and rhythms, costumes, and stories behind native dances from around the world. Includes an Afghan wedding dancer, the lion dance performed to welcome the Chinese New Year, country barn dances, break dancing, a Tibetan yak dance, and a woman's dance from Northern India. The book offers an attractive, active, and upbeat introduction about the ways in which people and cultures can be both very much the same and terrifically different from one another all at once. Reach out. Touch magic. Pass it on.

Keywords

Music, Multiracial, Festivals, Cultural History, Multicultural

Age Range:

Preschool, early school-age

Author/Illustrator:

George Ancona is the author of *Powwow; Let's Dance; Fiesta Fireworks; The Piñata Maker; Fiesta USA: Being Adopted* and more.

ISBN# 688162118 *Date Published:* 1998 *Price:* $ 16.00

Publisher: Morrow *Pages:* 40

Rating

MIXED UP CHAMELEON

Some say adopted people are like chameleons, able to change to fit in.

The chameleon wishes it could be like all the different animals in the zoo — and ends up being like all of them at once — with hilarious results.

Keywords

Adoption, Self-Esteem, Diversity

Age Range.

Preschool, early school-age

Author: Eric Carle

ISBN# 0-06-443162-2 Date Published. 1975 Price. $ 5.95
Publisher. HarperCollins Pages. 32

Rating

NINA BONITA

The white rabbit loved Nina Bonita .

Black is beautiful to a little white rabbit who tries to discover the secret that will make him black. He tries to color himself black but nothing works. Finally, he marries a black rabbit and has rabbit children with fur as black and pretty as that of Nina Bonita. This book is from Brazil.

Keywords

Transracial Adoption, Multiracial, Race Relations, Self-Esteem

Age Range.

Preschool, early school-age

Author: Ana Maria Machado

Translator: Elena Iribarren

Ana Maria Machado wrote this book originally in Spanish. Elena Iribarren translated the story to English.

ISBN# 980-2571652 Date Published. Price. $ 6.95
Publisher. Kane Miller Pages.

NOW WE CAN HAVE A WEDDING!

Homey, warm celebration of ethnic diversity through food.

From Kirkus Reviews: "A small girl goes from one apartment to another in her building, helping friends of all nationalities prepare special foods for her sister's wedding. She makes dolmades with her Greek papa, tamales with the groom's father, steamed cakes with Mr. Chen in 5B, biscotti with Señora Theodora in 2C, and so on. The tradition behind and significance of every delicacy is described in a childlike and joyful manner, while the foods provide a mini-tour of world cultures.

Keywords

Multicultural, Family Life, Friendship, Holidays and Celebrations, Food

Age Range.

Preschool, early school-age

Author: Judy Cox

Author: Dyanne Di Salvo-Ryan

ISBN# 082341342X Date Published. 1998 Price. $ 15.95
Publisher. Holiday House Pages. 32

OUTSIDE INSIDE POEMS

Unique word pictures of how it feels to be young and growing.

Arnold Adoff is committed to making poetry easy to grasp for young and old alike. His unique voice, combined with John Steptoe's wonderful illustrations, make this a must-have introductory book for young readers.

Keywords

African American, Self-Esteem, Child Development, Poetry

Age Range.

Preschool, early school-age

Poet: Arnold Adoff

Illustrator: John Steptoe

Arnold Adoff, the winner of the 1988 NCTE Award for Excellence in Poetry for Children, is the author of over 30 books.

ISBN# 152002243 Date Published. 1995 Price. $ 5.00
Publisher. Voyager Pages.

Rating

PAPA TELLS CHITA A STORY

A family story about Chita, a biracial Black/Cuban girl.

Papa is an African American, Spanish American war veteran and Chita is his biracial Black/Cuban daughter. This is the story about how his battalion of newly-freed former slaves won glory in battle. One of the few books to address this topic for this age group.

Keywords

Multiracial Identity, Self-Esteem, Race Relations, Role Models, Cultural History

Age Range:

Preschool, early school-age

Author: Elizabeth Howard

ISBN# 27446239 *Date Published:* 1995 *Price:* $ 5.99

Publisher: Simon & Schuster *Pages:*

Rating

SNEETCHES AND OTHER STORIES, THE

For children of all ages.

Still timely and important, these four stories offer messages so subtle and solutions so obvious that kids of all ages enjoy endless rereadings. "The Sneetches" illustrates the silliness of racial elitism and what happens to those who subscribe to it, a matter particularly powerful for children of multiracial identity. "Too Many Daves" considers identity needs of twenty-three siblings named Dave. "Zax" presents what happens when the stubborn and inflexible run into each other. And "What Was I Scared Of?" about pale green pants with nobody inside them, is about fear as a reaction to the unknown. Dr. Seuss at his best.

Keywords

Multiracial Identity

Age Range:

Preschool, early school-age

Author-Illustrator: Dr. Scuss

Everyone loves Dr. Seuss! A true original, he wrote and illustrated over 50 classic children's books with sales of more than a100 million copies

ISBN# 394800893 *Date Published:* 1988 *Price:* $ 14.95

Publisher: Random House *Pages:* 64

YOU BE ME, I'LL BE YOU

A biracial child explores how it is to feel different from her parents.

Anna, the biracial child of a white father and Black mother, explores her questions and yearnings about her identity, learning a lesson about differences, pride and her family. This is one of the very few books to deal directly with a biracial child's not-uncommon desire to look like her white father because she does not feel pretty, but it offers a silly and rather demeaning solution. However, it could be an interesting conversation-starter for discussions with your children about how they feel about racial differences.

Keywords

Multiracial Identity, Transracial Adoption, International Adoption, Racial/Ethnic Identity

Age Range:

Preschool, early school-age

Author: Pili Mandlcbaum

ISBN# 0-916291-47-2 *Date Published:* 1993 *Price:* $ 6.95

Publisher: Kane-Miller *Pages:* 32

Rating

BABY RATTLESNAKE

What happens when you get something before you are ready for it?

This is the story about what happens when the Elders give in to a young reptile and let him have his rattle, even though they know he is not old enough to use it wisely. The story concludes with a sweet expression of parental forgiveness and acceptance rather than shame or an "I told you so." Lyrical repetition makes this appropriate for younger children. Colorful, southwestern-style illustrations. One of the few authentic Native American folk tales available in paperback for young readers. Recommended by the Elementary School Library Collection.

Keywords

Self-Esteem, Folk tales and Legends, Native American

Age Range.

Preschool, early school-age

Author: Te Ata

adapter: Lynn Moroney

Told by Te Ata, whose name means "Bearer of the Morning," a 92-year-old Chikasaw storyteller; adapted by Lynn Moroney.

ISBN# 0-89239-111-1 Date Published. 1993 Price. $ 6.95

Publisher. Children's Book Pages. 32

Rating

CROW AND HAWK

A Pueblo Indian story asking which of a baby's mothers is the "real" one?

Crow lays her eggs but does not sit on them to hatch them. Instead, Hawk hatches them and raises the babies. Then Crow comes back. Which mother should keep the babies? Eagle, King of the birds, helps decide — the baby stays with Hawk. This story should be read at the same time as *The Mulberry Bird*, to create a more sympathetic balance and feeling about cooperative possibilities between birth and adoptive parents. Nevertheless, it presents a wonderful opportunity to talk about adoption and about the views regarding adoption that are held by various cultures. Vivid cut-paper illustrations.

Keywords

Adoption, Folk tales and Legends, Triad Issues, Native American

Age Range.

Preschool, early school-age

Author: Michael J. Rosen

ISBN# 015200257X Date Published. Price. $ 15.00

Publisher. Harcourt Brace Pages.

FIRST STRAWBERRIES, THE

How did strawberries come to be? Retelling of a Cherokee legend.

From Joseph Bruchac, an award-winning Native American storyteller, comes this retelling of a Cherokee legend which explains how strawberries came to reunite the first man and woman after a quarrel. The sun sends various berries to reunite the first man and woman after a quarrel, but only ripe strawberries had the power. Whenever the Cherokee eat strawberries, they are reminded to be kind to one another. Kirkus Reviews calls it "altogether lovely," and the Horn Book says "the brief, readable story, accompanied by strong and spare illustrations, carries a valuable message about friendship and respect."

Keywords

Native American, Folk tales and Legends, Friendship

Age Range.

Preschool, early school-age

Author: Joseph Bruchac

Joseph Bruchac is the author of *A Boy Called Slow; Between Earth and Sky; The First Strawberries* and more.

ISBN# 140564098 Date Published. 1998 Price. $ 5.99

Publisher. Puffin Pages. 32

FOX SONG

An Abenaki Indian girl grieves the death of her great-grandmother.

When she remembers that her great-grandmother is dead, Jamie does not want to wake up in the morning. She remembers the times they spent together and what Grandma Bowen taught her: "When you see a fox, you will think of me and not be alone." This story is about the love between the young and the old and the beauty of the natural world. It will hold particular interest to any adopted child, touching on personal experiences of loss.

Keywords

Native American, Grief and Loss, Intergenerational, Family Life, Core Issues (Feelings)

Age Range.

Preschool, early school-age

Author: Joseph Bruchac

Author: Paul Morin

Joseph Bruchac is the author of *A Boy Called Slow; Between Earth and Sky; The First Strawberries* and more.

ISBN# 698115619 Date Published. 1997 Price. $ 5.95

Publisher. Paper Star Pages. 32

Rating

GIRL WHO LOVED WILD HORSES, THE

A Native American girl prefers to live among the wild horses where she is free.

This book has memorable characters, a tear-jerker ending and a just plain good story. It may connect with adopted children's deeper feelings about moving from one way of life to another, presenting a great opportunity to talk about the feelings involved. The Horn Book writes, "Universally praised by critics at its original publication 20 years ago, this is the story of a Native American girl who feels such kinship to a group of wild horses that she eventually becomes one of them.... Both storytelling and art express the harmony with and the love of nature which characterize Native American culture." A Caldecott Medal Book.

Keywords

Adoption, Core Issues (Feelings), Fiction, Native American

Age Range:

Preschool, early school-age

Author: Paul Goble

Clarita Kohen

Paul Goble is the author of *The Lost Children, Adopted By The Eagles, The Girl Who Loved Wild Horses.*

ISBN# 689716966 *Date Published:* 1993 *Price:* $ 5.99

Publisher: Aladdin *Pages:* 32

Rating

MAGIC OF SPIDER WOMAN, THE

Why generations of Navajo weavers have carefully woven mistakes into their traditional blankets.

Spider Woman warns Weaving Woman to keep her life in balance and avoiding weaving for too long at any one time, but Weaving Woman becomes so involved in making the most beautiful blanket in the world that she cannot pull herself away from her loom. Soon she is trapped in her own excess, her spirit woven into her weaving. Spider Woman releases her by loosening a thread, in the process making the blanket imperfect. "Long ago and far away" tales are a great way to introduce children to the spirit of a culture — but this one may have more meaning to adults than kids.

Keywords

Native American, Folk tales and Legends, Skill Mastery, Spiritual Meanings

Age Range:

Preschool, early school-age

Author: Ileana C. Lee

Author: Susan Roth

ISBN# 590461559 *Date Published:* 1996 *Price:* $ 14.95

Publisher: Scholastic *Pages:* 32

MAMA'S LITTLE ONE

A traditional Mohican story.

This story was adapted by Hendrick Aupaumut, a Mohican historian, from a history of the Muh-he-ka-ne-ok. According to Mohican tradition, every morning until the children were grown, the head of each family, man or woman, would wake the children and teach them the ways to please the Great Good Spirit. Heath's appealing version takes the reader on a culturally specific journey, disclosing in a simple way the details of ways of living that reflect Mohican values.

Keywords

Native American, Family Life, Folk tales and Legends

Age Range:

Preschool, early school-age

Author: Kristina Heath

ISBN# 935790055 *Date Published:* 1998 *Price:* $ 10.00

Publisher: Muh-he-con-neew Press *Pages:* 32

MUD FAMILY, THE

For the Anasazi, life depends on rain. Sosi's family may have to leave their land.

A first-person narrative from Sosi, a young girl of the Anasazi tribe, ancestors of the present day Pueblo peoples who lived in the harsh deserts of the American Southwest. The land is drying up and the corn is dying. Sosi's family will have to move and her parents are cross, tired, and have no patience for her. Sosi expresses her confusion, sadness and anger by running away and making a family of mud dolls. Unlike in her own family, the doll family never scolds. Sosi makes the mud girl dance for rain, and the rain comes, bringing Sosi back to the family that needs her most of all.

Keywords

Native American, Cultural History, Family Life, Girl Power, Core Issues (Feelings), Africa

Age Range:

Preschool, early school-age

Author: Betsy James

ISBN# 195124790 *Date Published:* 1994 *Price:* $ 10.95

Publisher: Oxford Paperbacks *Pages:* 32

Rating

ROUGH FACE GIRL, THE

A n Algonquin Indian version of the Cinderella story.

From Kirkus Reviews: "An Algonquin Cinderella story, with accomplished but sometimes overly literal illustrations. A powerful invisible being will marry the woman who can prove that she's seen him; a poor man's two proud daughters try and fail, but the third, her face and hands scarred from tending the fire, has the understanding to see him everywhere in the world and is lovingly received. Martin's retelling is spare and understated but never dry; the two sisters are richly comic figures, the climax and ending uncontrived yet magically romantic."

Keywords

Folk tales and Legends, Native American, Girl Power

Age Range.

Preschool, early school-age

Author: Rafe Martin

Illustrator: David Shannon

ISBN# 698116267 | Date Published. 1998 | Price. $ 5.99

Publisher. Penguin | Pages. 32

Rating

STORY OF JUMPING MOUSE, THE

"You will reach the far-off land if you keep hope alive," Magic Frog says.

This Native American legend from Seven Arrows tells the story of a mouse whose dreams carry him finally to the far-off land where no mouse goes hungry. Though he faces great obstacles, his own unselfish spirit, optimism, and faith in himself turns out to be his power. A classic picture book with delightful pencil-wash drawings which will engage you and your small child. A Caldecott Honor book.

Keywords

Folk tales and Legends, Native American

Age Range.

Preschool, early school-age

Illustrator: John Steptoe

John Steptoe, a two-time Caldecott Honor Book recipient, is the author of *Jumping Mouse; Baby Says; Creativity; Mufaro's Beautiful Daughter* and *Stevie.*

ISBN# 068808740X | Date Published. | Price. $ 4.95

Publisher. Morrow | Pages.

TWO PAIRS OF SHOES

Maggie, a child of two worlds, Cree and Anglo, learns each has its own rules.

Today is a special day of Maggie, for she has been given two pairs of shoes — moccasins and patent leather. As a child of two worlds, she must now "remember when and how to wear each pair." We feel that this book is especially valuable for transracial adoptive families, in which the children (and parents!) can benefit from learning how to feel comfortable in diverse settings and differing cultural contexts.

Keywords

Native American, Antiracist Strategies, Family Life, Transracial Adoption, Manners

Age Range.

Preschool, early school-age

Author: Esther Sanderson

David Beyer

Esther Sanderson is Cree.

ISBN# 0921827156" | Date Published. 1990 | Price. $ 11.00

Publisher. Pemmican | Pages.

WORRY STONE, THE

An original folk tale in the spirit of the Chumash tribe of California.

Amanda, an old woman, is troubled by a sad little boy she meets at the park. She gives him the worry stone her grandfather had given her as a child and tells him the story her grandfather had told her. In the story, the Indian bride Tokatu sheds tears for her dead husband — tears that became stones that, when rubbed slowly and thoughtfully, seemed to ease the holder's troubles. The realistic illustrations are wonderful and the understanding that develops between the generations is comforting. Winner of the Small Press Children's Book Award and Western Writers of America Storyteller Award, 1997.

Keywords

Native American, Intergenerational, Friendship, Folk tales and Legends, Grief and Loss

Age Range.

School-agers 9-12

Author: Marianna Dengler

Author: Sibyl Graber Gerig

ISBN# 873586425 | Date Published. 1996 | Price. $ 15.95

Publisher. Rising Moon | Pages. 32

Rating

ALL THE COLORS WE ARE

How we get our skin color. Por que tenemos diferentes colores de piel.

Demystifies skin color differences. This is the best book we have found to help children view coloration from a scientific point of view rather than a judgmental one. We feel it should be in every child's library. Human beings have different skin tones to protect us from the sun's harmful rays. Melanin gives us color; all human beings have melanin in their skin, eyes, and hair. Each page has a spectrum of colors, allowing kids to match their own color to the colors on the page. Bilingual in Spanish and English. A Pact bestseller.

Keywords
Diversity, Multicultural, Multiracial, Bilingual, Transracial Adoption, International Adoption

Age Range:
Preschool, early school-age

Author: Katie Kissinger

ISBN# 934140804 Date Published: 1994 Price: $ 9.95
Publisher: Redleaf Pages: 32

Rating

ALMOND COOKIES AND DRAGON WELL TEA

Making friends across cultural lines is fun for Erica and Nancy.

Erica, depicted as a blonde child wearing a pony tail, sunglasses, and stretch pants visits the house of her friend Nancy, a Chinese American girl, who is illustrated wearing a more conservative outfit. The visit allows Nancy to make many delightful discoveries about her friend's cultural heritage and the reader is pleased at the developing friendship between the two girls. Erica's favorable responses help Nancy feel extra pride in her Chinese background, though there does not seem to be any interest on the part of either girl in introducing Nancy to any traditions that might be part of Erica's family life.

Keywords
Race Relations, Asian American, Fiction, Chinese American, Cultural History, Friendship

Age Range:
Preschool, early school-age

Author: Cynthia Chin-Lee

Illustrator: You-Shan Tang

Cynthia Chin-Lee is the author of *Almond Cookies and Dragon Well Tea*, and *A is for Asia*.

ISBN# 1879965038 Date Published: 1993 Price: $ 12.95
Publisher: Polychrome Pages:

BIRTHDAYS!

Birthday parties in more than 20 different countries, illuminated with children's art.

Simple text and paintings by children show how birthdays are celebrated in different cultures around the world. We are alike in celebrating the miracle of life and the passing of time, but different countries have different customs. Endnotes provide additional information about the customs in each country.

Keywords
Birthdays, Family Life, Friendship, Multiracial, Multicultural, Holidays and Celebrations

Age Range:
Preschool, early school-age

Author: Eve B. Feldman

Eve B. Feldman is the author of *That Cat*, *Animals Don't Wear Pajamas*, and *Dog Crazy*. She lives in Rockville Center, NY.

ISBN# 0-8167-3494-1 Date Published: 1996 Price: $ 14.95
Publisher: Bridgewater Pages: 32

CHAG SAMEACH! — HAPPY HOLIDAYS

A photo book that features Jewish transracial families.

Text and photographs featuring multiracial, single-parent, and other families provide a secular, egalitarian introduction to such Jewish holidays as Rosh Hashanah, Yom Kippur, and Purim. This is the only book we are aware of that portrays multiracial Jewish families observing traditional Jewish holidays. It is reassuring to Jewish children of color to see that they are not the only Jews with brown skin and engages children of other religions who wonder what it's like to be a child in a Jewish family that enjoys celebrating traditions together.

Keywords
African American, Judaism, Multiracial, Asian, Holidays and Celebrations

Age Range:
Preschool, early school-age

Author: Patricia Schaeffer

Patricia Schaeffer is an adoptive mother.

ISBN# 935079165 Date Published: 1985 Price: $ 5.95
Publisher: Tabor Sarah Bks Pages: 32

Rating

COLOR OF HIS OWN, A

A perfect read-aloud story.

For the first time in paperback, here's the story of a chameleon who gets tired of constantly changing his color and wants to find a color all his own. Staying green forever by remaining on a leaf seems like a much better idea than always changing. And it works for a time, but when autumn comes, even the leaf changes color. Oh, dear. Then our hero meets another chameleon and learns to like himself by making a friend who shares his changing ways. This book creates a wonderful opportunity to talk with children four to eight years old about skin color and what it means.

Keywords

Racial/Ethnic Identity, Multiracial Identity, Core Issues (Feelings), Self-Esteem, Friendship

Age Range.

Preschool, early school-age

Author: Leo Lionni

Leo Lionni has written and illustrated 93 books for children.

ISBN# 679887857 Date Published. 1997 Price. $ 6.99
Publisher. Dragonfly Books, Random House Pages. 32

Rating

CRAYON BOX THAT TALKED, THE

Why two colors can be better than one.

One by one, each crayon is unique. Together, they are complete. In Shane DeRolf's deceptively simple poem, a child's box of crayons coveys the simple truth that when we all work together, the results are much more interesting and colorful. Soon to be a nationally syndicated television show.

Keywords

Antiracist Strategies, Core Issues (Feelings), Family Life, Multicultural, Diversity, Self-Esteem

Age Range.

Preschool, early school-age

Author: Shane DeRolf

Illustrator: Michael Letzig

ISBN# 670886117 Date Published. 1997 Price. $ 12.00
Publisher. Random House Pages. 32

ELEVEN NATURE TALES: A MULTICULTURAL JOURNEY

Ecologically conscious folk tales from around the globe.

Eleven multicultural folk tales to read or tell aloud, focusing on how things relate to each other, one to one. Originating from the *Alaskan Tlingit to Zaire*, each story is told in simple, direct language that young readers or listeners will enjoy. Joe Schlichta's scratchboard illustrations are great.

Keywords

Multicultural, Folk tales and Legends, Spiritual Meanings

Age Range.

Preschool, early school-age

Author: Pleasant De Spain

Illustrator: Joe Shlichta

ISBN# 874834589 Date Published. 1996 Price. $ 7.95
Publisher. August House Pages.

EVERYBODY COOKS RICE

What's for dinner? Yummy – rice.

At dinner time, Carrie is searching for her brother throughout their multicultural neighborhood. At each home, she visits with a family from a different culture and tastes a different rice dish. Cultures represented include Chinese, Vietnamese, Puerto Rican, Haitian, East Indian and more. Recipes from the story are included in the back of the book.

Keywords

Multicultural, Racial/Ethnic Identity, Diversity

Age Range.

Preschool, early school-age

Author: Noray Dooley

Noray Dooley is also the author of *Everybody Bakes Bread.*

ISBN# 876145918 Date Published. 1992 Price. $ 6.95
Publisher. First Ave. Editions Pages.

FAMILIES

Rating 

A multiracial group of friends, who are cared for within many different types of families.

From the publisher: "This charming book is a winning introduction to the rich variety of families. Realities such as divorce, stepfamilies, adoption, single parenting, and gay and Lesbian parenting are explored through the curious, affectionate and nonjudgmental eyes of six-year-old Angie." Publishers Weekly says, "Children should have a good time following the explanations of Angie, six years old, who tells everything she knows about families... She can help kids to understand their own situations and the various home lives of other boys and girls." Also available in Spanish, as *Familias*, 1-55861-183-5

Keywords

Adopted Child, Family Life, Diversity, Gay and/or Lesbian, Multiracial, Stepparents

Age Range:

Preschool, early school-age

Author: Meredith Tax

Author: Marylin Hafner

Meredith Tax is is cofounder and president of Women's WORLD, which combats gender-based censorship. Marylin Hafner won the National Jewish Book Award for *Passover Magic.*

ISBN# 1-55861-157-6 *Date Published:* 1998 *Price:* $ 7.95

Publisher: Oxford Paperbacks *Pages:* 32

HATS OFF TO HAIR

Rating 

No matter how you wear your hair, it's an important part of you.

Realistic and charming paintings of contemporary American kids from many races and ethnicities showing off their hairdos are not enough to keep young readers engaged. This book is too slight. The book is visually engaging but does not offer anything more than meets the eye. Dependent on its illustrations to tell its story, it fails to offer much more interest.

Keywords

Hair, Multicultural

Age Range:

Preschool, early school-age

Author: Virginia Kroll

Virginia Kroll is the author of *Beginnings, Hats Off To Hair, Masai and I*, and more.

ISBN# 881068683 *Date Published:* *Price:* $ 6.95

Publisher: Charlesbridge *Pages:*

HEROES

Donnie, a Japanese American, faces prejudice and learns about heroism.

When Donnie's friends play war after school, they want him to be the bad guy. They don't believe his father and uncle served in the US Army, and to make matters worse, his family won't help him because they say "real heroes don't brag." It all changes one exciting day when.... This book received a Teachers' Choice Award; was voted a Notable Children's Book by the Smithsonian; and was Editors' Choice, San Francisco Chronicle.

Keywords

Race Relations, Japanese American, Self-Esteem, Racial/Ethnic Identity, Asian, Fathers

Age Range:

Preschool, early school-age

Author: Ken Mochizuki

Illustrator: Don Lee

Ken Mochizuki is the author of *Heroes* and *Passage to Freedom: The Sugihara Story*

ISBN# 1880000504 *Date Published:* 1997 *Price:* $ 6.95

Publisher: Lee & Low Books *Pages:* 32

IN GOD'S NAME

The importance of diversity and the strength of unity.

In this appealing book relaying God's many names, the energetic illustrations enhance the feeling of celebration. The visual elements of this book invoke an implicit context which elicits a sense of wonder in the reader, the wondrous notion of a larger universal power, a notion all the more moving because people from many cultures share the belief in such a power and have named it in order to be able to communicate with and about it. The illustrations portray children of color and white children in reasonable balance. A Pact bestseller.

Keywords

African American, Self-Esteem, Multicultural, Spiritual Meanings, Black Identity

Age Range:

Preschool, early school-age

Author: Sandy Eisenberg Sasso

Illustrator: Phoebe Stone

ISBN# 1-879045-26-5 *Date Published:* 1994 *Price:* $ 16.95

Publisher: Jewish Light Publishing *Pages:* 32

Rating

JUST LIKE ME

Stories and self-portraits by fourteen artists.

This vibrant anthology highlights the art and inspirational paths of 14 contemporary artists of many cultural backgrounds who have shared their art and lives with children. It's a pleasure to be in their company! Each double-page spread contains a self-portrait, as well as simple text about the artist's personal story and reflections on what the art means to them. Engaging and filled with life, this book captures the essence of celebrating diversity and is sure to invite kids to create self-portraits of their own.

Keywords

Multicultural, Biography

Age Range,

Preschool, early school-age

Editor: Harriet Rohmer

Harriet Rohmer is the founding director of Children's Book Press, a nonprofit publisher.

ISBN# 0892391499 ; Date Published, 1997 Price, $ 15.95
Publisher, Children's Book Pages,

Rating

KIDS MULTICULTURAL ART BOOK, THE

Art & craft experiences from around the world.

Imagine if you could walk from Asia to North America, just how long it would take! begins this book introducing 100 craft projects from African, Native American, Eskimo, Asian, and Latino cultures. The projects range from easy-to-do to challenging and remain respectful of their origins. With this book, children learn by doing — reaching across continents with paper, paste, and paints while developing basic sensibilities about the cultures of others. Some projects encourage the child's own creativity, using the traditional craft as a jumping off place.

Keywords

Multicultural, Skill Mastery

Age Range,

Preschool, early school-age

Author-Illustrator: Alexandra M. Terzian

ISBN# 913589721 Date Published, 1993 Price, $ 12.95
Publisher, Williamson Pages, 160

LIKE LIKES LIKE

A lonely kitty finds another kitty to play with.

A white cat all alone watches the animal world pair off ("Two by two") and droops ("head and ears down"). But then he explores and succeeds in meeting another cat! Joy comes with connection. Booklist says, "Raschka at his most amenable. Can be read as a meditation on race... a joyful, comforting celebration of the beginning of friendship." Kirkus Reviews calls it "upbeat...about the happiness a soul mate brings." In a starred review, Publishers Weekly calls it "a marvel of lyrical vigor...playful and poetic rhymes, homonyms, alliteration and imagery." This book's colorful illustrations are quirky and fun.

Keywords

Friendship, Diversity, Race Relations

Age Range,

Preschool, early school-age

Author-Illustrator: Chris Raschka

Chris Raschka is the author of *Charlie Parker Played Be Bop; Like Likes Like;* and a *Caldecott Honor Book, Yo! Yes?*

ISBN# 789425645 Date Published, 1999 Price, $ 15.95
Publisher, DK Publishing Pages, 32

MAMA & PAPA HAVE A STORE

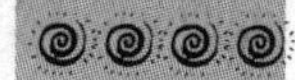

A remarkable story about a Chinese/Latin world.

Home is where the heart is! A Chinese family has fled a war in China and moved to Guatemala City, living behind their fabric store which sells Chinese silk thread (to be used in the best Guatemalan weavings) along with firecrackers, porcelain Buddhas and soy sauce. "This is how the day begins," says the youngest daughter, conveying the energy, affection, creativity, and resilience of her family through details of a typical day: the sound of chopping food, the game of sliding down the roof, her father's abacus; "and this is how it ends." Winner of the Americas Award for Children and Young Adult Literature.

Keywords

Multicultural, Latino/a, Chinese, Guatemalan

Age Range,

Preschool, early school-age

Author-Illustrator: Amelia Lau Carling

ISBN# 803720440 Date Published, 1998 Price, $ 15.99
Publisher, Dial Pages, 32

Rating

MANY COLORS OF MOTHER GOOSE, THE

At last! Mother Goose rhymes reflecting children of color.

This book collects 31 classic rhymes, presenting them in a way that reflects a variety of cultures and races.

Keywords

Antiracist Strategies, Self-Esteem, Multicultural, Racial/Ethnic Identity, Poetry, Multiracial

Age Range:

Preschool, early school-age

Author: Cheryl Willis Hudson

Cheryl Willis Hudson is the author of *Bright Eyes, Brown Skin* , *The Many Colors of Mother Goose* and *The Kids' Book of Wisdom*

ISBN# 940975777 *Date Published:* 1997 *Price:* $ 10.95

Publisher: Just Us Books *Pages:* 32

Rating

MY SONG IS BEAUTIFUL

A collection celebrating diversity which includes more white poets than poets of color.

"This small anthology of 14 poems celebrates diversity, not only in culture, but also in mood and genre (from invocation to nonsense verse) and in illustrator, artistic medium, and style... There are fine poems by Nikki Giovanni, Jack Prelutsky, A. A. Milne, and others, including a Brooklyn seventh-grader; and there are translations from Central Eskimo, ancient Mexico, Korea, and Chippewa Indian. Each poem is illustrated by a different artist, among them Ashley Bryan, David Diaz, and Keiko Narahashi." —The American Library Association

Keywords

Diversity, Racial/Ethnic Identity, Race Relations, Poetry, Multicultural, Multiracial

Age Range:

Preschool, early school-age

Editor: Mary Ann Hoberman

Mary Ann Hoberman is a poet.

ISBN# 316367389 *Date Published:* 1994 *Price:* $ 16.95

Publisher: Little Brown *Pages:* 28

NIGHT IS LIKE AN ANIMAL

Positive reflections for children of color.

Traveling across the earth, Night — in the form of an animal — brings peaceful sleep to children around the world. And when dawn comes, Night departs, leaving hidden paw prints in the shadows and elusive memories of sweet dreams. It is lovely to have a book representing the dark of night as something positive and peaceful rather than the more typical negative images associated with darkness. Particularly wonderful for all children of color. A New York Times Outstanding Book of the Year.

Keywords

African American, Latino/a, Self-Esteem, Black Identity, Native American, Multiracial

Age Range:

Preschool, early school-age

Author: Candace Whitman

ISBN# 374455024 *Date Published:* 1997 *Price:* $ 4.95

Publisher: Farrar-Strauss *Pages:* 32

PURPLE, GREEN AND YELLOW

Brigid's super-indelible-never-comes-off-till-you're-dead markers create new options about what color her skin could be.

Robert Munsch's wry humor could be a bridge to a conversation about your child's feelings about skin color. Brigid paints herself with her super-indelible never-comes-off-till-you're-dead markers. Nothing will remove the color, so she uses the purple marker to cover up all the other colors. She looks better than before — almost too good to be true. You might get some interesting answers if you ask your child what he thinks about these questions: Was being purple fun for Brigid? Would your child like to have a different color skin? What's good about the color he was born with? What's not so good about it?

Keywords

Core Issues (Feelings), Family Life, Racial/Ethnic Identity

Age Range:

Preschool, early school-age

Author: Robert Munsch

ISBN# 1550372564 *Date Published:* *Price:* $ 5.95

Publisher: Annick Press *Pages:* 32

Rating

SKIP ACROSS THE OCEAN

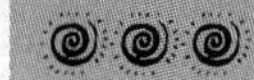

A truly international collection of verses for the very young, dazzlingly illustrated.

All over the world, parents entertain and comfort children with play rhymes and lullabies, and every country has its own unique store of them. Floella Benjamin has selected many of the most interesting of these — some familiar, some never before written down. The verses from six continents and twenty-three countries invite readers to skip across the ocean and dance with children from around the world.

Keywords

Racial/Ethnic Identity, Self-Esteem, Family Life, Poetry, Diversity

Age Range:

Preschool, early school-age

Author: Floella Benjamin

ISBN# 0-531-094553 Date Published: Price: $ 15.95
Publisher: Orchard Pages:

Rating

SMOKY NIGHT

What do riots mean to the kids who live through them?

This is a topical story about cats...and people...who couldn't get along until a night of rioting brings them together. Winner of the 1995 Caldecott Medal and many more awards. Fine illustrations!

Keywords

Race Relations, Racism, Friendship, Fiction

Age Range:

Preschool, early school-age

Author: Eve Bunting

Eve Bunting is the author of *Going Home, Smoky Night,* and many more.

ISBN# 0-15-269954-6 Date Published: Price: $ 6.00
Publisher: Harcourt Brace Pages:

SUBWAY SPARROW

A multicultural vignette about efforts to rescue a sparrow in trouble.

"There is a sparrow in the New York City subway. Four passengers, whose differences in age, culture, and language may appear insurmountable, find a way to catch it before the train gets into the next station and fills with people. Torres develops her story smoothly, weaving text and images into a simple, warm, and appealing plot." Booklist. Also available in Spanish, ISBN:0374827564.

Keywords

Multicultural, Latino/a

Age Range:

Preschool, early school-age

Author-Illustrator: Leyla Torres

Leyla Torres is the author of *Liliana's Grandmothers*, *Saturday Sancocho,* and *Subway Sparrow.*

ISBN# 374471290 Date Published: 1997 Price: $ 6.95
Publisher: Farrar-Strauss Pages: 32

TEA WITH MILK

How different cultures can blend

Say explores where home really is through the autobiographical story of his California-born mother's experiences when her family moves back to Japan. Respectful of the formality of Japan, Say captures the struggle between two cultures as May (his mother) seeks a place of her own by combining two cultures. May drinks her tea the western way, with milk and sugar.

Keywords

Multicultural, Japanese American

Age Range:

Preschool, early school-age

Author-Illustrator: Allen Say

Allen Say is the author/illustrator of *Allison; How My Parents Learned to Eat; Emma's Rug; Stranger In The Mirror; Boy of the Three Year Nap; Grandfather's Journey* and more.

ISBN# 395904951 Date Published: 1999 Price: $ 17.00
Publisher: Pages: 32

Rating

THIS IS OUR HOUSE

A great tool for teaching tolerance!

Natasha says, "I wish I'd known about his book when I taught preschool! It's great for when kids are starting to notice differences in each other." "This house is mine and no one else is coming in," George announces, taking over a large cardboard box on the playground and refusing entry to girls, twins, people with glasses, small people, etc. But when he leaves to go to the bathroom and comes back to find himself excluded, his hurt allows him to revisit his own ideas and discover that the box is a house for everyone.

Keywords

Multicultural, Race Relations, Antiracist Strategies

Age Range:

Preschool, early school-age

Author: Michael J. Rosen

Illustrator: Bob Graham

ISBN# 763602906 *Date Published:* 1996 *Price:* $ 5.99

Publisher: Candlewick *Pages:* 32

Rating

TODDLER'S BOOK OF FUN THINGS TO DO

Games, songs, and activities.

"Scurry along like a crab. Clap your hands. Do a somersault." Each page offers photos of toddlers of various heritages having fun and an invitation to your darling(s) to follow the cues and do the same.

Keywords

Multicultural, Games and Activities

Age Range:

Preschool, early school-age

Author: Sheila Hanly

Photographer: Stephen Shott

ISBN# 789439794 *Date Published:* 1999 *Price:* $ 12.95

Publisher: DK Publishing *Pages:* 48

TWO EYES A NOSE AND A MOUTH

Colorful photographs of many faces of many cultures.

Two eyes, a nose, and a mouth are the first things we see when we look at people's faces. This book contains over 100 photos of faces — young and old, light-skinned and dark-skinned — all smiling and all different. Of great interest to little ones. Beautiful photographs. A Pact bestseller.

Keywords

Multicultural, Racial/Ethnic Identity, Diversity

Age Range:

Preschool, early school-age

Author: Roberta Grobel Intrater

ISBN# 590482475 *Date Published:* *Price:* $ 12.95

Publisher: Scholastic *Pages:*

WE'RE DIFFERENT, WE'RE THE SAME

Created in cooperation with the producers of "Sesame Street."

Jim Henson's Sesame Street Muppets explore the many ways we're different and the many ways we're the same. Part of the "Sesame Street" series. Cartoon-like illustrations featuring Sesame Street Muppets. A very popular all-time favorite bestseller.

Keywords

Antiracist Strategies, Core Issues (Feelings), Diversity, Friendship, Multicultural

Age Range:

Preschool, early school-age

Author: Bobbi Jane Kates

ISBN# 679832270 *Date Published:* *Price:* $ 3.25

Publisher: Random House *Pages:* 32

Rating

WHO AM I?

A fun way to learn that things are seldom what they seem.

Here is a fun way to learn the concept that things are seldom what they seem, also suggested by the maxim, "Don't judge a book by its cover." As in *The Blind Man and the Elephant*, your child will come to realize that drawing conclusions without having enough information can lead to mistakes. Can you tell a zebra by its stripes or an elephant by its ear? Close up, animals don't always look like themselves. Lift the flaps to see their familiar faces in this extraordinary photographic book.

Keywords

Race Relations, Multicultural, Antiracist Strategies

Age Range:

Preschool, early school-age

Author: Sherrilyn Henning

ISBN# 0-14-055846-2 Date Published: Price: $ 5.99

Publisher: Puffin Pages: 16

Rating

WHO SAYS A DOG GOES BOW-WOW?

Words for animal sounds around the world are similar and very different.

The sounds animals make are described in the language people are speaking; thus even something as basic as "what an animal says" is determined by where people live and which language they speak. A good book to stimulate a conversation about culture with your young child.

Keywords

Multicultural, Multiracial, Friendship, Diversity

Age Range:

Preschool, early school-age

Author: Hank De Zutter

ISBN# 0-440-41338-9 Date Published: 1993 Price: $ 5.99

Publisher: Picture Yearling Pages: 32

WHOEVER YOU ARE

Celebrating diversity.

Whoever You Are urges readers to accept differences among people, to recognize similarities, and, most importantly, to rejoice in both. Kirkus Reviews writes that the book offers a "'we- are- all- the- same- under- the-skin' message for the very young. An essential book that acknowledges in the simplest of terms our common humanity," but Horn Book says, "A singsong voice speaks in vague, feel-good terms about how children around the world are different yet similar in fundamental ways. It is hard to argue with such general assertions, even though they somehow don't ring completely true. The whimsical, sunny paintings, surrounded by gold hand-carved frames, outshine the vapid text."

Keywords

Diversity

Age Range:

Preschool, early school-age

Author: Mem Fox

Illustrator: Leslie Staub

Mem Fox is the author of *Sophie, Whoever You Are* and more.

ISBN# 152997873 Date Published: 1997 Price: $ 16.00

Publisher: Harcourt Brace Pages: 32

WHY A DISGUISE?

Being different is fine.

The best-selling author of *If You Give A Mouse a Cookie* shows the many ways there are to enjoy being someone different, reminding us that it's nice to know we're still ourselves at the end of the day.

Keywords

Diversity, Multicultural, Core Issues (Feelings)

Age Range:

Preschool, early school-age

Author: Laura Numeroff

Illustrator: David McPhail

Laura Numeroff is the author of *What Mommies Do Best/ What Daddies Do Best; Why A Disguise?* and *If You Give A Mouse A Cookie.*

ISBN# 689825307 Date Published: 1999 Price: $ 5.99

Publisher: Aladdin Pages: 32

Rating

WHY AM I DIFFERENT?

If we were all the same, the world would be boring!

This book is about why each of us is different. Though not about adoption, it does mention adoption. A well-loved favorite. A Pact bestseller.

Keywords

Transracial Adoption, Diversity, Racial/Ethnic Identity, Multicultural, Multiracial, International Adoption

Age Range:

Preschool, early school-age

Author: Norma Simon

Norma Simon is the author of All Kinds of Families, Why Am I Different, and I Am NOT a Crybaby

ISBN# 0-8075-9076-2 Date Published: Price: $ 5.95

Publisher: Whitman Pages: 32

Rating

YO! YES?

Two boys, one Black and one white, meet on the street and become friends.

In a simple story that uses just nineteen words ("yo" appears twice, "yes" six times), two boys who meet as strangers strike up a spirited conversation on a city sidewalk. One hails the other, who is cautious. The first persists. The other responds. Gradually they begin to talk, ending up as friends. 1994 Caldecott Honor book.

Keywords

Race Relations, African American, Friendship, Multiracial, Black Identity

Age Range:

Preschool, early school-age

Author: Chris Raschka

Chris Raschka is the author of *Charlie Parker Played Be Bop; Like Likes Like;* and a*Caldecott Honor Book, Yo! Yes?*

ISBN# 531054691 Date Published: 1993 Price: $ 6.95

Publisher: Orchard Pages: 32

YOU'RE NOT MY BEST FRIEND ANYMORE

Molly is white; Ben is Black. What does being best friends mean?

Molly and Ben have always done everything together. But after a disagreement on how to spend the money they have saved together, the pair learns the true meaning of friendship.

Keywords

Core Issues (Feelings), Race Relations, Friendship, Multiracial

Age Range:

Preschool, early school-age

Author: Charlotte Pomerantz

ISBN# 803715595 Date Published: 1998 Price: $ 15.99

Publisher: Dial Pages: 32

Rating

52 SPECIAL TRADITIONS FOR FAMILY AND FRIENDS

Fun family activities that reinforce why you belong together.

This is a deck of cards rather than an actual book, with 52 appealing activities. One card suggests an adventure-of-the-month club, where you take turns planning surprise field trips. Another proposes a family memory day where family members gather old photos, letters, and memorabilia, then gather round and tell stories. These cards spur us on to make time for the people we care about. Families formed through adoption or foster care will grow stronger by taking the time to make conscious efforts to enhance their connections through the practice of family traditions and rituals. This book has many intriguing suggestions you can make your own.

Keywords

Family Life, Games and Activities, Rituals and traditions

Age Range.

Preschool, early school-age

Author: Lynn Gordon

Illustrator: Susan Synarski

ISBN# 811816230 Date Published. 1997 Price. $6.95

Publisher. Chronicle Books Pages. 52

Rating

A YOU'RE ADORABLE

A popular song of the 1940s is now a delightful picture book.

This picture book is not only an engaging introduction to the alphabet, but a perfect starting point for projects and activities. The multiracial illustrations are fresh and appealing, particularly because they are busy and the children in them are busy at a myriad of activities which appear to make them happy. This little book reflects an enthusiasm and an optimism about life that make it most enjoyable. We include it here because the images of children are multiracial and extremely vital. *A You're Adorable* remains a Pact bestseller.

Keywords

Diversity, Family Life, Multiracial, Self-Esteem

Age Range.

Preschool, early school-age

Author: Buddy Kaye

Bruce A. Jacobs is the author of Race Manners

ISBN# 1564025667 Date Published. 1996 Price. $3.99

Publisher. Candlewick Pages. 32

ALEXANDER AND THE TERRIBLE, HORRIBLE, NO GOOD, VERY BAD DAY

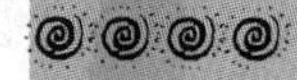

Knowing there's no avoiding some bad days makes having one a little bit easier.

One of life's more important and difficult messages is that the good times will inevitably be followed by the terrible, horrible, very bad days...and there's no way to avoid them. Alexander knew it was going to be a terrible day when he woke up with gum in his hair. And it got worse.... His best friend deserted him, there was no treat in his lunch bag, lima beans were for dinner and kissing was on TV! It isn't easy to learn the reality that "some days are like that." This is one of Judith Viorst's most popular books. "The clever text shines," says the School Library Journal in a starred review. ALA Notable Children's Book.

Keywords

Core Issues (Feelings), Family Life

Age Range.

Preschool, early school-age

Author: Judith Viorst

Illustrator: Patricia Mattozi

Judith Viorst is the author of *Alexander and the Terrible, Horrible, No Good, Very Bad Day;* and *Necessary Losses,* among many others.

ISBN# 0-689-71173-5 Date Published. 1987 Price. $4.99

Publisher. S&S Children's Pages. 32

ALEXANDER, WHO'S NOT (DO YOU HEAR ME? I MEAN IT!) GOING TO MOVE

Alexander's family is moving. He hates transitions. Guess what? He doesn't want to go.

The rest of Alexander's family is moving a thousand miles away, but there's no way Alexander is going to leave his best friend Paul, his babysitter or all the places and people he's known all his life. Even if he has to live in a tree house, Alexander is not — do you hear him? He means it! — not going to move. Moving is the worst. It means changing everything and losing everyone you know. Though it has nothing explicit to do with adoption, this story touches core issues for adopted kids, for change is often a sensitive issue with kids who have been adopted. This book should jump-start some interesting talk with your child.

Keywords

Grief and Loss, Family Life, Adopted Child, Boy Focus, Core Issues (Feelings), Friendship

Age Range.

Preschool, early school-age

Author: Judith Viorst

Robin Preiss Glasser

Judith Viorst is the author of *Alexander and the Terrible, Horrible, No Good, Very Bad Day;* and *Necessary Losses,* among many others.

ISBN# 689820895 Date Published. 1998 Price. $4.99

Publisher. Aladdin Pages. 32

Rating

ANNA IN CHARGE

Two Asian sisters playing in the park. Uh-oh.... Where's Katy?

While Anna is engrossed in drawing, her little sister Katy wanders off. After searching everywhere, Anna finds her in the park, and is tremendously relieved. *Anna in Charge* is a story about adoption that never mentions adoption at all. Use it to jump-start a conversation about being lost and then found, a core issue for many adopted children. This is also a story about family life and the relationship between an older child and a younger sibling she must take some responsibility for. In a world of children's books where there are more books about European-American families than any others, it is a bonus to all readers that the sisters are Asian.

Keywords

Core issues(feelings), Grief and Loss, Girl Power, Family Life, Sibling Issues

Age Range:

Preschool, early school-age

Author: Yoriko Tsutsui

Illustrator: Akiko Hayashi

ISBN# 1405007337 Date Published: 1989 Price: $ 3.95

Publisher: Puffin Pages: 32

Rating

ANNIE AND THE OLD ONE

It's never easy to make peace with losing someone you love.

Children who have been separated from their birth families may have even greater sensitivities than others to the enormous losses of a death. This powerful story provides a wonderful opportunity to talk about it. Book Talk says, "A poignant, understated, rather brave story of a very real child facing loss, set against a background of Navajo traditions and contemporary Native American life. Fine expressive drawings match the simplicity of the story." Newbery Honor Book; ALA Notable Children's Book.

Keywords

Diversity, Native American, Cultural History, Core Issues (Feelings), Grief and Loss

Age Range:

Preschool, early school-age

Author: Miska Miles

Illustrator: Peter Parnell

ISBN# 316571202 Date Published: 1972 Price: $ 7.95

Publisher: Little Brown Pages:

AUNT IN OUR HOUSE

A tender story about extended family love in a multiracial family.

Two biracial girls grow close to their Aunt when she comes to stay for awhile. Knowing she has to go home again, the sisters know they "will miss her like the sun that shines brighter when she is around them." We appreciate that although the sisters are of color and their Aunt is white, the story makes no particular mention of the multiracial element of this touching story. Books in Print writes, "The Aunt comes to stay, and the siblings' white father paints her portrait while their African American mother teaches her to weave.... The family happily absorbs her trumpet playing and tolerates her moods."

Keywords

Diversity, Multiracial, Family Life, Core Issues (Feelings), Black Identity

Age Range:

Preschool, early school-age

Author: Angela Johnson

Illustrator: David Soman

Angela Johnson is the author of *Mama Bird, Baby Bird; The Aunt In Our House; Julius, The Leaving Morning; Gone From Home; Heaven;* and more.

ISBN# 0-531-09502-9 Date Published: 1996 Price: $ 15.95

Publisher: Orchard Pages: 32

BABY ANIMALS

By the end of this story, all the baby animals are asleep.

Readers will be entranced by the tenderness of the baby animals' care. With few words, this picture story expresses the love and curiosity young children have about baby animals. This reassuring book makes a perfect bedtime story that parents will be able to read aloud again and again without getting bored. Charming text and wonderfully detailed and warm illustrations have made this book a Pact bestseller. The images of people throughout the book are multicultural in nature. Sure to become a classic baby shower or baby gift.

Keywords

Diversity, Multicultural, Multiracial, Self-Esteem

Age Range:

Preschool, early school-age

Author: Margaret Wise Brown

Margaret Wise Brown is the author of *Goodnight Moon; Baby Animals;* and more.

ISBN# 394820401 Date Published: Price: $ 16.00

Publisher: Random House Pages:

Rating

BEAR FOR MIGUEL, A

Maria's finds a special way to help her family in El Salvador.

A young girl in El Salvador goes to the market with her father and helps her family obtain necessities by trading a precious item of her own, her stuffed bear Paco. Maria understands her father can't work for either the government or the guerrillas without the possibility of reprisals from the other side. The only way for the family to survive is to barter their handiwork and their furniture for food. When a couple whose son, Miguel, has been injured by soldiers bargain for Paco, Maria makes a brave decision to help both her family and Miguel. A glossary is provided for Spanish words used in the text, although generally their meanings are clear from the context.

Keywords

Self-Esteem, Latino/a, Cultural History, Bilingual

Age Range.

Preschool, early school-age

Author: Elaine Marie Alphin

Illustrator: Joan Sandin

ISBN# 0-06-444234-9 Date Published. 1997 Price. $ 3.75

Publisher. Harper Trophy Pages. 64

Rating

BEIN' WITH YOU THIS WAY

Differences just aren't as important as the fun kids can have together.

In this singsong verse that talks about differences in skin color, hair, noses and eyes, families have a chance to add a tune and make the song their own. This book delivers the opportunity to engage young children and underscores a powerful message. Child magazine award: Child's Best for Excellence in Family Issues. "An exuberant story... Children will clamor for an immediate reread," says Kirkus Reviews. And Child magazine calls it "Multicultural literature at its best."

Keywords

African American, Family Life, Diversity, Multicultural, Black Identity

Age Range.

Preschool, early school-age

Author: W. Nikola-Lisa

Illustrator: Michael Bryant

ISBN# 188000059 Date Published. 1997 Price. $ 6.95

Publisher. Lee & Low Books Pages. 32

BIG BOX, THE

Toni Morrison's first book for kids, beautifully illustrated.

When Slade Morrison was six, he and his mother Toni, the Pulitzer Prize-winning author and Nobel Laureate, wrote a poem about the kinds of stuff kids need to be happy. The poem tells about three kids who "can't handle their freedom" and the grown-ups who create a world for them inside a box: a world with toys and games and treats and gifts to help them learn to live by the rules.

Keywords

Family Life, Manners, Multicultural

Age Range.

Preschool, early school-age

Author: Toni Morrison

Illustrator: Giselle Potter

ISBN# 786804165 Date Published. 1999 Price. $ 19.99

Publisher. Hyperion Pages. 48

BUBBE AND GRAM: MY TWO GRANDMOTHERS

Here is a supportive story for children who have one Jewish and one Christian parent.

From Booklist: "Shows a child enriched by her bonds with her Jewish and Christian grandmothers. As in Newman's *Heather Has Two Mommies*, the didacticism is heavy. Bubbe tells stories about Moses and the Maccabees. Gram tells about Jesus and recites the Lord's Prayer. Sometimes on Shabbat, the child goes to temple with Bubbe and lights candles, says blessings, and eats challah. Sometimes she goes to church with Gram, and then has a big midday dinner and says grace. The loving message is clear: this child is lucky to have Christmas and Hanukkah, Passover and Easter, and stories from everywhere."

Keywords

Intergenerational, Judaism, Christianity, Family Life, Interfaith Relationships, Religion

Age Range.

Preschool, early school-age

Author: Joan C. Hawxhurst

Ilustrator: Jane K. Bynum-Nwula

ISBN# 965128423 Date Published. 1997 Price. $ 12.95

Publisher. Allen & Unwin Pages.

Rating

BUILDING A BRIDGE

Anna, a white child, goes to a new school with Native Americans.

Anna, who is white, is anxious on her first day of school because she doesn't look like most of her classmates, who are Native American. A very perceptive teacher knows how she can help Anna make friends and provides the support and directions to help her. Through the "magic" of green and purple blocks, a new friendship develops when Anna and Juanita learn by working together that difference can be the source of joy, not just mistrust. *Building A Bridge* encourages young children to think about this issue for themselves. It is refreshing to see that is the white child who feels in the minority, rather than the children of color.

Keywords

Race Relations, Native American, Diversity, Friendship, Core Issues (Feelings)

Age Range:

Preschool, early school-age

Author: Lisa Shook Begaye

Lisa Shook Begaye is an actress and writer married to a Native American man.

ISBN# 0-87358-557-7 R *Date Published:* 1993 *Price:* $ 14.95
Publisher: Northland *Pages:* 32

Rating

CAN'T SIT STILL

The world is a fun place to be.

Skipping, hopping, biking, and dancing her way through the seasons of the year, a young brown-skinned girl explores her big-city neighborhood. Upbeat text and art celebrate a child's relationship to her world.

Keywords

African American, Family Life, Girl Power, Black Identity

Age Range:

Preschool, early school-age

Author: Karen E. Lotz

Illustrator: Colleen Browning

ISBN# 014056361X *Date Published:* 1997 *Price:* $ 5.99
Publisher: Puffin *Pages:* 49

CELEBRATING FAMILIES

14 children celebrate the people who love and care for them.

Children from single- or two-parent families, adoptive families, foster families, families with a disabled parent, homeless families, extended families, or other kind of families tell their stories. Picture books that explore realistic topics can relieve the feeling of isolation that says, "I must be the only one." Full-color photographs lend the text a sense of immediacy and realism and are the key to children's interest in *Celebrating Families.* As the saying goes, one picture in this book truly is worth a thousand words, because it is the photos that excite the reader's imagination and encourage us to explore the feelings of the children reflected on the pages.

Keywords

Family Life, Diversity, Adoption, Foster Child

Age Range:

Preschool, early school-age

Author: Rosemarie Hausshcrr

ISBN# 0-590-48937-2 *Date Published:* 1997 *Price:* $ 16.95
Publisher: Simon & Schuster *Pages:* 32

CHAIR FOR MY MOTHER, A

Caldecott Honor book about a single working Mom and loss issues after a fire.

A child, her waitress mother, and her grandmother save dimes to buy a comfortable armchair after all their furniture is lost in a fire.

Keywords

Diversity, Multicultural, Family Life, Single Parent Families, Mothers, Grief and Loss

Age Range:

Preschool, early school-age

Author: Vera Williams

Vera Williams is the author of *A Chair for My Mother*, and *More More More, Said The Baby.*

ISBN# 0-688-04074-8 *Date Published:* *Price:* $ 16.00
Publisher: Morrow *Pages:*

CHICKEN SUNDAY

Rating

Wanting something and sacrificing for it.

Stewart, Winston, and their newly-adopted Russian American sister pool their money to thank their gramma, Miss Eula, for her wonderful Sunday chicken dinners. When they come up short, they sell decorated eggs to buy her a beautiful Easter hat. Though Miss Eula is African American and the children are white, their deep cross-racial connection is demonstrated through the strength of their relationship, rather than by taking center stage as the book's central concern. Children who perceive the ethnic or racial differences between themselves and others in their families will identify with the sense of belonging reflected by these characters.

Keywords

Family Life, Race Relations, Friendship, Multicultural, International Adoption

Age Range:

Preschool, early school-age

Author: Patricia Polacco

Patricia Polacco is the author of *Chicken Sunday, Mrs. Katz and Tush*, *Welcome Comfort* and more.

ISBN# 798116151 *Date Published:* 1992 *Price:* $ 5.99

Publisher: Philomel *Pages:* 32

DADDY MACHINE, THE

Rating

What would you do if you had 62 dads with maybe more coming?

Sue and her brother have two moms. One day, both moms are away and the kids have a new construction toy to play with. It made a daddy machine and the machine made 62 dads. Uh-oh! So the children pulled the plug and there were no more new dads. With help from daddy 1 and 2, they changed the belt and pin on the machine and all the dads left except for 1 and 2, who moved into the house next door. Currently out of print but if you would like, we will attempt to find a copy for you. Please inquire.

Keywords

Gay and/or Lesbian, Fathers, Family Life, Diversity

Age Range:

Preschool, early school-age

Author: Johnny Valentine

Johnny Valentine is the author of *The Daddy Machine, One Dad, Two Dads, Brown Dads, Blue Dads* and more.

ISBN# 1-55583-107-9 *Date Published:* 1992 *Price:* $ 6.95

Publisher: Alyson Wonderland *Pages:* 32

DADDY, WILL YOU MISS ME?

Daddy is going to be away for four weeks. Will he miss his son?

This reassuring picture book details the many different ways the boy and his father can stay connected while the father is away in Africa for four weeks. Dealing with separation from a parent can be particularly sensitive for children who have been touched by adoption, and this book provides an opportunity for you and your children to discuss your own children's feelings about this poignant issue.

Keywords

Family Life, Fathers, Core Issues (Feelings)

Age Range:

Preschool, early school-age

Author: Wendy McCormick

Illustrator: Jennifer Eachus

ISBN# 068981898X *Date Published:* 1999 *Price:* $ 16.00

Publisher: Simon & Schuster *Pages:* 32

DAYS WITH FROG AND TOAD

Great favorites that belong in all early reader's libraries.

Frog and Toad are sweeties who have terrific adventures in a series all their own including *Frog and Toad All Year* and *Frog and Toad Together.* Because Frog and Toad are different from each other, but get along as friends, they help in learning tolerance. Most kids really love them.

Keywords

Family Life

Age Range:

Preschool, early school-age

Author: Arnold Lobel

Arnold Lobel is the author of *Ming Lo Moves Mountains, Frog and Toad Are Friends* and many more.

ISBN# 64440583 *Date Published:* *Price:* $ 3.95

Publisher: Harper Trophy *Pages:*

Rating

DESIGNED BY GOD

African American children explore the gifts God has given them.

"God had something special in mind for me; he gave me all that I need to do whatever I need to do: eyes, ears, nose, skin, body, mind, heart, spirit." Illustrated with children's drawings. A very popular book.

Keywords

Self-Esteem, African American, Spiritual Meanings, Christianity, Black Identity

Age Range:

Preschool, early school-age

Author: Bonnie Sose

ISBN# 247179-0-9615279-4-3 Date Published: 1988 Price: $ 11.00
Publisher: Character Builder Pages: 16

Rating

DIA'S STORY CLOTH

A traditional Hmong embroidered story cloth, colorful and detailed, introduce us to the Hmong people.

Colorful embroidered pictures based on a traditional Hmong story cloth, created by Dia's aunt and uncle, tell the history of the Cha family: leaving China to settle in Laos, Dia's childhood in Laos, her family's escape to a refugee camp in Thailand, and finally their immigration to the United States. Author notes describe the history and ways of the Hmong people and how their art, combining needlework and storytelling, continues in the U.S.

Keywords

Asian, China, Cultural History, Family Life, Hmong/Laotian, Thai

Age Range:

Preschool, early school-age

Author: Dia Cha

Illustrator: Chiic Thao Cha

Illustrator: Nhia Thao Cha

ISBN# 1880000636 Date Published: 1998 Price: $ 6.95
Publisher: Lee & Low Books Pages: 24

DO I HAVE A DADDY?

A book for children being raised by their moms alone.

When Eric asked his mom, "Where's my daddy? Do I have a daddy?" she explained that all children have a daddy but that some daddies don't live with their children and why. We'd be much happier if some of the illustrations in this book reflected people of color. In spite of that lack, the topic is an important one and the presentation is adequate.

Keywords

Family Life, Fathers, Single Parent Families, Mothers, Core Issues (Feelings)

Age Range:

Preschool, early school-age

Author: Kathryn M. Miller

Kathryn M. Miller is the author of *Did My First Mother Love Me?* and *Do I Have A Daddy?*

ISBN# 0-930934 Date Published: Price: $ 5.95
Publisher: Morning Glory Pages:

DON'T GIVE UP KID AND LEARNING DIFFERENCES, THE

A book for any child who has difficulty learning.

What can you do if the words and letters jump around on the page when you're trying to read them, or even make themselves look backwards? Alex needed his own way to learn and his parents helped him find a special class at school where the teacher could help him learn in the way that suited him best. In the new class, he learns to read, makes some new friends and begins to believe that "keeping on keeping on" can make a difference.

Keywords

Special Needs, Learning Difficulties, Self-Esteem

Age Range:

Preschool, early school-age

Author: Jeanne Gehret, M.A.

Illustrator: Sandra A. DePauw

Jeanne Gehret, M.A. is the author of *The Don't Give Up Kid* and *Learning Differences* and *Eagle Eyes.*

ISBN# 1-884281-10-9 Date Published: 1996 Price: $ 9.95
Publisher: Verbal Images Pr. Pages: 40

Rating

DOUBLE DIP FEELINGS

Intended to help children understand that feeling contradictory emotions is natural, these stories fall flat.

From Horn Book: "Uninteresting, often depressing illustrations and text depict situations that present conflicting emotions. No hints for resolving problems are given. Part of a series billed as books to help parents help their children, this one falls short of its intended goal."

Keywords

Multiracial, Core Issues (Feelings)

Age Range.

Preschool, early school-age

Author: Barbara S. Cain

ISBN# 945354207 Date Published. 1990 Price. $ 8.95
Publisher. Magination Pages.

Rating

DUMPLING SOUP

A multiracial family in Hawaii celebrates a joyful mix of food, customs, and languages.

Marisa makes mandoo (dumpling soup) for her family's New Year's lunch. It is filled with a mix of delicious flavors, and each seasoning adds taste to the soup. Her family is Japanese, Chinese, Hawaiian and haole (white). Each adds love.

Keywords

Food, Multicultural, Racial/Ethnic Identity, Self-Esteem, Hawaii, Asian American

Age Range.

Preschool, early school-age

Author: Jama Kim Rattigan

Jama Kim Rattigan, a third generation Korean American, was born in Hawaii. She now lives in Herndon, Virginia.

ISBN# 316734454 Date Published. Price. $ 5.95
Publisher. Little Brown Pages.

EAGLE EYES

A child's guide to the challenges of paying attention.

This beautifully illustrated picture book has become a classic. Ben has trouble focusing his attention and often misses what he's supposed to notice. His dad says Ben has Eagle Eyes, his own special way of seeing the world, and in this story Ben rescues his Dad.

Keywords

Special Needs, Family Life, ADHD, Differently-abled, Learning Difficulties

Age Range.

Preschool, early school-age

Author: Jeanne Gehret, M.A.

Illustrator: Susan Covert

Jeanne Gehret, M.A. is the author of *The Don't Give Up Kid and Learning Differences* and *Eagle Eyes.*

ISBN# 962513652 Date Published. Price. $ 9.95
Publisher. Verbal Image Pages.

ELIZABETI'S DOLL

Elizabeti watched Mama take care of her new baby brother and wanted her own baby.

Elizabeti didn't have a doll but she found a stone that was good to hold and just the right size and named it Eva. Elizabeti took good care of Eva but one day Eva got lost and Elizabeti was very sad. This is a gentle story with a happy ending that provides a lovely introduction to contemporary village life in Tanzania and also presents some of the core issues of adoption without being a typical adoption story: connection, loss, extended family issues and reunion are all suggested by the text and present the opportunity to share ideas and offer reassurance within the gentle mood set by the story. Wonderful illustrations.

Keywords

Africa, Family Life, Sibling Issues, Adoption, Core Issues (Feelings)

Age Range.

Preschool, early school-age

Author: Stephanie Stuve-Bodeen

Author: Christy Hale

ISBN# 1-880000-70-9 Date Published. 1998 Price. $ 15.95
Publisher. Lee & Low Books Pages. 32

Rating

EMMA'S RUG

Emma loves drawing, painting, and the rug she has carried everywhere since she was born.

Is Emma's shaggy rug the source of her amazing talent? She thinks so because when her mother puts it in the washing machine and accidentally destroys it, she has a fit and stops drawing and painting, believing she can no longer create. But when she dreams that she is part of Monet's glorious garden, with all her imaginary creatures around her, she starts to draw again. Unfortunately, the ending of this story of an introspective and isolated little girl damages any sense of authenticity the author has created. Though it is gratifying to see Emma return to her skill at creating, there is something a bit too precious about this story.

Keywords

Asian American, Family Life, Japanese American, Core Issues (Feelings)

Age Range:

Preschool, early school-age

Author-Illustrator: Allen Say

Allen Say is the author/illustrator of *Allison; How My Parents Learned to Eat; Emma's Rug; Stranger In The Mirror; Boy of the Three Year Nap; Grandfather's Journey* and more.

ISBN# 395742943 Date Published: 1996 Price: $ 16.95

Publisher: Houghton Mifflin Pages: 32

Rating

EVERETT ANDERSON'S GOODBYE

After his daddy dies, Everett Anderson has a hard time with his grief.

Everett Anderson's father has died. This simple book demonstrates in a young African American boy's words the five stages of grief — Denial, Anger, Bargaining, Depression and Acceptance — and provides opportunities to discuss and process loss. An excellent resource. A Coretta Scott King Award-winner. A Reading Rainbow selection.

Keywords

Grief and Loss, African American, Black Identity, Fiction, Core Issues (Feelings)

Age Range:

Preschool, early school-age

Author: Lucille Clifton

ISBN# 805008004 Date Published: 1983 Price: $ 5.95

Publisher: Henry Holt Pages: 32

EVERYONE POOPS

A laugh-out-loud book with multicultural characters, about the universality of the need to poop.

This irreverent book helps children know how bodies function while reminding them that all living creatures have much in common. Kids love it because it's funny, deals with bathroom humor, and addresses a subject they are rarely allowed to talk about. Books in Print writes, "Well yes, they do [poop], but does anyone really need an entire book on the subject? Readers are informed on page one that 'an elephant makes a big poop, a mouse makes a tiny poop.' Later on, they are told that it comes in different shapes, colors, and smells, etc." Most adult reviewers think it's awful. You decide. A Pact bestseller.

Keywords

Multicultural, Diversity, Multiracial, Health

Age Range:

Preschool, early school-age

Author: Toro Gomi

ISBN# 0-916291-45-6 Date Published: 1993 Price: $ 11.95

Publisher: Kane-Miller Pages: 32

FAMILIES ARE DIFFERENT

What makes a family belong together? What if child and parents don't look alike?

Nico was born in Korea and adopted into her family in the United States. She looks a lot like her sister Angel who was also adopted from Asia, but she doesn't look like her mom and dad. Nico wishes she looked like her parents. Then her mom tells her that "there are different kinds of families, glued together with a special kind of glue called love."

Keywords

Family Life, Transracial Adoption, International Adoption, Korean American, Core Issues (Feelings), Diversity

Age Range:

Preschool, early school-age

Author: Nin Pellegrini

ISBN# 0-8243-0887-6 Date Published: Price: $ 16.95

Publisher: HLDH Pages:

Rating

FEELINGS

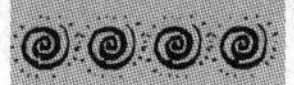

How do you feel? Happy?...Sad? This book will make you feel GREAT!

This wonderfully-illustrated book presents situations that awaken all kinds of feelings, offering a chance to see that most people share the same fears, pain, joys, and pleasures, whether they are children or adults. It covers a broad range of the feelings we all experience, implicitly "giving permission" to experience and express both the bad and the good. Strongly recommended as a springboard for talking about how kids feel and when. A Reading Rainbow feature book. A Pact bestseller.

Keywords

Core Issues (Feelings), Family Life

Age Range.

Preschool, early school-age

Author-Illustrator: Aliki

Aliki, who uses just one name, is the author of *Feelings; Marianthe's Story: Painted Words* and *Spoken Memories*; and *Manners.*

ISBN# 068806518X Date Published. Price. $ 4.95

Publisher. Scholastic Pages.

Rating

FROG AND TOAD ARE FRIENDS

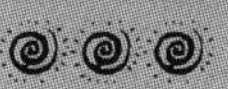

What makes a friend a friend? Hop along with frog and toad – you'll see.

Whether they are telling stories, taking walks, or writing letters, Frog and Toad always care for each other in good and decent ways, as best friends should. Here are five very short and irresistible stories about their adventures together looking for lost buttons, greeting the spring, making up a story, Toad's bathing suit, and waiting for mail. Caldecott Honor Book. ALA Notable Children's Books. School Library Journal Best of the Best. If you need even more of Frog and Toad, don't miss *Frog and Toad Together, Frog and Toad All Year,* and *Days with Frog and Toad.*

Keywords

Friendship, Multicultural

Age Range.

Preschool, early school-age

Author: Arnold Lobel

Arnold Lobel is the author of *Ming Lo Moves Mountains, Frog and Toad Are Friends* and many more.

ISBN# 6440206 Date Published. 1979 Price. $ 3.75

Publisher. HarperCollins Pages. 32

GARDENER, THE

Lydia Grace makes a family and a garden wherever she goes.

A good introduction to storytelling through letters. When hard times hit during the Depression, Lydia must stay with her mean uncle who owns a city bakery. She makes a secret roof garden, a surprise that make her uncle smile — in a very unusual way. Grouchy old uncle turns into a loving gardener, baker, and friend. The New York Times Book Review calls it "a moving, wonderfully rich illustrated story. It is that rarity, a pictorial delight that in 20 double pages gives more and more of itself each time it's read, and whose silent complexities reveal themselves with continuing pleasure." How does all of that fit into such a little book? Caldecott Award winner.

Keywords

Family Life, Extended Family, Core Issues (Feelings)

Age Range.

Preschool, early school-age

Author: Sarah Stewart

Illustrator: David Small

ISBN# 374325170 Date Published. 1997 Price. $ 15.00

Publisher. Farrar-Strauss Pages.

GENIE IN THE JAR

A lovely riff on two African-infused traditions: music and weaving.

This spirited poem to the power of music and of love celebrates images of Black songs and Black weaving. Take a note and spin it around, spin it around...careful baby, don't prick your finger. This book makes you wanna dance. The illustrations are done in bright pastels on brown paper; a visually exciting combination that adds a great deal to the text. African American children will see that this book is specific to them, and all children will be able to appreciate the self-affirming values of the culture.

Keywords

Poetry, African American, Racial/Ethnic Identity, Self-Esteem, Girl Power, Black Identity

Age Range.

Preschool, early school-age

Poet: Nikki Giovanni

Nikki Giovanni is the author of *Genie in the Jar* and *Racism 101.*

ISBN# 0-8050-4118-4 Date Published. Price. $ 6.95

Publisher. Henry Holt Pages.

Rating

GOOD FAMILIES DON'T

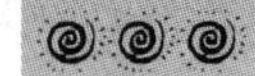

Munsch makes us laugh at adult attempts to take life too seriously.

Just the use of the term "fart" will have your children in stitches, as mom, dad and eventually the police investigate the "fart" in the upstairs bedroom. The illustrations indicate that the family is multiracial.

Keywords

Family Life, Diversity, Transracial Adoption, Multicultural, International Adoption

Age Range:

Preschool, early school-age

Author: Robert Munsch

ISBN# 0-440-40565-3 Date Published: Price: $ 4.99

Publisher: Dell Pages:

Rating

HEATHER HAS TWO MOMMIES

Having two mommies is "different."

A description of how Heather's two mommies fall in love, decide to have a baby, go through a pregnancy with Heather and then love her during her first three years. The second half of the book answers the questions and addresses the sadness Heather feels when her preschool class draws pictures of their families and it occurs to her she doesn't have a daddy like most of the other kids. Ultimately, the story validates differences, affirming that every family is special.

Keywords

Gay and/or Lesbian, Family Life, Mothers, Girl Power, Diversity

Age Range:

Preschool, early school-age

Author: Lesléa Newman

ISBN# 155583180X Date Published: 1989 Price: $ 7.95

Publisher: Alyson Wonderland Pages:

HOUSE BY THE RIVER

How Belinda and her mom survived the storm and Belinda came to love her home.

Belinda didn't like living by the river, especially when a storm threatened. Her mom, a single parent, shares her warm memories of how well the rickety old house has served their family, proving stronger than the storm. When the sun comes back in the morning, Belinda is glad as she's never been before to see their muddy yard, even finding a perfect egg deep in the crevices under the house where she doesn't usually like to go. A testimony to the bond between mother and child, *House By The River* evokes the power of rich African American family traditions. Illustrations add much to enhance the subtleties of the story.

Keywords

African American, Family Life, Single Parent Families

Age Range:

Preschool, early school-age

Author: William Miller

Author: Cornelius Van Wright

Author: Ying-Hwa Hu

William Miller is the author of *Frederick Douglass; Richard Wright and the Library Card; Zora Hurston and the Chinaberry Tree; The Bus Ride;* and *House by the River.*

ISBN# 1880000482 Date Published: 1997 Price: $ 15.95

Publisher: Lee & Low Books Pages: 32

HUNDRED PENNY BOX, THE

A boy's struggle with the emotional tug-of-war caused by divided family loyalties.

It's a pleasure to spend time in Michael's company. He honestly loves his 100-year-old, great great Aunt Dew, and the reader will fall into the same warm bath of affection. Aunt Dew's one-hundred-penny box holds a penny from each year of her life and she has a family story to go along with each one, but Michael's momma considers the hundred-penny box just a piece of junk. Michael is caught between the two women he loves most, neither of whom can understand or appreciate the other. His struggle is to help them reconcile. The family just happens to be African American.

Keywords

African American, Family Life, Extended Family, Core Issues (Feelings), Intergenerational, Mothers

Age Range:

Preschool, early school-age

Author: Sharon Mathis

Illustrator: Diane Dillon

Illustrator: Leo Dillon

Sharon Mathis is the author of *Running Girl; I Wish for You;* and *The Hundred Penny Box*

ISBN# 14032169 Date Published: 1986 Price: $ 4.99

Publisher: Viking Pages: 47

Rating

I AM NOT A CRYBABY

In the right circumstance, crying can be a positive experience.

Written by an elementary class, this is a multicultural book which gives permission to cry when it works or not cry if it doesn't. A boy cries when his divorced dad leaves after a Sunday visit and a mom cries when her son gets a hearing aid and hears for the first time. Very good.

Keywords

Core Issues (Feelings), Multiracial

Age Range:

Preschool, early school-age

Author: Norma Simon

Norma Simon is the author of *All Kinds of Families, Why Am I Different,* and *I Am NOT a Crybaby*

ISBN# 140542167 Date Published: Price: $ 3.95

Publisher: Centering Corp. Pages:

Rating

I HAVE A NEW FRIEND

Discovering we're more the same than different.

A story of two little girls from different cultures: one is Japanese and the other is Caucasian American. The two girls meet in school and begin a special friendship. Although they are from different parts of the world, they find that they have lot in common.

Keywords

Japanese American, Multiracial, Friendship, Diversity

Age Range:

Preschool, early school-age

Author: Kathleen Allan-Meyer

ISBN# 0-8120-6532-8 Date Published: Price: $ 10.95

Publisher: Barrons Pages:

I HAVE TO GO

Preschoolers who are in the throes of toilet training will appreciate Andrew's predicament.

Children who have joined their families through adoption Issues often have special sensitivity to issues of control and transition, and toilet training certainly falls into this category. Books can be helpful when they provide opportunity to discuss the importance of being responsible for one's own actions without necessarily targeting the child's personal experiences. *I Have To Go* provides lots of opportunity. In this amusing story, little Andrew maintains his own individual sense of timing and appropriateness in the task of learning to control his bladder, despite all the anxious preparations and inquiries of his parents.

Keywords

Child Development, Core Issues (Feelings), Family Life, Skill Mastery

Age Range:

Preschool, early school-age

Author: Robert Munsch

Illustrator: Michael Martchenko

ISBN# 920303 Date Published: Price: $ 5.95

Publisher: Annick Press Pages: 32

I LIKE BEING ME

Poems for children about feeling special, appreciating others, and getting along.

New from the author of "Make Someone Smile," this collection of poems for children is perfect for reading aloud. Simple, memorable rhyming poems explore issues important to the everyday lives of young children — being kind, solving problems, learning from mistakes, being a friend, and more. Photographs include children of multicultural backgrounds.

Keywords

Family Life, Poetry, Core Issues (Feelings)

Age Range:

Preschool, early school-age

Author: Judy Lalli

ISBN# 1575420252 Date Published: 1999 Price: $ 8.95

Publisher: Free Spirit Pages: 64

Rating

I LIKE ME!

I can do it! I'm okay!

An easy-to-read book for young children about an exuberant pig who loves herself and everything she can do. A great book about self-esteem and positive reinforcement. This pig does a cartwheel, paints, rides her bike fast, and reads good books. She likes her round piggy body and she takes good care of it by keeping clean, eating well, and brushing her teeth. When she falls down, she gets up again and when she makes a mistake, she tries again. The pictures are cheerful and upbeat, and the simple text is appealing to kids.

Keywords

Self-Esteem, Skill Mastery

Age Range:

Preschool, early school-age

Author: Nancy Carlson

ISBN# 0-14-050819-8 Date Published: Price: $ 4.99
Publisher: Viking Pages:

Rating

I LOVE YOU, LITTLE ONE

How parents tell their little ones all the ways they are loved, forever and always.

Detailed and serene illustrations make this a reassuring bedtime favorite. Booklist concurs, writing that "With her signature evocative watercolor and pencil images, child's eye level, and delicate close-ups, Tafuri has created a rockabye picture book that sings. One by one, a little deer, duck, rabbit, child, and others ask, 'Do you love me, Mama?' And each is answered 'yes' in a most reassuring way." And Kirkus Reviews writes: "Six beautiful mother-and-baby animal pairs illustrate parallels between the mother's love and the nurturing, protecting environment that is the animal's home."

Keywords

Family Life, Mothers, Fathers, Core Issues (Feelings), Diversity

Age Range:

Preschool, early school-age

Author: Nancy Tafuri

ISBN# 590921592 Date Published: 1998 Price: $ 15.95
Publisher: Scholastic Pages: 32

I LOVE YOU, STINKY FACE

"Would you love me if I smelled so bad my name was Stinky Face?"

At bedtime, a sleepy child tests mama's love in more ways than you can imagine. A warm and reassuring book you and your bunny can laugh at together. All kids want reassurance of their parents' love; adopted kids may want it just that much more.

Keywords

Adopted Child, Core Issues (Feelings), Family Life

Age Range:

Preschool, early school-age

Author: Lisa McCourt

Illustrator: Cyd Moore

ISBN# 816743924 Date Published: 1997 Price: $ 5.95
Publisher: Bridgewater Pages: 32

I PROMISE I'LL FIND YOU

"I promise I'll find you" offers important reassurance to adopted children.

Most children are afraid of being lost or separated from loved ones, whether separated in a crowd, wandering away from home, frightened in a strange new place. The fear is often even more acute for children who have been adopted. This book offers reassurance and the absolute promise: "If we are ever apart, I promise I'll find you, no matter what."

Keywords

Core Issues (Feelings), Attachment, Family Life, Grief and Loss

Age Range:

Preschool, early school-age

Author: Heather Patricia Ward

Illustrator: Sheila McGraw

Heather Patricia Ward lives in Alberta, Canada. She is the mother of four children. This is her first book.

ISBN# 1-55209-094-9 Date Published: Price: $ 5.95
Publisher: Fire Fly Pages: 24

Rating

I SHOULD BE ME!

Limericks tell a little girl's story and her struggle to accept herself.

A rhyming self-esteem story to enhance children's belief in themselves.

Keywords

Adopted Child, Self-Esteem, Poetry

Age Range.

Preschool, early school-age

Author: Julianne des Autels

ISBN# 965252701 Date Published. 1996 Price. $ 4.95

Publisher. Make Me Believe Books Pages. 32

Rating

I WANT TO BE

"I want to be a new kind of earthquake, rocking the world..."

Young readers will find exciting words and ideas to encourage them to stretch their own imaginations, to experience the joy of reaching, touching, tasting, listening, and learning. Together, these wonderful original words from a distinguished poet and vibrant illustrations from an award-winning illustrator make for a moving book. A Literary Guild selection.

Keywords

African American, Self-Esteem, Black Identity, Poetry

Age Range.

Preschool, early school-age

Author: Thylias Moss

ISBN# 0-8037-1286-3 Date Published. Price. $ 5.99

Publisher. Dial Pages.

I'LL ALWAYS LOVE YOU

One morning, Elfie, a dachshund, does not wake up.

This story of loss and grief for little ones is certain to help kids talk about their feelings through the window of Elfie's special boy. The School Library Journal writes, "In this gentle, moving story, Elfie, a dachshund, and her special boy progress happily through life together. One morning, Elfie dies. The family grieves and buries her. The watercolor illustrations, tender and warm in color and mood, suit the simple text perfectly."

Keywords

Boy Focus, Core Issues (Feelings), Grief and Loss

Age Range.

Preschool, early school-age

Author: Hans Wilhelm

ISBN# 517572656 Date Published. 1997 Price. $ 5.99

Publisher. Crown Pages. 32

JOJO'S FLYING SIDE KICK

How can JoJo get her yellow belt in Tae Kwon Do when she's afraid?

How refreshing to have a book about Tae Kwon Do, a Korean martial art form, in which the heroine just happens to be an African American girl. Pinkney's distinctive scratch board technique is colorful, realistic, and filled with culturally authentic details of life in a middle class Black family, making up a most positive big picture. Unfortunately, JoJo is not a fully developed character, and because it's hard to care about her, the plot line seems a bit contrived. Nonetheless, this book is worthy for the illustrations alone.

Keywords

Sports, African American, Self-Esteem, Family Life

Age Range.

Preschool, early school-age

Illustrator: J. Brian Pinkney

J. Brian Pinkney is the award-winning illustrator of *Shake Shake Shake; Watch Me Dance; Happy Birthday, Dr. Martin Luther King; Max Found Two Sticks;* and *Mirandy & Brother Wind.*

ISBN# 689821921 Date Published. 1998 Price. $ 5.99

Publisher. Aladdin Pages. 32

Rating

JULIUS

What happens when Maya's grandfather brings Julius as a gift?

When Maya's grandfather comes for a visit, he brings a surprise in a crate — something, he says, to teach her "fun and sharing." Maya hopes it's a horse or a big brother. But instead it's Julius, a big, cool pig. Maya's parents see Julius as a slob, but Maya sees another Julius altogether: a playmate, a protector, and a sharer in all that's magical and wild. The family just happens to be African American.

Keywords

Family Life, African American

Age Range:

Preschool, early school-age

Author: Angela Johnson

Angela Johnson is the author of *Mama Bird, Baby Bird; The Aunt In Our House; Julius, The Leaving Morning; Gone From Home; Heaven;* and more.

ISBN# 531054659 *Date Published:* 1993 *Price:* $ 6.95
Publisher: Orchard *Pages:*

Rating

K IS FOR KISS GOODNIGHT

A bedtime alphabet.

This cozy and reassuring bedtime story introduces young children to the alphabet while taking toddlers through their nighttime routines. The wonderful wonderful illustrations reflect a fine celebration of diversity.

Keywords

Family Life, Multicultural, Asian, Chinese American, Korean American

Age Range:

Preschool, early school-age

Author: Jill Sardegna

ISBN# 0-440-41218-8 *Date Published:* *Price:* $ 4.99
Publisher: bdd-Juvies *Pages:*

KISSING HAND, THE

A story for the child in each of us who sometimes needs reassurance.

This is a story about the way love works to give us strength in a sometimes scary world. When Chester the raccoon is reluctant to go to kindergarten for the first time, his mother reassures him by sharing a very special secret to help him always remember that he is loved and that wherever he goes, her love goes with him. An appropriate gift for a child entering school or going to camp for the first time or for any occasion when the child will be temporarily separated from home and loved ones.

Keywords

Attachment, Core Issues (Feelings), Family Life, Grief and Loss

Age Range:

Preschool, early school-age

Author: Audrey Penn

Audrey Penn is the author of four children's books including *The Kissing Hand* and *Sassafras.*

ISBN# 0-87868-585-5 *Date Published:* 1993 *Price:* $ 16.95
Publisher: Child Welfare League *Pages:*

LEAVING MORNING, THE

When moving day finally comes, leaving is hard.

Words and pictures catch exactly the mixture of excitement and wistfulness that "good-bye" can mean for young children, especially for adopted children. On the leaving morning, a child watches for the movers, has a cup of cocoa in the deli across the street, and leaves lip marks on the window of the apartment before departing for the new home.

Keywords

Core Issues (Feelings), Grief and Loss, Adopted Child, Attachment

Age Range:

Preschool, early school-age

Author: Angela Johnson

Illustrator: David Soman

Angela Johnson is the author of *Mama Bird, Baby Bird; The Aunt In Our House; Julius, The Leaving Morning; Gone From Home; Heaven;* and more.

ISBN# 531070727 *Date Published:* 1996 *Price:* $ 5.95
Publisher: Orchard *Pages:*

Rating

LEO THE LATE BLOOMER

Leo couldn't do anything right. Then one day, he made it.

Leo couldn't do anything right. He couldn't read. He couldn't write. He couldn't draw. Leo's dad is afraid he never will do things like these. Leo's mom explains that he's simply a late bloomer — but Leo's dad asks if Leo is a bloomer at all. In his own good time, though, Leo reads, writes, speaks in paragraphs, eats neatly and draws. Everyone is very happy. "Reassuring for late bloomers," says The Saturday Review.

Keywords

Special Needs, Learning Difficulties, Self-Esteem

Age Range.

Preschool, early school-age

Author: Robert Kraus

Author: Jose Aruego

Robert Kraus is the author of *Leo the Late Bloomer* and *Little Louie and the Baby Bloomer*

ISBN# 0-06-443348-X Date Published. Price. $ 4.95
Publisher. Harper Trophy Pages.

Rating

LILIANA'S GRANDMOTHERS

Mima lives down the street and Mama Gabina lives in South America.

Gentle watercolor illustrations work well with the text to describe Liliana's relationship with her grandmothers, each very different from the other. This reassuring and sweet story about family differences will hold appeal for children of adoption, many of whom may have a special sensitivity to questions of "matching" — and whether families that do not match can belong together absolutely. It provides a gentle opportunity to talk about differences within the family circle without focusing on your child's personal circumstances. A very pleasant book, also available in a Spanish edition as Las abuelas de Liliana.

Keywords

Latino/a, Intergenerational, Family Life, Extended Family

Age Range.

Preschool, early school-age

Author: Leyla Torres

Leyla Torres is the author of *Liliana's Grandmothers*, *Saturday Sancocho*, and *Subway Sparrow.*

ISBN# 374351058 Date Published. 1998 Price. $ 16.00
Publisher. Farrar-Strauss Pages. 32

LION WHO HAD ASTHMA, THE

"Encourage your child's imagination! It's ... an asset in the treatment of asthma" –J. London

Sean the lion has asthma, and suddenly it's hard for him to breathe. The whole family pitches in to help deliver the treatment and son Sean is King of the Jungle again — roaring louder than ever. Sean's nebulizer mask and his imagination aid in his recovery following an asthma attack. The story, which includes information on childhood asthma and how to control its symptoms, is honest, direct, and encouraging.

Keywords

Special Needs, Self-Esteem, Asthma, Skill Mastery, Health

Age Range.

Preschool, early school-age

Author: Jonathan London

Illustrator: Nadine Wescott

Jonathan London is the author of A Koala for Katie and The Lion Who Had Asthma.

ISBN# 0-8075-4560-0 Date Published. 1997 Price. $ 5.95
Publisher. Whitman Pages. 32

LITTLE LOUIE AND THE BABY BLOOMER

Leo the late bloomer has a baby brother.

Little Louie, Leo's baby brother, can't do anything right, according to Leo. His parents tell him to be patient. This book is a repeat of *Leo, The Late Bloomer.* Though charming, it does not present any additional ideas or information. From Booklist: "The old favorite *Leo the Late Bloomer* has helped many children feel better about not being ready to read or write at the same time as their peers. This book has the same charm and feel-good message as Leo's story. The illustrations are a combination of watercolors and pen-and-ink, though here they are noticeably brighter."

Keywords

Differently-abled, Sibling Issues, Special Needs, Family Life, Boy Focus

Age Range.

Preschool, early school-age

Author: Robert Kraus

Author: Jose Aruego

Robert Kraus is the author of *Leo the Late Bloomer* and *Little Louie and the Baby Bloomer*

ISBN# 60262931 Date Published. 1998 Price. $ 15.95
Publisher. HarperCollins Pages. 32

Rating

LOVABLES IN THE KINGDOM OF SELF-ESTEEM, THE

We all have some special gift to contribute to the world.

Of these twenty-four different animals, each has a special trait, and each can help children can identify themselves with being lovable and building self-esteem.

Keywords

Self-Esteem

Age Range:

Preschool, early school-age

Author: Diane Loomans

Illustrator: Kim Howard

Diane Loomans is the author of *Positively Mother Goose, Full Esteem Ahead,* and *The Laughing Classroom.*

ISBN# 915811250 *Date Published:* 1991 *Price:* $ 15.95

Publisher: H.J. Kramer *Pages:* 32

Rating

LOVE AS STRONG AS GINGER

Intergenerational family ties.

When they spend a day together at the cannery cracking crabs, a Chinese American girl comes to realize how hard her grandmother works to fulfill her dreams. The warmth and realism of Johnson's illustrations add a great deal to this reassuring story of family life.

Keywords

Asian American, Chinese American, Family Life, Extended Family, Intergenerational

Age Range:

Preschool, early school-age

Author: Lenore Look

Illustrator: Stephen T. Johnson

ISBN# 689812485 *Date Published:* 1999 *Price:* $ 15.00

Publisher: Athenaeum *Pages:* 40

LOVING TOUCHES

A book for children about positive, caring kinds of touching.

Shows children ways to ask for and receive loving touches. Stresses the fact that we all have the same needs to be touched as we move along from infancy to old age. Teaches respect for one's own and others' bodies.

Keywords

Core Issues (Feelings), Sexual Abuse, Self-Esteem

Age Range:

Preschool, early school-age

Author: Lory Freeman

ISBN# 0-943990-20-3 *Date Published:* 1986 *Price:* $ 5.95

Publisher: Parenting *Pages:* 24

MAKING FACES

An interactive funny book about feelings and how to process them.

Eleven short stories that encourage children to make funny faces using the mirror that folds out from the book's back cover. "Butterworth's inventiveness and sense of fun make reading this a delightfully silly time," says the Horn Book Guide. American Bookseller says, "Nick Butterworth's unique book helps children experiment with expressing their feelings. This is a fun, creative book."

Keywords

Self-Esteem, Core Issues (Feelings), Games and Activities

Age Range:

Preschool, early school-age

Author: Nick Butterworth

Nick Butterworth is also the author of *My Dad Is Awesome* and *Making Faces.*

ISBN# 1-56402-846-1 *Date Published:* *Price:* $ 7.99

Publisher: Candlewick *Pages:*

Rating 

MAMA, DO YOU LOVE ME?

Combines a universal theme with a backdrop of Arctic culture.

As her daughter's imagined infractions increase, mother becomes annoyed but the ultimate answer is always a resounding YES — I will love you forever. A bestseller in children's book sales in bookstores nationally.

Keywords

Family Life, Mothers, Multicultural, Core Issues (Feelings)

Age Range.

Preschool, early school-age

Author: Barbara M. Joosse

ISBN# 0-87701-759-X Date Published. 1991 Price. $ 14.95
Publisher. Chronicle Pages. 32

Rating 

MAMA, IF YOU HAD A WISH

A reassuring bedtime picture story!

A series of tender exchanges between a mama rabbit and her young bunny, asking, "Would you love me more if I were different?" The familiar, predictable text and simple illustrations will make this a popular bedtime or story-hour offering.

Keywords

Family Life, Mothers, Core Issues (Feelings)

Age Range.

Preschool, early school-age

Author: Jean Modessit

Illustrator: Robin Spowart

The author and the illustrator are a husband and wife team who live in California.

ISBN# 0-671754378 Date Published. Price. $ 5.99
Publisher. Simon & Schuster Pages.

MAMA, MAMA

Who needs a mother? All living creatures.

Gentle poetic verse gives voice to the childhood need for mother in soothing sound and rhythm, accompanied by colorful illustrations.

Keywords

Family Life, Poetry

Age Range.

Preschool, early school-age

Author: Jean Marzolla

Illustrator: Laura Regan

ISBN# 694012450 Date Published. 1999 Price. $ 5.95
Publisher. HarperCollins Pages. 14

MANNERS

Manners show thinking of others as well as yourself.

Good manners are a useful tool to help people get along together and enjoy one another. Books in Print writes that "Every page brims with etiquette tips, expressed by small-sized figures drawn in Aliki's customarily cheery style. If there is a problem here, it is one of excess! the dos and don'ts fly by so thick and fast that readers may have difficulty grasping them. Culture, gender, and age are well represented, and contribute to the book's wide appeal."

Keywords

Core Issues (Feelings), Self-Esteem, Multicultural, Manners

Age Range.

Preschool, early school-age

Author-Illustrator: Aliki

Aliki, who uses just one name, is the author of *Feelings; Marianthe's Story: Painted Words* and *Spoken Memories;* and *Manners.*

ISBN# 68804579 Date Published. 1997 Price. $ 4.95
Publisher. Morrow Pages. 40

Rating

MAX LOVES SUNFLOWERS

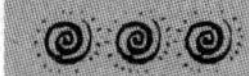

Growing things is fun.

Sturdy pull-tabs and flaps allow young readers to help Max plant seeds and water them, and then enjoy the pleasure of watching patiently until the beautiful sunflowers open. The simple text and illustrations provide reassuring sense that all is right in the world, in this text whose main character just happens to be African American.

Keywords

Family Life, African American

Age Range:

Preschool, early school-age

Author: Ken Wilson-Max

ISBN# 786804130 *Date Published:* 1999 *Price:* $ 12.95
Publisher: Hyperion *Pages:* 14

Rating

MOMMY, DON'T GO

Help decide what to do. If you don't like what happens, choose again.

Telling children what to do doesn't help them learn to think for themselves. This fun game book lets them make decisions and choose their own ending. Your child gets to see the results of his or her choices and think about behavior in a non-threatening way. This book illustrates the use of problem-solving skills, critical thinking, and conflict resolution through an example of mother-child separation.

Keywords

Core Issues (Feelings), Attachment, Mothers, Games and Activities

Age Range:

Preschool, early school-age

Author: Elizabeth Crary

ISBN# 0-943990-26-2 *Date Published:* 1978 *Price:* $ 6.95
Publisher: Parenting Press *Pages:* 30

MONSTER MAMA

One person's monster is another's Mom!

Patrick Edward's mother is a monster. When she's angry, she has the power to waste the world. When you need her, she can protect you from every danger. With satisfying results, she helps her child deal with some obnoxious bullies. It's a nice role-reversal, especially for an adopted child, to have mumsy, rather than the child, be the one seen as different. Appeals to offbeat humor. "Both Patrick Edward, a self-sufficient, fearless little boy, and his mother are shy and retiring except when roused by necessity. The story has humor, suspense, and magic. Shows a warm, supportive relationship between a son and his unique mother," says Books in Print.

Keywords

Family Life, Transracial Adoption, Mothers, International Adoption, Core Issues (Feelings)

Age Range:

Preschool, early school-age

Author: Liz Rosenberg

Illustrator: Stephen Gammell

ISBN# 0-698-11429-9 *Date Published:* 1992 *Price:* $ 5.95
Publisher: Putnam-Paperstar *Pages:* 32

MONSTER MANNERS

A guide to monster etiquette.

Children who are adopted are often challenged in today's world about where they belong and if they fit in. Manners, the knowledge of acceptable, thoughtful and desirable ways to behave in relation to other people, can be special armor for children who face extra scrutiny in their everyday lives. However, this book is not as engaging as *Manners* by Aliki, intended for this same age group.

Keywords

Adopted Child, Parenting, Self-Esteem, Manners, Family Life

Age Range:

Preschool, early school-age

Author: Bethany Roberts

Illustrator: Andrew Glass

ISBN# 395866227 *Date Published:* 1997 *Price:* $ 5.95
Publisher: Clarion *Pages:* 32

Rating

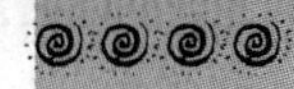

MORE MORE MORE, SAID THE BABY

Three multicultural family love stories.

This wonderful, funny multicultural full-color large-size picture book shows three babies in three families having fun with their parents and grandparents. Sometimes the child and adult are of the same race; sometimes they're not. But in every case, what's reaffirmed is the love between adults and the children in their families. A heartwarming imagination-tickler that all kids should experience. Caldecott Honor book. Paper and hardcover.

Keywords

Family Life, Multicultural, Multiracial, Transracial Adoption, Core Issues (Feelings)

Age Range.

Preschool, early school-age

Author: Vera Williams

Vera Williams is the author of *A Chair for My Mother,* and *More More More, Said The Baby.*

ISBN# 0-688-147365 *Date Published.* 1990 *Price.* $ 4.95
Publisher. Tupelow/Wm. Morris *Pages.* 32

Rating

MRS. KATZ & TUSH

Another multicultural winner from Patricia Polacco.

This is the story of how a young African American boy and Mrs. Katz, the boy's elderly Jewish neighbor, come to care about and for one another and the good times they share. The Jewish widow and the young boy become fast friends and spend a special Passover together in this warm book rich in language and imagery. An emotionally evocative but unsentimental picture book with great illustrations.

Keywords

Multicultural, Race Relations, African American, Judaism, Multiracial, Intergenerational

Age Range.

Preschool, early school-age

Author: Patricia Polacco

Patricia Polacco is the author of *Chicken Sunday, Mrs. Katz and Tush* , *Welcome Comfort* and more.

ISBN# 0-440-40936-5 *Date Published.* 1994 *Price.* $ 5.99
Publisher. Dell *Pages.*

MY BEST FRIEND

Best friends don't always get along – but most of the time, they do!

Who wants to be friends with Omar? He doesn't say, "I'm sorry." He always takes the biggest piece of cake. And he's usually the first to grab the window seat on the bus! But lots of times he's helpful and caring, and he tells the funniest jokes.

Keywords

Core Issues (Feelings), Self-Esteem, Friendship

Age Range.

Preschool, early school-age

Author: P. Mignon Hinds

ISBN# 307114414 *Date Published.* *Price.* $ 6.99
Publisher. Essence *Pages.*

MY DAD IS AWESOME

Let's all praise dads.

A book about a father's most endearing qualities, this offers the perfect opportunity to consider the things that make one's own dad special. Multicultural illustrations.

Keywords

Family Life, Fathers

Age Range.

Preschool, early school-age

Author: Nick Butterworth

Nick Butterworth is also the author of *My Dad Is Awesome* and *Making Faces.*

ISBN# 1564020339 *Date Published.* 1998 *Price.* $ 4.99
Publisher. Candlewick *Pages.* 32

Rating 

MY KIND OF FAMILY: SINGLE PARENT HOMES

Single-parent homes and the people who live in them.

This book helps children cope with the emotional confusion of being in a changing family. Divorce, remarriage, new surroundings, and new relatives are a few of the changes presented for discussion. Written from children's perspectives and including children's art, this book encourages children to identify and record their thoughts about growing up with a single parent.

Keywords

Family Life, Single Parent Families

Age Range:

Preschool, early school-age

Author: Michelle Lash

Author: Sally Ives Loughridge

Illustrator: David Fassler

ISBN# 0-914525-12-3 Date Published: Price: $ 14.95

Publisher: Waterfront Pages:

Rating 

NEW MOON

A little girl's love for the moon and her brother's love for her.

As her older brother recounts, his little sister Vincena has just learned two words to name the glowing disk in the night sky— "la luna" and "moon," and she searches for it, through the month, as it changes shape, disappears, and finally returns. She wakes from her nap to find her big brother at the crib-side: "'Moon?' she asked, rubbing sleepies from her eyes. "'Yes, yes!' I said, swinging her high. 'La luna has come out to play with you while it's still light.'" The cut paper collage illustrations depict a warm view of the pleasures of a child's world and the lovely gifts a big brother can offer.

Keywords

Sibling Issues, Latino/a, Multiracial, Family Life

Age Range:

Preschool, early school-age

Author: Peggy Deitz Shea

Illustrator: Cathryn Falwell

ISBN# 1-56397-410-X Date Published: 1996 Price: $ 14.95

Publisher: Boyds Mill Press Pages: 32

OLD DOG, THE

Simple words with a poignant message about loss.

Ben, a young African American boy, discovers his dog unmoving and unresponsive. "He's dead," says Ben's father. This book does a good job of describing the experience of missing Old Dog. We wish that Ben's parents had not so quickly replaced Old Dog at the end of the book— but the sentiments of loss are easily and comfortingly portrayed.

Keywords

Grief and Loss, Core Issues (Feelings), Friendship

Age Range:

Preschool, early school-age

Author: Charlotte Zolotow

Illustrator: James E. Ransome

ISBN# 0-06024409-7 Date Published: 1994 Price: $ 15.95

Publisher: Harper Row Pages: 32

ON MOTHER'S LAP

Is there's room for one more?

This book about a mom (who just happens to be Asian) explores the sibling issue of whether Mom has room on her lap for both of her children. The answer is, "There's always enough room for us both." A book to cuddle by.

Keywords

Family Life, Core Issues (Feelings), Multicultural, Sibling Issues, Mothers

Age Range:

Preschool, early school-age

Author: Ann Herbert Scott

Ann Herbert Scott is the author of *On Mother's Lap* and *Sam.*

ISBN# 0-395-62976-4 Date Published: Price: $ 5.95

Publisher: Clarion Pages: 39

Rating

ONE DAD, TWO DADS, BROWN DADS, BLUE DADS

Some kids have two dads. Some kids have blue dads!

Two children —one with blue dads, one from a more traditional family— compare notes in this lighthearted, easy-to-read book about parents who are different. In the end of course, they discover that blue dads aren't really that different from other dads. Except for one thing....

Keywords

Gay and/or Lesbian, Family Life, Fathers, Diversity

Age Range.

Preschool, early school-age

Author: Johnny Valentine

Johnny Valentine is the author of *The Daddy Machine, One Dad, Two Dads, Brown Dads, Blue Dads* and more.

ISBN# 1-55583-253-9 Date Published. Price. $ 10.95

Publisher. Alyson Wonderland Pages.

Rating

OTTO LEARNS ABOUT HIS MEDICINE

A story about medication for children with ADHD.

This is a story about the positive effects of medication on hyperactivity. Otto is a car that has trouble listening long enough to learn. He and his parents visit a special mechanic who tells Otto about a special medicine that can help.

Keywords

ADHD, Special Needs

Age Range.

Preschool, early school-age

Author: Matthew Galvin, M.D.

ISBN# 0-945354-04-5 Date Published. Price. $ 11.95

Publisher. Magination Pages.

PAPER BOATS

An excellent introduction to Indian culture.

A young boy from India dreams of the wonders of the world that lie far beyond the confines of his small village. Very appealing illustrations in a full-color picture-book format. An excellent introduction to Indian culture.

Keywords

India, Racial/Ethnic Identity, Family Life

Age Range.

Preschool, early school-age

Author: Rabindranath Tagore

ISBN# 1878093126 Date Published. 1992 Price. $ 14.95

Publisher. Boyds Mill Press Pages. 32

PETER'S CHAIR

New baby in the family? This book is for you.

The new baby is home and Peter's world has really changed. So Peter runs away until his parents welcome him home with his own grown-up chair. Peter eventually realizes his status as big brother is very special. As in all of Keats' beautiful books, the family is African American.

Keywords

African American, Sibling Issues, Family Life, Black Identity, Core Issues (Feelings)

Age Range.

Preschool, early school-age

Author: Ezra Jack Keats

ISBN# 0-06-553040-5 Date Published. Price. $ 5.99

Publisher. Harper-Trophy Pages.

PLACE FOR EVERYONE, A

Rating 

You don't have to look the same to fit in.

A charming animal fable about looking different from the group yet finding acceptance. Recommended by Darlene Powell Hopson and Derek S. Hopson, authors of *Different and Wonderful* and *Raising the Rainbow Generation.*

Keywords

Folk tales and Legends, Diversity, Racial/Ethnic Identity

Age Range:

Preschool, early school-age

Author: Barbara Resch

Illustrator: Philomena Korbutt

ISBN# 161820229 *Date Published:* 1991 *Price:* $ 9.95
Publisher: Atomium Books *Pages:* 28

ROSH HASHANAH WALK, A

Rating 

Jewish children of multiracial heritage celebrate.

Reflects Jewish children of various racial backgrounds. The children's faces vary from peachy white to brown. A group of children take a Rosh Hashanah walk and learn about the custom of "tashlich," the Jewish New Year ritual of throwing one's sins into the water and asking others' forgiveness for the failings of the year past.

Keywords

Judaism, Multiracial, Spiritual Meanings

Age Range:

Preschool, early school-age

Author: Carol Levin

ISBN# 930494709 *Date Published:* 1987 *Price:* $ 4.95
Publisher: Kar Ben *Pages:*

SAM

Everyone was too busy to play with Sam ...until they noticed how he felt.

Sam wants to play, but no one in his family wants him around: not his mother, his brother, not even his sister. Finally, when his father turns him away, Sam begins to cry, and only then does his family realize that Sam needs his own special job. This story projects positive images children will identify with. African American children will see that this book is specific to them, and all children will be able to appreciate the familiar picture of family distraction and family love.

Keywords

African American, Self-Esteem, Core Issues (Feelings), Family Life, Black Identity

Age Range:

Preschool, early school-age

Author: Ann Herbert Scott

Ann Herbert Scott is the author of On Mother's Lap and Sam.

ISBN# 0-698-11387-X *Date Published:* 1992 *Price:* $ 5.95
Publisher: Putnam-Paperstar *Pages:* 32

SASSAFRAS

Poor Sassafras: he hides because he is a skunk, and little skunks can stink.

With some help from his friends, Sassafras discovers that all animals have something that makes them special. Being stinky is what makes Sassafras so "skunk-special." This charming picture story supports a child's need to feel accepted and loved, even when different from others. *Sassafras* is a warm, sweet story.

Keywords

Core Issues (Feelings), Racism, Self-Esteem

Age Range:

Preschool, early school-age

Author: Audrey Penn

Illustrator: Ruth E. Harper

Audrey Penn is the author of four children's books including *The Kissing Hand* and *Sassafras.*

ISBN# 878685782 *Date Published:* 1995 *Price:* $ 16.95
Publisher: Child Welfare League *Pages:*

Rating

SECRET ROOM, THE

Prize-winning story of wisdom's triumph over greed, set in a desert kingdom.

A king discovers the difference between cleverness and wisdom. "The spare telling and completely enchanting and distinctive character portrayals in the glowing illustrations make this folk tale another winner," says the Horn Book. An American Bookseller Pick of the Lists, New York Times Outstanding Book of the Year, and Horn Book Honor Book.

Keywords

Folk tales and Legends, Arab, Cultural History

Age Range:

Preschool, early school-age

Author: Uri Shulevitz

ISBN# 0-374-46596-7 *Date Published:* 1996 *Price:* $ 5.95
Publisher: Farrar-Strauss *Pages:* 32

Rating

SHELLEY, THE HYPERACTIVE TURTLE

The latest book in the Woodbine Special-Needs Collection.

Imaginatively written and beautifully illustrated, this delightful book tells the story of Shelley and his family as they face the challenges presented by his hyperactivity. From Shelly's initial visit to the doctor, through diagnosis and treatment, the book explains hyperactivity directly to children.

Keywords

Special Needs, ADHD

Age Range:

Preschool, early school-age

Author: Deborah Moss

The author has dedicated this story to her very special son, Ryan.

ISBN# 0-933149-31-X *Date Published:* *Price:* $ 12.95
Publisher: Woodbine *Pages:*

SO MUCH

Everybody loves the baby so much!

Mom and baby (who happen to be brown-skinned), are home alone when Auntie and then Uncle and Nannie and Gran-Gran and the cousins come to visit. And they all want to hug and kiss and squeeze and eat the baby right up because everybody loves the baby so much! A wonderful evocation of a moment in a Black family's life. A Child magazine Best Children's Book. A Parenting magazine Reading Magic Award Winner. A Booklist Editor's Choice. A Pact bestseller.

Keywords

Family Life, African American, Holidays and Celebrations, Black Identity

Age Range:

Preschool, early school-age

Author: Trish Cooke

Trish Cooke was inspired by her own baby to write *So Much*. "He's a chubby baby, really pinchable," she says, "and he gets a lot of attention from everybody in my family."

ISBN# 1-56402-344-3 *Date Published:* 1994 *Price:* $ 6.99
Publisher: Candlewick *Pages:* 42

SOMEONE SPECIAL, JUST LIKE YOU

Photo essay of children who are differently-abled.

Brown and Ortiz show that the differences that seem to separate children from others are not important. What is important is the common delight in life — a desire to love, learn and play, and to be accepted for themselves as other children are.

Keywords

Differently-abled, Special needs, Family Life, Diversity

Age Range:

Preschool, early school-age

Author: Tricia Brown

Photographer: Fran Ortiz

ISBN# 805042687 *Date Published:* 1995 *Price:* $ 5.95
Publisher: Owlet *Pages:*

Rating

SOMETHING BEAUTIFUL

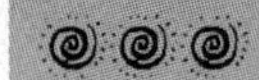

"Beautiful! I think it means 'something that when you have it, your heart is happy.'"

A young girl lives in a building with writing in the halls trash in the yard, and danger on the streets. On the front door, someone writes the word DIE. But when her teacher teaches her the word b-e-a-u-t-i-f-u-l, she asks friends in the community whether they have anything beautiful. Their answers create hope and new strength for her. Resisting saccharine platitudes, this story makes vital the message that attitude matters most. Soentpiet's lifelike illustrations, in which the main character just happens to be African American, convey a sense of joy that greatly deepens the impact of the text.

Keywords

African American, Family Life, Girl Power

Age Range:

Preschool, early school-age

Author: Sharon Dennis Wyeth

Author: Chris Soentpiet

Sharon Wyeth is the author of *World of Daughter McGuire* and *Something Beautiful.*

ISBN# 385033299 Date Published: 1998 Price: $ 16.95
Publisher: Bantam Pages: 32

Rating

SOMETHING GOOD

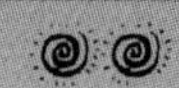

Makes kids and grown ups laugh together ... what could be better for a family?

In this book, lots of thing happen when Daddy and all the kids go to the supermarket. Tyra wants sweets while Daddy says they have to choose "something good." When Tyra gets in trouble and has to stand still, she is mistaken for a doll and is given a price tag; finally Daddy ends up "buying" her from the clerk. She finds this validating and reassuring, that after all she is "something good." The illustrations show a transracial family — children of color with a white dad.

Keywords

Transracial Adoption, Family Life, Multiracial, International Adoption, Core Issues (Feelings), Self-Esteem

Age Range:

Preschool, early school-age

Author: Robert Munsch

ISBN# 1-55037-100-2 Date Published: Price: $ 4.95
Publisher: Annick Press Pages:

SOMETHING ON MY MIND

The winning team of Grimes and Feelings presents prose poems about African American kids.

Replete with poetry and illustrations that reflect the fears, hopes, and yearnings of African American children, *Something On My Mind* has received an American Library Association Notable Children's Book citation and a Coretta Scott King Award. These emotion-packed prose poems provide a rich experience for both ear and eye. Words and pictures connect readers to children's intimate experiences and suggest how the spirit shines through, regardless of the difficulty of the circumstances. Children of Black heritage will identify with these works and children of other cultural backgrounds will gain a better understanding of the issues that affect Black Americans.

Keywords

African American, Core Issues (Feelings), Racial/Ethnic Identity, Poetry, Black Identity

Age Range:

Preschool, early school-age

Author: Jan Piénknowski

Nikki Grimes is the author of *Baby's Bedtime, Meet Danitra Brown, Something On My Mind,* and *Wild Wild Hair.* Tom Feelings is the illustrator of *Something On My Mind.*

ISBN# 140547053 Date Published: 1998 Price: $ 4.99
Publisher: Puffin Pages:

SOMETHING SPECIAL

Charlie takes his new baby sister to school for show-and-tell.

A cheerful big brother-little sister story with a multicultural group of characters. Its vibrantly colored collage illustrations give life to this engaging tale of the challenges — and developing pleasures — of life as a new big brother. From Horn Book: "Charlie finally realizes that his new baby sister, though she takes up all his mother's time, is kind of special, particularly when she smiles. The story meanders a bit, but readers will be drawn to the idea of taking a baby to show-and-tell. Colorful collage illustrations aptly reflect the childlike perspective of the story."

Keywords

Sibling Issues, Multiracial, Multicultural, Family Life, Diversity

Age Range:

Preschool, early school-age

Author: Nicola Moon

Illustrator: Alex Ayliffe

ISBN# 1561451371 Date Published: 1998 Price: $ 14.95
Publisher: Peachtree Pages: 32

Rating

SOPHIE

Birth, death, and birth in an African American family.

Booklist writes, "Simple language tells of the love between grandfather and granddaughter, from the beginning of her life to the end of his. 'Once there was no Sophie. And then there was. Sophie's hand curled round Grandpa's finger. Grandpa and Sophie loved each other.' As Sophie grows taller, Grandpa grows smaller, until at last, 'there was no Grandpa....'" "In each of Robinson's striking acrylic paintings, the eye is drawn to the oversized hands, which symbolize continuity," says the Horn Book. But Kirkus Reviews writes that "Children grieving from the loss of a grandparent will find little comfort in the distant eventuality of having a child of their own. A story that will appeal more to parents than to the target audience."

Keywords

African American, Family Life, Grief and Loss, Core Issues (Feelings), Extended Family

Age Range,

Preschool, early school-age

Author: Mem Fox

Mem Fox is the author of *Sophie, Whoever You Are* and more.

ISBN# 152015981 *Date Published,* 1997 *Price,* $ 6.00
Publisher, Harcourt Brace *Pages,* 32

Rating

SYLVESTER AND THE MAGIC PEBBLE

Touches on a child's desire to believe his parents can save him from anything.

In a moment of fright, Sylvester the donkey asks his magic pebble to turn him into a rock — but then he cannot hold the pebble so as to wish himself back to normal again! He is rescued by his mother and father in an amazing story that touches on deep feelings without ever articulating them expressly. For years, this book was the bedtime favorite of four out of four of our children.

Keywords

Core Issues (Feelings), Family Life, Grief and Loss

Age Range,

Preschool, early school-age

Author: William Steig

William Steig has written and illustrated 27 books for children, including *Sylvester and the Magic Pebble; Pete's A Pizza;* and *Pebble and Toby, Where Are You?*

ISBN# 671662694 *Date Published,* 1969 *Price,* $ 5.95
Publisher, Aladdin *Pages,* 32

TENTH GOOD THING ABOUT BARNEY, THE

"My cat cat Barney died. My mother said... think of ten good things about Barney...."

Keywords

Core Issues (Feelings), Family Life, Parenting, Grief and Loss

Age Range,

Preschool, early school-age

Author: Judith Viorst

Author: Eric Blevgard

Judith Viorst is the author of *Alexander and the Terrible, Horrible, No Good, Very Bad Day;* and *Necessary Losses,* among many others.

ISBN# 689712030 *Date Published,* 1988 *Price,* $ 4.99
Publisher, Aladdin *Pages,* 24

THANK YOU, MR. FALKER

A story about learning challenges.

This autobiographical book is the author's tribute to her fifth-grade teacher. Overjoyed to start school and learn to read, Trish is dismayed when all she can see on the page are "wiggling shapes." As she falls further and further behind her classmates, reading becomes torture. She "hated hated hated school" and the kids who called her dummy. Coming from a family of readers, she becomes convinced she is dumb. Although from kindergarten on she hides the fact that she can't read, Mr. Falker, her fifth-grade teacher, discovers Trisha's problem, gets her special help, and changes her life.

Keywords

Family Life, Learning Difficulties, Biography, Special Needs

Age Range,

Preschool, early school-age

Author: Patricia Polacco

Patricia Polacco is the author of *Chicken Sunday, Mrs. Katz and Tush, Welcome Comfort* and more.

ISBN# 399231668 *Date Published,* 1998 *Price,* $ 16.99
Publisher, Philomel *Pages,* 36

Rating

TORTILLAS AND LULLABIES/ TORTILLAS Y CANCIONCITAS

How traditions continue through the generations.

Reiser infuses a sense of tradition in a bilingual picture book that captures the rhythms of life. A young girl's great-grandmother makes tortillas for the girl's grandmother, then moves through each successive generation to the present day, as the child makes tortillas for her doll. Gathering flowers, washing clothes, and singing lullabies accompanied by the reassuring mantra, "Every time it was the same, but different." A unique border is formed by placing the English text at top of every page and the Spanish text at the bottom. The lush, colorful illustrations were created by a consortium of Costa Rican women.

Keywords

Bilingual, Costa Rica, Family Life, Rituals and Traditions, Food

Age Range:

Preschool, early school-age

Author: Lynn Reiser

Author: Rebecca Hart

ISBN# 688146287 *Date Published:* 1998 *Price:* $ 16.00

Publisher: Greenwillow *Pages:*

Rating

TUCKING MOMMY IN

A simple story of mommy-love that kids read over and over for sheer delight.

An affectionate slice of reality: Mommy says she is "so tired that I can't think straight," so her two small daughters help out by putting her to bed. The characters appear to be Asian or Latino. The story is very engaging for young children who are delighted with the role reversal. Beautiful, soothing illustrations, lots of pages for small hands to turn.

Keywords

Family Life, Mothers, Core Issues (Feelings)

Age Range:

Preschool, early school-age

Author: Morag Loh

Illustrator: Donna Rawlins

This highly pleasurable story is by Morag Loh.

ISBN# 0-531-07025-5 *Date Published:* 1991 *Price:* $ 5.95

Publisher: Orchard *Pages:* 40

WAY MOTHERS ARE, THE

Kitty realizes his mother loves him no matter what, because "That's the way mothers are."

A little cat tries to understand the depth of his mother's devotion. And over and over, his mother reassures him of the most important fact of his life: her unconditional love.

Keywords

Family Life, Mothers, Core Issues (Feelings)

Age Range:

Preschool, early school-age

Author: Miriam Schlein

ISBN# 0-8075-8691-9-R *Date Published:* *Price:* $ 14.95

Publisher: Whitman *Pages:*

WELCOME COMFORT

A foster child and Santa Claus.

Welcome Comfort, a lonely foster child, is assured by his friend, the school custodian, that there is a Santa Claus, but he does not discover the truth until one wondrous and surprising Christmas Eve.

Keywords

Family Life, Foster Child, Holidays and Celebrations

Age Range:

Preschool, early school-age

Author-Illustrator: Patricia Polacco

Patricia Polacco is the author of *Chicken Sunday, Mrs. Katz and Tush, Welcome Comfort* and more.

ISBN# 399231692 *Date Published:* 1999 *Price:* $ 16.99

Publisher: Philomel *Pages:* 40

Rating

WHAT MOMMIES DO BEST/ WHAT DADDIES DO BEST

Two books in one, back to back, shows that mothers and fathers are equally important.

Five different animal pairs demonstrate the skills that mothers possess; then, turn the book over and children see fathers doing the same things in their own way. Children from any kind of family will be able to relate to the familiar domestic scenes portrayed with plenty of whimsy and warmth.

Keywords

Family Life, Diversity, Fathers, Mothers

Age Range.

Preschool, early school-age

Author: Laura Numeroff

Illustrator: Lynn Munsinger

Laura Numeroff is the author of *What Mommies Do Best/ What Daddies Do Best; Why A Disguise?* and *If You Give A Mouse A Cookie.*

ISBN# 689805772 Date Published. 1998 Price. $ 13.00

Publisher. Simon & Schuster Pages. 32

Rating

WHEN I WAS LITTLE LIKE YOU: SEXUAL ABUSE

Help young children know what to do if someone tries to touch them inappropriately.

Jane Porett is a survivor of childhood sexual abuse. She relates her own story, including her feelings of shame, fear, and isolation and encourages children to tell a grown-up if any sexually inappropriate event happens to them, so that they no longer need to feel afraid or hurt.

Keywords

Special Needs, Core Issues (Feelings), Sexual Abuse, Self-Esteem

Age Range.

Preschool, early school-age

Author: Jane Porett

ISBN# 0-87868-530-8 Date Published. 1993 Price. $ 14.95

Publisher. Child Welfare League Pages. 28

WHERE'S MY MOM?

"Diffuses the common anxiety children harbor about being separated from mom." –Kirkus Reviews.

Waking from his nap, a child wants his mommy. Is she in the bathroom? Is she behind the curtains or in the garden? Is she in the refrigerator with the strawberry jelly? Where can she be? Teddy bear in hand, the young protagonist searches for his "missing" Mom (don't worry; Dad is keeping an eye on the intrepid searcher). Children who have joined their family through adoption may have a special sensitivity about needing to know their mothers are available. This book provides good opportunities to talk about how your little one feels when Mom can't be quickly found. although we wish the illustrations reflected multiracial characters.

Keywords

Core Issues (Feelings), Family Life, Mothers

Age Range.

Preschool, early school-age

Author: Leon Rosselson

Illustrator: Priscilla Lamont

ISBN# 1-56402-8356 Date Published. 1994 Price. $ 5.99

Publisher. Candlewick Pages.

WHO'S IN A FAMILY?

"Who's in a family? The people who love you the most!"

Come meet diverse families from all over the world. Many kinds of families, both human and animal, are represented: elephant families, dog families, chimp families, single parent families, multiracial families, gay and Lesbian families, and more. Space is provided for children to draw in pictures of their own families. Books in Print writes, "Animal families are juxtaposed with the human, presumably to show that certain situations are natural. For instance, one double-page spread shows a grandmother caring for her two grandsons while their mother is at work. The following page explains that the eldest female is also in charge in elephant families."

Keywords

Core Issues (Feelings), Family Life, Diversity, Extended Family

Age Range.

Preschool, early school-age

Author: Robert Skutch

ISBN# 188367266X Date Published. 1998 Price. $ 6.95

Publisher. Tricycle Press Pages. 32

WILL YOU COME BACK FOR ME?

Rating 

Four-year-old Suki is worried about being left in day care for the first time.

Four-year-old Suki is not happy to be going to Mrs. Clara's Child Care Center. She is afraid her mother will forget to pick her up. With a big red paper heart, her mother shows Suki how she can know.

Keywords

Core Issues (Feelings), Asian American, Mothers

Age Range:

Preschool, early school-age

Author: Ann Tompert

Ann Tompert has written 12 books for children.

ISBN# 0-8075-9113-0 Date Published: 1988 Price: $ 5.95
Publisher: Whitman Pages: 32

WILL YOU TAKE CARE OF ME?

Rating 

What "if I became a grown-up and could do everything myself?" asks little kangaroo.

In the tradition of *Mama, Would You Love Me,* Mama assures Baby that she will always care for him, no matter what. Sunny paintings and collages and Mama's imaginative answers make this bedtime book a treat. From Booklist: "Bridges manages to be both lyrical and fresh in constructing her heartwarming dialogue, which is buttressed by Sweet's fetching watercolors."

Keywords

Family Life, Core Issues (Feelings)

Age Range:

Preschool, early school-age

Author: Margaret Park Bridges

Illustrator: Melissa Sweet

ISBN# 688151949 Date Published: 1999 Price: $ 16.00
Publisher: Morrow Pages: 32

YOU GO AWAY

Separation and reunion stories for little ones.

Being away from parents is one of the most challenging issues for most young children and may be even more so for adopted kids. *You Go Away* conveys everyday experiences of a multicultural crew of children briefly separated from their parents or caretakers, then reunited. The repetition and pattern will reassure and comfort youngsters in this situation.

Keywords

Family Life, Core Issues (Feelings), Multicultural

Age Range:

Preschool, early school-age

Author: Dorothy Corey

Illustrator: Diane Paterson

ISBN# 807594423 Date Published: 1999 Price: $ 14.95
Publisher: Whitman Pages: 32

ZA-ZA'S BABY BROTHER

With a new baby, Za-Za's parents are too busy to pay any attention to her.

Meet Za-Za, a brand new big sister. Za-Za's parents are busy so she plays by herself and she plays with the baby. At last, when it's time for the baby to go to sleep, Mom and Dad give Za-Za just what she needs: a big hug! With her childlike sensibility and bright, bold art, Lucy Cousins reassures young children that while life changes when a new baby arrives, Mom's and Dad's love will always stay the same.

Keywords

Sibling Issues, Family Life, Core Issues (Feelings)

Age Range:

Preschool, early school-age

Author: Lucy Cousins

ISBN# 1-56402-582-9 Date Published: 1995 Price: $ 16.95
Publisher: Candlewick Pages: 32

School-Agers

At this age, many readers come into their own, finding a new ease with and interest in words on paper as their reading skills cohere and their reading speed increases. The world of literature holds a wonderful array of books written expressly for this age group, making it an exciting time for kids who love to read. In this collection, we try to offer many books that depict everyday, real-world situations to help children make sense of their own experience. In developing our collection, we've carried several goals in mind. Peer pressure and judgmental interpersonal evaluations intensify in the elementary and middle-school years; often, during this stage, children develop strong and persistent attitudes about who and what is okay or unacceptable. In response to these pressures, we want to offer books that address the particular concerns of our special constituency, stimulating questions and encouraging critical thinking about adoption, family life, social values and racial identity. We want to offer role models, grand and famous or simple and unsung, reminding children of others like them — whether adopted, or of color, or from difficult beginnings — who have struggled toward some personal goal. Children identify with heroes willing to make tough choices to do what is right and to face the consequences of their own actions. Thus, our selection of biographies introduces characters of diverse races, genders, classes, and religions, illuminating these inspiring figures while introducing kids to lifestyles and cultures that might otherwise remain unfamiliar. We also want to offer texts that challenge or complicate typical accounts of social history; many of the books in this selection offer new, positive, and non-traditional accounts of a culture, historical event or daily situation, freed from the chains of stereotypes. In this section of the BookSource, you'll find that pictures begin to give way to words, as children move away from a dependence on pictures to hold their interest and develop the narrative.

Rating

ABBY AND THE BEST KID EVER

Baby-Sitters Club, No. 116

When Lou McNally, a foster child, was last in Stoneybrook, she was the Worst Kid Ever. Her mother left when she was little, then her father died, her dog died, and they took her brother to another foster family. Lou was just horrible: never obeying, being mean to the animals. Now she's back...and Abby is going to be her baby-sitter. She's prepared for the worst, but Lou is a perfect angel. Lou is trying as hard as she can to be perfect so her Aunt and Uncle will keep her. She's wearing dresses and is pretty, proper, and neat. This book is filled with myths and stereotypes about adoption. Don't bother with it.

Keywords

Adopted Child, Foster Child

Age Range,

School-agers 9-12

Author: Ann Martin

Ann Martin is the author of *Claudia and the Great Search* and *Abby and the Best Kia Ever.*

ISBN# 590059947 Date Published, 1998 Price, $ 3.99

Publisher, Apple Pages,

Rating

ADOPTED BY THE EAGLES

A Plains Indian story of friendship and treachery.

Two friends go out hunting for horses — but only one returns. With the help of the eagles, the lost one survives and comes back later to regain his place in the tribe. A story based on Lakota Indian traditions, it is said to have been a favorite story of Chief Edgar Red Cloud. Brightly-colored illustrations depict authentic, minutely detailed portraits of people, animals, and insects. Native American children will appreciate their connection to this moving and powerful tale, and all children will be able to appreciate the affirming values of the culture.

Keywords

Adoption, Core Issues (Feelings), Native American, Cultural History, Self-Esteem, Friendship

Age Range,

School-agers 9-12

Author: Paul Goble

Paul Goble is the author of *The Lost Children, Adopted By The Eagles, The Girl Who Loved Wild Horses.*

ISBN# 689820860 Date Published, Price, $ 5.99

Publisher, Macmillan Pages, 40

ADOPTED ONE, THE

What an adopted child doesn't know – unless someone tells him – is his whole story.

In his attempts to make sense of his past, an adopted child will create explanations which are often more frightening than the truth. This book provides keys to the ways children try to make sense of being adopted. Each page contains adult text and child text. The adult text offers uncomplicated ways to respond to children's ideas. Issues include being physically different from other family members; not knowing about one's birth; not knowing one's birth parents; not being satisfied with the story of how one came to be adopted; temperamental fit; values; the adopted child's anger, and more.

Keywords

Adoption, Core Issues (Feelings), Family Life, Self-Esteem, Triad Issues, Parenting

Age Range,

School-agers 9-12

Author: Sara Bonnett Stein

Photographer: Erica Stone

ISBN# 802772242 Date Published, 1984 Price, $ 8.95

Publisher, Walker & Co. Pages, 48

AWAKE AND DREAMING

Theo wanted to be part of a real family. Finally, she was.

From Booklist: "Pearson's unusual novel shifts smoothly from Theo's miserable existence to the romantic idealism she craves and finally back to the difficult but ultimately satisfying new actuality that she creates. Strong, believable characters, the hint of the supernatural, and Pearson's poignant commentary on the writer's craft all add up to a compelling and memorable read," while Kirkus Reviews says, "Theo, nine, has not had a gentle life. She escapes via daydreams and voracious reading. While parts of the tale are clumsily drawn, Theo's longings are unmistakably clear, and the shaky shifts in point of view won't matter to readers, for this is a real page-turner."

Keywords

Family Life, Adoption

Age Range,

School-agers 9-12

Author: Kit Pearson

ISBN# 670869546 Date Published, 1997 Price, $ 13.99

Publisher, Viking Pages, 228

BECAUSE YOU'RE LUCKY

Rating 

Kevin comes to live with his Jonathon, who has to share everything – even his mother.

Sharing his toys, his room, his school, even his mother with his cousin Kevin isn't easy for Jonathon and it looks like a permanent arrangement. This appealing story of two boys stretching and growing into a new sense of family with one another covers territory not often reflected in picture books — kinship adoption. Wonderful illustrations of characters who just happen to be African American.

Keywords

African American, Adoption, Family Life, Extended Family, Sibling Issues, Fiction

Age Range:

School-agers 9-12

Author: Irene Smalls

Illustrator: Michael Hays

Irene Smalls and Michael Hays are the author/illustrator team of *Jonathon and His Mommy.*

ISBN# 316708673 Date Published: 1997 Price: $ 15.95

Publisher: Little Brown Pages: 32

BEING ADOPTED

Rating 

What does it feel like to grow up adopted? Listen to the children.

This book about identity documents the inner lives of three children: their doubts, fears, satisfactions, and triumphs, normalizing the feelings and experiences common to adoption. One little girl reviewing *Being Adopted* said, "I especially like the part where Rebecca's sad because someone made fun of her because she's adopted and her brother told her not to worry because their mommy and daddy will never give them up." — adding that she too is adopted but knows her parents will never give her up.

Keywords

Adoption, Adopted Child, Family Life, Core Issues (Feelings)

Age Range:

School-agers 9-12

Author: Maxine Rosenberg

Maxine Rosenberg is the author of *Living In Two Worlds,* and *Growing Up Adopted.*

ISBN# 688026729 Date Published: Price: $ 16.00

Publisher: Morrow Pages:

BONESY AND ISABEL

Isabel, adopted from El Salvador, must face the death of her dear dog Bonesy.

Isabel is welcomed into her new home by the family dog, Bonesy. Bonesy is always at her side and understands how she's feeling. And he always waits under the table for her leftover scraps. But one night, Bonesy takes his last breath and Isabel must deal with his death. Books in Print: "A child learns that communication goes beyond the spoken word and a loss cements a loving relationship. Bonesy becomes Isabel's true compasero when she joins her new household. When she realizes something is wrong, she tries to wake him, without success. Eventually her parents join her on the floor, and tears are the language they share."

Keywords

Adoption, Core Issues (Feelings), Grief and Loss, International Adoption, Fiction, Adopted Child

Age Range:

School-agers 9-12

Author: Michael J. Rosen

Author: James E. Ransome

ISBN# 0-15-209813-5 Date Published: Price: $ 15.00

Publisher: Knopf Pages: 36

CHARLOTTE'S WEB

Was there ever a birth mother in literature more touching than Charlotte?

Wilbur, a lovable pig, is rescued from a cruel fate by a beautiful and intelligent spider named Charlotte. Later, when Charlotte becomes ill, Wilbur agrees to care for her babies. Charlotte is a very positive birth mother role model. Adopted children will find reassurance in this story.

Keywords

Adoption, Friendship, Diversity, Birth Parent, Triad Issues, Fiction

Age Range:

School-agers 9-12

Author: E. B. White

Illustrator: Garth Williams

ISBN# 6440557 Date Published: Price: $ 4.95

Publisher: HarperCollins Pages:

Rating

CLAUDIA AND THE GREAT SEARCH

Volume 33 of the "Babysitter's Club" Series.

Since she sees no resemblance between herself and the brainy older sister whom she rivals, thirteen-year-old Claudia concludes that she is adopted.

Keywords

Adoption, Sibling Issues, Girl Power, Fiction

Age Range:

School-agers 9-12

Author: Ann Martin

Ann Martin is the author of *Claudia and the Great Search* and *Abby and the Best Kia Ever.*

ISBN# 590731904 Date Published: 1990 Price: $ 3.99

Publisher: Scholastic Pages:

Rating

COPING AS A FOSTER CHILD

Is foster care okay for me?

A discussion of ways to make living with foster parents a better experience. Books in Print: "An accurate, in-depth look at several teens in foster care, presented through case studies. Included are explanations of the variety of options available, their specific purposes, and reasons behind placement in each. Successes as well as failures are showcased as readers are given a closer look at many options within both foster care and adoption. This readable account offers necessary facts for researchers while doubling as a resource for teens facing similar situations. The adolescents speak eloquently and often with a wisdom beyond their years as they share their current plights and hopes for the future."

Keywords

Foster Child, Core Issues (Feelings), Adoption Reform, Family Life

Age Range:

School-agers 9-12

Author: Geraldine M. Blomquist

Author: Paul Blomquist

ISBN# 0-8239-1346-5 Date Published: 1992 Price: $ 17.95

Publisher: Rosen Group Pages:

DOUBLE PLAY AT SHORTSTOP

Twelve-year-old Danny's curiosity leads him to a surprising discovery about his own adoption.

But will he want to believe what he discovers? From Booklist: "Danny Walker feels he is a shoo-in for the all-star team, until he meets Tammy Aiken, the shortstop for the opposition. They're both great players, but other similarities (both have red hair, a similar stance, etc.) make Danny uneasy. When he learns that both are adopted and share the same birthday, Danny becomes convinced they're twins, separated at birth. While the long-lost twins subplot offers few surprises, the outcome of the baseball series will hold the reader's interest, and Christopher's unusual ending will satisfy sports fans. The inclusion of many female players is a bonus."

Keywords

Adoption, Sports, Sibling Issues, Fiction

Age Range:

School-agers 9-12

Author: Matt Christopher

ISBN# 316142018 Date Published: 1997 Price: $ 3.95

Publisher: Little Brown Pages: 160

ECHOHAWK

Echohawk was small when he was taken from his White family and adopted by Mohicans.

After Echohawk is adopted into a Mohican tribe, his world becomes the Mohican culture, customs and beliefs. Then he gets the chance to choose whether to go back to white culture or stay in the only world he's every known. What will he do? A book sure to raise questions and create a great opportunity for a discussion of adoption, the role of the birth family, and the role of the adoptive family.

Keywords

Adoption, Native American, Fiction, Racial/Ethnic Identity, Transracial Adoption, Triad Issues

Age Range:

School-agers 9-12

Author: Lynda Durrant

ISBN# 440414385 Date Published: 1996 Price: $ 4.50

Publisher: Yearling Books Pages: 182

Rating

GINGER BROWN: THE NOBODY BOY

Ginger is a biracial child. Will Nobody Boy be her friend?

After her parents divorce, seven-year-old Ginger spends the summer at her grandparents' home in the county. Her visit is enlivened by the appearance of a sad little boy who calls himself Nobody. This story offers a compassionate look at the growth of their friendship and at what friendship, love and family really mean. A First Stepping Stone chapter book for young readers.

Keywords

Core Issues (Feelings), Multiracial, Friendship, Self-Esteem, Fiction

Age Range:

School-agers 9-12

Author: Sharon Dennis Wyeth

Sharon Wyeth is the author of *World of Daughter McGuire* and *Something Beautiful.*

ISBN# 0-679-85645-5 *Date Published:* *Price:* $ 3.99
Publisher: Random House *Pages:*

Rating

GINGER BROWN: TOO MANY HOUSES

Ginger is a seven-year-old biracial child whose mom and dad have gotten a divorce.

Everything changes for Ginger after her parents divorce. She has to say good-bye to her kitten and live with her grandparents while her mom finds a new home for the two of them. Trying to make sense of the differences in skin color within her family, she is confused by the fact that her grandparents, named Brown, are really pinkish white like Daddy, while Nana and Granddaddy, named Gray, are brown like Mommy. It is these age-appropriate thoughts, revealed through Ginger's bittersweet first-person narration, that make the story work so well, though occasionally Ginger seems far too wise for her years.

Keywords

Multiracial, Core Issues (Feelings), Divorce, Fiction, Racial/ Ethnic Identity

Age Range:

School-agers 9-12

Author: Sharon Dennis Wyeth

Sharon Wyeth is the author of *World of Daughter McGuire* and *Something Beautiful.*

ISBN# 679954376 *Date Published:* 1996 *Price:* $ 3.99
Publisher: Random House *Pages:*

GREAT GILLY HOPKINS, THE

Gilly is a tough cookie, but underneath, she yearns for a family of her own.

Tells the story of an 11-year-old foster child who tries to cope with her longings and fears as she schemes against everyone who tries to be friendly. Winner of the 1979 National Book Award for Children's Literature. 1979 Newbery Honor Book.

Keywords

Foster Child, Girl Power, Family Life, Foster Care, Friendship, Fiction

Age Range:

School-agers 9-12

Author: Katherine Paterson

ISBN# 0-06-440201-0 *Date Published:* 1987 *Price:* $ 4.50
Publisher: Harper Trophy *Pages:* 192

HALINKA

A displaced child's search for home.

Halinka, 12, is a Jewish girl living in a welfare home in Germany, left alive and alone after the Holocaust. In this account of her survival, written in the first-person by one of Germany's most honored children's authors, brings readers inside her secrets, dreams and lies to herself and the people around her. Halinka suffers abuse; her story is about the walls she builds to hide from pain and about how she learns to let love in when it's finally offered. She is as sympathetic a character as the great Gilly Hopkins because of her honesty with herself, her resiliency and her optimism. Not many will read her story with dry eyes.

Keywords

Sexual Abuse, Core Issues (Feelings), Fiction, Foster Child, Friendship, Grief and Loss

Age Range:

School-agers 9-12

Author: Mirjam Pressler

Translator: Elizabeth D. Crawford

Mirjam Pressler won the German Youth Literature Prize in 1994 for the body of her work. A translator and biographer of Anne Frank, she lives in Israel and Germany.

ISBN# 805058613 *Date Published:* 1998 *Price:* $ 16.95
Publisher: Henry Holt *Pages:* 192

Rating

HEAVEN

Who Is Marley? Where did she come from? Where does she belong?

"Last night Momma and Pops kept saying they should have told me what they had to tell me sooner. It's what people who haven't told the truth always say...." At fourteen, Marley is shocked to find out she was adopted. The truth seems to change everything. How could her parents have lied? Is her brother really her brother? Does she belong? As she processes the disclosure, Marley finds peace, realizing that her relationships with her family remain the same. She comes to understand both that they belong to each other as they always have and that it is important to know about her birth family and her birth heritage.

Keywords

African American, Family Life, Adoption, Triad Issues, Core Issues (Feelings), Attachment

Age Range:

School-agers 9-12

Author: Angela Johnson

Angela Johnson is the author of *Mama Bird, Baby Bird; The Aunt In Our House; Julius, The Leaving Morning; Gone From Home; Heaven;* and more.

ISBN# 689822294 Date Published: 1998 Price: $ 16.00

Publisher: Simon & Schuster Pages: 138

Rating

HOW BABIES AND FAMILIES ARE MADE

"A family is people caring about each other."

This multicultural book explains different ways families are formed and gives explicit information about fetal development, anatomy, conception and more. Technical information is well presented, but there is a lot of it, perhaps more than a child in this age range will choose to follow.

Keywords

Adoption, Family Life, Health

Age Range:

School-agers 9-12

Author: Patricia Schaeffer

Patricia Schaeffer is an adoptive mother.

ISBN# 935079173 Date Published: Price: $ 6.95

Publisher: Tabor Sarah Bks Pages:

I LOST MY BEAR

Jules Feiffer knows that a stuffed animal is far more than a bear.

Jules Feiffer knows some things about feelings. This picture book describes the travails of an unnamed young girl who can't find her special bear. Using the cartoon style common to all his work, this fun book creates an opportunity to talk about loss — one of the core issues of adoption — without ever using the word adoption or expressly invoking your child's personal story. What did the girl feel like when she couldn't find her bear? What did she feel like when she was looking? How did she solve her problem? What did she feel like when the bear was found?

Keywords

Adopted Child, Core Issues (Feelings), Grief and Loss

Age Range:

School-agers 9-12

Author: Jules Feiffer

Jules Feiffer is the creator of syndicated cartoons for adults. He also wrote The Man In The Ceiling for children.

ISBN# 688151477 Date Published: 1998 Price: $ 16.00

Publisher: Morrow Pages: 40

IS THAT YOUR SISTER?

A six-year-old's understanding of transracial adoption.

Six-year-old Catherine tells in her own words what it is like to be adopted. Since she is in a multiracial family, no one looks alike. She talks matter-of-factly about her friends' questions and her answers.

Keywords

Adoption, Sibling Issues, Transracial Adoption, International Adoption, Family Life, Diversity

Age Range:

School-agers 9-12

Author: Catherine Bunin

Author: Sherry Bunin

Author: Martha G. Welch

ISBN# 961187263 Date Published: 1993 Price: $ 14.95

Publisher: Our Child Press Pages: 32

Rating

JOURNEY

Coping with abandonment, finding family.

Journey is eleven the summer his mother leaves him and his sister with his grandparents. Angry and sad, he searches for answers in old photos and in new ones his grandfather Marcus takes to prove that the love that still binds the family is for real. Journey realizes that it was inevitable for Mama to split and that it was his grandfather who had always been his parent. The bottom line is that he becomes able to see that his family, though not perfect, is good enough; he tells his Mama so when she eventually phones. This poignant book is sure to hit some core issues for kids who have been separated from their birth families.

Keywords

Adoption, Family Life, Fiction, Mothers, Core Issues (Feelings)

Age Range:

School-agers 9-12

Author: Patricia MacLachlan

Patricia MacLachlan won the 1986 Newbery Medal for *Sarah, Plain and Tall.*

ISBN# 440408091 *Date Published:* 1993 *Price:* $ 4.50

Publisher: Yearling Books *Pages:*

Rating

JOURNEY HOME

A 10-year-old Vietnamese American girl journeys to Vietnam to find her mother's birth family.

This multigenerational book about adoption is one of the few to address the feelings of a child whose parent joined their family through adoption. Mai's story is presented with great sensitivity. Perhaps that's why it's such a shock when grampa is referred to as a foster parent — it feels like a shower of cold water, when a writer who seemed to understand reveals that he does not. Sigh. Nonetheless, this is a good book which offers the opportunity to talk with your child about how outsiders see adoptive families.

Keywords

Vietnam, Adoption, Adopted Child, Family Life, International Adoption, Intergenerational

Age Range:

School-agers 9-12

Author: Lawrence McKay

Illustrator: Don Lee

ISBN# 1880000652 *Date Published:* 1998 *Price:* $ 15.95

Publisher: Lee & Low Books *Pages:* 32

LIFE APART, A

Gail's marriage falters when the daughter she placed for adoption fifteen years ago finds her.

This book was not available for review in time for publication in this edition of the BookSource. If you would like updated information, please call Pact at 415 221-6957.

Keywords

Adoption, Birth Parent, Triad Issues, Search and Reunion, Core Issues (Feelings)

Age Range:

School-agers 9-12

Author: Shirlee Evans

ISBN# 836135369 *Date Published:* 1990 *Price:* $ 6.99

Publisher: Herald Pr *Pages:*

LONG JOURNEY HOME, THE

For any child who has been separated from a loved one.

Mayla is separated from his mom by a raging flood. Will the mother bear who finds him take care of him? Every time she has to leave, he's afraid he'll never see her again. A gripping story that will hold the attention of any child and that will have special poignancy for a child who has been separated from a birth parent, even at birth. Without focusing on the individual details of your child's own story, this book promotes discussions of the core feelings in adoption and foster care transitions. The affirming underlying messages are that children are braver and more resourceful than they may realize and that the universe will support us.

Keywords

Foster Child, Adoption, Role Models, Core Issues (Feelings), Foster Care

Age Range:

School-agers 9-12

Author: Richard Delaney

Dr. Rick Delaney, a practicing psychologist, is the author of *Fostering Changes; Troubled Transplants;* and *Long Journey Home.*

ISBN# 0-590-41433-X *Date Published:* 1997 *Price:* $ 7.95

Publisher: Wood Barnes *Pages:* 44

Rating

LOST CHILDREN, THE

A Blackfoot Indian myth about the constellations reminds us that all children are sacred.

The archetype of the orphan appears throughout literature; encountering it for the first time while sheltered in the comfort and safety of a parent's lap can help prepare adopted children for outsiders' responses to their origins. It also provides an opportunity to talk informally about adoption without focusing directly on the child's personal story. The School Library Journal writes, "Goble's illustrations — dazzling in color, crisp and clean in design — prove typically arresting," and Kirkus Reviews concurs: "A grand addition to a notable oeuvre, with a powerful contemporary message."

Keywords

Adoption, Core Issues (Feelings), Folk tales and Legends, Native American, Orphan

Age Range.

School-agers 9-12

Author: Paul Goble

Paul Goble is the author of *The Lost Children, Adopted By The Eagles, The Girl Who Loved Wild Horses.*

ISBN# 689819994 Date Published. 1998 Price. $ 5.99

Publisher. Simon & Schuster Pages. 40

Rating

MANDY

Look out for Mandy! She'll capture your heart.

Mandy is ten and lives in an orphanage. One day in the woods, she finds a tiny, deserted cottage that she makes her secret home. But on one stormy night, she gets sick at the cottage and no one can find her.

Keywords

Adoption, Girl Power, Fiction

Age Range.

School-agers 9-12

Author: Julie Andrews Edwards

Julie Andrews Edwards is the star of many films and Broadway theater productions including "Mary Poppins" and "The Sound of Music."

ISBN# 0-06-440296-7 Date Published. Price. $ 4.95

Publisher. Harper Row Pages. 279

ME AND MY NAME

A sensitive look at the effects of divorce and adoption.

Erin, a sixth grader, faces difficult decisions: about adoption by her stepfather; about choosing between two boys at school; about a game of truth or dare at a slumber party; and about being true to herself and fitting in.

Keywords

Core Issues (Feelings), Adoption, Family Life, Fiction, Self-Esteem

Age Range.

School-agers 9-12

Author: Mary Jane Miller

ISBN# 0-14-034374-1 Date Published. Price. $ 3.99

Publisher. Puffin Pages.

ME, MOP, AND THE MOONDANCE KID

Three orphans try to make their wishes come true in this funny story.

A feel-good story about resilient characters who just happen to be African American and orphans. The publisher writes, "Myers combines wit, sensitivity and insight to create this funny, fast-paced story about three orphaned children and the Elks, a Little League baseball team," and Publishers Weekly concurs, writing, "Myers' keen sense of humor, quick, natural dialogue and irresistible protagonists make this novel a winner." An ALA Notable Children's Book.

Keywords

Adoption, Orphan, Sports, African American, Friendship, Black Identity

Age Range.

School-agers 9-12

Author: Walter Dean Myers

Illustrator: Rodney Pate

Walter Dean Myers is the author of *One More River To Cross; Brown Angels; Me, Mop, and the Moondance Kid s, Slam, Malcolm X , Hoops,* and many more.

ISBN# 440403960 Date Published. 1991 Price. $ 4.50

Publisher. Yearling Books Pages.

MISSING SISTERS

Twelve-year-old Alice, an orphan, is shocked to find out she has an identical twin.

From Booklist: "At first glance, Alice Colossus doesn't have much going for her. Her best friend is the elderly Sister Vincent De Paul. When the sister is injured in a fire, Alice feels more lost than ever. What she needs is some sort of miracle, and it comes in a big way with the discovery of an identical twin sister she never knew she had. Though the plot sounds contrived, Maguire's story is anything but, because his characters transcend their material.... Sister Vincent De Paul delivers the author's message: 'Don't mind the choices, Alice; mind the details!... Mind the moments, Alice, and the choices don't make a whit of difference.'"

Keywords
Adoption, Special Needs, Friendship, Girl Power, Intergenerational, Sibling Issues
Age Range:
School-agers 9-12
Author: Gregory Maguire

ISBN# 0-689-50590-6 *Date Published:* 1994 *Price:* $ 4.95
Publisher: Simon & Schuster *Pages:* 152

MOLLY BY ANY OTHER NAME

Molly is Asian, adopted, and doesn't know her origins, but her search scares her parents.

Seventeen-year-old Molly Fletcher has a chance to find her birth mother. Her adoptive parents are afraid everyone may get hurt if she searches. Can she make them understand her need to learn about her roots? She has to try. Books in Print writes, "Arranged in three sections, the story relates Molly's search, her birth mother's reactions, and their eventual meeting. Much like Hadley Irwin's *Kim/Kimi*, Molly finds she is of Japanese descent. Okimoto's treatment of the subject, however, does a far better job of describing the feelings of the characters. A book that goes beyond the adoption topic to encompass family feelings and dynamics."

Keywords
Adoption, Search and Reunion, Girl Power, Triad Issues, Core Issues (Feelings), Japanese American
Age Range:
School-agers 9-12
Author: Jean Davies Okimoto

ISBN# 0590-429940-9 *Date Published:* 1990 *Price:* $ 2.95
Publisher: Scholastic *Pages:* 276

MULBERRY BIRD

"'All grownups have one problem that stands out above all others,' mother bird thought."

Although she loves her baby very much, a young mother bird chooses adoption because she is unable to give him the home that he needs. This gentle story shows her struggle with this decision and illustrates her hope that her baby's life can be fulfilled through adoption. This new, beautifully illustrated version of a beloved classic offers a reassuring answer to every adopted child's question, "Why is there adoption and why was I adopted?"

Keywords
Adoption, Birth Parent, Core Issues (Feelings), Grief and Loss
Age Range:
School-agers 9-12
Author: Anne Braff Brodzinsky

An adoptive parent, Anne Braff Brodzinsky was part of the Rutgers team which produced the definitive research study on what children understand about adoption.

ISBN# 944934153 *Date Published:* *Price:* $ 16.00
Publisher: Perspectives *Pages:*

NEVER NEVER NEVER WILL SHE STOP LOVING YOU

The story of a birth mother and her baby.

This reassuring story tells the adopted child that he or she is loved and wanted. Not only does the new family love the child; the birth mother loves the child, too. "Your birth mother wanted to hold and hug and kiss you forever. She wanted to rock you to sleep, kiss you awake, watch you grow, and dry your tears. Annie knew she would be happier if she kept you. But what about you? What did you need?"

Keywords
Triad Issues, Adoption, Open Adoption, Birth Parent, Core Issues (Feelings), Grief and Loss
Age Range:
School-agers 9-12
Author: Jolene Durrant

ISBN# 966356756 *Date Published:* 1998 *Price:* $ 9.95
Publisher: JoBiz Books *Pages:* 32

Rating

OCEAN WITHIN, THE

Learning trust, becoming part of a family.

"Elizabeth, 11, barely speaks and views her adoption by the Sheridans as just another temporary situation, to be endured without getting emotionally entangled. The Sheridans are a raucous and deeply affectionate family, and Elizabeth is overwhelmed by their noise and their joy. Elizabeth's passion is the ocean, which she has dreamed of seeing; too afraid to actually let the water touch her, she watches the ocean for hours while the others swim and play. It is four-year-old Petey who begins to reach Elizabeth; too young to be deceived, he recognizes both her loneliness and her fear. Absorbed young readers will find they are holding their breath at the end." — Booklist

Keywords

Family Life, Foster Child, Adopted Child

Age Range:

School-agers 9-12

Author: V.M. Caldwell

Illustrator: Erica Magnus

ISBN# 1571316248 *Date Published:* 1999 *Price:* $ 6.95

Publisher: Milkweed Editions *Pages:* 236

Rating

ONE THING THAT'S TRUE

Adoption, race and class in a novel for school-agers.

From Booklist: "Roxanne, 13, can't work out what's gone wrong.... Why are her parents acting so weird, especially with her older brother, Joel? When it turns out that Joel is adopted and that they had kept it secret, Joel runs away. Set in Canada, this first novel is told in a fresh, funny, contemporary voice that blends the suspenseful plot with Roxanne's coming-of-age struggles ('Are you, like, in love or something?'). Race and class are part of the story: as one of the few Black families in the community, the Jacobs are always wary of prejudice. Foggo dramatizes serious issues without sermonizing and captures the joy and muddle of growing up."

Keywords

Adopted Child, Adoption, Family Life

Age Range:

School-agers 9-12

Author: Cheryl Foggo

ISBN# 1550744119 *Date Published:* 1998 *Price:* $ 14.95

Publisher: *Pages:* 128

ONLY THE BEST (GIRLS ONLY NO. 2)

Jenna is a winner. What happens when there are problems:

Jenna is elated when she's made captain of her gymnastics team. The only problem is that she's having trouble with her aerial cartwheels — and the next meet is just ten days away. In this story, which is told from a Christian perspective, Jenna just happens to be Korean American and adopted.

Keywords

Sports, Christianity, Korean American, Adopted Child, Transracial Adoption

Age Range:

School-agers 9-12

Author: Beverly Lewis

ISBN# 764220594 *Date Published:* 1998 *Price:* $ 5.99

Publisher: Bethany *Pages:* 128

ORPHAN BOY

An old man becomes insatiably curious about the boy's mysterious powers.

At dawn, the planet Venus appears in the east as the morning star. At nightfall, it is the evening star in the west. The Masai call this star Kileken, the orphan boy. This traditional story from Africa explains the reason the orphan boy appears in the sky both morning and night. "This ancient myth, told to Mollel by his grandfather, is accompanied by magnificent oil paintings of Africa in which the colorfully clad old tribesmen and the lush green grassland contrast with pictures of arid, sun-drenched plains, baked dry by heat and drought. The design is beautiful," says Books in Print.

Keywords

Adoption, Fiction, Folk tales and Legends, Africa, Black Identity, Orphan

Age Range:

School-agers 9-12

Author: Tololwa M. Mollel

Tololwa M. Mollel is author of *Orphan Boy, Big Boy, The Princess Who Lost Her Hair* and more.

ISBN# 0-395-72079-6 *Date Published:* 1990 *Price:* $ 5.95

Publisher: Clarion *Pages:*

Rating

ORPHAN TRAIN QUARTET, THE

Power-packed adventures, set in the 1850s, of siblings on the Orphan Train to be adopted.

This is a series about the more than 100,000 homeless children taken from the streets of New York and sent to new families. Danny and his younger sister Peg feel lucky to be adopted by the Swensons, but when Mrs. Swenson dies, Danny plots to get Mr. Swenson to marry his widowed mother. Book 1 is called *A Family Apart* and revolves around six brothers and sisters whose mother makes the ultimate sacrifice to give them hope for a better future. It can be ordered separately. ISBN#:0440226767: $ 4.50

Keywords

Adoption, Fiction, US History, Orphan

Age Range:

School-agers 9-12

Author: Joan Lowery Nixon

ISBN# 553284851 *Date Published:* 1990 *Price:* $ 16.50

Publisher: Bantam *Pages:*

Rating

OUT OF THE BLUE

Megan's 12th birthday surprise is a new half-sister reunited with the family after adoption!

Kids ages 10-14 will appreciate Ellis' latest story of a family changed by the addition of a long-lost half-sister. When her birth mother finally locates 24-year-old Natalie, Megan resents her new older sibling in this portrait of how change affects all members of a family.

Keywords

Adoption, Birth Parent, Sibling Issues, Fiction, Core Issues (Feelings), Search and Reunion

Age Range:

School-agers 9-12

Author: Sarah Ellis

ISBN# 140380663 *Date Published:* 1996 *Price:* $ 3.99

Publisher: Putnam-Paperstar *Pages:*

RAIN FOREST GIRL

Daiane didn't want to be adopted. She wanted to stay in Brazil with her family.

Daiane was adopted as a nine-year-old and moved from Brazil to America. Though this story raises important questions, we are concerned by its presentation. The photographs and format seem to suggest that this story is told in Daiane's own voice and reflects her own self-expression, but details of the story suggests otherwise: for example, Daiane did not speak English, yet the text has her quoting the English words spoken to her by an American official. And the text offers no indication that she thinks about her birth family. Most troubling, the cover suggests Daiane was removed from her birth family because "an American family wanted to adopt her." We hope not.

Keywords

Adoption, International Adoption, Latino/a, Brazil

Age Range:

School-agers 9-12

Author: Chalise Miner

Chalise Miner is the adoptive mother of Daiane, the central character in this story.

ISBN# 1883845815 *Date Published:* 1998 *Price:* $ 12.95

Publisher: Mitchell Lane Publishers *Pages:* 48

SARAH, PLAIN AND TALL

A book about expanding a family, filled with gentle humor and sweetness.

Mama died the day after Caleb was born. Their house on the prairie was quiet. Then Papa put an ad in the paper asking for a wife. Sarah decides to come for a month. This classic has captured young children's hearts through the years. Newbery Medal winner.

Keywords

Adoption, Fiction, Girl Power

Age Range:

School-agers 9-12

Author: Patricia MacLachlan

Patricia MacLachlan won the 1986 Newbery Medal for *Sarah, Plain and Tall.*

ISBN# 0-06-440205-3 *Date Published:* *Price:* $ 3.95

Publisher: Harper Row *Pages:*

Rating

SPOTTY

Is it more important to please Grampa or take care of Spotty?

Afraid that Grandpa won't accept her new baby's spots, Mother Bunny leaves Spotty at home while she and his siblings go to Grandpa's birthday party. Spotty runs away. This book can provide practice for your child in spotting prejudice. You might say, "People who don't know better sometimes think there is something wrong with people who are different from them. This attitude is not okay, and we use the word racism to talk about it. When we read this book together, let's see if we can find out if there's racism in this story. If there is, let's think what we could do to make it stop."

Keywords

Core Issues (Feelings), Race Relations, Family Life, Extended Family, Intergenerational, Parenting

Age Range:

School-agers 9-12

Author: Margret Rey

Illustrator: H. A. Rey

ISBN# 395837324 Date Published: 1997 Price: $ 5.95

Publisher: Houghton Mifflin Pages:

Rating

STEALING HOME: THE STORY OF JACKIE ROBINSON

The inspiring story of the first Black player in the major leagues.

This reissue corresponds with the 50th anniversary of the year Jackie Robinson joined the Brooklyn Dodgers. The first Black man to join the major leagues, he had the courage to confront racism and fight for the rights of all Black people both on and off the baseball diamond. Jackie Robinson was a great athlete, but his destiny went far beyond the baseball diamond. He was a symbol of courage, hope, and unity for all Black and white Americans and for people throughout the world. A fresh new look at an American hero. Illustrated.

Keywords

African American, Biography, Role Models, Self-Esteem, Race Relations, Black Identity

Age Range:

School-agers 9-12

Author: Barry Denenberg

ISBN# 590045539 Date Published: 1997 Price: $ 3.99

Publisher: Scholastic Pages: 128

STORY OF ADOPTION

Adoption from Korea from a young child's point of view.

This small book helps children understand how they came to have new families and to appreciate that their heritage is positive. This book is out of print, but if you place an order we may be able to find you a used copy within 2-6 months. We will notify you and request your approval of the price and condition. We will also notify you if we are unable to locate this title within six months.

Keywords

Adoption, Racial/Ethnic Identity, Transracial Adoption, International Adoption, Korean American

Age Range:

School-agers 9-12

Author: Darla Lowe

Illustrator: Christina Carney

ISBN# 960609024 Date Published: 1988 Price: $ 4.95

Publisher: EastWest Press Pages:

SUDDEN CHANGE OF FAMILY, A

When Katy discovers her mom was adopted, she learns what makes a family belong together.

For Katy, summertime means going out to Whitemarsh Point to visit her grandparents. But this year, Katy finds out that her mom was adopted — and her mom drags Katy off to find her "real" family. Katy learns that being a "family" means more than just blood relationships — and that love and responsibility can be just as important.

Keywords

Adoption, Family Life, Fiction, Adopted Child, Core Issues (Feelings)

Age Range:

School-agers 9-12

Author: Mary Jane Auch

ISBN# 0671748920" Date Published: 1993 Price: $ 2.99

Publisher: Pocket Books Pages:

Rating

TURNS ON A DIME

This book was not available for review in time for publication in this edition of the BookSource. If you would like updated information, please call Pact at 415 221-6957.

Keywords

Adoption, Adopted Child

Age Range:

School-agers 9-12

Author: Julie Lawson

Julie Lawson is the author of *Too Many Suns* and *Turns on a Dime.*

ISBN# 773759425 Date Published: 1999 Price: $ 6.95

Publisher: Stoddart Publications Pages: 176

Rating

VISITING MISS PIERCE

An adopted teen becomes engrossed in a senile woman's stories of her lost brother.

"As Barry learns more about Willie, he begins to idolize the rebellious, independent young man, who apparently stood up to his parents by marrying a servant and fathering her child before being killed in World War I. Barry's ideals are shattered, however, when he discovers that Willie allowed his parents to have the marriage annulled and the child given away for adoption so that he could marry the woman of their choice. This hits the boy especially hard, as he himself is adopted and has questions about his birth parents. Barry's abilities, insecurities and actions are on target; his changing feelings about volunteering in the convalescent home are especially well drawn," says Books in Print.

Keywords

Adoption, Fiction, Birth Parent, Intergenerational, Core Issues (Feelings)

Age Range:

School-agers 9-12

Author: Pat Derby

ISBN# 0-374-48156-3 Date Published: 1989 Price: $ 3.50

Publisher: Farrar-Strauss Pages: 144

WE DON'T LOOK LIKE OUR MOM AND DAD

Why did you adopt Korean kids? If my birth mom came would she recognize me?

This is a question and answer book for adoptive parents from their Korean-born sons, in the form of a photo essay of a transracial adoptive family. Covers a host of questions from children to parents and imparts the message that other adopted children share their experiences — adopted children are not alone.

Keywords

Transracial Adoption, International Adoption, Korean American, Fathers, Mothers, Family Life

Age Range:

School-agers 9-12

Author: Harriet Sobol

Illustrator: Patricia Agre

ISBN# 0-698-20608-8 Date Published: 1984 Price: $ 11.95

Publisher: Putnam-Paperstar Pages: 32

WHAT MY SISTER REMEMBERED

When their parents died, Molly was adopted by relatives and Beth by a rich family.

While visiting her younger sister Molly for the first time in eight years, Beth confronts painful memories of the sudden death of their parents and the subsequent adoption of the sisters by different families. Molly doesn't understand why Beth seems to hate her so much. Beth remembers more of their past than Molly — and she's going to tell the truth, no matter whom it hurts. This story for young teens is a page turner, if a bit overly dramatic. It should hold the interest of any adopted children. Availability: This item usually ships within six weeks. Please note that items occasionally go out of print or publishers run out of stock. We will notify you within three weeks if we have trouble obtaining this book.

Keywords

Adoption, Sibling Issues, Family Life, Fiction, Core Issues (Feelings), Grief and Loss

Age Range:

School-agers 9-12

Author: Marilyn Sachs

ISBN# 0-525-44953-1 Date Published: 1992 Price: $ 6.95

Publisher: Dutton Pages: 122

WHEN THE ROAD ENDS

Rating 

Three foster children must find a way to become a family.

They're an unlikely mix: serious, sensible Mary; hostile and rebellious Adam; and Jane, a tiny frightened girl who refuses to speak. Foster care has placed them, one by one, in a home where they are abandoned by their caretaker and must learn to survive on their own.

Keywords
Foster Child, Family Life, Fiction, Foster Care, Core Issues (Feelings)

Age Range
School-agers 9-12

Author: Jean Thesman

ISBN# 380720116 Date Published 1995 Price $ 3.99
Publisher Camelot Pages

WHERE IS HOME?

Rating 

A first-person account of living through foster care.

Pam Jones was six when her father left her. She then spent 13 years moving in and out of New York state foster homes, mental wards, police stations, and the homes of a few friends and family members. This book is about her memory of those intolerable years and offers a call to action to keep other children from having the kinds of experiences of rejection that shaped her life as an African American child caught in a system that was not designed to serve her needs. Though this book does not offer clues to Pam's resilience and ability to grow up healthy in spite of the system's failings, it is a poignant account of the pain of growing up without a family.

Keywords
Family Life, Foster Care, Adoption Reform, Social Welfare, Biography

Age Range
School-agers 9-12

Author: E. P. Jones

ISBN# 941423530 Date Published 1991 Price $ 9.95
Publisher Four Walls Eight Windows Pages

WHERE THE EAGLES FLY

Life as a foster child.

When 12-year-old Greg and his sister Jenny arrive at their new foster home, Greg is cautious until he makes a friend.

Keywords
Foster Child, Family Life, Fiction, Attachment

Age Range
School-agers 9-12

Author: Ruth Nulton Moore

ISBN# 836136640 Date Published 1994 Price $ 5.99
Publisher Herald Press Pages

WHO FRAMED LORENZO GARCIA?

Lorenzo is being framed and Ramón needs to get him freed.

Ramón is a tough, smart, gay 15-year-old who is ready to start a new life with Lorenzo Garcia, a gay police officer who wants to adopt him. But Lorenzo is too close to the truth about a drug ring, and is framed to get him out of the way. With brains and courage, Ramón and the Pride Pack risk their lives to find the real criminals and free Lorenzo.

Keywords
Boy Focus, Latino/a, Fathers, Fiction, Gay and/or Lesbian

Age Range
School-agers 9-12

Author: R.J. Hamilton

ISBN# 1555836089 Date Published 1995 Price $ 5.95
Publisher Alyson Wonderland Pages 144

Rating

WINDOW, THE

Rayona has a birth family she never knew existed.

In this prequel to the author's *Yellow Raft in Blue Water*, eleven-year-old Rayona is sent to live for awhile with her grandmother and the family she never knew existed. This is a children's book that is absolutely not just for children. Written by Michael Dorris, whose book *The Broken Cord* offers insights no adoptive parent can do without, this book speaks to the deeper feelings of separation from and reconnection to family.

Keywords

Native American, Family Life, Extended Family, Adoption, Core Issues (Feelings), Grief and Loss

Age Range:

School-agers 9-12

Author: Michael Dorris

Michael Dorris is an adoptive father and the author of The Broken Cord, Morning Girl, The Window and numerous others.

ISBN# 786803010 *Date Published:* 1997 *Price:* $ 4.99

Publisher: Hyperion *Pages:* 112

Rating

WRITING TO RICHIE

A poignant story of loss and connection.

David and Richie are brothers in foster care. Then one day Richie has a severe allergy attack and David's world will never be the same again. In a poignant story of loss and connection, this book really captures some of the feelings children in foster care experience as well as some of the strategies like being "good enough" or "too tough to hurt" and "never taking the risk to care." The book ends on a hopeful note but it is not sugarcoated or fake.

Keywords

Fiction, Foster Child, Foster Care, Family Life, Sibling Issues, Core Issues (Feelings)

Age Range:

School-agers 9-12

Author: Patricia Calvert

ISBN# 0-684-19764-2 *Date Published:* *Price:* $ 13.95

Publisher: Scribners *Pages:*

YEAR OF THE SAWDUST MAN, THE

Can a child's love make her mother stay?

This is the story of Nissa, who is coping with her mother's departure from the family. Though it does not expressly address adoption, this book deals with the core issues that come up for those who lose a parent, no matter the circumstances. Sure to touch the deep places in a young reader's heart, providing new understandings.

Keywords

Birth Parent, Core Issues (Feelings), Family Life, Divorce, Fiction, Mothers

Age Range:

School-agers 9-12

Author: A. LaFaye

ISBN# 689831064 *Date Published:* 1998 *Price:* $ 4.99

Publisher: Simon & Schuster *Pages:* 224

ZOE AND COLUMBO

Being wanted is what makes you special.

Zoe and Columbo are brother and sister, each aged nine. Zoe was born into the family; Columbo adopted. Columbo wants to keep his adoption a secret and is feeling "less-than." His rediscovery that belonging comes from being wanted makes an absorbing story.

Keywords

Adoption, Fiction, Sibling Issues, Adopted Child, Core Issues (Feelings), Family Life

Age Range:

School-agers 9-12

Author: Susan Shreve

ISBN# 0-688-13552-8-R *Date Published:* 1995 *Price:* $ 15.00

Publisher: Morrow *Pages:* 96

Rating

ADDY, AN AMERICAN GIRL

Come with Addy and her family in their escape from slavery.

An engaging set of six chapter books that chronicle the story of Addy, a nine-year-old slave girl, and her family as they escape slavery via the underground railroad and make a new life in Philadelphia in 1864. In this realistic and triumphant story, the family faces separation, poverty and continued bigotry. This series, balancing fiction and fact, includes concise historical notes to each volume. These are wonderful books to read together as a family. Other books in the series are: *Meet Addy; Addy Learns a Lesson; Addy's Surprise; Happy Birthday, Addy!; Addy Saves the Day;* and *Changes for Addy.*

Keywords

African American, Cultural History, Girl Power, Black Identity, Fiction, US History

Age Range.

School-agers 9-12

Author: Connie Porter

ISBN# 1-56247-0779 Date Published. 1993 Price. $ 5.95

Publisher. Pleasant Company Pages. 69

Rating

AFRICAN BEGINNINGS

Surveying African cultures (including Egyptian) in chronological order, covering 11 in total.

The American Library Association writes that this book offers "separate sections on music and dance; the spread of Islam, slavery, trade with Europeans, and art and religion are included, along with a bibliography. Oil-and-wash paintings, which reflect Cooper's exceptional ability to capture people's faces, portray the varied cultures with dignity and spirit. Both the authors and the artist have done their research, but as Haskins notes, the book is 'only a glimpse.' It is a place to begin." Kirkus Reviews adds, "This sumptuously packaged first volume in a projected series makes a strong first impression, but Cooper's golden-hazed paintings, which are strongly atmospheric, are less rewarding on cultural and historical details."

Keywords

African American, Black Identity, Cultural History

Age Range.

School-agers 9-12

Author: James S. Haskins

Author: Kathleen Benson

Illustrator: Floyd Cooper

ISBN# 688102565 Date Published. 1998 Price. $ 18.00

Publisher. Lothrop Pages. 48

AMAZING GRACE

A must, the story of Grace, an amazing girl who believes in herself.

When told she cannot be Peter Pan in the school play because she's a girl and because she's Black, Grace challenges the racist, sexist attitudes at her school (with the help of her family) and prevails. Grace's mother and grandmother teach her to fight bias by preparing, not by trying to protect her — a lesson useful for all parents. An inspiring favorite that should be in every child's library! A Pact bestseller.

Keywords

Black Identity, Self-Esteem, Role Models, Girl Power, Core Issues (Feelings), Skill Mastery

Age Range.

School-agers 9-12

Author: Mary Hoffman

Mary Hoffman is the author of *Amazing Grace* and *An Angel Just Like Me.*

ISBN# 0-8037-1040-2 Date Published. 1994 Price. $ 15.99

Publisher. Dial Pages. 32

AND NOT AFRAID TO DARE

Biographical sketches of ten Africa American Women

This book helps to fill in the missing history of African American women, offering ten who overcame racism and sexism in their determination to achieve. The collection ranges from escaped slave Ellen Craft to Olympic Gold Medalist Jackie Joyner-Kersee and includes Charlotte Forten Grimke, Mary Fields, Ida B. Wells, Mary McLeod Bethune, Clara Hale, Leontyne Price, Toni Morrison, and Mae C. Jemison. Bolden's "compelling stories read like fiction, with dynamic protagonists who are portrayed as ordinary women doing extraordinary things.... They repeatedly convey the message that with hard work and dedication, every door can be opened," says the American Library Association.

Keywords

Biography, African American, Rituals and Traditions, Role Models

Age Range.

School-agers 9-12

Author: Tonya Bolden

ISBN# 590480804 Date Published. 1998 Price. $ 16.95

Publisher. Scholastic Pages. 210

Rating

BROWN ANGELS

A celebration of childhood, offering endearing photographs of beautiful brown – angelic– children.

Turn-of-the-century photographs of African American children star in a book about "a time of innocence, a time of giving, and an unfettered love of life." Combines eleven original poems with a selection of turn-of-the century photographs collected by the author. Winner of the Pact Press Parents' Choice award for 1995. Paperback and hardcover both available.

Keywords

African American, Racial/Ethnic Identity, Cultural History, Black Identity, Poetry

Age Range:

School-agers 9-12

Author: Walter Dean Myers

Walter Dean Myers is the author of *One More River To Cross; Brown Angels; Me, Mop,* and the *Moondance Kid s, Slam, Malcolm X, Hoops*, and many more.

ISBN# 0-06-022917-9 *Date Published:* 1993 *Price:* $ 5.95

Publisher: HarperCollins *Pages:* 36

Rating

BROWN HONEY IN BROOMWHEAT TEA

A collection of poems exploring African American identity, celebrating family, individuality, and heritage.

This moving collection of poems addresses the importance of remembering history, cherishing the present, and maintaining hope for the future. Kirkus Reviews calls it "A must.... Framed by two maxims ('Broomwheat tea: good for what ails you...when poured by loving hands,' and 'A cup of loving kindness/helps keep a family going'), a cycle of a dozen lyrical poems. Laden, but never overburdened, with meaning, the poetry is significant and lovely. Cooper's full-bleed paintings, with vibrant, unsentimentalized characters, are warm, contemplative — a beautiful complement to Thomas' eloquence." 1994 Coretta Scott King Author and Illustrator Honor Book.

Keywords

Family Life, African American, Racial/Ethnic Identity, Poetry, Black Identity

Age Range:

School-agers 9-12

Author: Joyce Carol Thomas

Joyce Carol Thomas is the author of *Brown Honey in Broomwheat Tea* and *I Have Heard of a Land.*

ISBN# 64434397 *Date Published:* 1996 *Price:* $ 4.95

Publisher: Trophy Press *Pages:* 28

BUILDING A NEW WORLD

One of the twelve volumes of the series entitled The Kingdoms of Africa.

Illuminated by maps, artifacts, and period paintings, this book accomplishes a challenging task: cover 400 years of the deeply troublesome history of Black America while maintaining an even, non-polemical and engaging tone. Its tone and style skillfully engage those readers who may not ordinarily consider themselves historians; this history is one of real people and conditions: "The workday on a typical sugar plantation...was highly regimented. Well before the sun came up, slaves were roused by the blowing of a horn or a conch shell." A great introduction to the Black experience in the New World for middle-school-aged (and older) readers. Includes an index, a careful bibliography and a short glossary.

Keywords

African American, Cultural History, US History, Race Relations, Black Identity, Educational Issues

Age Range:

School-agers 9-12

Author: Philip Koslow

Philip Koslow wrote the preceding 11 volumes of *The Kingdoms of Africa*, and he is the author of *Centuries of Greatness: The West African Kingdoms, 750-900.*

ISBN# 0-7910-3144-6 *Date Published:* 1997 *Price:* $ 8.95

Publisher: Chelsea House Publishers *Pages:* 64

BY ANY MEANS NECESSARY: MALCOLM X

A biography of a leader who saw Whites as the enemy.

From Kirkus Reviews: "The author sees most of Malcolm X's life as a search for self-respect.... A sense of outrage permeates Myers's book — at social inequities; at our biased system of justice; at the FBI's close surveillance of black organizations; at the way so many black leaders came to violent ends.... Readers can look to Myers for a sense of the rage and frustration that fueled Malcolm X's brief career." A Coretta Scott King Honor Book. An ALA Notable Children's Book.

Keywords

African American, Biography, Race Relations, Racial/Ethnic Identity, Racism, Role Models

Age Range:

School-agers 9-12

Author: Walter Dean Myers

Walter Dean Myers is the author of *One More River To Cross; Brown Angels; Me, Mop, and the Moondance Kid s, Slam, Malcolm X , Hoops*, and many more.

ISBN# 590987593 *Date Published:* 1999 *Price:* $ 5.99

Publisher: Polaris *Pages:* 224

Rating

COMING HOME

From the life of Langston Hughes

Compelling text and illustrations create an inspiring portrait of James Langston Hughes' childhood. Hughes lived with his grandmother when his father moved to Mexico (as a Black man, he had not been allowed to become a lawyer in Oklahoma) and his mother moved to New York to become an actress. Grandma was very poor and didn't like Langston playing with other kids, so his dream was to live with his parents. But this dream was never realized, instilling in him a lifelong search for home. The book expresses both Hughes' sadness and his solution: to find home within himself. An ALA notable book.

Keywords
African American, Role Models, Family Life, Grief and Loss, Core Issues (Feelings), Poetry

Age Range.
School-agers 9-12

Author: Floyd Cooper

Floyd Cooper is the author of *Coming Home; Cool Melons Turn To Frogs* and more.

ISBN# 698116127 *Date Published.* 1994 *Price.* $ 5.99
Publisher. Paper Star *Pages.* 32

Rating

CORNROWS

Every hair design has a name and rich meaning in Black tradition.

As Great Grandmaw braids the children's hair, she tells them stories they love to hear about the symbolism of braided hair. Beautiful black and white drawings. An essential book for every girl of African American heritage. Unfortunately, perhaps because of the style of illustrations, this book appears old-fashioned and is not as visually appealing as other books about hair, but it is the only one specifically for a school-age reader. Coretta Scott King Award winner.

Keywords
African American, Hair, Black Identity, Self-Esteem, Cultural History

Age Range.
School-agers 9-12

Author: Camille Yarbrough

Camille Yarbrough is the author of *Cornrows* and *The Shimmershine Queens.*

ISBN# 6928207092 *Date Published.* *Price.* $ 5.95
Publisher. Putnam-Paperstar *Pages.*

DEAR MRS. PARKS

Through her heartfelt correspondence, Rosa Parks challenges children to embrace life's possibilities.

"Mother Parks has assembled a treasure. In this wonderful collection of her responses to letters from young people, she teaches, she inspires, she challenges, and above all, she loves," says General Colin Powell. "The letters illustrate young people's genuine concern about personal and societal conditions.... (Readers) will walk away from this book with respect for a woman whose life works and courage are an example to us all," says the School Library Journal.

Keywords
Biography, Racial/Ethnic Identity, Race Relations, Role Models, Civil Rights, US History

Age Range.
School-agers 9-12

Author: Rosa Parks

Author: Gregory J. Reed

Rosa Parks, whose simple act changed the course of American history, lives in Detroit and travels in the U.S. on behalf of civil rights.

ISBN# 188000061X *Date Published.* 1997 *Price.* $ 8.95
Publisher. Lee & Low Books *Pages.* 120

DREW AND THE HOMEBOY QUESTION

Deerwood is a rich White kids' school – Drew will be the only Black student.

When Drew Taylor wins a scholarship to Deerwood Hall, his three best friends give him a hard time. Not only is Deerwood Hall a rich kids' school, it's a rich White kids' school — and Drew will be the only Black student there. It's a challenge Drew knows he's got to face, but why aren't his homeboys helping? This book will hold particular interest for children growing up in transracial adoptive families, sure to raise questions and create a great opportunity for a discussion of race relations, the role of the child, and the role of the adoptive family. Illustrated with cartoons.

Keywords
African American, Family Life, Core Issues (Feelings), Black Identity

Age Range.
School-agers 9-12

Author: Robb Armstrong

ISBN# 0-06-442047-7 *Date Published.* *Price.* $ 3.95
Publisher. Harper Trophy *Pages.* 96

Rating

ERNESTINE AND AMANDA

A series book intended for school-aged girls

In the first book that chronicles the lives of two girls growing up in the segregated South of the 1950s, Ernestine and Amanda agree on one thing — they aren't going to be friends. But as the year goes by, the girls are amazed to discover how much they are beginning to need each other. Part of a series of chapter books including *Ernestine & Amanda: Mysteries on Monroe Street* and *Ernestine & Amanda: Summer Camp Ready Or Not!*

Keywords

Civil Rights, African American, Cultural History, Friendship, Black Identity, Self-Esteem

Age Range:

School-agers 9-12

Author: Sandra Belton

ISBN# 068980847X Date Published: 1998 Price: $ 3.99

Publisher: Aladdin Pages: 128

Rating

FROM SLAVE SHIP TO FREEDOM ROAD

The inner lives of Black slaves in America.

Beginning with the ships sailing from Africa and continuing through the Civil War, Lester and Brown reveal the inner life of the slaves, as expressed in their secret worship meetings, their heroic escapes, their invocation of memories of ancestors whose names they didn't know, and their joy about freedom.

Keywords

Black Identity, Africa, US History, Race Relations, Racism, Spiritual Meanings

Age Range:

School-agers 9-12

Author: Julius Lester

Rod Brown

Julius Lester is the author of *To Be A Slave; Sam and the Tigers; From Slave Ship To Freedom Road; What A Truly Cool World; Black Cowboy; Wild Horses*, and more.

ISBN# 803718934 Date Published: 1998 Price: $ 17.99

Publisher: Dial Pages:

GIRL NAMED DISASTER, A

The story of eleven-year-old Nhamo, a wonderfully resourceful Shona orphan fleeing an arranged marriage.

From Horn Book: "An extraordinarily rich novel set in contemporary Mozambique and Zimbabwe and featuring a most remarkable heroine begins with her life in a traditional, remote village; follows her journey to escape an arranged marriage; and concludes with her experiences in civilized Zimbabwe." Publisher's Weekly writes, "Fromer returns to Africa for the setting of this gripping adventure, equally a survival story and a spiritual voyage.... Nhamo herself is a stunning creation — while she serves as a fictional ambassador from a foreign culture, she is supremely human. An unforgettable work."

Keywords

Africa, Spiritual Meanings, Girl Power, Orphan, Fiction

Age Range:

School-agers 9-12

Author: Nancy Fromer

ISBN# 140386351 Date Published: 1998 Price: $ 4.99

Publisher: Puffin Pages: 320

HARRIET AND THE PROMISED LAND

Harriet Tubman's courageous story, told through spectacular artwork and rhythmic verse.

Harriet Tubman's struggles as she courageously leads slaves to freedom on the Underground Railroad. Dynamic and powerful illustrations. A New York Times Best Illustrated Children's Book. 1993 Parent's Choice award.

Keywords

Black Identity, Self-Esteem, African American, Biography, Role Models, Girl Power

Age Range:

School-agers 9-12

Author: Jacob Lawrence

ISBN# 0-689-80965-4 Date Published: 1997 Price: $ 5.99

Publisher: Aladdin Paperbacks Pages: 40

Rating

HARRIET TUBMAN

Harriet Tubman is a historical leader all children should learn about.

An introduction to the inspirational life and deeds of Harriet Tubman, "the Moses of her people." This book revolves around an entertaining first visit between Harriet Tubman, eight-year-old Kumi and his sister Chanti, who is six. Despite the simple text that reveals the skills, courage, and humility of a great American heroine, this book is flawed by a presentation of characters who seem more like cartoons than real people. We find that young readers have difficulty remaining fully engaged.

Keywords

Black Identity, Self-Esteem, African American, Biography, Role Models, Girl Power

Age Range:

School-agers 9-12

Author: Empac Staff

ISBN# 922162921 *Date Published:* *Price:* $ 3.49

Publisher: Empac *Pages:*

Rating

HER STORIES

African American tales focused on the magical lore and wondrous imaginings of African American women.

Twenty-five compelling folk tales, tall tales and true tales from the female African American storytelling tradition. Each story focuses on the role of women — both historical and fantastic — and their particular strengths, joys and sorrows. These stories offer positive images that hold special appeal for African American children, while all children will be able to appreciate the affirming values of this cultural tradition. Coretta Scott King Award winner. A Pact bestseller.

Keywords

Racial/Ethnic Identity, Self-Esteem, Folk tales and Legends, African American, Girl Power, Black Identity

Age Range:

School-agers 9-12

Author: Virginia Hamilton

ISBN# 0-590-47370-R *Date Published:* 1995 *Price:* $ 19.95

Publisher: Blue Sky/Scholastic *Pages:* 110

I AM ROSA PARKS

Rosa Parks always wanted fair treatment for everyone, even when she was young.

When Rosa Parks refused to give up her seat on a bus to a white man one December day in 1955, she made history. Mrs. Parks' brave act sparked the bus boycott in Montgomery, Alabama, propelling Martin Luther King to national attention. This book sets these events in the context of Mrs. Parks' life, from childhood to the present.

Keywords

African American, Self-Esteem, Black Identity, Biography, Role Models, US History

Age Range:

School-agers 9-12

Author: Rosa Parks

Author: James S. Haskins

Rosa Parks, whose simple act changed the course of American history, lives in Detroit and travels in the U.S. on behalf of civil rights.

ISBN# 0-8037-1206-5 *Date Published:* 1997 *Price:* $ 12.99

Publisher: Dial *Pages:* 48

I HAVE HEARD OF A LAND

A Black female pioneer describes setting up home in early Oklahoma.

A National Book Award-winning author draws on family history for this lyrical account of America's little-known past. In the late 1880s, thousands of pioneers, many former slaves, raced to the Oklahoma Territory to stake their claim. "I Have Heard of a Land," a hymn to liberty and unity, commemorates the strength of the African American pioneers.

Keywords

African American, Cultural History, History, US History

Age Range:

Adult

Author: Joyce Carol Thomas

Author: Floyd Cooper

Joyce Carol Thomas is the author of *Brown Honey in Broomwheat Tea* and *I Have Heard of a Land.*

ISBN# 60234776 *Date Published:* 1998 *Price:* $ 14.95

Publisher: HarperCollins *Pages:* 32

Rating

I SEE THE RHYTHM

A history of African American music, winner of the Newbery Award.

From Booklist: "A useful timeline describes music from African origins and slave songs through ragtime; the blues; big band, bebop, and cool jazz; gospel; rhythm and blues; and the contemporary sounds of rock, hip-hop, and rap. Igus uses lyrics to communicate how the styles played to emotions of musicians and their fans ('I see the cool tones of modern jazz/escape the city heat'). Wood's paintings are equally suggestive. Mixing modernist and primitive styles, her art not only complements the text but vivifies it. Audience may be a problem: the text is too sophisticated for younger readers and the format may alienate some older readers."

Keywords

Music and Dance, African American, Cultural History

Age Range:

School-agers 9-12

Author: Toyomi Igus

Illustrator: Michele Wood

ISBN# 892391510 *Date Published:* 1998 *Price:* $ 15.95

Publisher: Children's Book *Pages:* 32

Rating

I WAS BORN A SLAVE

The story of Harriet Jacobs.

This is the story of Harriet Jacobs, who was born a slave and escaped to the North and freedom. Based on her autobiography and illustrated with bold block prints, the story captures the feelings of a child who didn't realize she was a slave until she was six, who spent seven years hiding, and who developed a remarkable life as a free woman. Her story is one that will help children of African American heritage feel deep pride in the accomplishments of their people, while children of other racial groups will gain a much better understanding of the terrible history of slavery in the United States and of the difficulty for all people in our country to overcome this legacy.

Keywords

African American, Race Relations, US History, Racism, Biography, Role Models

Age Range:

School-agers 9-12

Author: Jennifer Fleischner

ISBN# 7613011119 *Date Published:* 1998 *Price:* $ 24.90

Publisher: Millbrook Press *Pages:* 96

JOSHUA'S MASAI MASK

Joshua uses the magical Masai mask to discover the grass is not always greener.

Joshua loves playing his kalimba, a traditional African musical instrument. But when his family suggests he bring it to the school talent show, he thinks it's a terrible idea — all his classmates like rap. Then his Uncle Zambezi gives Joshua a magical mask to boost his confidence. Through the power of the mask, Joshua is able to realize it's always better to be true to oneself. The New York Times says, "Its message is splendidly universal. Gently, without didacticism, it urges us to make the best of our talents in ways that should engage any American child."

Keywords

African American, Cultural History, Fiction, Race Relations, Black Identity, Self-Esteem

Age Range:

School-agers 9-12

Author: Dakari Hru

ISBN# 1880000326 *Date Published:* 1996 *Price:* $ 5.95

Publisher: Lee & Low Books *Pages:* 32

JOURNEY TO FREEDOM

Every child needs to learn about the history of slavery in the United States.

Booklist: "Told in the first person by eight-year-old Joshua, this picture book for older readers follows the family from safe house to safe house until they finally cross the river to their destination." Kirkus Reviews writes, "Well-meaning but flat. Wright assumes readers will know more of the historical background than is likely. Drawings make the people seem stiff. And why is the narrative voice — ostensibly that of an eight-year-old former slave — in lyrical, perfect [standard] English while Tubman speaks in dialect? A worthy but muddled attempt."

Keywords

African American, Cultural History, Racial/Ethnic Identity, Self-Esteem, Black Identity, US History

Age Range:

School-agers 9-12

Author: Courtni C. Wright

Illustrator: Gershom Griffith

ISBN# 823413330 *Date Published:* 1997 *Price:* $ 6.95

Publisher: Holiday House *Pages:*

Rating

JUBA THIS AND JUBA THAT

Wanna play? This treasure trove draws on traditional resources, all updated for today.

Let *Juba This and Juba That* transport you to the music and the beauty of Africa. Here are authentic outdoor sporting games, crafts projects, and unfamiliar songs and dances guaranteed to delight for hours on end. Celebrating the wealth and diversity of the African American heritage, these activities and games are organized by type, offering each game's history along with easy-to-follow instructions and lists of any necessary equipment.

Keywords

Folk tales and Legends, Games and Activities, African American, Role Models, Black Identity, Cultural History

Age Range,

School-agers 9-12

Author: Darlene Hopson, Ph.D.

Author: Derek S. Hopson, Ph.D.

Darlene and Derek S. Hopson are the authors of *Raising the Rainbow Generation, Juba This and Juba That*, and *Different and Wonderful.*

ISBN# 684807815 Date Published, 1996 Price, $ 10.00
Publisher, S&S Children's Pages, 160

Rating

KIDS' BOOK OF WISDOM, THE

Quotes from African American tradition.

Easy-to-read proverbs include information about the origins of the wise words in this handsome anthology directed at school aged children. Children of African American heritage will take pride in these uplifting words which comes from their culture. Children from other backgrounds will gain new understanding of some of the values inherent to African American life. To expand their world, we must introduce all our children to the rich contributions of the many peoples of the earth, contributions that connect us to the past, to each other, and to the future.

Keywords

African American, Self-Esteem, Racial/Ethnic Identity, Black Identity, Proverbs, Cultural History

Age Range,

School-agers 9-12

Author: Cheryl Willis Hudson

Author: Bernette G. Ford

Cheryl Willis Hudson is the author of *Bright Eyes, Brown Skin , The Many Colors oj Mother Goose* and *The Kids' Book of Wisdom*

ISBN# 940975610 Date Published, 1997 Price, $ 5.95
Publisher, Just Us Books Pages, 64

KIDS EXPLORE AMERICA'S AFRICAN AMERICAN HERITAGE

Adults as well as kids will enjoy this fun and informative book.

Written by kids for kids. Includes history, biographies, celebrations, food, art, dance, music, and folk stories that have been passed down through the years. A wonderful introduction to African American culture.

Keywords

African American, Cultural History, Racial/Ethnic Identity, Black Identity

Age Range,

School-agers 9-12

Author: Westridge Kids

ISBN# 1-56261-090-2 Date Published, 1996 Price, $ 9.95
Publisher, John Muir Pub. Pages, 149

LEON'S STORY

Leon Tillage was a sharecropper's son in North Carolina and a civil-rights protester.

Leon's father was murdered by White teenagers out to "have some fun," and Leon himself faced brutality while following Martin Luther King's ideas of nonviolent protest. In spite of his horrific experiences, his attitude toward life remained optimistic. Kids will remember this simple book as a testament to human resiliency. The emotional impact of Leon's look at humanity's inhumanity is moving, powerful, and healing.

Keywords

African American, Race Relations, Racism, History, US History, Civil Rights

Age Range,

School-agers 9-12

Author: Susan Roth

Author: Leon Walter Tillage

ISBN# 374343799 Date Published, 1997 Price, $ 14.00
Publisher, Farrar-Strauss Pages, 112

MANY THOUSAND GONE

Rating

35 stories about famous former slaves including Nat Turner, Harriet Tubman, Frederick Douglass, etc.

Kirkus Reviews: "Taking as her theme the 'joyous anthem of freedom,' beginning with 'No more auction block for me,' Hamilton samples documented African American lives from 1619 through the Civil War. Hamilton presents what is known with a cool austerity that makes her subtext even more forceful: though the injustices are representative, these lives are exceptional in having left traces, however meager. The anecdotal fragments are masterfully chosen to illustrate the cruel commonplace, as well as to rehearse pivotal events and examine extremes. As always, Hamilton's prose is concise, lucid, and fresh. A compelling book, outstanding in every way."

Keywords

African American, Self-Esteem, Cultural History, Race Relations, US History, Role Models

Age Range:

School-agers 9-12

Author: Virginia Hamilton

Illustrator: Leo Dillon

Illustrator: Diane Dillon

ISBN# 679879366 Date Published: 1993 Price: $ 12.00

Publisher: Knopf Pages:

MY BLACK ME

Rating

Understandable and penetrating poems on being Black.

This classic anthology of African American poetry for young readers offers brief, to-the-point poems by such greats as Langston Hughes, Lucille Clifton, Nikki Giovanni, and others. Adoff's collection offers a brilliant mix of work capturing a range from high-pitched and piercing to transparent and moving. A warm bath in racial pride for young people which will hold the interest of readers of all ages.

Keywords

African American, Race Relations, Racial/Ethnic Identity, Racism, Poetry

Age Range:

School-agers 9-12

Poet: Arnold Adoff

Arnold Adoff, the winner of the 1988 NCTE Award for Excellence in Poetry for Children, is the author of over 30 books.

ISBN# 140374434 Date Published: 1995 Price: $ 4.99

Publisher: Puffin Pages:

NATHANIEL TALKING

Spunky rhyming poems, smart and full of a Black child's insights.

Nathaniel's rap about life as he knows it: Being nine, life knowledge, missing his mama who has died, making friends, misbehaving, family. Coretta Scott King award winner.

Keywords

African American, Self-Esteem, Black Identity, Family Life, Friendship, Core Issues (Feelings)

Age Range:

School-agers 9-12

Author: Eloise Greenfield

Eloise Greenfield is the author of *Nathaniel Talking; Big Friend, Little Friend* and many more.

ISBN# 0-86316-201-0 Date Published: 1990 Price: $ 6.95

Publisher: Writers & Readers Pages:

NEW YORK PUBLIC LIBRARY AMAZING AFRICAN AMERICAN HISTORY

A book of answers for kids.

Who were the Buffalo soldiers? What was the Harlem Renaissance? Who were the Little Rock Nine? The New York Public Library, one of the most respected names in reference libraries, recounts history from Africa through slavery, the Civil War to the Civil Rights movement, and up through the present.

Keywords

US History, African American, Black Identity

Age Range:

School-agers 9-12

Author: Diane Patrick Wexler

ISBN# 471192171 Date Published: 1998 Price: $ 12.95

Publisher: Wiley Pages: 192

Rating

NOW LET ME FLY

Minna was sold as a slave. She must help her children be free.

Books in Print says, "In an author's note, Johnson writes that this 'is not a pleasant story, nor does it have a happy ending. Yet it is a story that must be told'.... In her powerful, heartbreaking first-person narrative, Minna tells how her husband is suddenly sold to another master 'before I could even say good-bye. I was never to hear another word from him again.' The next year, her oldest son is also sold, after which Minna allows two other children to 'steal away' to freedom. As the tale closes, Minna and her youngest daughter still live in 'this prison of slavery' that ended 20 years later."

Keywords

Cultural History, Fiction, US History, Race Relations, African American, Family Life

Age Range.

School-agers 9-12

Illustrated by the Author: Dolores Johnson

Dolores Johnson is the author and illustrator of *The Children's Book of Kwanzaa*, *Your Dad Was Just Like You*, *Now Let Me Fly*, *Seminole Diary* and more.

ISBN# 0-689-80966-2 Date Published. 1997 Price. $ 5.99

Publisher. S&S Children's Pages. 32

Rating

ONE MORE RIVER TO CROSS

The story of twelve Black Americans.

The highly respected, award-winning author of *Black Dance in America* tells the triumphant stories of twelve African-Americans who have made important contributions to American life and culture, including Crispus Attucks, Malcolm X, Madame C.J. Walker (the first Black woman millionaire) and Eddie Robinson (the winningest football coach ever). A Notable Children's Trade Book in the Field of Social Studies.

Keywords

African American, Cultural History, Self-Esteem, Racial/Ethnic Identity, Black Identity, Biography

Age Range.

School-agers 9-12

Author: James S. Haskins

ISBN# 590428977 Date Published. 1993 Price. $ 4.50

Publisher. Scholastic Pages.

PEOPLE COULD FLY, THE

You will enjoy these delightful tales as much as the kids do.

Four groups of stories: Animal Tales; Tales of the Real, Extravagant and Fanciful; Tales of the Supernatural; and Slave Tales of Freedom. Excellent. Coretta Scott King Award winner.

Keywords

African American, Racial/Ethnic Identity, Folk tales and Legends, Self-Esteem, Race Relations, Black Identity

Age Range.

School-agers 9-12

Author: Virginia Hamilton

ISBN# 679843361 Date Published. Price. $ 12.00

Publisher. Knopf Pages.

PHILLIP HALL LIKES ME, I RECKON, MAYBE

A book about warm family relationships, first love and community life in rural Arkansas.

Philip Hall is the cutest, smartest boy in the class, and Beth Lambert loves him. The fact that he's academically superior doesn't particularly bother Beth at first. Then she realizes she's letting him beat her at schoolwork. But coming out on top is just too natural to Beth, and she doesn't hold herself back for very long, especially when it comes to catching turkey thieves, or winning calf-raising contest, or making mountaintop rescues, or capturing the affections of a young boy. Characters just happens to be African American. A Newbery Honor book and A New York Times Outstanding Book of the Year.

Keywords

African American, Friendship, Family Life, Core Issues (Feelings), Black Identity, Fiction

Age Range.

School-agers 9-12

Author: Bette Greene

ISBN# 440457556 Date Published. 1975 Price. $ 4.99

Publisher. Yearling Books Pages.

Rating

PLACE CALLED FREEDOM, A

An introduction to slavery and the courage of those who fought against it.

When young James Starman and his slave family are set free, they travel north to Indiana where they build a house, a farm, and a new life for themselves. In the years before the Civil War, Papa keeps making dangerous trips south to bring back relatives. So many people arrive that soon they form a village. Inspired by the true story of the founding of Lyles Station, Indiana, *A Place Called Freedom* celebrates the courage, compassion and wisdom that create strong communities. It is very important that the history of slavery in the United States be understood by all of our children. This full-color book provides a good starting opportunity.

Keywords

African American, Biography, US History, Family Life, Black Identity, Role Models

Age Range:

School-agers 9-12

Author: Scott Russell Sanders

Illustrator: Thomas B. Allen

ISBN# 0689804709˚ *Date Published:* 1997 *Price:* $ 16.00

Publisher: S&S Children's *Pages:*

Rating

RUNNING GIRL

For girls who can't go slow.

A girl's love of running is linked to the great tradition of African American women athletes who competed before her. Ebonee Rose is portrayed as a well-rounded character progressing toward self realization and carrying on a legacy of honor and achievement. This story projects a clear and positive perspective for young people in general and a role model that African American children will identity with.

Keywords

African American, Role Models, Sports, Self-Esteem, Black Identity

Age Range:

School-agers 9-12

Editor: Sharon Mathis

Sharon Mathis is the author of *Running Girl; I Wish for You*; and *The Hundred Penny Box*

ISBN# 152996745 *Date Published:* 1997 *Price:* $ 17.00

Publisher: Harcourt Brace *Pages:*

SALUTE TO BLACK SCIENTISTS AND INVENTORS

Promoting cultural heritage, pride, and self-esteem.

Features inspiring, in-depth biographies and illustrated portraits of historically significant African Americans.

Keywords

African American, Role Models, Black Identity, Self-Esteem, Biography, Cultural History

Age Range:

School-agers 9-12

Author: Empac Staff

ISBN# 092216276X *Date Published:* 1996 *Price:* $ 3.49

Publisher: Empac *Pages:* 60

SALUTE TO HISTORIC BLACK FIRSTS, A

Promoting cultural heritage, pride, and self-esteem.

Featuring brief biographies and illustrated portraits of historically significant African Americans, this booklet highlights the achievements and contributions of the heroes and heroines of our times. *A Salute To Historic Black Firsts* provides a positive introduction to a host of important people every young person should know about. Children who are of Black heritage will identify with these leaders and feel pride in their achievements. Children of other racial and ethnic groups will gain a new understanding of the tremendous achievements of the people represented.

Keywords

Racial/Ethnic Identity, Self-Esteem, African American, Biography, Role Models, Black Identity

Age Range:

School-agers 9-12

Author: Empac Staff

ISBN# 922162824 *Date Published:* 1996 *Price:* $ 2.29

Publisher: Empac *Pages:*

Rating

SAM AND THE TIGERS

Marvelous version of the Little Black Sambo story, free of racial stereotypes.

A boy's triumph over powerful and greedy tigers, retold by Julius Lester. Wordy and wonderful retelling of Helen Bannerman's classic, *Little Black Sambo,* told in a Black southern storytelling voice — a voice readers may recognize from Lester's retellings of *The Tales of Uncle Remus*, among others. He turns Sam's deals with hungry tigers into an exuberant battle of wits and transforms his pancake dinner into a glorious feast for the whole community. African American children in particular will enjoy their connection to this storytelling history, and all children will enjoy this refreshing retelling of a much-maligned tale.

Keywords

Racial/Ethnic Identity, Self-Esteem, Folk tales and Legends, African American, Black Identity

Age Range.

School-agers 9-12

Author: Julius Lester

Julius Lester is the author of To Be A Slave; Sam and the Tigers; From Slave Ship To Freedom Road; What A Truly Cool World; Black Cowboy; Wild Horses, and more.

ISBN# 803720289 *Date Published.* 1996 *Price.* $ 15.99

Publisher. Dial *Pages.* 40

Rating

SHIMMERSHINE QUEENS, THE

"When we in trouble, our get-up gift come to our rescue."

Angie and Michelle are best friends, facing the very real problems of growing up in a tough inner city neighborhood where it's sometimes not considered cool to be smart or to have kinky hair and dark skin — that is, until 90-year-old Cousin Beatta comes to visit and teaches Angie and Michelle about the shimmershine feeling, that good feeling and pride that people have for their racial heritage and physical features.

Keywords

Racial/Ethnic Identity, Self-Esteem, Fiction, Girl Power

Age Range.

School-agers 9-12

Author: Camille Yarbrough

Camille Yarbrough is the author of *Cornrows* and *The Shimmershine Queens.*

ISBN# 0-698-11369-1 *Date Published.* 1996 *Price.* $ 4.95

Publisher. Putnam-Paperstar *Pages.* 144

SKIN I'M IN, THE

Winner of the John Steptoe Award for best new African American voice in children's literature.

"Maleeka Madison feels like a freak in her inner-city middle school. The kids pick on her because she is 'the darkest, worst-dressed thing in school' and because she gets good grades. Funny and clever, Flake is honest about how mean people are. The characters are complex.... The gum-smacking, wisecracking dialogue in the hallways, the girls' bathroom, and the classroom will pull readers into a world too rarely represented in middle-grade fiction. Every outside kid will get it," says Booklist. "This first novel bristles with attitude that is both genuine and alarming," says School Library Journal.

Keywords

African American, Core Issues (Feelings), Fiction, Friendship

Age Range.

School-agers 9-12

Author: Sharon Flake

ISBN# 786804440 *Date Published.* 1999 *Price.* $ 14.95

Publisher. Jump At The Sun *Pages.*

SOJOURNER TRUTH AND THE VOICE OF FREEDOM

From her beginnings in slavery to her tireless campaign for the rights of the freed.

The School Library Journal cautions, "Disturbing aspects include the textual disunity caused by full-page discussions of Frederick Douglass and the early women's movement, which appear almost as fillers. Also troublesome is the author's presumption that her subject believed slavery to be honorable. While this may be intended to show the attitudes of a slave girl as opposed to those of an abolitionist, it is a difference that will be lost on the intended audience."

Keywords

African American, Cultural History, Black Identity, Biography, Role Models, US History

Age Range.

School-agers 9-12

Author: Jane Shumate

ISBN# 1878841718 *Date Published.* 1992 *Price.* $ 6.95

Publisher. Millbrook Press *Pages.* 32

Rating

SWEET CLARA AND THE FREEDOM QUILT

Clara's quilt secretly helped slaves find the underground railroad and their road to freedom.

Clara, a slave on Home Plantation, knows that the Underground Railroad can lead her to freedom. The only problem is, how can she find it? While piecing together the scraps of information gathered from other slaves, she makes a powerful quilt so secret that even the master won't suspect.

Keywords

Black Identity, Self-Esteem, African American, Cultural History, Fiction, Girl Power

Age Range:

School-agers 9-12

Author: Deborah Hopkinson

ISBN# 0-679-87472-0 Date Published: Price: $ 6.99
Publisher: Knopf Pages:

Rating

THE WELL: DAVID'S STORY

Every child who has cried, "That's not fair!" should read this book.

From Booklist: "From the first line, this short, intense novel of racist violence is told with immediacy. David Logan tells a story of his boyhood in Mississippi at a time when 'uppity niggers' can be hanged for thinking themselves equal to whites. The Logans are among the few black families to own land, and they have a well of sweet water, which they share with their neighbors, black and white. Most people are grateful, but the white Simms family hates being beholden to blacks. The well of the title is a metaphor for the bigotry that lies beneath the surface and the sweet strength of family ties."

Keywords

African American, Race Relations, Racism, History

Age Range:

School-agers 9-12

Author: Mildred D. Taylor

Mildred D. Taylor is the author of *The Friendship* and *The Well: David's Story.*

ISBN# 140386424 Date Published: 1995 Price: $ 4.99
Publisher: Penguin Pages: 95

THROUGH MY EYES

Ruby will grab you by the heart and not let go.

This moving history in sepia photos and in Ruby's own words takes the reader by the hand to share Ruby Bridge's intense experience as she enters first grade in New Orleans, 1961, the first Black student in an all- white school. It doesn't try to paint a pretty picture; the hate, protesting, and burning crosses are vividly portrayed as well as Ruby's love for the white teacher who sat with her, all alone that first year, and taught her. Ruby's memories about that year and her thought's today about that time are unforgettable.

Keywords

African American, History, Race Relations, Racism

Age Range:

School-agers 9-12

Author: Ruby Bridges

ISBN# 590189239 Date Published: 1999 Price: $ 16.95
Publisher: Scholastic Pages:

UNDERGROUND RAILROAD, THE

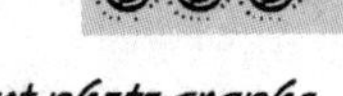

The Underground Railroad in clear text, elegant photographs and stirring historic artifacts.

Along with an accessible narrative history of the Underground Railroad, this book offers beautiful and stirring photographs of artifacts of slavery and the Underground Railroad; its photographs — of things as simple as a well-worn wooden pair of slave shoes or the signal light shining from a safe-house's upstairs window — bring this important piece of American history to life. The inclusion of photographs brings a greater sense of immediacy and realism to the text.

Keywords

African American, Cultural History, Civil Rights, Race Relations, Racism, Black Identity

Age Range:

School-agers 9-12

Photographs by the Author: Raymond Bial

ISBN# 0-395-69937-1 Date Published: 1995 Price: $ 15.95
Publisher: Houghton Mifflin Pages: 48

Rating

WATSONS GO TO BIRMINGHAM – 1963, THE

Kenny tells what happened when Grandma's church is bombed.

Enter the hilarious world of 10-year-old Kenny and his family, the Weird Watsons. When Momma and Dad decide it's time for Grandma to help Byron shape up, the Watsons set out on a trip like no other. They're going to Birmingham, Alabama, toward one of the darkest moments in America's history, and it's a funny, intimate, powerful and magical ride. In the midst of the warmth of the Watson family, readers encounter some of our searing history when the Watsons' venture South leads them into unexpected violence. 1996 Newbery Honor Book. 1996 Coretta Scott King Honor Book. An ALA Notable Book. An ALA Best Book for Young Adults. A New York Times Book Review Best Book. A Horn Book Fanfare.

Keywords

African American, Race Relations, Black Identity, Racism, Self-Esteem, Family Life

Age Range.

School-agers 9-12

Author: Christopher Ford Curtis

Christopher Paul Curtis received the Avery Hopwood and Jules Hopwood Prize for major essays and for an early draft of *The Watsons Go to Birmingham-1963.*

ISBN# 0440414121" Date Published. 1995 Price. $ 5.50

Publisher. Delacorte Pages. 224

Rating

WHITE WASH

The book's a shocker, and it means to be.

Young readers will be upset by what happens but reassured by being given words to talk about it. From Kirkus Reviews: "The Hawks, a white gang, knock Mauricio aside and spray-paint Helene-Angel's brown face white. At home, Grandma cleans her up and allows her sanctuary in her room, whispering comforting words through a closed door. After a week, Grandma insists she open the door 'and be strong.' Believing herself an embarrassment, Helene-Angel opens the door to find her whole class there, pledging support."

Keywords

Fiction, Antiracist Strategies, Race Relations, Racial/Ethnic Identity, Racism, Core Issues (Feelings)

Age Range.

School-agers 9-12

Author: Ntozake Shange

Illustrator: Michael Sporn

Ntozake Shange is the author of *For Colored Girls Who Have Considered Suicide When the Rainbow Is Enuf.*

ISBN# 802784909 Date Published. 1998 Price. $ 15.95

Publisher. Walker & Co. Pages. 32

WHY MOSQUITOES BUZZ IN PEOPLE'S EARS

Children chuckle over the tattletale quality of the conclusion.

A West African fable, with wide-eyed illustrations of animals that provide just the right sort of kaleidoscopic, jungle safari experience. Winner of the Caldecott Medal; the 1975 ALA Notable Children's Book; The NY Times Outstanding Book of the Year 1975; and School Library Journal Best Book of the Year 1975.

Keywords

African American, Folk tales and Legends, Black Identity, Africa

Age Range.

School-agers 9-12

Author: Verna Aardema

Verna Aardema is the author of *Borreguita and the Coyote, Bringing The Rain To Kapiti Plain,* and *Why Mosquitoes Buzz In People's Ears.*

ISBN# 0-14-054905-6 Date Published. 1975 Price. $ 59.00

Publisher. Puffin Pied piper Pages.

WILMA UNLIMITED

An award-winning book featuring Caldecott medalist Davia Diaz's striking paintings and Kathleen Krull's stirring text.

This easy-reader biography reveals the drama in the story of Wilma Rudolph's life. Born small and sickly into a poor family with twenty children living in the segregated south, and then stricken as a baby with both scarlet fever and polio, Wilma defied these limitations and became the world's fastest woman, capturing the world's attention by earning triple gold medals in track and field at the 1960 Olympic games. Diaz's brilliant design make this book a visual feast. Superimposed are striking paintings, whose visual interest and impulse toward graphic abstraction invite close scrutiny. Diaz designed the text's font, as well. A wonderful addition to all family libraries.

Keywords

African American, Biography, Cultural History, Role Models, Girl Power, Black Identity

Age Range.

School-agers 9-12

Author: Kathleen Krull

Illustrator: David Diaz

Kathleen Krull, known for her unconventional approach to biography, wrote *Lives of the Musicians: Good Times, Bad Times,* and *What the Neighbors Thought.*

ISBN# 0-15-201267-2 Date Published. 1996 Price. $ 16.00

Publisher. Harcourt Brace Pages. 36

WOMEN OF HOPE

Rating 

African Americans Who Made A Difference

Including a series of thirteen remarkable photographs from posters created by Bread and Roses, the radiant faces and inspiring stories of Ida B. Wells-Barnett, the Delaney sisters, Septima Poinsette Clark, Ella Josephine Baker, Fannie Lou Hamer, Ruby Dee, Maya Angelou, Toni Morrison, Marian Wright Edelman, Alice Walker, Alexa Canady, and Mae C. Jemison are vitally alive, reverberating in the mind long after the book is closed. As Gloria Steinem writes, "Women of Hope will inspire all Americans, especially our youth, who have been denied the knowledge that greatness looks like them."

Keywords

African American, Race Relations, Role Models, Biography, Girl Power

Age Range:

School-agers 9-12

Author: Joyce Hansen

ISBN# 590939734 | Date Published: 1998 | Price: $ 16.95

Publisher: Scholastic | Pages: 32

WORDS BY HEART

Rating 

Lena learns hard lessons when her Papa dies.

Hoping to make her adored Papa proud of her and to make her White classmates notice her "Magic Mind" rather than her Black skin, Lena vows to win the Bible-quoting contest. But winning does not bring Lena what she expected. Instead of honor, violence and death result, striking the one she loves most dearly. Lena, who has believed in vengeance, must now learn how to forgive. An ALA Best Book for young adults. School Library Journal Best Book of the year. A Booklist Reviewers' Choice.

Keywords

Black Identity, Core Issues (Feelings), Fathers, Fiction, Grief and Loss, Self-Esteem

Age Range:

School-agers 9-12

Author: Ouida Sebestyen

Ouida Sebestyen is the author of *Out of Nowhere: A Novel* and *Words by Heart.*

ISBN# 044041346X | Date Published: 1997 | Price: $ 4.50

Publisher: Dell | Pages: 144

YOLANDA'S GENIUS

How Yolanda makes the world safe for her little brother Andrew.

Yolanda is smart, tough, and big for her age. Her younger brother, Andrew, doesn't talk very much and has trouble learning to read, but is able to create beautiful music with the old harmonica left to him by their father. When bullies destroy Andrew's cherished harmonica, it falls to Yolanda to replace the instrument and reveal her brother's musical genius to the world. Yolanda and Andrew just happen to have brown skin. 1996 Newbery Honor Book, 1996 ALA Notable Children's Book.

Keywords

African American, Family Life, Girl Power, Self-Esteem, Black Identity, Skill Mastery

Age Range:

School-agers 9-12

Author: Carol Fenner

ISBN# 689821727 | Date Published: 1997 | Price: $ 2.65

Publisher: Aladdin | Pages: 224

ZORA HURSTON AND THE CHINABERRY TREE

A famous African American writer, who learned about hope and strength from her mother.

"This storybook...emphasizes the awareness of family, nature and community that is reflected in (Hurston's) writing," says The New York Times. Books in Print writes, "A stern father tells Zora that she should wear a dress (she wears overalls), read the Bible daily and obey him, but Zora listens only to her mother, who teaches her young daughter to remember the stories, which 'kept their people alive. As long as they were told, Africa would live in their hearts.'" Reading Rainbow Selection; "Pick of the Lists," American Bookseller; Notable Children's Trade Book in the Field of Social Studies.

Keywords

Biography, African American, Role Models, Family Life, Black Identity, Grief and Loss

Age Range:

School-agers 9-12

Author: William Miller

Author: Cornelius Van Wright

Author: Ying-Hwa Hu

William Miller is the author of *Frederick Douglass; Richard Wright and the Library Card; Zora Hurston and the Chinaberry Tree; The Bus Ride;* and *House by the River.*

ISBN# 1-880000-33-4 | Date Published: 1994 | Price: $ 6.95

Publisher: Lee & Low Books | Pages: 32

AANI AND THE TREE HUGGERS

Rating 

A girl in India inspires the women around her to save their beloved forest.

"A testament to heroism, based on events in northern India in the 1970s. When cutting crews came to slash the forest, women and girls faced down the developers and halted the destruction. More books of this caliber might help save the planet." —Smithsonian

Keywords

Role Models, India, Core Issues (Feelings), Cultural History, Self-Esteem, Girl Power

Age Range

School-agers 9-12

Author: Jeannine Atkins

Jeannine Atkins is the author of *Get Set! Swim!*, *Aani* and the *Tree Huggers*, and more.

ISBN# 1880000245 Date Published 1996 Price $ 14.95
Publisher Lee & Low Books Pages 32

ANGEL CHILD, DRAGON CHILD

Rating 

A young Vietnamese girl learns touching lessons about understanding difference.

This story of a Vietnamese family who moves to the U.S. offers one daughter's way of facing racism and changing the attitudes of other kids in her class. It's a heart opener that feels very good. A Reading Rainbow book. This book is out of stock indefinitely at the publisher, but if you place an order we may be able to find you a used copy within 2-6 months. We will notify you and request your approval of the price and condition. We will also notify you if we are unable to locate this title within six months.

Keywords

Vietnamese, Race Relations, Racism, Asian American, Core Issues (Feelings), Family Life

Age Range

School-agers 9-12

Author: Michele M. Surat

ISBN# 0-590-42271-5 Date Published 1989 Price $ 4.99
Publisher Scholastic Inc. Pages 40

ASHOK BY ANY OTHER NAME

How an Indian child copes with responses to his name.

This book will appeal to any child with an uncommon name. Taking pride in a name coming from one's cultural history is sometimes difficult, and Ashok serves as a positive role model for all kids. Availability: This title is currently on back order. We expect to be able to ship it to you within 3-5 weeks of ordering.

Keywords

India, Names, Core Issues (Feelings), Role Models, Self-Esteem, Racial/Ethnic Identity

Age Range

School-agers 9-12

Author: Sandra Ymate

Sandra S. Ymate is the author of *Children of Asian America* and *Ashok By Any Other Name.*

ISBN# 1879965011 Date Published 1992 Price $ 12.95
Publisher Polychrome Pages

BAT 6

12-year-old girls focus racist feelings for their town. Engrossing, no hearts and flowers.

From Booklist: "Three years after the end of World War II, Aki Mikami and her family return to their home. They've been gone for six years — since they were forced to join tens of thousands of other Americans of Japanese ancestry in internment camps.... The Japanese-hating Shazam, whose father died at Pearl Harbor, comes to live with her grandmother. The ultimate, explosive meeting of the two girls on a softball field...will demonstrate that wars may end, but the passions they foster — if unexamined — can make victims of the survivors.... [This story offers] an extraordinarily artful portrait of a moment in American history that challenged our comfortable assumptions about who we were and what we believed."

Keywords

Fiction, US History, Race Relations, Racism, Japanese American, Core Issues (Feelings)

Age Range

School-agers 9-12

Author: Virginia Euwer Wolff

Illustrator: Joseph Layden

ISBN# 590897993 Date Published Price $ 16.95
Publisher Scholastic Pages 256

Rating

BELIEVERS IN AMERICA

Poems about Americans of Asian and Pacific Islander descent (Many Voices, One Song)

Poems about Asian Americans such as Patsy Mink, Kristi Yamaguchi, and Wang Laboratories founder Dr. An Wang.

Keywords

Asian American, Biography, Poetry, Multiracial, Chinese American, Korean American

Age Range:

School-agers 9-12

Author: Steven Izuki

Illustrator: Bill Fukada McCoy

ISBN# 516451529 *Date Published:* 1995 *Price:* $ 7.95

Publisher: Children's Book *Pages:* 48

Rating

BLIND MEN AND THE ELEPHANT, THE

A great way to learn that a part of something may not define its whole.

Each member in a group of blind men thinks he knows what an elephant is like — but the impressions are based only on the part of the elephant each has encountered. A great story for jump-starting a conversation about prejudice.

Keywords

Folk tales and Legends, India, Racism

Age Range:

School-agers 9-12

Author: Karen Backstein

ISBN# 0-590-45813-2 *Date Published:* 1992 *Price:* $ 3.50

Publisher: Scholastic *Pages:* 48

BREAKAWAY

Racism, and the struggle of an adolescent to create his own identity.

With rare honesty, this hard-hitting and unsettling story of a Chinese Canadian boy captures the conflicts of an outsider's search for identity. At 18, Kwok bitterly resents the racism he experiences as the only Chines boy at his school and in his bid for a university scholarship in order to realize his dream of joining a Chinese soccer team. Caught as he is between two worlds, his transition occurs when Kwok comes to understand what his parents are trying to do for the family, to respect his father's struggle and to embrace his complex heritage.

Keywords

Asian, Race Relations, Racial/Ethnic Identity, Racism, Sports, Fiction

Age Range:

School-agers 9-12

Author: Paul Yee

ISBN# 888992017 *Date Published:* 1993 *Price:* $ 7.95

Publisher: Douglas & McIntyre Ltd. *Pages:*

CHI-LIN PURSE: A COLLECTION OF ANCIENT CHINESE STORIES

Retelling of nine Chinese stories.

From Booklist (starred review): "Legends, novels, and operas hundreds of years old are the source material for Linda Fang's stories. Dramatic, funny, and touching, the stories often concern difficulties overcome by characters who are kind or clever or both."

Keywords

China, Chinese, Folk tales and Legends

Age Range:

School-agers 9-12

Author: Linda Fang

Author: Jeannie M. Lee

ISBN# 374411891 *Date Published:* 1997 *Price:* $ 4.95

Publisher: Farrar-Strauss *Pages:* 160

Rating

CHILDREN IN CHINA

A rather somber portrayal of Chinese children.

In these black-and-white photographs of children's faces and activities, Chinese culture and history are represented as challenging, formal, and contained. Of the ninety photographs, only fifteen show smiling faces. Above all else in the eyes of Michael Karhausen, a German photographer/journalist, the lives of children in China appear to be serious. The text reinforces this message. It's easy to imagine that Chinese children being raised in the US may feel lucky to escape some of the soberness and hard work portrayed. We wish there had been more balance in the book and more images of children having fun than looking wistful. Does not compare well to *Children of China*, a photograph book in full color.

Keywords

Asian, China, Chinese, Cultural History

Age Range.

School-agers 9-12

Photographer: Michael Karhausen

Michael Karhausen is a photographer and journalist who lives in Germany.

ISBN# 1570751447 Date Published. 1998 Price. $ 25.00
Publisher. Orvis Books Pages.

Rating

CHILDREN OF CHINA, THE

An artist's journey through China. A must-have book for parents with children from China.

This dramatically illustrated book gives us beautiful glimpses of Chinese family life. The book opens and closes by depicting Song Nan's own son as a baby, reflecting the book's theme of children and art as the continuity of life. Many different ethnic groups are presented in detail through drawings of beautiful children in action. An end-leaf map, locating various Chinese subcultures, creates a unique tool for talking about the grand scope of Chinese culture. This book belongs in the home library of every child born in China.

Keywords

Cultural History, Asian, Core Issues (Feelings), International Adoption, China, Chinese American

Age Range.

School-agers 9-12

Author: Song Nan Zhang

This is Song Nan Zhang's third book.

ISBN# 887763634 Date Published. 1995 Price. $ 14.95
Publisher. Tundra Pages.

CHILDREN OF INDIA, THE

Daily life in India, as seen through a child's eyes.

Through descriptions of the daily lives of children from different regions and social levels, these profiles of the lives of children in India help children get a feel for what it would be like to grow up in India, in this introduction to the variety and richness of its culture. Availability: This item usually ships within six weeks. Please note that items occasionally go out of print or publishers run out of stock. We will notify you within three weeks if we have trouble obtaining this book.

Keywords

Cultural History, Racial/Ethnic Identity, Diversity, India, International Adoption, Asian

Age Range.

School-agers 9-12

Author: Jules M. Hermes

ISBN# 876147597 Date Published. 1993 Price. $ 7.95
Publisher. Lerner Pages.

CHINA'S BRAVEST GIRL

The legend of Hua Mu Lan.

In this adaptation of the beloved Chinese legend of the maiden warrior, Hua Mu Lan convinces her father that she must go to war to protect the family's honor — because there is no eldest son. The heroine is courageous and wise, respectful and loving, and able to meet men on equal terms.

Keywords

Folk tales and Legends, Asian, Self-Esteem, Chinese American, Girl Power, Chinese

Age Range.

School-agers 9-12

Author: Charlie Chin

The author, Charlie Chin, is a writer, musician, composer and actor.

ISBN# 892391200 Date Published. Price. $ 6.95
Publisher. Children's Book Pages.

CHINESE NEW YEAR'S DRAGON

Rating 

Our heroine finds herself on a dragon's back soaring over ancient China.

From Booklist: "This book deals with the holiday as a family event — from cleaning and shopping to food preparation and gifts. Street parades and fireworks are only incidental; this story takes place in a middle-class kitchen, living room, and dining room. The girl cleans the house in her jeans, but she wears traditional clothing (with red sneakers) for the family party. The magical happening is a tiny, dreamy moment when the girl feels she's back in ancient China, watching the celebration from a dragon's back. The pictures show a world in which tradition intersects a nontraditional world: the New Year's fireworks explode against an urban skyscape."

Keywords

China, Chinese, Cultural History, Holidays and Celebrations, International Adoption, Family Life

Age Range:

School-agers 9-12

Author: Rachel Sing

ISBN# 671886029 *Date Published:* 1994 *Price:* $ 5.99

Publisher: Little Simon *Pages:* 32

DRAGON PRINCE, THE

Rating 

A Chinese "Beauty and the Beast" tale.

From Kirkus Reviews: "The subtitle says all: A dragon ambushes a poor farmer and promises to eat the unfortunate man unless one of the farmer's seven daughters marries him. Six daughters run away in fear, but Seven can't bear to see her father suffer. The dragon transforms into a handsome prince. Mak's splendid, realistic paintings, in dark jewel tones bordered with white, extend the text elegantly." From Booklist: "Mak's illustrations dramatically combine realism and fantasy. The suspense of the story and the charm of its language should appeal to readers of different ages. A good choice for reading aloud."

Keywords

Folk tales and Legends, Chinese, Asian

Age Range:

School-agers 9-12

Author: Lawrence Yep

Illustrator: Kam Mak

ISBN# 64435180 *Date Published:* 1997 *Price:* $ 5.95

Publisher: Harper Collins *Pages:* 32

FAMOUS ASIAN AMERICANS

Biographies of Asian American role models.

"Ethnic pride shines through in these fourteen sketches of contemporary Asian Americans. The different walks of life covered range from sports to music, from politics to letters." — Kirkus Reviews

Keywords

Asian American, Biography, Sports, Role Models, Self-Esteem

Age Range:

School-agers 9-12

Author: Janet Nomura Morey

Illustrator/Photographer: Wendy Dunn

ISBN# 525650806 *Date Published:* 1992 *Price:* $ 5.99

Publisher: Cobblehill *Pages:*

GIRL WHO LOVED THE WIND, THE

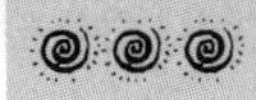

Prepare, don't protect. Living all of life – the happy and the sad.

Danina is surrounded by happy music, beautiful paintings and always-smiling servants. Her wealthy father has so ordered it, to keep the daughter he loves from ever being hurt. But even the high walls of the house cannot keep Danina from hearing the voice of the wind. Its song is sometimes sad and harsh, sometimes sweet, like life itself. And now that Danina has heard the song, the palace feels like a prison. What lies beyond the walls?

Keywords

Folk tales and Legends, Asian, Girl Power, Fiction, Core Issues (Feelings)

Age Range:

School-agers 9-12

Author: Jane Yolen

Jane Yolen is the award-winning author of more than 100 books including *Girl Who Loved The Wind* and has been called "America's Hans Christian Anderson."

ISBN# 006443088X *Date Published:* *Price:* $ 5.95

Publisher: Harper Trophy *Pages:*

GIRL-SON, THE

Rating

The heroine of this true story finds courage to fight traditions that hold children back.

"This fictionalized biography of Korean educator Induk Pahk is told as if by the woman herself. She was initially educated by being disguised as a boy, since girls at the time were thought to be unworthy or unable to learn to read and write. Children may be astounded at the lengths to which Pahk and her mother went to achieve the education that we take for granted. An epilogue and directions for determining one's own birth sign according to the Chinese zodiac are included," writes Books in Print about this inspiring story.

Keywords

Cultural History, Korean American, Self-Esteem, Biography, Role Models, Korean

Age Range.

School-agers 9-12

Author: Anne E. Neuberger

ISBN# 1575050773 Date Published. Price. $ 6.95

Publisher. Carolrhoda books Pages. 132

GRANDFATHER TANG'S STORY

Rating

A tale told with tangrams.

"Drawing on a Chinese form of storytelling with seven shapes cut from a square of paper, Tompert recounts the tale of two fox fairies. Parker's pen-and-watercolor art adds drama, wile the tangram insets will motivate children to try their own versions." —The Bulletin of the Center for Children's Books.

Keywords

Asian, China, Chinese, Intergenerational, Games and Activities, Folk tales and Legends

Age Range.

School-agers 9-12

Author: Ann Tompert

Illustrator: Robert A. Parker

Ann Tompert has written 12 books for children.

ISBN# 517885581 Date Published. 1999 Price. $ 6.99

Publisher. Dragonfly Books, Random House Pages. 32

GUNG HAY FAT CHOY

Happy Chinese New Year.

Story of Chinese New Year told with color photos and simple text. Includes family traditions, the Lion Dance, Dragon parade, and the Chinese Zodiac. The Chinese New Year is a time of rejoicing, family reunions, gift giving, and feasting. It is a birthday party for everyone. Chinese American children will see that this book is specific to them, and all children will be able to appreciate the values of the culture.

Keywords

Chinese American, Cultural History, Holidays and Celebrations, Festivals

Age Range.

School-agers 9-12

Author: June Behrens

June Behrens has written more than 50 books, plays, and filmstrips for children.

ISBN# 516488422 Date Published. 1982 Price. $ 4.95

Publisher. Children's Press Pages. 32

HELLO, MY NAME IS SCRAMBLED EGGS

Who is Tuan and what is he going to do next?

Tuan is a Vietnamese refugee and Harvey's family is his host. Harvey wants to be his friend, but right from the start everything goes wrong. Tuan thinks hot dogs are really made from dogs and that hair dryers are guns. Iced tea, forks, and escalators amaze him. This is a great book to help kids understand the ways that being different can be hard but also wonderful.

Keywords

Race Relations, Asian, Core Issues (Feelings), Fiction, Vietnamese American, Asian American

Age Range.

School-agers 9-12

Author: Jamie Gilson

ISBN# 0-671-74104-7 Date Published. Price. $ 3.99

Publisher. Simon & Schuster Pages.

Rating

HIROSHIMA

Hiroshima and its people's struggles to survive as seen through the eyes of a twelve-year-old.

Young people and adults alike will be captivated by this simply told but highly emotional story. "The facts are dramatic and told with controlled intensity.... The account is fair, non-hectoring, and totally devastating. Though accessible to middle-grade readers, this will also interest older readers, who will find nothing condescending in content or format," writes the American Library Association. Readers who have been separated from loved ones or from their culture of origin may take special interest in this rendition of how bad things can happen to good people.

Keywords

Japanese, History, Biography, Core Issues (Feelings), Asian American, Cultural History

Age Range:

School-agers 9-12

Author: Lawrence Yep

ISBN# 590208330 *Date Published:* 1996 *Price:* $ 3.99

Publisher: Apple *Pages:* 64

Rating

HOANG ANH: A VIETNAMESE AMERICAN BOY

Living in two cultures: American and Vietnamese.

From Kirkus Reviews: "Hoang Anh Chau was born in a refugee camp in Malaysia during his family's odyssey from the Mekong Delta to their current home in San Rafael, California. He's now a photogenic junior-high student, youngest in a large, hardworking family. Vivid color photos and first-person text demonstrate that in most respects Hoang Anh is like any middle-class American boy, yet he maintains ties to his traditional culture (the Tet New Year's celebration is featured). With well-captioned photos in varied sizes and an unusually attractive layout, this appealing portrait has strong visual interest. Helpful phonetic pronunciations of Vietnamese words and names; glossary; map; index."

Keywords

Vietnam, Family Life, Cultural History, Biography, Boy Focus, Multicultural

Age Range:

School-agers 9-12

Author: Diane Hoyt-Goldsmith

Diane Hoyt-Goldsmith is the author of *Hoang Anh: A Vietnamese American Boy; Buffalo Days;* and *The Day of the Dead.*

ISBN# 823409481 *Date Published:* 1992 *Price:* $ 16.95

Publisher: Holliday House *Pages:*

IF IT HADN'T BEEN FOR YOON JUN

Alice, adopted from Korea, is the only Asian person in her school and family.

Seventh-grader Alice Larsen wants to deny her Korean ancestry. Adopted as a baby by a Minnesota family, she is a happy, popular cheerleader. When another Korean, Yoon Jun Lee, begins attending Bainer Junior High, Alice thinks he is weird. Then he becomes her partner for International Day. Together they prepare a report about Korea to present to students and parents, accompanied by samples of Mrs. Lee's cooking. Alice's interest in her heritage is piqued, and Yoon Jun becomes a friend, especially after he pushes her out of the path of a speeding car. Alice's emotions are genuine and believable as she denies her Korean heritage but wonders, too... about birth parents, about what might have been.

Keywords

Adoption, Asian American, Korean American, Friendship, International Adoption, Self-Esteem

Age Range:

School-agers 9-12

Author: Marie Lee

Marie Lee is the author of *If It Hadn't Been For Yoon Jun* and *Finding My Voice*

ISBN# 0-380-72347-6 *Date Published:* 1995 *Price:* $ 3.99

Publisher: Avon *Pages:* 144

IN THE YEAR OF THE BOAR AND JACKIE ROBINSON

A ten-year-old Chinese girl emigrates to Brooklyn in 1947.

Making friends in this strange new world is very difficult for Shirley, until she discovers baseball, the Brooklyn Dodgers and a wonderful hero and role-model in Jackie Robinson. "Poignant but outrageously funny," says the School Library Journal. ALA Notable Children's Book.

Keywords

Asian American, Chinese American, Sports, Fiction

Age Range:

School-agers 9-12

Author: Bette Bao Lord

ISBN# 0064401758 *Date Published:* 1986 *Price:* $ 5.95

Publisher: Trophy Press *Pages:*

JAR OF DREAMS, A

Rating 

Rinko does not want to be Japanese. What can she do?

The Horn Book: "An ingenious simplicity and grace mark the first-person telling of the story of eleven-year-old Rinko and her Japanese family in Berkeley, CA. Times are hard for everyone in 1935, but being Japanese is for Rinko an added burden.... Compared with many worldly-wise book heroines, Rinko is genuine and refreshing, and her worries seem wholly natural, honest, and convincing."

Keywords
Antiracist Strategies, US History, Core Issues (Feelings), Fiction, Japanese American, Race Relations

Age Range:
School-agers 9-12

Author: Yoshiko Uchida

Yoshiko Uchida is the author of *A Jar of Dreams, The Bracelet* and *Long Journey Home.*

ISBN# 689716729 | Date Published: 1993 | Price: $ 3.95
Publisher: Aladdin | Pages: 144

JAWS OF THE DRAGON, THE

Rating 

A family must leave Vietnam and make a new home.

From Horn Book: "Tra, a Vietnamese boy of Chinese descent, is confused about his identity and about his father's role in the Vietnam War. Seeking freedom, his family escape by boat to Hong Kong, where they find continued hardship. However, after a fight with his father's old enemy, Tra comes to understand and take pride in his father. Although detailed, the narrative lacks authenticity and the power to convince."

Keywords
Vietnam, Family Life, Fathers, Fiction, Core Issues (Feelings), Cultural History

Age Range:
School-agers 9-12

Author: Alan Gibbons

ISBN# 822507374 | Date Published: 1994 | Price: $ 19.95
Publisher: Lerner | Pages: 153

JOURNEY HOME

The cruel treatment inflicted upon Japanese Americans during World War II by their fellow Americans.

After their release from an American concentration camp, a Japanese American girl and her family try to reconstruct their lives amidst strong anti-Japanese feelings which breed fear, distrust, and violence.

Keywords
Japanese American, Race Relations, Racism, Cultural History, US History, Fiction

Age Range:
School-agers 9-12

Author: Yoshiko Uchida

Yoshiko Uchida is the author of *A Jar of Dreams, The Bracelet* and *Long Journey Home.*

ISBN# 0689716419" | Date Published: 1992 | Price: $ 3.95
Publisher: Aladdin | Pages: 131

KNEELING CARIBOU & DANCING GIANTS

Mabuhay! Welcome! Come celebrate Filipino Festivals!

This is a feel-good book — a lively introduction to Filipino culture, tradition and history that provides both candy for the eye and delight for the mind. Ileana Lee's lively yet delicate illustrations complement Rita Krasno's engaging text; they join together to bring life to the celebration of caribou at the Farmer's Festival, the Ati-Atihan Festival, a Moslem Festival, a Christmas Festival, Philippine Independence Day, and the Festival of the Higantes. Games, songs, folk tales, crafts, activities, and recipes add hands-on appeal to make a winner of this jubilant presentation, a book most kids and their parents will enjoy spending time with.

Keywords
Filipino American, Multicultural, Holidays and Celebrations, Family Life, Festivals, Asian

Age Range:
School-agers 9-12

Author: Rita Krasno

Author: Ileana C. Lee

Rita Krasno is the author of *Kneeling Caribou & Dancing Giants* and *The Lost Boy.*

ISBN# 1881896153 | Date Published: 1997 | Price: $ 19.95
Publisher: Pacific View Press | Pages: 48

Rating

LITTLE WEAVER OF THAI-YEN VILLAGE, THE

Simply told, a story of the tragic outcome of war and of human resilience.

Hien, who lost her family in the war, is brought to the United States. The story recounts her efforts to remain true to her background while trying to adjust to a new country. Bilingual in English and Vietnamese.

Keywords

Foster Child, Racial/Ethnic Identity, Self-Esteem, Vietnam, Bilingual, Girl Power

Age Range:

School-agers 9-12

Author: Raintree Staff

ISBN# 0-89239-030-1 *Date Published:* 1977 *Price:* $ 14.95

Publisher: Children's Book *Pages:* 24

Rating

LOOK WHAT WE BROUGHT YOU FROM INDIA

Crafts, games, recipes, stories, and other cultural activities from Indian Americans

A hands-on approach to learning about Indian culture, this book invites the reader to explore the fun of floor painting and tie-dying, cooking traditional recipes, the games of Five Shells and Kabaddi and the festivals of Diwali and Holi.

Keywords

India, International Adoption, Festivals, Cultural History

Age Range:

School-agers 9-12

Author: Phyliss Shalant

ISBN# 382394631 *Date Published:* 1998 *Price:* $ 11.00

Publisher: Julian Messner *Pages:* 48

LOOK WHAT WE BROUGHT YOU FROM KOREA

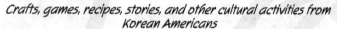

Crafts, games, recipes, stories, and other cultural activities from Korean Americans

A hands-on approach to learning about Korean culture, this book invites the reader to explore the fun of kite-making, seesaws, kimchi and more.

Keywords

Asian, Asian American, Korean, Korean American, Cultural History

Age Range:

School-agers 9-12

Author: Phyliss Shalant

Author: Soyoo Hunjoo Park

ISBN# 671887025 *Date Published:* 1995 *Price:* $ 11.00

Publisher: Julian Messner *Pages:*

LOOK WHAT WE BROUGHT YOU FROM VIET NAM

Crafts, Games, Recipes, Stories, and Other Cultural Activities from New Americans

A hands-on approach to learning about Vietnamese culture, this book invites the reader to explore the fun of Vietnamese crafts and culture.

Keywords

Vietnam, International Adoption, Asian, Asian American

Age Range:

School-agers 9-12

Author: Phyliss Shalant

Author: Joana Roy

ISBN# 671659782 *Date Published:* 1998 *Price:* $ 11.00

Publisher: Addison-Wesley *Pages:*

Rating

MADE IN CHINA

Who invented paper? crossbows? the first printing press? silk making? compasses:

"This colorfully illustrated book focuses on specific topics related to ancient Chinese culture, history, tradition, and invention. These topics include watercolors, drawings, and diagrams as well as many excellent photos of artifacts and reproductions of period artwork," says Booklist. Kirkus Reviews writes, "A concise history of Chinese thought and creativity, covering not only scientific ideas and inventions, but religion and philosophy, government, trade, farming, and more. Information is presented clearly and spans centuries. Each page contains extended information on a given topic, such as the relationship between salt production and natural gas lighting. The book is intriguing, as much fun to browse as it is to sink into for research."

Keywords

China, Chinese, Self-Esteem, Cultural History

Age Range:

School-agers 9-12

Author: Suzanne Williams

Illustrator: Andrea Fong

ISBN# 1881896145 Date Published: 1997 Price: $ 18.95

Publisher: Dragon Books Pages:

Rating

MOON LADY

Ying-ying discovers the best wishes are those you make come true yourself.

Amy Tan is one of our favorite writers of books for adults because of her ability to communicate feelings. Her children's stories, in contrast, are plot-driven; though exciting, they are long, wordy, and complex and not appropriate for a picture-book audience. The illustrations are wonderful, however. Aladdin's mistake may have been to pair two fine talents in the wrong venue; a wonderful storyteller writing for the wrong age range with a wonderful illustrator who can make the most of a picture-book format. Still, for those seeking books reflecting Chinese culture, *Moon Lady* has much to offer if for nothing other than its dramatic pictures.

Keywords

China, Chinese, Girl Power, Fiction, Intergenerational, Family Life

Age Range:

School-agers 9-12

Author: Amy Tan

Gretchen Shields

Amy Tan is the author of *The Joy Luck Club, Moon Lady* and more.

ISBN# 689806167 Date Published: 1995 Price: $ 5.99

Publisher: Aladdin Pages:

ONION TEARS

Being separated from her family makes it hard for Nam-Huong to trust anyone.

Vietnamese girl Nam-Huong wants to adjust to her new life, but she misses her family too much. When kids try to be friends, she rejects them, so they begin to tease. Soon she doesn't talk at all. Finally she makes one friend — but when it seems that her refusal to speak may cost her this friendship, she tells about the horrors of her escape from Vietnam and how she lost her grandfather in the sea in this story about trying to trust again. A forceful view of the Vietnamese war from a child's perspective, similar to *The Little Weaver of Thai-Yen Village.*

Keywords

Adoption, Vietnam, Friendship, International Adoption, Transracial Adoption, Foster Child

Age Range:

School-agers 9-12

Author: Diana Kidd

ISBN# 0-688-11862-3 PA Date Published: 1990 Price: $ 3.95

Publisher: Morrow Pages: 72

PASSAGE TO FREEDOM: THE SUGIHARA STORY

The true story of the "Japanese Schindler" who saved thousands of Jews during W.W.II.

From the author and illustrator of Baseball Saved Us comes a story of courageous humanity. "In 1940, Chiune Sugihara, a Japanese diplomat living in Lithuania, issued thousands of visas to Jewish refugees — against the recommendations of his government — to allow them to flee the Nazis. Told through the eyes of his son Hiroki, who was five at the time, it is a touching account of how one person's courage can make a difference." *Passage to Freedom* highlights the important influence of the opinions of Sugihara's sons on his decision. According to American Bookseller, it is "a powerful story that needs to be told."

Keywords

Race Relations, Self-Esteem, Japanese American, Biography, Role Models, Asian

Age Range:

School-agers 9-12

Author: Ken Mochizuki

Illustrator: Don Lee

Ken Mochizuki is the author of *Heroes* and *Passage to Freedom: The Sugihara Story*

ISBN# 1880000490 Date Published: 1997 Price: $ 15.95

Publisher: Lee & Low Books Pages: 32

Rating

SACHIKO MEANS HAPPINESS

A Japanese American granddaughter's struggle to understand her grandmother's Alzheimer's-induced behavior.

A young girl is frustrated because grandma no longer acts like grandma. After much anger, she realizes that grandma's childlike transformation stems from the fact that she has Alzheimer's disease; after this realization, she is then able to build a new kind of relationship with her. Beautiful illustrations depict Japanese culture.

Keywords

Asian American, Core Issues (Feelings), Japanese American, Girl Power, Intergenerational

Age Range:

School-agers 9-12

Author: Kimiko Sakai

ISBN# 0-89239-122-7 *Date Published:* 1995 *Price:* $ 6.95

Publisher: Children's Book *Pages:* 32

Rating

SADAKO AND THE THOUSAND PAPER CRANES

Courage and spirit make Sadako a heroine. Peace day was created in her honor.

Sadako Sasaki was two years old when the atom bomb was dropped on her home city of Hiroshima. When she was twelve, she developed leukemia. Facing long days in bed, Sadako spent the time folding paper cranes, for the legend holds that if a sick person folds 1000 cranes, the gods will make her well again. She folded 644 cranes before she died. Children all over Japan helped collect money to build a monument to her. An inspiring story of one child's courage in the face of adversity and the tremendous outpouring of support she received from the people around her. A Pact bestseller.

Keywords

Asian, History, Girl Power, Biography, Japanese, Cultural History

Age Range:

School-agers 9-12

Author: Eleanor Coerr

After learning that Sadako's letters to her classmates had been published in a book called *Kokeshi*, Eleanor Coerr decided to bring the story to American readers.

ISBN# 0-440-47465-5 *Date Published:* 1990 *Price:* $ 3.99

Publisher: BDD Books *Pages:* 64

SONG OF MU LAN, THE

Mu Lan proves girls can do as much as boys.

A powerful and vibrant retelling of the ancient story recently made famous by Disney's film. From Booklist: "Although originating between AD 420 and 589, this Chinese folk poem is more than a historical treasure — it is topical enough to prompt some rather interesting discussions about sex roles and women in the military. Written in both English and Chinese with beautiful calligraphy and wonderful illustrations."

Keywords

China, Girl Power, Folk tales and Legends, Bilingual

Age Range:

School-agers 9-12

Author: Jeannie Lee

Jeannie Lee is the author of *Silent Lotus* and *The Song of Mu-Lan.*

ISBN# 1886910006 *Date Published:* 1995 *Price:* $ 15.95

Publisher: Front Street Press *Pages:*

TALES OF A CHINESE GRANDMOTHER

An aged Chinese grandmother tells Chinese folk tales and legends.

Chinese culture as explained by a grandmother to two young children as they grow up in old China, explaining traditions and origins of Chinese folklore.

Keywords

China, Folk tales and Legends, Chinese, Family Life, Racial/Ethnic Identity, Cultural History

Age Range:

School-agers 9-12

Author: Frances Carpenter

Illustrator: Malthe Hasselriis

ISBN# 804810427 *Date Published:* 1991 *Price:* $ 8.96

Publisher: Tuttle, Charles E. *Pages:* 261

Rating

TYE MAY AND THE MAGIC BRUSH

A Chinese folk tale.

Tye May has a magic paint brush: the images she paints with it becomes real. When the greedy emperor and the nasty landlord try to take the brush for themselves, she finds a way to outsmart them.

Keywords

Folk tales and Legends, Self-Esteem, Chinese American, Asian, Girl Power, Chinese

Age Range.

School-agers 9-12

Author: Molly Bang

Author of *Ten, Nine, Eight; The Grey Lady and the Strawberry Snatcher*; *The Paper Crane* and more.

ISBN# 688115047 Date Published. 1981 Price. $4.95

Publisher. Morrow Pages. 55

Rating

WEAVING OF A DREAM, THE

Chinese folk tale retold in jewel-like illustrations and colorful text.

Long ago in China lived a very poor widow and her three sons. The widow was very talented and could weave beautiful brocades. One day she began weaving a very special tapestry. She worked on it day and night for three years, but when she was finished, it was carried off by the wind. Her three sons set out on a magical journey to retrieve it.

Keywords

Folk tales and Legends, Girl Power, Asian, Chinese

Age Range.

School-agers 9-12

Author: Marilee Heyer

ISBN# 140505288 Date Published. Price. $5.99

Publisher. Puffin Pages. 32

YANG THE THIRD AND HER IMPOSSIBLE FAMILY

Mary wants to be like everyone else and make a friend.

Recent immigrant Yingmai changes her name to Mary Yang and is trying to be more "American" so she can get to be friends with her popular classmate, Holly Hansen, but her impossible family is making it hard. Mary gets her chance by adopting one of Holly's kittens. The only problem is that cats aren't allowed in the Yang house. Sequel to Yang the Youngest and His Terrible Ear.

Keywords

Asian American, Chinese American, Self-Esteem, Friendship

Age Range.

School-agers 9-12

Author: Lensey Namioka

Illustrator: Kees De Kiefte

Lensey Namioka is the author of Yang the Third and Her Impossible Family and Yang the Youngest and His Terrible Ear

ISBN# 0440412315" Date Published. 1996 Price. $3.99

Publisher. Yearling Books Pages.

YANG THE YOUNGEST AND HIS TERRIBLE EAR

"A lively music and sports story about being a new kid in a new culture.'

Everyone in the Yang family is a talented musician except for nine-year-old Yingtao, the youngest Yang, who is tone-deaf. His family has moved from China to Seattle, and Yingtao want to make new friends. He must get better on the violin to help his father get more students. His parents — professional musicians — assume the problem is lack of practice and chide him for playing baseball (he's a natural) when he could be rehearsing. Together, he and his new friend Matthew think of a sure way to save his father's recital. But is it sure? This is an engrossing and funny story, sure to hold a young reader's attention.

Keywords

Racial/Ethnic Identity, Chinese American, Race Relations, Family Life, Fiction, Sports

Age Range.

School-agers 9-12

Author: Lensey Namioka

Illustrator: Kees De Kiefte

Lensey Namioka is the author of *Yang the Third and Her Impossible Family* and *Yang the Youngest and His Terrible Ear,*

ISBN# 0-440-40917-9 Date Published. 1993 Price. $4.50

Publisher. Dell Pages. 144

Rating

ALL FOR THE BETTER

A story of El Barrio

Evelina Lopez, age 11, is sent from Puerto Rico to New York to live with her aunt and uncle during the depression because her family is too poor to provide for her. Though she is very sad, she is a resilient soul and makes a smooth transition, emerging as an inspiring figure with great courage. This story will encourage discussion of separation and loss and be of particular interest to children who have had to separate from their own birth families. Filled with authentic details of Puerto Rican family life, it presents a voice not often heard in books for school-age children.

Keywords

Puerto Rico, Latino/a, Adopted Child, Grief and Loss

Age Range:

School-agers 9-12

Author: Nicholasa Mohr

Illustrator: Rudy Gutierrez

ISBN# 811480607 *Date Published:* *Price:* $ 6.75

Publisher: Raintree *Pages:* 56

Rating

BARRIO: JOSE'S NEIGHBORHOOD

What is it like to grow up as a Mexican American?

This vibrant and captivating book presents Jose, an eight-year-old boy flying through life in the barrio of San Francisco. Its bright and detailed photographs and engaging text depict Jose's life — his school, recreation, holidays, family, and the vital street and neighborhood life. George Ancona is the author/photographer of many big colorful books for children that explore various cultural groups and communities. His photographs add excitement, a dimension of reality very useful for children trying to put themselves in the picture.

Keywords

Latino/a, Mexican American, Family Life

Age Range:

School-agers 9-12

Author/Illustrator: George Ancona

George Ancona is the author of *Powwow; Let's Dance; Fiesta Fireworks; The Piñata Maker; Fiesta USA: Being Adopted* and more.

ISBN# 152010483 *Date Published:* 1998 *Price:* $ 9.00

Publisher: Harcourt Brace *Pages:* 48

BREAKAWAY

Luke's dreams of becoming a great soccer star seem impossible – unless....

Twelve-year-old Luke Espinosa dreams of becoming a great soccer player but he can't afford a ball. Then Luke discovers that his father, who left when Luke was a baby, is a professional soccer player, and he is sure that soccer is in his genes. He decides to go live with his father and learn to play the game he loves. But when his father says there's no room in his life for Luke, the boy must find the inner courage to make his dreams come true. An absorbing story that will have particular meaning for adopted children who may wonder how their genetic heritage contributes to their talents and skills.

Keywords

Latino/a, Sports, Fathers, Core Issues (Feelings), Fiction

Age Range:

School-agers 9-12

Author: Kimberly Griffiths Little

ISBN# 380792257 *Date Published:* 1998 *Price:* $ 3.99

Publisher: Camelot *Pages:* 160

CALLING THE DOVES

This book will answer children's questions about immigrant-bashing and Latino stereotyping.

The author, one of the most prominent Mexican American poets of our day, describes growing up as an immigrant to the United States and as the son of a migrant farm worker. This book captures the love and warmth of Mexican American family life despite great hardships and poverty. It extols the values of hard work, caring for others and family tradition. Written in both Spanish and English in side-by-side texts.

Keywords

Self-Esteem, Latino/a, Family Life, Cultural History, Bilingual, Mexican American

Age Range:

School-agers 9-12

Author: Juan Felipe Herrera

ISBN# 892391324 *Date Published:* 1997 *Price:* $ 14.95

Publisher: Children's Book *Pages:* 32

Rating

CIRCUIT, THE

Stories from the life of a migrant child.

Francisco Jimenez emigrated with his family to California from Tlaquepaque, Mexico. As a child he worked in the fields of California, and these twelve deceptively simple short stories help us understand a child's view of the struggles and triumphs of life in a migrant family. There is no sense of complaint in these stories; rather, readers are charged with the opportunity to bear witness to the tenacity and courage of a family determined to make it under the most inhumane and taxing circumstances. Winner 1998 Boston Globe-Horn Book Award for Fiction.

Keywords

Mexican American, Family Life, Latino/a

Age Range:

School-agers 9-12

Author: Francisco Jiménez

Francisco Jiménez was born in Mexico. He is now chairman of the Modern Language Department at Santa Clara, University.

ISBN# 826317979 Date Published: 1997 Price: $ 10.95

Publisher: University of New Mexico Press Pages: 134

Rating

DAY OF THE DEAD, THE

A Mexican American celebration.

From Booklist: "Ten-year-old twins from Sacramento, California tell the story of their family's Day of the Dead celebration. In contrast to books that portray the holiday in rural Mexico, this explains the holiday's history while focusing on celebrations of an American family in a Mexican American community. The twins and their mother are photographed in ordinary clothes, with the State Capitol in the background, as well as in costume and in a procession. Aztec beliefs and their intermingling with Catholic rituals are explained, and descriptions of dancing, art, and prayer repeatedly illustrate the unity of past and present during festival days. A glossary of terms with clear phonetic pronunciations follows."

Keywords

Latino/a, Mexican American, Festivals, Cultural History, Spiritual Meanings

Age Range:

School-agers 9-12

Author: Diane Hoyt-Goldsmith

Author: Lawrence Migdale

Diane Hoyt-Goldsmith is the author of *Hoang Anh: A Vietnamese American Boy; Buffalo Days;* and *The Day of the Dead.*

ISBN# 823412008 Date Published: 1995 Price: $ 6.95

Publisher: Holiday House Pages:

DESERT MERMAID

A contemporary folk tale about the ecology of the desert and the importance of nature.

A desert mermaid living in an oasis seeks to save her people by rediscovering the forgotten songs of their ancestors. An original story written in the style of a folk tale and set in Mexico's Sonora Desert. Bilingual in English and Spanish.

Keywords

Bilingual, Latino/a, Folk tales and Legends, Mexican

Age Range:

School-agers 9-12

Author: Alberto Blanco

Alberto Blanco is one of Mexico's most notable poets. He wrote *Desert Mermaid* and *Angel's Kite/La Estrella De Angel.*

ISBN# 0-89239-106-5 Date Published: Price: $ 13.95

Publisher: Children's Book Pages:

EVERYBODY HAS FEELINGS/ TODOS TENEMOS SENTIMIENTOS

Photographs of children of all races underscored with simple adjectives in Spanish and English.

Told in the first person, this simply worded bilingual text leads children into an exploration of their own feelings as depicted in candid photographs. Happy, sad, lonely, strong, safe, and many more. The feelings are universal, and the children are from a diverse set of racial backgrounds. Bilingual in English and Spanish.

Keywords

Adoption, Core Issues (Feelings), Bilingual, Multicultural, Multiracial, Latino/a

Age Range:

School-agers 9-12

Photographer: Charles E. Avery

ISBN# 0-940880-34-2 Date Published: 1992 Price: $ 7.95

Publisher: Open Hand Pages: 42

Rating

FAMOUS HISPANIC AMERICANS

Inspiring stories of fourteen outstanding Latinos are chronicled.

Booklist says, "Morey and Dunn have written an interesting and useful collective biography that contains 14 chapters, each featuring an accomplished American man or woman of Hispanic heritage, from a variety of professions. Included are politicians (Ileana Ros-Lehtinen, Frederico Pena), scientists and physicians (Antonia Novello, Ellen Ochoa), artists and performers (Gloria Estefan, Andy Garcia, Carolina Herrera, Lourdes Lopez, Paul Rodriguez), athletes (Gigi Fernandez, Felipe Alou), and others. Illustrated with black-and-white photos, the prose is clear, and the book's format easily lends itself to students' biographical research.

Keywords

Biography, Latino/a, Role Models, Self-Esteem

Age Range:

School-agers 9-12

Author: Janet Nomura Morey

Illustrator/Photographer: Wendy Dunn

ISBN# 05256519X *Date Published:* 1996 *Price:* $ 15.99

Publisher: Cobblehill *Pages:*

Rating

FAMOUS MEXICAN AMERICANS

Biographies of Chicano role models.

Biographies of nine Mexican Americans "who show their determination to succeed amidst stereotypes, discrimination, and prejudices.... The book provides young readers with role models to be admired and emulated." —School Library Journal

Keywords

Biography, Mexican American, Role Models, Self-Esteem, Cultural History

Age Range:

School-agers 9-12

Author: Janet Nomura Morey

Illustrator/Photographer: Wendy Dunn

ISBN# 140384375 *Date Published:* 1989 *Price:* $ 5.99

Publisher: Cobblehill *Pages:*

FELITA

Everyday experiences of an eight-year-old Puerto Rican girl growing up in a close-knit, urban community.

Felita is part of a strong and loving Puerto Rican family living in New York. Her story deals with her encounters her with some racist Irish and Germans and with the death of her beloved grandmother. Though this book should be of interest to any child, transracially- adopted children likely be particularly responsive to the many core adoption issues suggested in the story.

Keywords

Latino/a, Puerto Rico, Intergenerational, Grief and Loss, Race Relations, Racism

Age Range:

School-agers 9-12

Author: Nicholasa Mohr

Illustrator: Ray Cruz

ISBN# 141306432 *Date Published:* 1996 *Price:* $ 4.99

Publisher: Puffin *Pages:*

FIESTA U.S.A.

Come celebrate! Four fiestas celebrated by Latinos in the United States.

This book introduces readers to The Day of The Dead in San Francisco; las Posadas in Albuquerque, New Mexico; the dance of the Matachines in El Rancho, New Mexico; and Three Kings' Day in New York City. The author explores how Spanish-speaking people keep their traditions alive and find new ways to celebrate their cultures. The inclusion of photographs brings a sense of immediacy and realism to the text. This story projects positive images children will identify with. Latino children will see that this book is specific to them, and all children will be able to appreciate the affirming values of this culture.

Keywords

Holidays and Celebrations, Latino/a, Cultural History, Self-Esteem

Age Range:

School-agers 9-12

Author/Illustrator: George Ancona

George Ancona is the author of *Powwow; Let's Dance; Fiesta Fireworks; The Piñata Maker; Fiesta U.S.A: Being Adopted* and more.

ISBN# 515674985 *Date Published:* 1995 *Price:* $ 15.99

Publisher: Lodestar *Pages:*

Rating

GATHERING THE SUN

An Alphabet in Spanish and English.

Twenty-eight poems celebrate the harvest. Awash with light, sun-drenched paintings take the reader into the fields and orchards and into the lives of the people who work them. Alma Flor Ada's newest work conveys her deep love and respect for people of Spanish heritage, while the glowing illustrations by Simón Silva capture the spirit of the poetry, creating a rich experience for the reader. Children of Latino descent will feel pride in their connection to this heritage and children of al backgrounds will benefit from discovering the ways and accomplishments of other worlds. Named as a notable children's trade book in the field of social studies by the Children's Book Council and National Council for the Social Studies.

Keywords

Language, Bilingual, Latino/a, Racial/Ethnic Identity, Poetry

Age Range.

School-agers 9-12

Author: Alma Flor Ada

Alma Flor Ada is author of *Gathering The Sun; My Name is Maria Isabel; Lizard and the Sun; The Gold Coin* and many other important books about Latino heritage.

ISBN# 699139035 Date Published. 1998 Price. $ 16.00

Publisher. Lothrop Pages.

Rating

I HATE ENGLISH

Mei Mei comes to understand English, but has conflicts about speaking it.

Mei Mei moves from Hong Kong to New York and is afraid that if she learns to speak English, she will lose something — so she decides to speak only Chinese. One day, her teacher Nancy finds an unusual way to help Mei Mei begin to be bilingual. Read it to find out how a simple and engaging resolution to her conflict came about.

Keywords

Race Relations, Racial/Ethnic Identity, Asian American, Chinese American, Language

Age Range.

School-agers 9-12

Author: Ellen Levine

ISBN# 0-590-42304-5 Date Published. Price. $ 3.95

Publisher. Scholastic Pages.

IF YOU WERE THERE: AZTEC TIMES

An illustrated guide to Aztec culture. Includes a fold-out game board.

Part of the *If You Were There* series filled with interesting information.

Keywords

Cultural History, Mexico, History, Games and Activities

Age Range.

School-agers 9-12

Author: Anthony Mason

ISBN# 689811993 Date Published. 1997 Price. $ 16.95

Publisher. Simon & Schuster Pages. 32

KIDS EXPLORE AMERICA'S HISPANIC HERITAGE

An enthusiastic and genuine glimpse into Hispanic history and culture.

Written by a group of young students in Westridge, Colorado, this book helps Latino American children identify with their culture. The text's photographs are further enriched by drawings from the students. Chapters include history, food, stories, jokes and famous people. Very appealing.

Keywords

Cultural History, Latino/a, Self-Esteem, Racial/Ethnic Identity

Age Range.

School-agers 9-12

Author: Westridge Kids

ISBN# 1562610341 Date Published. 1996 Price. $ 9.95

Publisher. John Muir Pages. 149

Rating

KIDS WHO WALK ON VOLCANOES

What do kids in Central America do everyday?

Colorful photo journal of Central American kids playing, working, celebrating, and having fun. 60 color photos.

Keywords

Guatemalan, Latino/a, Honduran

Age Range:

School-agers 9-12

Author: Paul Otteson

ISBN# 1562613081 Date Published: 1996 Price: $ 6.95

Publisher: John Muir Pages:

Rating

LA MARIPOSA

A simple and touching story of a boy's struggle to learn a new language.

This story touches the core issues around transition faced by every adopted child. In his first year of school, Francisco understands little of what his teacher says. But he is drawn to the silent, slow-moving caterpillar in the jar next to his desk. He knows that caterpillars turn into butterflies, but how? This honest, unsentimental account of Francisco's struggle to learn the new language reveals our imaginations' great power to sustain us. Both poignant and true, *La Mariposa* makes a subtle plea for tolerance. This book is also available in a Spanish edition, ISBN 095917387.

Keywords

Adoption, Latino/a, Core Issues (Feelings), Language, Self-Esteem, Diversity

Age Range:

School-agers 9-12

Author: Francisco Jiménez

Illustrator: Simon Silva

Francisco Jiménez was born in Mexico. He is now chairman of the Modern Language Department at Santa Clara, University.

ISBN# 395816637 Date Published: 1998 Price: $ 16.00

Publisher: Houghton Mifflin Pages: 48

LEGEND OF FOOD MOUNTAIN

La montaña del alimento.

"A pre-Columbian tale from Mexico in which muralist Graciela Carrillo creates an enormously complicated colorful and fascinating system of communications between the character, readers, gods and animals of that legendary land." —San Francisco Chronicle

Keywords

Cultural History, Latino/a, Folk tale and Legends

Age Range:

School-agers 9-12

Editor: Harriet Rohmer

Harriet Rohmer is the founding director of Children's Book Press, a nonprofit publisher.

ISBN# 892390220 Date Published: 1997 Price: $ 14.95

Publisher: Children's Book Pages: 24

LLAMA'S SECRET

A legend of Peru.

A Peruvian rendition of the Great Flood story, in which a llama warns the people and animals to seek shelter on Huillcacato to avoid the rising sea, Mamacocha. "Once upon a time" and "long ago and far away" tales are a great way to introduce children to the spirit of a culture.

Keywords

Latino/a, Peru, Folk tales and Legends, Cultural History

Age Range:

School-agers 9-12

Author: Argentina Palacios

Author: Charles Reasoner

ISBN# 816730504 Date Published: Price: $ 4.95

Publisher: Troll Pages: 32

Rating

MAGIC WINDOWS

Ventanas Magicas.

Through the magic windows of her cut-paper art, Garza shows us her family, her life as an artist, and the legends of her Aztec past. Children catch a glimpse of the hummingbirds that carry the souls of the ancestors; look into the artist's studio and see her paint a Mexican jarabe tapato dancer; and watch her teach her nieces and nephews how to make their own magic windows. The text is in Spanish and English. The Bulletin of the Center for Children's Books said that "vivid examples and simple explanations make this unusual art form intriguing and accessible."

Keywords

Bilingual, Mexico, Mexican American, Latino/a

Age Range.

School-agers 9-12

Author: Carmen Lomas Garza

Carmen Lomas Garza is a renowned American painter and graphic artist. Garza lives in San Francisco, CA.

ISBN# 089239157X Date Published. 1999 Price. $ 15.95
Publisher. Children's Book Pages. 32

Rating

MAKING MAGIC WINDOWS: CREATING CUT PAPER PROJECTS

Creating cut paper projects.

Carmen Lomas Garza is teaching the traditional Mexican craft of papel picado in the United States and developing it into a sophisticated art form. This workbook shows children how to create beautiful papel picado designs and banners by simply folding and cutting tissue paper. Directions are included for creating eight different traditional designs, including The Four Cardinal Points, a design reminiscent of the four points of a compass; Tiles, echoing the colorful hand-painted tiles that decorate many Mexican buildings; and The Fan, one of the artist's favorite designs, consisting of leaves, hummingbirds, and flowers.

Keywords

Mexican, Mexican American, Games and Activities, Festivals, Latino/a, Skill Mastery

Age Range.

School-agers 9-12

Author: Carmen Lomas Garza

Carmen Lomas Garza is a renowned American painter and graphic artist. Garza lives in San Francisco, CA.

ISBN# 892391596 Date Published. 1999 Price. $ 9.95
Publisher. Children's Book Pages. 32

MARIANTHE'S STORY

Marianthe struggles to tell her American classmates of her story of immigration.

Kirkus Reviews writes: "The first story, 'Painted Words,' follows Marianthe, new to the U.S., and her mother on the dreaded first day of school. Knowing no English, Marianthe draws pictures about herself during the art period, communicating in the only way she can. A patient teacher, some not-always-nice classmates, and success in English give Marianthe the courage to take part in Life-Story Time, in the 'Spoken Memories' section of the book. She tells the class of the baby brother who died before she was born, the village where she lived, the closeness of friends and neighbors."

Keywords

Latino/a, Language, Core Issues (Feelings), Fiction, Cultural History

Age Range.

School-agers 9-12

Author-Illustrator: Aliki

Aliki, who uses just one name, is the author of *Feelings; Marianthe's Story: Painted Words and Spoken Memories;* and *Manners.*

ISBN# 688156614 Date Published. 1998 Price. $ 16.00
Publisher. Morrow Pages. 64

MEET JOSEFINA

Engaging stories about Josefina Montoya, the newest American Girl.

Josefina's stories are set in New Mexico in 1824, exploring how the opening of the Santa Fe Trail brought Anglo traders into a land rich with Hispanic and Indian traditions. Stories show how these cultures encountered and enriched each other. Josefina is the newest character in The American Girls Collection. Wonderful books to read together as a family and for any "American Girl" fan to enjoy again and again. All books available in English or Spanish. *Meet Josefina* (1562475150) or *Así Es Josefina* (1562474960); *Josefina Learns A Lesson* (1562475157) or *Josefina Aprenda Una Lección* (1562474979); *Josefina's Surprise* (1562475193) or *Una Sorpresa Para Josefina* (1562474987).

Keywords

Family Life, Latino/a, Mexican American, Fiction

Age Range.

School-agers 9-12

Author: Valerie Tripp

ISBN# SEE ABOVE Date Published. 1997 Price. $ 5.95
Publisher. Pleasant Company Publication Pages.

MY NAME IS MARIA ISABEL

Cuban American author Alma Flor Ada explores a theme common among children in multicultural settings.

Maria Isabel is hurt when her teacher decides to call her Mary to distinguish her from two other Marias in the class. Maria is proud of her name and heritage and must find a way to make her teacher understand. Kirkus Reviews says, "Ada captures the authentic flavor of Latino culture in this warm, yet never sentimental, story: an entire family genealogy is encapsulated in a Latino name, as well as special connections between its bearer and the relatives for whom she was named. Presented in realistic terms, Maria Isabel's struggles will ring true to many children in the US. Pair this with Barbara Cohen's *Molly's Pilgrim* for a fine multicultural comparison."

Keywords

Cultural History, Latino/a, Extended Family, Self-Esteem, Racial/Ethnic Identity

Age Range:

School-agers 9-12

Author: Alma Flor Ada

Alma Flor Ada is author of *Gathering The Sun; My Name is Maria Isabel; Lizard and the Sun; The Gold Coin* and many other important books about Latino heritage.

ISBN# 068980217X Date Published: 1995 Price: $ 3.95

Publisher: Aladdin Pages: 32

NERDLANDIA

Kids will identify with Martin and Ceci.

Wearing a calculator on his belt, Martin is a total Chicano nerd who is totally in love with Ceci, the coolest chola in school. Ceci, in turn, has developed her own secret crush on this geeky muchacho. Helped by their bumbling but well-meaning friends, both Martin and Ceci transform themselves in the name of love, with Martin becoming cool just as Ceci becomes a nerdish beauty. There's lots of hip dialogue and plenty of playing up to the audience, so teenagers will have a ball with Soto's Chicano version of Grease, updated and set in Fresno, California... All the world's Nerdlandia!" — Booklist

Keywords

Latino/a, Mexican American

Age Range:

School-agers 9-12

Author: Gary Soto

Gary Soto is an acclaimed poet and fiction writer. He is the author of *Living Up The Street; Jesse; Nerdlandia, Chato's Kitchen* and *Baseball in April.*

ISBN# 698117840 Date Published: 1999 Price: $ 5.99

Publisher: Paper Star Pages: 88

PIÑATA MAKER, THE/EL PIÑATERO

A fascinating glimpse of life in a Mexican village.

This festive bilingual photo essay and how-to guide tells the story of 77-year-old Don Ricardo, who turns old newspapers and brown paper cement bags into elaborate piñatas for his Southern Mexican village, Ejutla de Crespo. This fascinating historical and cultural look at piñata-making has broad appeal. Side-by-side bilingual Spanish and English text.

Keywords

Racial/Ethnic Identity, Latino/a, Bilingual, Cultural History, Mexican

Age Range:

School-agers 9-12

Author/Illustrator: George Ancona

George Ancona is the author of *Powwow; Let's Dance; Fiesta Fireworks; The Piñata Maker; Fiesta USA: Being Adopted* and more.

ISBN# 0-15-2000060-7 Date Published: 1995 Price: $ 9.00

Publisher: Harcourt Brace Pages:

SAY HOLA TO SPANISH, OTRA VEZ (AGAIN)

More fun and learning from the creators of Say Hola to Spanish.

With its lively illustrations and humorous verse, this companion volume to the acclaimed *Say Hola to Spanish* makes language-learning a fun activity for the whole family. The colorful format and pages packed with action will appeal to a child's sense of humor while fans of children's verse in the tradition of Dr. Seuss will appreciate the style and art of this engaging educational storybook. "Together, text and illustrations create a fiesta of lively language fun, perfect for spicing up a story hour or sneaking in a first Spanish lesson," says Booklist. And Children's Book Review Service suggests, "Want to learn Spanish the fun way? Then read this cleverly illustrated book."

Keywords

Family Life, Latino/a, Educational Issues, Bilingual, Language

Age Range:

School-agers 9-12

Author: Susan Middleton Elya

ISBN# 1880000598 Date Published: 1997 Price: $ 6.95

Publisher: Lee & Low Books Pages: 32

Rating

SEA SERPENT'S DAUGHTER

A legend of Brazil

Relates the traditional Brazilian legend of how the King of the Sea's magical gift of darkness to his daughter brings night to the people of the rain forest.

Keywords

Latino/a, Brazil, Folk tales and Legends

Age Range

School-agers 9-12

Author: Margaret Lippert

ISBN# 816730547 Date Published 1993 Price $ 4.95

Publisher Troll Pages 32

Rating

STANDING TALL

The stories of ten Latino Americans who have become American heroes.

Biographies of ten men and women who have made important contributions to history as Latino Americans. From the very first Admiral of the Navy, David Farragut, to the baseball hero Roberto Clemente, to pop star Gloria Estefan, this book tells the captivating stories of ten important and influential Hispanic Americans who have made and are making history. Black-and-white photos.

Keywords

Racial/Ethnic Identity, Latino/a, Cultural History, Biography, Role Models, US History

Age Range

School-agers 9-12

Author: Argentina Palacios

ISBN# 590471406 Date Published 1994 Price $ 3.50

Publisher Scholastic Pages

THIS TREE IS OLDER THAN YOU ARE

Poems and stories in Spanish and English.

Sixty-four great Mexican writers and painters, including Rosario Castellanos, Alberto Blanco, Octavio Paz, and Julio Galan, are collected in this book.

Keywords

Poetry, Latino/a, Self-Esteem, Mexican American, Mexican, Bilingual

Age Range

School-agers 9-12

Editor: Naomi Shihab Nye

Naomi Shihab Nye is an acclaimed poet and the author of *This Tree Is Older Than You Are* and *Habibi*.

ISBN# 689820879 Date Published 1998 Price $ 12.00

Publisher Aladdin Pages 112

UNDER THE ROYAL PALMS

A childhood in Cuba.

It's hard to find biographies for this reading level and this one is filled with great photographs of Alma Flor Ada's childhood in Cuba. Exploring her heritage through stories of family and friends, Ada encourages children to discover the stories in their own lives. Few authors capture the powerful memories that are triggered by scent as clearly as Ada, the night jasmine, coffee, ylang-ylang, and her grandmother's perfume of lavender and sage. It's easy to picture the young Ada with grandma, attempting to count bats as they fly by, or smashing her favorite doll when her uncle dies in a plane crash. This book invites introspection and discussion.

Keywords

Latino/a, Cuba, Family Life

Age Range

School-agers 9-12

Author: Alma Flor Ada

Alma Flor Ada is author of *Gathering The Sun; My Name is Maria Isabel; Lizard and the Sun; The Gold Coin* and many other important books about Latino heritage.

ISBN# 689806310 Date Published 1998 Price $ 15.00

Publisher Athenaeum Pages 80

DESDEMONA'S FIRE

Rating 

Poems about biracial identity.

This first collection of poetry by Koecher, exploring biracial identity in a style rich in imagery and finely-crafted detail, won the 1999 winner of the Naomi Long Madgett Poetry Award.

Keywords
Poetry, Multiracial, Multiracial Identity

Age Range:
School-agers 9-12

Author: Ruth Ellen Koecher

Ruth Ellen Koecher's poems have appeared in African American Review, Antioch Review, Gettysburg Review, Ploughshares, Prairie Schooner, and others.

ISBN# 916418839 Date Published: 1999 Price: $ 12.00
Publisher: Lotus Press Pages: 61

I AM WHO I AM

Rating 

Speaking out about multiracial identity.

There are few books for children on this topic, and *I Am Who I Am* is a positive attempt to present this complex issue to young readers. Despite its rather dry text, it covers the history of racism, the function of racial categories and the role of heritage in the development of racial identity. Transracial adoption is discussed as a positive option when racial matching adoptive parents are not available. Though mention is made of the need for same-race role models for transracially adopted young people, the author does not review the differing ways in which transracial adoption affects multiracial children as compared with those families in which the parent(s) and child do not share any racial heritage.

Keywords
Multiracial Identity, Race Relations, Racial/Ethnic Identity, Transracial Adoption

Age Range:
School-agers 9-12

Author: Kathleen Gay

Kathleen Gay is also the author of *Adoption and Foster Care* and numerous other books for young people.

ISBN# 0531112144/6811 Date Published: 1996 Price: $ 22.70
Publisher: Franklyn-Watts Pages: 144

LIVING IN TWO WORLDS

Kids tell of the benefits and challenges of growing up with more than one culture.

Biracial children grow up with an everyday awareness that they are living in two worlds. In this book, kids tell of the relationship between the benefits and challenges of growing up with more than one world view, but it's not particularly engaging.

Keywords
Diversity, Transracial Adoption, International Adoption, Multicultural, Multiracial Identity

Age Range:
School-agers 9-12

Author: Maxine Rosenberg

Maxine Rosenberg is the author of *Living In Two Worlds,* and *Growing Up Adopted.*

ISBN# 688062792 Date Published: Price: $ 11.95
Publisher: Lothrop, Lee & Shepard Pages:

PROUDLY RED AND BLACK

Brief biographies of people of mixed African and Native American heritage.

Biographical sketches of colonial trader Richard Cuffe, Senator Robert Smalls, sculptor Edmonia Lewis, frontiersman Edward Rose, Seminole leader John Horse, and Bill Pickett, rodeo star: six people who made significant contributions to United States history in spite of barriers they faced because of their racially mixed heritage. "Entertaining as well as informative," says Booklist.

Keywords
African American, Native American, Multiracial Identity, Role Models, US History, Biography

Age Range:
School-agers 9-12

Author: William Loren Katz

Author: Paula Franklin

ISBN# 689318014 Date Published: 1993 Price: $ 15.00
Publisher: Athenaeum Pages: 88

Rating

SUN DANCE AT TURTLE ROCK

Cody is biracial. Will his white grandfather accept him?

Cody, 12, has an African American mother and a white father, now dead. When he visits his relatives on his father's side, the town is clearly unacquainted with African Americans and Cody feels certain that his white grandfather is ashamed of his brown skin, though his aunts and cousins are welcoming. ALA Booklist writes that this book handles complicated feelings with humor and warmth and deals with racial issues with sensitivity and honesty. Multicultural Review gave it a very positive review.

Keywords

Extended Family, Multiracial, Intergenerational, Race Relations, Racial/Ethnic Identity, Fiction

Age Range:

School-agers 9-12

Author: Patricia Costa Viglucci

ISBN# 964591499 Date Published: 1996 Price: $ 4.95

Publisher: Stone Pine Pages: 128

Rating

TREVOR'S STORY

Ten-year-old Trevor describes what he likes and does not like about being biracial.

There are so few books written for biracial children that this one, though lacking in the excitement we wish all books would generate, is worthwhile simply as a conversation-starter. Talking with your child about his or her responses to Trevor's feelings can free your child to express her own feelings indirectly, by discussing Trevor rather than herself. Every means you can find to help you comprehend your child's feelings about these issues is valuable. Does your child agree or disagree with what Trevor likes and does not like about being biracial? Do Trevor's examples of how this comes up in his daily life ring true for your child?

Keywords

Biography, Multiracial Identity, Racial/Ethnic Identity

Age Range:

School-agers 9-12

Author: Bethany Kandel

Illustrator: Carol Halebian

ISBN# 0-8225-2583-6 Date Published: 1996 Price: $ 14.95

Publisher: Lerner Pages: 32

TWO MRS. GIBSONS

A biracial girl describes her Japanese mother and her African American grandmother.

A touching tribute to the two most important women in Ms. Igus' life — her Japanese mother and her African American grandmother. This heartwarming story is a celebration of family heritage and bonds that know no boundaries. Through simple language and metaphor, the story demonstrates that the Mrs. Gibsons are as different as a pot of rice and a pot of greens, as different as Japan and Tennessee. Books in Print: "The story is a loving mood piece, telling of strength through difference as together mother and grandmother provide a loving and nurturing environment. Igus' simple, affecting prose speaks directly to the heart and is well matched by Wells' warm, lush paintings."

Keywords

Multicultural, Fiction, Racial/Ethnic Identity, Family Life, Diversity, Multiracial Identity

Age Range:

School-agers 9-12

Author: Toyomi Igus

Editor: Sue Wells

ISBN# 892391359 Date Published: 1996 Price: $ 14.95

Publisher: Children's Book Pages: 32

WORLD OF DAUGHTER MCGUIRE

Daughter McGuire, an eleven-year-old biracial child, finds a way through some tough real-life issues.

Daughter's parents are trying to decide if they will get divorced. A school report about her heritage makes her wonder who she really is, not an easy task for a girl whose grandparents are African American, Italian, Irish-Catholic and Russian Jews. Then someone calls her "zebra," and it all seems to be getting to be just too much.... Is it okay to be different? Most preteens will identify with at least one of Daughter's issue and be reassured when they find out how Daughter gets through it.

Keywords

Multiracial, Racial/Ethnic Identity, Core Issues (Feelings), Race Relations, Racism, Fiction

Age Range:

School-agers 9-12

Author: Sharon Dennis Wyeth

Sharon Wyeth is the author of *World of Daughter McGuire* and *Something Beautiful.*

ISBN# 0-440-41114-9 Date Published: 1995 Price: $ 3.99

Publisher: BDD Books Young Readers Pages: 176

Rating

AS LONG AS THE RIVERS FLOW

The stories of nine Native Americans.

This collection offers the stories of nine Native Americans, from Geronimo to Louise Erdrich, who overcame difficult obstacles to make history. Each person is presented in the context of the community in which he or she lived. The title is taken from the language of many treaties between Native Americans and the US government; though it was meant by the Natives to mean "forever," it has seldom lasted in the long history of violated trust and broken promises. Kirkus Reviews says "this distinguished book merits a place on every shelf, not just those built to meet multicultural needs."

Keywords

Native American, Role Models, Race Relations, Cultural History, US History, Biography

Age Range:

School-agers 9-12

Author: Paula Gunn Allen

Author: Patricia Clark Smith

ISBN# 590478699 *Date Published:* 1996 *Price:* $ 15.95

Publisher: Scholastic *Pages:*

Rating

BEADED MOCCASINS, THE

12-year-old Mary Campbell was kidnapped by Delaware Indians and lived with them six years.

Booklist says, "Mary's first-person narrative will hold readers fast: the terror of her capture, the candor about her inner struggle as a captive who begins to feel part of her new family. Few of the Delaware are individualized, except for her adoptive grandfather, but there is no reverential stereotyping. Mary has seen him order the scalping of a baby, but he is gentle with her, and she comes to love and respect him.... Readers will be moved by the psychological truth of her adjustment and her yearning to prove herself and belong." For adopted children, this story will touch many core issues of belonging and resiliency.

Keywords

Native American, Adopted Child, Core Issues (Feelings), Fiction

Age Range:

School-agers 9-12

Author: Lynda Durrant

ISBN# 395853982 *Date Published:* 1998 *Price:* $ 15.00

Publisher: Clarion *Pages:* 183

BOY CALLED SLOW, A

As he grew, his people came to call him by a new name – Sitting Bull.

Dramatic text and rich paintings bring this legendary hero to life. Full color. From Booklist: "Being named Slow hardly slowed this protagonist: he became Sitting Bull. Bruchac's sensitively told history of Slow's coming-of-age reassures boys that success comes through effort, not birth. Slow yearns for a strong name like his father's. Slow does his best in everything and ends up racing ahead of the war party in his first raid to attack the Crows, who quickly flee. Slow's father proudly renames him Sitting Bull. In brilliant counterpoint to the story's emotional timelessness is Baviera's vision of the Lakotas as spiritually and culturally distant from us. His illustrations brilliantly portray a vanished culture."

Keywords

Native American, Cultural History, Biography, Role Models

Age Range:

School-agers 9-12

Author: Joseph Bruchac

Illustrator: Rocco Baviera

Joseph Bruchac is the author of *A Boy Called Slow; Between Earth and Sky; The First Strawberries* and more.

ISBN# 69811616 *Date Published:* 1995 *Price:* $ 5.99

Publisher: Putnam-Paperstar *Pages:* 32

BROTHER EAGLE/SISTER SKY

Chief Seattle calls upon us to take care of the earth.

An inspirational story from Native American lore with attractive illustrations. Books in Print: "Jeffers has paired Seattle's eloquent text with her dreamy, meticulous illustrations and the result is haunting... This thoughtful book deserves to be pondered and cherished by all." But another reviewer writes, "Alas, Jeffers' entire stock of characters appear to have come from Sioux Central Casting, complete with Plains ponies and teepees.... The beautiful, important words of the text are not well served by images that ignore the rich diversity of Amerind cultures in favor of cigar-store redskins." Winner of the 1992 ABBY Award.

Keywords

Native American, Folk tales and Legends, Self-Esteem, Spiritual Meanings

Age Range:

School-agers 9-12

Author: Susan Jeffers

ISBN# 0-8037-0969-2 *Date Published:* 1991 *Price:* $ 17.00

Publisher: Dial *Pages:* 32

Rating

BUFFALO DAYS

Clarence Three Irons, Jr., is a Crow Indian boy, living in Lodge Grass, Montana.

The buffalo has always been essential to Crow culture and the tragic impact of the loss of the herd and how the tribe acquired and maintains its current herd is brought to life in this stirring book. Descriptions of the annual Crow Fair and Rodeo reflect the grand buffalo days — showing Clarence building and camping in tipis, wearing ceremonial clothing, and participating in sacred dances. Horn Book says, "Both text and color photos are clear, informative, and appealing."

Keywords

Native American, Music and Dance, Rituals and traditions

Age Range

School-agers 9-12

Author: Diane Hoyt-Goldsmith

Author: Lawrence Migdale

Diane Hoyt-Goldsmith is the author of *Hoang Anh: A Vietnamese American Boy; Buffalo Days*; and *The Day of the Dead.*

ISBN# 823413276 | Date Published 1997 | Price $ 16.95

Publisher Holiday House | Pages 32

Rating

CHEROKEES PAST AND PRESENT, THE

An authentic guide to the Cherokee people.

This small book offers a lot of information on Cherokee history, language, food, dwellings, clothing, arts and crafts, government, religion, legends, and games in this accurate and accessible account of the Cherokee people.

Keywords

Native American, Language, Guidebook

Age Range

School-agers 9-12

Author: Shirley J. Simmons

Author: J. Edward Sharpe

ISBN# 935741046 | Date Published 1997 | Price $ 3.95

Publisher Cherokee Pubns. | Pages 32

COYOTE STORIES FOR CHILDREN

Tales of the clever coyote – a classic character in Native American oral traditions.

This picture book will hold broad appeal to children of any ethnic or racial heritage. Books in Print writes, "This collection of four Native American stories joins a growing body of retellings of the exploits of this clever but exasperating trickster. Both wise and foolish, this mythic figure is presented in a fast-flowing, read-aloud style. Border panels and full-page black-and-white pen-and-ink drawings are in an entertaining cartoon style that perfectly complements these rollicking adventures. There is also a brief introduction explaining who Coyote is and the Native conception of storytelling. Ideally suited for story hours and reading aloud."

Keywords

Native American, Folk tales and Legends

Age Range

School-agers 9-12

Author: Susan Strauss

Illustrator: Gary Lund

ISBN# 0-941831-62-0 | Date Published 1991 | Price $ 7.95

Publisher Beyond Words | Pages 50

GREAT ENCOUNTER, THE

An enlightening look at history!!!

With the help of this book, children will learn that long before Columbus came to America, Africans and Native Americans lived together, peacefully.

Keywords

Race Relations, Cultural History, African American, Native American, Fiction, Black Identity

Age Range

School-agers 9-12

Author: Patricia A. Piercy

Illustrator: Napoleon Wilkerson

ISBN# 913543268 | Date Published 1991 | Price $ 6.95

Publisher African American Images | Pages 52

PEOPLE SHALL CONTINUE, THE

Rating 

"Best overview of Native history for younger children I have ever seen..." –Books Without Bias

An epic story of Native American people, in the rhythms of traditional oral narration. Its purpose is to instill a sense of responsibility, of all people, for life, and to give hope.

Keywords

Self-Esteem, Native American, Cultural History, Racial/Ethnic Identity

Age Range:

School-agers 9-12

Author: Simon J. Ortiz

Illustrator: Sharol Graves

ISBN# 892391251 Date Published: 1994 Price: $ 6.95

Publisher: Native American/Acoma Pages:

POWWOW

Rating 

Montana's vibrant Crow's Fair, the largest powwow in the United States.

From Kirkus Reviews: "Photographer Ancona is at his experienced best. Featured is a boy transformed from T-shirted kid to warrior-dancer; but the real focus is on the four kinds of dancers — Traditional, Fancy, Grass, and Jingle-dress — and on the grace and excitement of their performances. Particularly moving are some individual ceremonies: a giveaway of items for an honored dancer; a family dance to welcome a little girl into the ranks of the dancers. The unity of the many tribes engaged in the ceremony, the sense of family, and the cherishing of actively participating children are all themes young people will appreciate. A lively, positive portrayal of contemporary Native Americans."

Keywords

Native American

Age Range:

School-agers 9-12

Author/Illustrator: George Ancona

George Ancona is the author of *Powwow; Let's Dance; Fiesta Fireworks; The Piñata Maker; Fiesta USA: Being Adopted* and more.

ISBN# 152632697 Date Published: 1998 Price: $ 9.00

Publisher: Harcourt Brace Pages: |

THANKSGIVING, A NATIVE PERSPECTIVE

An authentic Native American view of Thanksgiving.

This book belongs in the home libraries of all Americans. If we do nothing to teach our children the true history we have shared, we do nothing to create a better today. "All Native nations have celebrations of the harvest that come from ancient tradition. The U.S. holiday perpetuates a myth which is a bitter reminder for all Native people of 500 years of betrayal returned for friendship. This source book of essays, speeches, poetry, stories and activities will help teachers and students think critically about what has been, and continues to be, taught as the 'first' Thanksgiving." —Oyate

Keywords

Native American, Holidays and Celebrations, Educational Issues, Self-Esteem, Spiritual Meanings, Antiracist Strategies

Age Range:

School-agers 9-12

Author: Loretta Lopez

ISBN# Date Published: 1997 Price: $ 8.00

Publisher: Oyate Pages:

WE ARE MESQUAKIE, WE ARE ONE

A fact-based novel about a Native American girl's experiencing of forced migration in the 1830s.

From the publisher: "This powerful, fact-based story is seen through the eyes of Hidden Doe, a young Native American girl who grows to maturity during the 1840s, when the US government forces her people to leave their homeland in Iowa and to make the long and bitter journey to a Kansas reservation. As she comes of age during this painful time, Hidden Doe is counseled in the ways of her people by Gray Gull, her courageous grandmother, and by Great Eagle, the wise chief, and soon also grows to know Bright Eagle, the young man who will win her love."

Keywords

Biography, Cultural History, Girl Power, US History, Native American, Race Relations

Age Range:

School-agers 9-12

Author: Hadley Irwin

Hadley Irwin is the pen name of Lee Hadley and Annabelle Irwin who teach English at Iowa State University.

ISBN# 1-55861-148-7 Date Published: 1997 Price: $ 9.95

Publisher: Oxford Paperbacks Pages: 128

Rating

ALL KINDS

It's much more fun when we share.

Race and color have nothing to do with being "good or bad, kind or mean, fast or slow, strong or weak, clever or stupid." We all belong equally and we all belong together, as this book demonstrates, embracing the idea that "Friendships and new ideas are the best things." Bright illustrations. Easy-to-read text.

Keywords

Multiracial, Race Relations, Racial/Ethnic Identity

Age Range:

School-agers 9-12

Author: Pam Adams

ISBN# 0-85953-353-0 *Date Published:* 1990 *Price:* $ 3.99

Publisher: Child's Play *Pages:*

Rating

ALL THE COLORS OF THE RACE

Poems of the inner feelings of a biracial girl.

Let yourself and your family be filled by these poems, written from the perspective of a biracial young girl. Her voice is wry and confident but not cocky, as she recounts experiences so familiar to people with multiple racial and ethnic identities: "When they asked if I was black or white or what, I said: I was black and white and what difference did it make to them. And they said: did I have the answers to the math problems? And I had the answers." A wonderful way to help children give voice to their own claims of identity, these inspiring, musical, and enduring poems are filled with power for all who are unique (which means every last one of us). Don't miss them.

Keywords

Multicultural, Self-Esteem, Racial/Ethnic Identity, African American, Core Issues (Feelings), Multiracial Identity

Age Range:

School-agers 9-12

Poet: Arnold Adoff

Arnold Adoff, the winner of the 1988 NCTE Award for Excellence in Poetry for Children, is the author of over 30 books.

ISBN# 0-688-11496-2 *Date Published:* 1982 *Price:* $ 4.95

Publisher: Shepard *Pages:*

BLACK AND WHITE

A multilayered nonlinear picture story; winner of the 1991 Caldecott Medal.

Black and White is not "about" something; it is an exciting experience with endless options and possibilities. Kids get to navigate the unknown relationships between words and pictures, gathering new clues each time they look with care. Each page has four panels concerning parents, trains, and cows. Are they separate stories or one interrelated narrative? This is an interactive, thought-provoking book that experiments with time, and interaction — a wonderful opportunity to immerse oneself in open-minded exploration. Isn't that the key to true multicultural understandings? Horn Book calls it "a freewheeling and free-spirited escape from the ordinary."

Keywords

Multicultural, Core Issues (Feelings), Race Relations

Age Range:

School-agers 9-12

Author: David Macaulay

David Macaulay is the author of *The Way Things Work*.

ISBN# 395521513 *Date Published:* 1990 *Price:* $ 16.00

Publisher: Houghton Mifflin *Pages:* 32

CHILDREN JUST LIKE ME

A lively book of vivid photographs showing we're all more alike than we are different.

Photographs of children in more than 30 countries show their families, homes, clothes, food, friends, favorite games, and other aspects of their lives. Focused on concrete aspects of everyday life from children's perspectives. Readers will enjoy learning about the dreams, beliefs, hopes, fears, and day-to-day lives of other children as they discuss them with the authors, a teacher and a photographer. Includes interviews with youngsters from all walks of life, revealing their diverse cultural backgrounds and universal similarities. Published in association with UNICEF to coincide with UNICEF's fiftieth anniversary.

Keywords

Multicultural, Multiracial, Diversity, Cultural History, Family Life

Age Range:

School-agers 9-12

Photographer: Barnabas Kindersley

Author: Sue Copsey

ISBN# 0-7894-0201-7 *Date Published:* 1995 *Price:* $ 16.95

Publisher: Dorling Kindersley *Pages:* 79

Rating

CHILDREN OF ASIAN AMERICA

Rare stories about contemporary young people from various Asian American communities.

Writes Horn Book, "Compiled on behalf of the Asian American Coalition; though didactic, the twelve stories and poems in this oversized book will nevertheless affirm the experiences of many young Asian Americans. Many of the pictures reflect communities other than the specific one being featured." And the Midwest Book Review says, "Children from Thai, Vietnamese, and other Asian communities as well as biracial Asian American families form the basis for various multicultural themes in this excellent collection."

Keywords

Asian American, Multiracial, Thai, Vietnamese, Family Life, Cambodia

Age Range:

School-agers 9-12

Author: Sandra S. Ymate

Author: Gene H. Mayeda

Sandra S. Ymate is the author of *Children of Asian America* and *Ashok By Any Other Name.*

ISBN# 1879965151 Date Published: 1995 Price: $ 18.95

Publisher: Polychrome Pages:

Rating

FRIENDSHIP

A wonderful book to jump-start conversations about racism.

This brief but poignant story about friendship and betrayal in the relationship between a White store owner and an elderly Black customer in Mississippi in the racist climate of 1933 won the 1998 Coretta Scott King Award. The characters are strong, the situation moving. Horn Book Magazine writes, "Eloquent in both its brevity and understatement, the story draws from her family's experiences to enlarge her readers' understanding of a still unresolved heritage."

Keywords

Race Relations, Racism, US History, Core Issues (Feelings), Friendship, Fiction

Age Range:

School-agers 9-12

Author: Mildred D. Taylor

Illustrator: Max Ginsberg

Mildred D. Taylor is the author of *The Friendship* and *The Well: David's Story.*

ISBN# 140389644 Date Published: 1998 Price: $ 3.99

Publisher: Puffin Pages: 56

FROM FAR AWAY

A collaboration between Robert Munsch and a child who immigrated from Beirut to Canada.

Escaping with her family from war-torn Lebanon, Saoussan finds life in Canada is sometimes scary, in this story about cultural acclimation and perseverance. "I got a letter from Saoussan," says Munsch. "She wanted me to come to her school and tell stories. She wrote that 'many strange things happened when I could not speak English.' I asked, 'What strange things?' She sent back a very touching letter about her first Halloween in Canada. I liked the letter so much I asked her let me make it into a book. We worked on the story together. She was a savage editor. We split royalties 50/50."

Keywords

Multicultural, Language, Grief and Loss, Core Issues (Feelings), Biography

Age Range:

School-agers 9-12

Author: Saoussan Askar

Author: Robert Munsch

Illustrator: Michael Martchenko

155037396X

ISBN# 1995 Date Published: $ 4.95 Price: Annick

Publisher: Press Pages:

GOLEM

The story of the Golem created from river clay to protect the people against persecution.

A Caldecott Medal Book told in a warm Yiddish colloquial idiom about a Rabbi who created a giant to protect the Jewish people against the "Blood Lie," the myth perpetuated by anti-Semitic gentiles that Jews were mixing the blood of Christian children with the flour and water of matzo. This well-told story will be interesting to anyone who wants to understand race relations and coping strategies.

Keywords

Race Relations, Racism, Religion, Judaism, Cultural History, Folk tales and Legends

Age Range:

School-agers 9-12

Author: Barbara Rogasky

Author: David Wisniewski

ISBN# 395726182 Date Published: 1996 Price: $ 15.95

Publisher: Clarion Pages: 32

Rating

HIDE AND SEEK

Rachel and her family go into hiding after other Jewish children are taken away.

Rachel Hartog is eight years old in 1940 when she begins to notice changes around her and the innumerable restrictions placed on the lives of Jews. This is a good introduction for young children to the story of the Holocaust, a story that must be told.

Keywords

Judaism, Grief and Loss, Family Life, Cultural History, Core Issues (Feelings), Racial/Ethnic Identity

Age Range.

School-agers 9-12

Author: Ida Vos

ISBN# 140369082 Date Published. 1994 Price. $ 3.99
Publisher. Puffin Pages.

Rating

HONORING OUR ANCESTORS

Fourteen outstanding artists remember the ancestors who most touched their lives.

It helps to know where you've come from to figure out where you're going and this high-spirited tribute to a lively and diverse group of family or spiritual ancestors is designed to inspire kids to find out about and honor their own ancestors. Creative and filled with life, this is a reach out and take action book that will encourage kids to draw, paint, write, or find their own way to honor those who have made a difference in their lives.

Keywords

Multicultural, Intergenerational, Family Life

Age Range.

School-agers 9-12

Editor: Harriet Rohmer

Harriet Rohmer is the founding director of Children's Book Press, a nonprofit publisher.

ISBN# 892391588 Date Published. 1999 Price. $ 15.95
Publisher. Children's Book Pages.

IT'S OUR WORLD, TOO

Stories of young people who are making a difference.

True stories of children who are making a REAL difference to meet challenges of crime, racism, homeless people, saving rain forests, etc. Inspiring and stimulating.

Keywords

Self-Esteem, Multicultural, Role Models

Age Range.

School-agers 9-12

Author: Phillip Hoose

ISBN# 0-316-37245-5 Date Published. 1994 Price. $ 13.95
Publisher. Little Brown Pages. 166

KID'S MULTICULTURAL COOKBOOK, THE

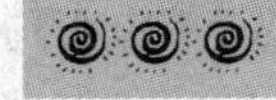

Food and fun around the world. Let's get cooking. Kids can.

Meet kids and share the delicious foods they cook in their kitchens. Recipes for over 75 multicultural dishes along with games, traditions, customs and more. Sample Sherpa popcorn from Nepal, Mexican hot chocolate, real ginger ale from Liberia, Thai watermelon slush and more. The illustrations are a combination of cartoons and photographs.

Keywords

Diversity, Cultural History, Multicultural, Games and Activities, Skill Mastery, Food

Age Range.

School-agers 9-12

Editor: Deanna Cook

ISBN# 913589917 Date Published. 1995 Price. $ 12.95
Publisher. Williamson Pages. 160

LET'S COOK

Rating 

A multicultural cookbook.

This book, with its clear step-by-step instructions, illustrations, and photos of the finished dishes, is packed with ideas, hints, and shortcuts. Full color.

Keywords

Multicultural, Self-Esteem, Games and Activities, Skill Mastery, Food

Age Range:

School-agers 9-12

Author: World Book

ISBN# 716656019 Date Published: 1997 Price: $ 4.95

Publisher: World Book Pages: 24

MORNING GIRL

Rating 

What does your child think about strangers taking over someone's home?

Michael Dorris writes about the deeper feelings that accompany life's experiences. The story of *Morning Girl*, which was developed from a brief entry in Christopher Columbus' diary, is set in the Bahamas in 1492. Two island children grow up in this tropical paradise and become very close to one another and very trusting of the world. When Europeans arrive, intending to take over the Bahamas, the children innocently welcome them. This view of Europeans as conquerors can provide a springboard to a discussion which will help you know how much your child understands about racism and about the history of the United States as it relates to indigenous people and slavery.

Keywords

Fiction, European History, Race Relations, Racial/Ethnic Identity, Racism, Cultural History

Age Range:

School-agers 9-12

Author: Michael Dorris

Michael Dorris is an adoptive father and the author of *The Broken Cord, Morning Girl, The Window* and numerous others.

ISBN# 1562826611 Date Published: Price: $ 3.99

Publisher: Hyperion Pages:

SABBATH GARDEN, THE

Intergenerational friendship between an African child and an elderly Jewish man.

"Opal Tyler, a 13-year-old African American, lives in a world of drugs, crime, and squalor.... Opal forges a friendship with Solomon Leshko, an elderly Jewish man who is trapped in his memories and his grief, and yes, trapped in a neighborhood he has watched change from a clean, solid place to a filthy crime-ridden slum.... The story deals with racial and religious relations, but it is also a book that looks at pride and dignity." —School Library Journal

Keywords

African American, Filipino American, Judaism, Intergenerational, Race Relations, Fiction

Age Range:

School-agers 9-12

Author: Patricia Baird Greene

ISBN# 525674306 Date Published: 1993 Price: $ 15.99

Publisher: Lodestar Pages:

STRING FIGURES FROM AROUND THE WORLD

All about string figures and how to make them.

Skill mastery is a great way to build self-esteem — and making string figures is fun! Directions for how to make string figures from many cultures. A unique way of learning about people from around the world. String figures from New Guinea, New Caledonia, Africa, Hawaii, Native Americans, Japan and South America with easy-to-follow instructions, stories, and the fun of learning something new.

Keywords

Multiracial, Self-Esteem, Games and Activities, Skill Mastery

Age Range:

School-agers 9-12

Author: Serena DeWitt

Illustrator: Robin Michel

ISBN# 893463566 Date Published: 1992 Price: $ 5.95

Publisher: Helan Pages: 27

Rating

TALKING WALLS: THE STORIES CONTINUE

Do walls talk? If they did, what would they tell us?

This sequel to the award-winning *Talking Walls* will spark the curiosity of young readers. Explore the mysteries of the unfinished Mayan murals, started a thousand years ago in Bonampak, Mexico. March along a wall in Northern England, built with fortresses and towers by the Roman Emperor Hadrian. The world is full of interesting walls, from the mighty dikes of the Netherlands, to the Wall of Messages in Chile. Beautifully illustrated by Anne Sibley O'Brien, these stories help us explore and understand the diversity of our world and its people. Full color.

Keywords

Race Relations, Multicultural, Diversity

Age Range:

School-agers 9-12

Author: Margy Burns Knight

Illustrator: Anne Sibley O'Brien

Margy Burns Knight also wrote *Welcoming Babies* and *Talking Walls*, illustrated by Anne Sibley O'Brien.

ISBN# 884481689 Date Published: Price: $ 8.95

Publisher: Tilbury Pages: 40

Rating

TO BE A KID

Around the world, kids will be kids.

In a truly multicultural book, wonderful photographs contributed by Peace Corps volunteers and John D. Ivanko, an award-winning photographer, illustrate a spirited look at the universal joys and activities shared by children in forty countries around the world from playing ball with friends to being carried on a parent's shoulders. SHAKTI for Children, a nonprofit organization to teach children to value diversity and the publisher Charlesbridge, will each donate a portion of their profits to The Global Fund for Children, supporting community-based educational projects for children around the world.

Keywords

Multicultural, Diversity

Age Range:

School-agers 9-12

Author: Maya Ajmera

Photographer: John D. Ivanko

Maya Ajmera is the founder and executive director of SHAKTI for Children. She is the coauthor of *Children from Australia to Zimbabwe*.

ISBN# 8810688411 Date Published: 1999 Price: $ 15.95

Publisher: Charlesbridge Pages: 32

UNDER OUR SKIN: KIDS TALK ABOUT RACE

Teens talk about race.

A companion book to *What I Believe: Kids Talk About Faith*, this book explores one of the most explosive issues of our time — race — through the eyes and words of six teenagers of different ethnic backgrounds. Tad, a Caucasian; Rosa, a Hispanic; Akram, an Arab; Jenny, a Chinese; Jason, an African American; and Janell, a Native American, candidly discuss how the traditions of their different cultural heritages affect their daily lives, their views on race, and their experiences with prejudice. These six young voices celebrate the best of our multicultural society and offer words of wisdom and hope for the future.

Keywords

Multicultural, Latino/a, Racial/Ethnic Identity, Arab, Native American

Age Range:

School-agers 9-12

Author: Debbie Holsclaw Birdseye

Illustrator/ Photographer: Robert Crum

Author: Tom Birdseye

Debbie Holsclaw Birdseye and Tom Birdseye have collaborated on two previous books.

ISBN# 082341325X Date Published: 1997 Price: $ 15.95

Publisher: Holiday House Pages: 32

WHY DOES THAT MAN HAVE SUCH A BIG NOSE?

Give your curious child a chance to have questions answered straight.

Kids have a natural curiosity about people who look different from them. This book answers questions without embarrassing the asker, answerer or the person being asked about. It helps kids understand that different does not have to mean bad, wrong, ugly or scary, but can be a reflection of everyone's uniqueness, heritage, charm and value. A Pact bestseller.

Keywords

Diversity, Multicultural, Racism

Age Range:

School-agers 9-12

Author: Mary Beth Quinsey

ISBN# 0-943990-24-6 Date Published: Price: $ 5.95

Publisher: Parenting Press Pages: 36

ASHA'S MUMS

Rating 

Asha has two mothers and has to answer the other kids' questions.

Asha has two mothers. When she tells the kids at school about it, there are more questions than she first anticipated. This story tells how she comes to deal with issues she has to face with friends about being in a Lesbian family. Nicely illustrated.

Keywords

Adoption, Gay and/or Lesbian, Family Life, Girl Power

Age Range:

School-agers 9-12

Author: Rosamund Elwin

Author: Dawn Lee

Illustrator: Michele Paulson

ISBN# 088961143-2 Date Published: 1996 Price: $ 5.95
Publisher: Women's Press Pages: 24

BE GOOD TO EDDIE LEE

Rating 

Eddie Lee has Down Syndrome. Christy wants to be good to him, but....

Christy and JimBud are off to find frogs' eggs on a hot summer day. Eddie Lee tags along, cheerfully oblivious to being unwanted. Unexpectedly, he takes Christy to a little pond she didn't know about and finds a beautiful lily. When they see her distorted reflection in the water, he tells Christy, "Î like you anyway." Christy discovers that good things can be found in unusual places. Kirkus Reviews says, "What makes Fleming's first book so effective are the carefully selected detail and authentic portrayal of the children's attitudes — as well as Cooper's luminous full-bleed art, summoning up all the enchantment of a lovely summer day and presenting Eddie Lee as believably endearing."

Keywords

Differently-abled, Friendship, Special Needs, Core Issues (Feelings)

Age Range:

School-agers 9-12

Author: Virginia Fleming

ISBN# 0698115821* Date Published: 1997 Price: $ 5.95
Publisher: Putnam-Paperstar Pages: 32

BOUNDLESS GRACE

The importance of family: those we live with and those we don't.

Grace, whose parents are divorced, has the opportunity to visit her father in Africa along with his new wife and their two children. After traveling there with her grandma, and after much initial uncertainty as to whether she belongs, finds a way to feel connected to this family while still remaining part of her family at home. The obvious linkages to adoption make this a useful book for any child with more than one family, but it lacks the life force of *Amazing Grace.*

Keywords

African American, Family Life, Self-Esteem, Racial/Ethnic Identity, Girl Power, Fiction

Age Range:

Preschool, early school-age

Author: Mary Hoffman

Mary Hoffman is the author of *Amazing Grace* and *An Angel Just Like Me.*

ISBN# 803717156 Date Published: 1995 Price: $ 14.99
Publisher: Dial Pages:

FAMILIES

Children and parents openly discuss the challenges and benefits of contemporary family life.

Families — what are they? Each of the kids in this book has learned some important things about families. Adam knows you can survive the death of a parent. Jody knows you can grow to love someone you thought you'd hate. They all know that it isn't important who makes up a family; what's important is how members feel about each other and what they do for each other.

Keywords

Adoption, Family Life, Diversity, Core Issues (Feelings)

Age Range:

School-agers 9-12

Author-Illustrator: Aylette Jenness

Aylette Jenness is an author and photographer. This book began as a photographic exhibition at The Children's Museum in Boston, Mass.

ISBN# 0-395-66952-9 Date Published: Price: $ 4.95
Publisher: Houghton Mifflin Pages:

FOREVER FRIENDS

Rating

A poignant story about a young African American girl's first encounter with death.

This portrait of a rich, full, yet ordinary life, its collapse, and its hard-won reconstruction will help young people realize that going on is possible. This inspiring story, for any young person who has experienced a loss of any kind, should be a catalyst for discussion of losses akin to those experienced in adoption.

Keywords

Grief and Loss, African American, Family Life, Self-Esteem, Fiction, Core Issues (Feelings)

Age Range:

School-agers 9-12

Author: Candy Dawson Boyd

ISBN# 140320776 Date Published: 1986 Price: $ 4.99

Publisher: Puffin Pages:

GIRLS TO THE RESCUE

Rating

Tales of clever, courageous girls from around the world.

The girls in these stories entertain us, inspire us, make the difference, save the day and never wait to be rescued by Prince Charming. Magic or violence are never the solutions. These are girls who are resourceful and fair and who make the reader proud (and sometimes laugh out loud). A wonderful read. This is book one of what has become a series of four and possibly growing of multicultural self-esteem- building books about girls.

Keywords

Multicultural, Self-Esteem, Cultural History, Racial/Ethnic Identity, Girl Power

Age Range:

School-agers 9-12

Editor: Paul Schmid

Editor: Bruce Lansky

ISBN# 671899791 Date Published: 1995 Price: $ 3.95

Publisher: Simon & Schuster Pages:

I KNOW I MADE IT HAPPEN

Keeping "I made it happen" thoughts from turning into "I should have" and "If only."

This book is written in the voice of a child worrying that by thinking or feeling "mean" things, he or she may have caused a brother's hurt, a sister's fall, a grandma's death or a mom and dad's divorced. The book reassures the reader that these fears, though common, are not true.

Keywords

Core Issues (Feelings)

Age Range:

School-agers 9-12

Author: Lynn B. Blackburn

ISBN# 1561230162 Date Published: 1990 Price: $ 3.95

Publisher: Centering Corp. Pages: 24

IF THEY CAN DO IT, WE CAN, TOO

Kids write about famous people who overcame learning differences similar to theirs.

Inspiration and support for children with special needs. Eighteen elementary school students with learning differences wrote this book about famous people who needed to learn in different ways as children. The heroes they chose include figures as diverse as Leonardo da Vinci, Babe Ruth, Nelson Rockefeller, Gerald Ford, Stevie Wonder, Ann Bancroft, Greg Louganis, and Tom Cruise. This story projects positive images children will identify with. Differently-abled children will identify with this book, and all children will appreciate the importance of self-affirmation. Currently on back order from the publisher. We do not have a reprint date, but we expect to be able to ship it to you within 5 weeks.

Keywords

Special Needs, Role Models, Self-Esteem, Learning Difficulties, Biography, Differently-abled

Age Range:

School-agers 9-12

Author: Margo Dineen

ISBN# 0-925190-61-6 Date Published: 1992 Price: $ 5.95

Publisher: Deaconness Press Pages: 87

Rating

IT'S PERFECTLY NORMAL

Changing bodies, growing up, sex, and sexual health.

This is an informative, well crafted guide that addresses kids' concerns about their changing bodies and how they they function. Best of all, it includes multicultural models and promotes an acceptance of difference beyond the norm including wheelchair- bound people, aged people, Gay and Lesbian people, skinny people, fat people, people of all races — in short, a great diversity, and all treated with respect. Both physiological and psychological aspects of the issues are covered. Though topics of sexuality and sexual development are difficult for some, this book provides a positive foundation for discussion.

Keywords

Family Life, Diversity, Health

Age Range:

School-agers 9-12

Author: Robie H. Harris

Illustrator: Michael Emberley

ISBN# 1564021599 *Date Published:* 1996 *Price:* $ 10.99

Publisher: Candlewick *Pages:* 89

Rating

LILY'S CROSSING

Friendship and shared losses heighten the impact of this fast moving story.

This story, set in the summer of 1944, tells of Lily, whose mom died when she was little and whose father has enlisted in the Army. Alone with her grandmother, Lily meets Albert, a refugee from the Nazis, his family lost, who carries a grief of his own. The friendship they develop is based in part on their shared losses, heightening this book's appeal for adopted or foster children. From the New York Times Book Review: "With Ms. Giff's usual easygoing language and swift, short paragraphs, the impact of the war on an American child is brilliantly told." A Children's Books Editor's Recommended Book and a Newbery Honor Book.

Keywords

Grief and Loss, Girl Power, Intergenerational, Family Life, Friendship, Core Issues (Feelings)

Age Range:

School-agers 9-12

Author: Patricia Reilly Giff

ISBN# 440414539 *Date Published:* 1999 *Price:* $ 4.99

Publisher: Yearling Books *Pages:*

MY FAMILY TREE: A BIRD'S EYE VIEW

A book for blended families.

An activity kit for kids and their families, allowing room for families created through remarriage. Although it doesn't directly address adoptive and birth families, there is room for modification to allow for an adopted child's genealogical history. Multiracial illustrations.

Keywords

Family Life, Blended Family, Games and Activities

Age Range:

School-agers 9-12

Author: Nina Laden

ISBN# 811815285 *Date Published:* 1997 *Price:* $ 9.95

Publisher: Chronicle Books *Pages:*

NO KISS FOR MOTHER

"This fierce, funny book will make toes curl with horrified delight." – New York Times

In families formed by adoption, mothers often receive kid's anger. This book encourages talk about mother-child stuff from the child's view. From Horn Book: "The ornery protagonist Piper Paws hates his overly sweet mother's kisses and is a perfect enfant terrible at school. But Piper really loves his mother; in the end, they are reconciled, and Piper sells his stink bombs, slingshot, and firecrackers. Few have ever equaled Tomi Ungerer's dark genius when it comes to creating books for children." Winner of the American Institute for Graphic Arts Prize for illustration.

Keywords

Boy Focus, Core Issues (Feelings), Family Life, Mothers, Fiction

Age Range:

School-agers 9-12

Author: Tomi Ungerer

Tomi Ungerer is the author/illustrator of over 50 books for children.

ISBN# 1570982082 *Date Published:* 1998 *Price:* $ 5.95

Publisher: Roberts Rinehart *Pages:*

Rating

OUT OF THE DUST

A Newbery Medal Book

Written in freeform verse in a journal format, this novel is set in the Oklahoma dust bowl during the Great Depression. Billie Jo Kelby, the 14-year-old narrator, is "left out in the dust." She feels as if everything is her fault, blaming herself for the death of her mother and the baby and fearing that she will lose her father as well. Horn Book says that this book, with "nearly every word informed by longing, provides an immediacy that expressively depicts both a grim historical era and one family's healing." Children who have experienced loss on any level are likely to identify with Billie Jo.

Keywords

Poetry, Core Issues (Feelings), Grief and Loss, Girl Power, Fathers, US History

Age Range.

School-agers 9-12

Author: Karen Hesse

ISBN# 590371258 Date Published. 1997 Price. $ 4.99

Publisher. Scholastic Pages. 227

Rating

SOMETHING VERY SORRY

A story of family members supporting one another through the worst.

In this true story of nine-year-old Rosemyn, a horrifying accident rips Rosemyn's world apart. Mom died in the accident, Rose's little sister was brain injured, Dad has had an iron pin put in his leg and Rose's arm has been put in traction. Rose's diary, written after the accident, describes her feelings in simple, unadorned language and shows how she comes to mend. Children who have experienced loss are likely to be intensely interested in Rose's struggle to manage her grief, anger, and fear of the future. *Something Very Sorry* is a poignant survival story, one that deeply touches core issues.

Keywords

Grief and Loss, Core Issues (Feelings), Family Life, Biography

Age Range.

School-agers 9-12

Author: Arno Bohlmeijer

Author: Daniel Nevins

ISBN# 698116100 Date Published. Price. $ 5.95

Publisher. Paper Star Pages. 175

SURVIVAL GUIDE FOR KIDS WITH LD

Answers to frequently asked questions about learning difficulties for kids.

What happens to kids with learning difficulties when they grow up? Does LD ever go away? Why is it so hard to learn if you have LD? Why me? Is there more than one kind of LD? These and many more questions about learning difficulties are answered for kids in this survival guide.

Keywords

Core Issues (Feelings), Family Life, Special needs, Learning Difficulties

Age Range.

School-agers 9-12

Author: Gary Fisher

Author: Rhoda Cummings

Illustrator: Jackie Urbanovic

ISBN# 0-915793-18-0 Date Published. 1992 Price. $ 9.95

Publisher. Free Spirit Pub. Pages. 104

WHEN SOMETHING TERRIBLE HAPPENS

This hands-on workbook helps children learn to cope with grief.

Children touched by adoption often have a greater sensitivity than others to issues of guilt. This book, a hands-on workbook for children, deals with guilt for very young kids. Parents or counselors can work directly with children to explore complicated and strong emotions associated with very difficult things that happen to children.

Keywords

Grief and Loss, Core Issues (Feelings), Adopted Child, Foster Child, Orphan

Age Range.

School-agers 9-12

Author: Marge E. Heegaard

ISBN# 962050237 Date Published. 1992 Price. $ 6.95

Publisher. Woodland Press Pages. 32

Books for Teens and Young Adults

"You tell a story because a statement would be inadequate."
—Flannery O'Connor

Teens and young adults can be inspired to new thoughts or actions by immersing themselves in a good read about a character with whom they can identify. The best of books written for teens and young adults are more sophisticated in plot than are books for younger children and may depict complex characters, reflecting deepening levels of meaning. For these readers, poised on the high-wire of autonomy and individuation, we want to offer books that explicitly address issues which may tilt the balance, exploring questions like, "Who am I?" and "Where do I fit?" and "What do I want to make of myself?" These questions, and their answers, can be complicated, intensified, and perhaps enriched by the additional issues of race and adoption; the adolescent's developing preoccupation with identity and sexuality can be especially challenging for young adults as they realize the implications of their genetic and family heritages, including issues of their birth parents' sexuality and perhaps of their adoptive parents' infertility.

Although in this age group many of life's issues increasingly reach conscious consideration, these young adults may also be drawn to the power of metaphor; poetry and analogy can sometimes best express their interior world. Given this multitude of interests — ranging from analytic consideration of sexuality and identity, to realistic representation of their own lives, to metaphoric expression of universal human concerns — we have striven to offer not only a variety of topics but topics considered through a variety of forms: fictional, analytical, biographical, poetic and metaphoric. Our hope is that every teenager or young adult, in whatever circumstance, expressed in any language style, and struggling with any issue involving race, adoption, and identity, will find those concerns matched in the pages of a book that seems written "just for me." It's a tall order; we hope this guide helps you fill it.

Rating

ADAM AND EVE AND PINCH ME

Sara- the- Ice- Queen bounced between foster homes for 15 years.

Fifteen-year-old Sara Moone, abandoned at birth and shunted from one foster home to another, finds herself wanting to stay with her latest family. Then she learns that her birth mother has searched her out. Will she be asked to give up her new life?

Keywords

Attachment, Foster Child, Fiction, Core Issues (Feelings), Birth Parent, Foster Care

Age Range:

Teenagers

Author: Julie Johnston

ISBN# 0-14-037588-0 *Date Published:* 1994 *Price:* $ 4.99

Publisher: Puffin *Pages:* 180

Rating

ADOPTED FROM ASIA

Eleven young people share their experiences of being adopted from Korea.

Discusses prejudice, friends and dates, racial identity, self-esteem, family relationships and more. The tone is positive, optimistic and self-aware. "I consider myself as Korean American, but wouldn't try too hard to be either Korean or American. Until two years ago, I'd been trying so hard to be integrated into American society and to become Americanized. That's really who I am. I was so good in upgrading myself, being the norm, wearing right clothes, right looks, all that stuff, to be acceptable to my Caucasian peers. Because I was so different from others, I wanted to be like everyone else and wanted to fit into my peer group. Probably that's why I'm so Americanized."

Keywords

Transracial Adoption, International Adoption, Asian American, Korean American, Racial/Ethnic Identity, Adoption

Age Range:

Teenagers

Author: Frances Koh

ISBN# 960609067 *Date Published:* 1994 *Price:* $ 15.95

Publisher: EastWest Press *Pages:* 96

BABY

A heartwarming story about loss, connection, and the healing powers of language.

Larkin and her friend Lalo find a baby in a basket with this note: "This is Sophie. She is good.... I love her. I will come back for her one day." Larkin's family welcomes Sophie but her arrival forces them to come to terms with a secret loss. Some are afraid to love Sophie, always wondering if her mother will return for her. In time, though, Larkin learns to make peace with love and loss. This story of a family's responses to an abandoned baby is told with a child's voice and focuses on the child's role. Holding the reader captive from start to finish, it is sure to inspire discussion about family building through adoption and foster families. Highly recommended.

Keywords

Adoption, Family Life, Fiction, Foster Child, Friendship, Girl Power

Age Range:

Teenagers

Author: Patricia MacLachlan

Patricia MacLachlan won the 1986 Newbery Medal for *Sarah, Plain and Tall.*

ISBN# 0-385-31133-8 *Date Published:* 1993 *Price:* $ 4.95

Publisher: Delacorte Press *Pages:* 132

CAIRO HUGHES (LIVEWIRE)

A young-adult novel about transracial adoption in England.

This book was not available for review in time for publication in this edition of the BookSource. If you would like updated information, please call Pact at 415 221-6957.

Keywords

Africa, Adoption, Fiction, Transracial Adoption, Racial/Ethnic Identity

Age Range:

Teenagers

Author: Millie Murray

ISBN# 704349361 *Date Published:* 1997 *Price:* $ 9.30

Publisher: Trafalger Square *Pages:*

CELEBRATING THE HERO

Rating

An American teenager seeks her identity in her homeland, Colombia.

When an American teen travels to her mother's birthplace in Colombia to attend a ceremony for her illustrious grandfather, she attempts to come to terms with her mother's death and make peace with her own feelings of guilt. "Jenkins weaves a dreamy...narrative that explores the uses — and abuses — of power, loyalty and trust within a family, and that also examines the workings of imagination and memory," says Publisher's Weekly.

Keywords

Grief and Loss, Latino/a, Self-Esteem, Colombia, Family Life

Age Range:

Teenagers

Author: Lyll Becerra de Jenkins

ISBN# 140376054 Date Published: 1993 Price: $ 4.99

Publisher: Lodestar/Puffin Pages:

CINDY'S GLORY

Rating

A teen fantasy about adoption.

Cindy Blake is happy living at Whitebrook Farm and riding Glory, the colt that she rescued from abuse — until her worst nightmares begin to come true: her adoption to the McClean family is not approved and Glory is put up for sale. What can Cindy do? Since the author has created a highly unlikely scenario in which young Cindy is the trainer of a thoroughbred race horse, it's likely she can do anything, but some young adults will enjoy her heroic role.

Keywords

Adoption, Adopting Older Child, Girl Power, Fiction

Age Range:

Teenagers

Author: Joanna Campbell

ISBN# 61063258 Date Published: 1997 Price: $ 4.50

Publisher: Harper Row Pages:

COPING WITH BEING ADOPTED

One of the few books to help young adopted adults cope with adoptism in society.

Discusses feelings and questions associated with being adopted, taking into account both birth parents and adoptive parents and dealing with issues from the beginning of placement onward.

Keywords

Adoption, Core Issues (Feelings), Triad Issues

Age Range:

Teenagers

Author: Shari Cohen

ISBN# 823907708 Date Published: 1988 Price: $ 17.95

Publisher: Rosen Pub. Group Pages: 126

DETOUR FOR EMMY (AND STUDY GUIDE)

Inspiring story of a young girl, alone and pregnant.

Realistically portrays the struggles of teenage love and teenage motherhood. A well-written story that will be recognizable to a teen facing unplanned pregnancy and that presents positive options without falling into melodrama.

Keywords

Birth Parent, Fiction, Placement, Adoption, Core Issues (Feelings)

Age Range:

Teenagers

Author: Marilyn Reynolds

Marilyn Reynolds is the author of *Detour for Emmy* and *Too Soon For Jeff.*

ISBN# 0-930934-76-8 Date Published: Price: $ 8.95

Publisher: Morning Glory Pages:

Rating

DON'T THINK TWICE

Living in a maternity home gives 17-year-old Anne plenty to think about.

Set in the late 1960s in a rural Texas home for pregnant teens, this story's characters include a California "hippie," a 12-year-old who was raped by her father, a sorority girl from Mississippi, and Anne, the narrator. Though Anne's dysfunctional family offer her no support, she slowly builds friendships among the disparate girls at the home. One by one, the girls have their babies, place them in adoptions, and move on, but it's never an easy journey. There are no saviors and no happy endings.

Keywords

Birth Parent, Placement, Fiction, Friendship, Birth Parent

Age Range:

Teenagers

Author: Ruth Pennebecker

ISBN# 805044078 *Date Published:* 1996 *Price:* $ 3.99

Publisher: Henry Holt *Pages:*

Rating

EDGAR ALLAN

It's not easy being a brother when a new child is adopted into your family.

Edgar Allan is one of the first stories about an African American family adopting a new child and has become a classic of its genre. It presents the story of a minister's family told by the minister's son, who is troubled when he has to share his privileges and position with a newly adopted child.

Keywords

Transracial Adoption, Sibling Issues, Adoption

Age Range:

Teenagers

Author: J. Neufeld

ISBN# 0-451-16775-9 *Date Published:* 1987 *Price:* $ 3.99

Publisher: Mass Market Paperback *Pages:*

FACE IN MY MIRROR, THE

At 15, Mai, an adopted Vietnamese American girl, is having an identity crisis.

Mai Houston is a Vietnamese American child who has been adopted by a loving couple from California. Now, at 15, she is having an identity crisis, especially after some racial incidents. She goes to spend some time with her biological aunt in Boston, where she learns — in a most dangerous way — that life is more than just one culture or another. Original.

Keywords

Adoption, Asian American, Fiction, Girl Power, Vietnamese American, Transracial Adoption

Age Range:

Teenagers

Author: Maureen Wartski

ISBN# 449704432 *Date Published:* 1994 *Price:* $ 3.99

Publisher: Mass Market Paperback *Pages:*

FACE ON THE MILK CARTON

Oh, my God, that's me! Why is my face on the milk carton?

A young girl is shocked to discover that the photo depicted on a milk carton is of herself as a young girl. Are her parents her real parents, or was she kidnapped as a young child? This plot touches on one of the questions that many adopted teens secretly wonder: Did my birth parents place me for adoption, or was I kidnapped?

Keywords

Adoption, Family Life, Core Issues (Feelings), Fiction

Age Range:

Teenagers

Author: Caroline B. Cooney

ISBN# 440220653 *Date Published:* 1999 *Price:* $ 5.50

Publisher: Dell *Pages:*

FAMILY SECRETS (DEAR DIARY)

Rating

Will Sarah find her birth family in time to save her life?

Sarah Davenport's only hope for life is a bone marrow transplant from a family member. But Sarah is adopted and does not even know her birth family's name. In the fight to save her life — and to learn more about her roots — Sarah travels across the country looking for her birth mother and a miracle.

Keywords

Adoption, Fiction, Triad Issues

Age Range:

Teenagers

Author: Cheryl Zach

ISBN# 425152928 *Date Published:* 1996 *Price:* $ 4.50
Publisher: Mass Market Paperback *Pages:*

FILLING IN THE BLANKS

Rating

A guided look at growing up adopted.

A life book/work book designed for use with an adult helper. Useful whether children have been adopted as infants or at an older age, domestically or internationally, through agencies or independently, by single parents or couples. *Filling In The Blanks* makes a particularly good preparation tool for children who are moving between placements. Parents will find that the questions presented in this book offer them terrific preparation to help their adopted child as he or she approaches preadolescence. It's important for an adopted child's success that adults involved with them become conscious of the issues of adoption as they arise in every young person's development.

Keywords

Adoption Reform, Memory Book, Child Development, Adopted Child, Parenting

Age Range:

Teenagers

Author: Susan Gabel

ISBN# 0-9609504-8-6 *Date Published:* *Price:* $ 15.00
Publisher: Perspectives Press *Pages:*

FIND A STRANGER, SAY GOODBYE

Who is Natalie's real mother?

17-year-old Natalie Armstrong begins a journey to find her past when she searches for her birth mother in this fast-moving account of her fears and about the responses of the people who love her. At first, Natalie's adoptive parents do not support her desire to search, but in the end they come around despite their own fears. The reunion with and depiction of her birth mother seem unrealistic and are disappointing, although overall the book is an enjoyable read.

Keywords

Search and Reunion, Adoption, Girl Power, Fiction, Grief and Loss, Triad Issues

Age Range:

Teenagers

Author: Lois Lowrey

ISBN# 440205417 *Date Published:* 1990 *Price:* $ 4.00
Publisher: Dell *Pages:*

HEART KNOWS SOMETHING DIFFERENT, THE

Young writers (ages 15-20) provide an insider's view of growing up in "the system."

How well can a bureaucracy replace the family? For the more than 450,000 children living in foster care, this question is crucial. Yet when the public tries to peer into this largely hidden world, administrators frequently invoke the need for "confidentiality." And the young people themselves — those who really know what foster care is like — are rarely heard. Now, for the first time, *The Heart Knows Something Different* gives them a voice. These well-crafted narratives are remarkable for their candor, range of experience, and hard-won insights. Shows us, from the inside looking out, the mix of pain and fear, and sometimes hope and happiness, of the foster care experience.

Keywords

Foster Child, Core Issues (Feelings), Family Life, Foster Care

Age Range:

Teenagers

Editor: Al Desetta

ISBN# 892552182 *Date Published:* 1996 *Price:* $ 13.95
Publisher: Persea Books *Pages:* 232

I SEE THE MOON

Rating 

When her sister decides to place her baby for adoption, Bitte asks, "What is love?"

Unlike the rest of her family,12-year-old Bitte is thrilled when her 15-year-old sister Kari is pregnant. When she learns of Kari's decision to make an adoption plan, Bitte is devastated. Then she comes to accept Kari's decision and to understand that love is not as simple as she'd thought. The family are Norwegian Americans. An ALA Notable Children's Book. An ALA Quick Pick.

Keywords

Placement, Fiction, Family Life, Adoption, Birth Parent, Sibling Issues

Age Range:

Teenagers

Author: C. B. Christiansen

ISBN# 0-689-80441-5 *Date Published:* 1995 *Price:* $ 3.99

Publisher: Athenaeum *Pages:* 115

I'M PREGNANT, NOW WHAT DO I DO?

Rating

A new book for pregnant teens.

This book discusses abortion, adoption and parenting as options when facing an unplanned pregnancy. Case studies of young mothers bring life to the difficult issues of teen pregnancy.

Keywords

Birth Parent, Adoption, Grief and Loss, Core Issues (Feelings), Parenting, Pregnancy

Age Range:

Teenagers

Author: Robert W. Buckingham

Mary P. Derby

ISBN# 1573921173 *Date Published:* 1997 *Price:* $ 12.95

Publisher: Prometheus Bks. *Pages:*

KIM/KIMI

Kim, struggling with identity issues, needs to understand all of her heritage.

Even a warm, loving relationship with her mother, stepfather, and half-brother can't give 16-year-old Kim/Kimi all the answers she needs. She must find out more about her Japanese American father, who died before she was born. "Readers will be drawn by the inherent drama of Kim's conflict and her painful discoveries," says Booklist.

Keywords

Multiracial Identity, Japanese American, Family Life, Core Issues (Feelings), Racial/Ethnic Identity, Fiction

Age Range:

Teenagers

Author: Irwin Hadley

ISBN# 1432593 *Date Published:* 1988 *Price:* $ 4.99

Publisher: Puffin *Pages:*

LOST IN THE SYSTEM

Lost in the system *is a powerful commentary on the foster care system.*

Most children, just by virtue of being born, can count on the love, support and stability of a family. But for other children, this is not the case. *Lost in the System* recounts the author's rise from foster child to Miss Teen USA 1993, and her long-awaited realization of her greatest dream — being adopted at age 17. It voices the universal fears and frustrations of children who grow up navigating the foster care system, and who often end up feeling lonely and overlooked.

Keywords

Adoption, Foster Child, Biography, Core Issues (Feelings), Role Models

Age Range:

Teenagers

Author: Charlotte Lopez

Author: Susan Dworkin

ISBN# 684811995 *Date Published:* 1996 *Price:* $ 11.00

Publisher: Simon & Schuster *Pages:* 189

Rating

M.C. HIGGINS THE GREAT

M.C. Higgins has to choose between his family and his home.

Fifteen-year-old Mayo Cornelius Higgins lives in the Ohio countryside where there are beautiful rolling hills and shady valleys. But the unsightly results of strip mining seem to be taking over. M.C. feels torn between trying to get his family out and saving the land he loves. M.C. just happens to be African American.

Keywords

Fiction, Foster Child, Girl Power

Age Range:

Teenagers

Author: Virginia Hamilton

ISBN# 689821689 *Date Published:* 1995 *Price:* $ 2.65

Publisher: Aladdin *Pages:* 288

Rating

MOST WANTED, THE

When Andy discovers he's adopted, he uses the Internet to find his birth parents.

The Internet... a world without rules, without boundaries. Where you can be anyone you want, whoever you aren't. And it's all just a click away.... Andy MacFarland thought he knew everything. But his mom just showed him how stupid he really is. Well, not stupid, just ignorant of the facts — and deliberately kept that way. At the age of 16, Andy has found out that he's adopted. It seems like his life is not his life, and there's only one way to reclaim what he's lost: Andy's got to find his birth parents. The place to start: the Net. Different people in different places. The one thing they have in common is a new address on the Internet.danger.com. Where all your fears come true.

Keywords

Family Life, Fiction, Mothers, Fathers, Adoption, Search and Reunion

Age Range:

Teenagers

Author: Jordan Cray

ISBN# 689820402 *Date Published:* 1998 *Price:* $ 3.99

Publisher: S&S Children's *Pages:* 208

OUT OF NOWHERE: A NOVEL

Abandoned by his mother, 13-year-old Harley finds a family of friends.

Out of Nowhere has strong characters and an offbeat and memorable story, unusual for this age group. Booklist: "Harley, at 13, has just parted company with his promiscuous mother. May, at sixty-something, has just been abandoned by her husband of 40 years. A dog, later to be called Ishmael, has just been booted out of a pickup truck. A chance meeting at an Arizona rest stop throws these outcasts together, and they set off in May's car for a house she owns across the mountains.... Sebestyen redeems this too tidily balanced cast and too tidily contrived plot with lively dialogue, liberally laced with ironic wit [and offering a] keen depiction of Harley's obstinacy and need."

Keywords

Foster Child, Friendship, Fiction, Family Life, Core Issues (Feelings)

Age Range:

Teenagers

Author: Ouida Sebestyen

Ouida Sebestyen is the author of *Out of Nowhere: A Novel* and *Words by Heart.*

ISBN# 140376402 *Date Published:* 1995 *Price:* $ 3.99

Publisher: Puffin *Pages:*

PINBALLS, THE

You can't always decide where life will take you if you're stuck in foster care.

A hopeful story of how a child came to see she could take control of her own life. "Three kids in foster care — Pinballs, as wisecracking Carly dubs them — collide in a warm and caring home and learn to pin their hopes on each other," says the School Library Journal. ALA Notable Children's Book, School Library Journal Best Books of 1977. 58,000 kids in Georgia voted *Pinballs* their favorite book.

Keywords

Foster Child, Core Issues (Feelings), Self-Esteem, Foster Care, Family Life

Age Range:

Teenagers

Author: Betsy Byars

ISBN# 0-06-4401918-7 *Date Published:* *Price:* $ 4.50

Publisher: Harper Row *Pages:*

PLACE TO CALL HOME, A

Rating 

A book for teens about biracial heritage and family connection.

Anna is devoted to her younger siblings and will sacrifice anything to keep the three of them together so when her mother disappears, Anna hides the evidence from the authorities. Review, Books in Print: "Anna's desperate struggle to make a home for her two younger siblings leads her to Mississippi to trace her mother's escape route from her abused childhood and to seek her family and milieu. Anna, the Black child of a white mother and unknown father, loves her two white siblings passionately, though she can't forget she's different. A Place to Call Home is a fast-paced, compelling read, with a memorable and feisty heroine and satisfying social values."

Keywords

Multiracial Identity, African American, Core Issues (Feelings), Fiction, Family Life, Racial/Ethnic Identity

Age Range:

Teenagers

Author: Jackie French Koller

ISBN# 0-689-81395-3 Date Published: 1997 Price: $ 4.50

Publisher: S&S Children's Pages: 208

PLACING YOUR BABY FOR ADOPTION

Rating 

An easy-to-understand book about making a placement plan.

Provides teenage expectant parents the information needed to make an informed decision regarding placing their baby for adoption.

Keywords

Birth Parent, Triad Issues, Placement, Parenting, Adoption, Family Life

Age Range:

Teenagers

Author: Aliza Sherman

ISBN# 823922669 Date Published: 1997 Price: $ 17.95

Publisher: Rosen Pages: 64

PREGNANT? ADOPTION IS AN OPTION

For anyone facing an untimely pregnancy.

Planning is the key — whether it's a parenting plan or an adoption plan. Encourages counseling with a professional for help in making a plan, someone who will be there whether a birth parent decides to parent or to place a child in adoption. Help with building open adoption relationships.

Keywords

Placement, Birth Parent, Adoption, Triad Issues, Open Adoption

Age Range:

Teenagers

Author: Nancy Thorndike Greenspan

ISBN# 1-885356-08-0 Date Published: Price: $ 11.95

Publisher: Morning Glory Pages: 224

SCARIEST NIGHT, THE

A mystery driven by sibling jealousy.

When her family decides to spend the summer in Milwaukee so that her adopted brother can attend a special piano school, Erin finds herself jealous. Like many fictional books with an adoption theme, this one an unrealistic tone, as if the adoption issues were tacked on to round out the plot rather than out of a deeper understanding of the issues. Even so, regardless of a book's approach, the chance to meet characters who are adopted is valuable, if only to stimulate questions and discussion. We feel less alone in the world when we are aware of others who share our circumstances, even when they deal with them quite differently.

Keywords

Sibling Issues, Family Life, Adopted Child, Adoption, Adoptive Parent, Fiction

Age Range:

Teenagers

Author: Betty Wright

ISBN# 0-8234-0904-X Date Published: Price: $ 15.95

Publisher: Holiday House Pages:

Rating

SECOND BEST (LIFE AT SIXTEEN)

Another teen romance about adoption.

Meeting her birth mother for the first time, adopted teen Tessa is shocked to discover that she has an identical twin sister, who, to Tessa's disappointment, is spoiled and moody and who drinks too much.

Keywords
Adoption, Sibling Issues, Birth Parent, Core Issues (Feelings), Fiction

Age Range:
Teenagers

Author: Cheryl Lanham

ISBN# 425155455 Date Published: 1997 Price: $ 4.50
Publisher: Berkley Pub. Group Pages: 201

Rating

SECRETS

T.J. must choose between his birth mother and his adoptive father.

T.J. must make a painful choice between his birth mother and his adoptive father. Books for teens with an adoption theme often have an unrealistic tone, as if the superficial events are the whole story rather than an opportunity for deeper understanding of the issues. Even so, finding books that include adopted characters, no matter a book's approach, is useful if only to stimulate questions and discussion. We feel less alone in the world when we are aware of others who share our experiences, even when they deal with them quite differently.

Keywords
Fathers, Adoption, Family Life, Fiction, Birth Parent

Age Range:
Teenagers

Author: Alane Ferguson

ISBN# 689803133 Date Published: Price: $ 16.00
Publisher: Simon & Schuster Pages: 160

SHOULD I KEEP MY BABY?

Caring, practical help for teenage girls facing pregnancy alone.

Offering girls a Christian message upholding a strong biblical emphasis on the preciousness of life, this book explores the issues of economic support, parental approval, marriage, health, adoption, and much more. Written specifically for the Christian teenage girl, this book preaches a message of love and acceptance.

Keywords
Core Issues (Feelings), Birth Parent, Parenting, Placement, Christianity

Age Range:
Teenagers

Author: Martha Zimmerman

ISBN# 1556619839 Date Published: 1997 Price: $ 7.99
Publisher: Bethany House Pages:

SNAKESTONE

James, at fifteen, decides to find his birth mother.

From Booklist: "Doherty's latest novel centers on a teen coming to terms with his adoption. Fifteen-year-old James investigates the few personal articles that accompanied him to his adoptive home — some baby clothes, a note reading 'Look after Sammy,' a partial address, and a small shell-shaped stone. What drama there is comes mainly from snippets of the story of James' birth mother, which are interwoven among James' own experiences, and from the brief encounter that eventually takes place between her and James. It's Doherty's credible characterizations and her strong, clear prose that keep the pages turning; they beckon readers who appreciate a solid story."

Keywords
Adoption, Fiction, Search and Reunion, Birth Parent, Adopted Child, Family Life

Age Range:
Teenagers

Author: Berlie Doherty

ISBN# 531088626 Date Published: 1996 Price: $ 16.99
Publisher: Orchard Books Pages:

Rating

SOMEONE TO LOVE

15-year-old Sara rebels against her parents' decision to adopt a baby through open adoption.

Books in Print writes, "An open adoption sets into motion this overwrought story. Written as a series of letters from 15-year-old Sara to the unborn child her parents are planning to adopt, the novel describes Sara, who wears Question Authority T-shirts and is aggressively vegetarian and who does combat with her parents when they decide to adopt the child of 18-year-old Iris. Following a fight with her parents, Sara runs away with Iris. Sara's narration can be excessively detailed and narrow, and the format poses a strain, particularly in the conclusion, where Sara tidily distills her soap-opera-ish adventures into a string of obvious psychological insights."

Keywords

Adoption, Sibling Issues, Fiction, Adopted Child, Birth Parent, Family Life

Age Range:

Teenagers

Author: Francess L. Lantz

ISBN# 380974770 *Date Published:* 1997 *Price:* $ 4.00

Publisher: Avon *Pages:* 224

Rating

SPECIAL KIND OF LOVE, A

Jennifer, at seventeen, has just been told she was adopted.

Lexi's friend Jennifer Golden plans a surprise party for her parents' anniversary. But nothing prepares Jennifer for the secret she uncovers regarding her own birth. Now Lexi and her friends must help Jennifer cope with her anger, shock and confusion. Suddenly she feels like a stranger in her own home. Can she ever forgive her mom and dad? What will Jennifer do next?

Keywords

Adoption, Christianity, Fiction, Family Life, Foster Child, Foster Care

Age Range:

Teenagers

Author: Judy Baer

ISBN# 1-55661-367-9 *Date Published:* 1993 *Price:* $ 4.99

Publisher: Bethany *Pages:* 126

THIS TIME IT'S ME

For pregnant teens.

Discusses choices, problems, and worries. Sections on boyfriends and parents.

Keywords

Core Issues (Feelings), Birth Parent, Placement

Age Range:

Teenagers

Author: Mary Vondra

ISBN# (TTIC) *Date Published:* *Price:* $ 3.25

Publisher: Centering Corp. *Pages:*

TOO SOON FOR JEFF

A novel for teenage birth fathers.

A story about becoming a father too soon and all the feelings involved, this is the only book we know of on this topic for young birth fathers.

Keywords

Birth Parent, Fathers, Fiction, Placement, Adoption

Age Range:

Teenagers

Author: Marilyn Reynolds

Marilyn Reynolds is the author of *Detour for Emmy* and *Too Soon For Jeff.*

ISBN# 0-930934-91-1 *Date Published:* 1994 *Price:* $ 8.95

Publisher: Morning Glory *Pages:* 223

Rating

WHERE ARE MY BIRTH PARENTS?

A guide for adopted teenagers.

A sensitive guide to help adopted people make informed decisions about if and how to search for their birth parents. Includes why people search; telling your parents; the first contact; birth mothers; reunion and post reunion, and more.

Keywords

Adoption, Search and Reunion, Birth Parent, Core Issues (Feelings), Family Life

Age Range:

Teenagers

Author: Karen Gravelle

Author: Susan Fisher, M.D.

ISBN# 0-8027-7453-9 Date Published: 1993 Price: $ 8.95

Publisher: Walker & Co. Pages: 120

Rating

WHO AM I?

...and other questions of adopted kids.

Should I search for my birth parents? Why did my biological mother give me up for adoption? This book gives adopted children reassuring answers to common questions about their birth families and includes advice from experts and quotes from adopted teenagers.

Keywords

Adoption, Adopted Child

Age Range:

Teenagers

Author: Charlene C. Giannetti

Illustrator: Larry Ross

ISBN# 084317529X Date Published: 1999 Price: $ 4.99

Publisher: Price, Stern, Sloan Pages: 128

WHY DIDN'T SHE KEEP ME?

Firsthand narratives by birth mothers who explain why they placed their children for adoption.

Firsthand narratives by mothers who reveal the practical and emotional motivations that led them to place a child for adoption. Recurring theme: the child is never placed without pain, love, and great sacrifice.

Keywords

Adoption, Adopted Child, Birth Parent, Triad Issues, Core Issues (Feelings)

Age Range:

Teenagers

Author: Barbara Burlingham-Brown

ISBN# 0-912083-66-2 Date Published: 1994 Price: $ 12.95

Publisher: Langford Books Pages: 170

WILL THE REAL ME PLEASE STAND UP

Mira's mom is Japanese American. Her dad is African American.

The story of how Mira learns to cope with her loneliness and being different. This book is currently available on special order from the publisher. We expect to be able to ship it to you within 5 weeks.

Keywords

Biracial, Multiracial Identity, Core Issues (Feelings), Fiction, Family Life

Age Range:

Teenagers

Author: Elizabeth Van Steenwyck

ISBN# 9995152398 Date Published: 1994 Price: $ 2.99

Publisher: Willowisp Press Pages:

Rating

ARILLA SUN DOWN

Arilla tells her own story of growing up in a multiracial family.

Arilla is a seventh-grader with a mother who is a Black dancer, a father who is part Native American and part Black, and a radical 16-year-old brother who strongly and positively identifies with his Indian heritage. Everyday life gets rather complicated in this coming of age story about a biracial child.

Keywords

Multiracial Identity, Racial/Ethnic Identity, Family Life, Fiction, Multicultural

Age Range:

Teenagers

Author: Virginia Hamilton

ISBN# 0-590-22223-6 Date Published: 1995 Price: $ 4.99

Publisher: Scholastic Pages: 272

Rating

BLACK BOOK, THE

Bill Cosby called this a scrapbook kept by a 300-year-old Black man.

A provocative account, through words, pictures, songs, stories, and advertisements, of Black life in America and of America's history of racism. For those of us who were taught the white man's version of American history, this book offers a powerful and disturbing corrective. Not so much a reference book — there is no index, and the composition is more collage than linear — as a scrapbook that informs and challenges at the same time.

Keywords

African American, Civil Rights, Cultural History, Race Relations, Racism, Black Identity

Age Range:

Teenagers

Author: Middleton A. Harris

ISBN# 0-394-70622-6 Date Published: 1974 Price: $ 22.95

Publisher: Random House Pages:

FORGED BY FIRE

When his aunt dies, Gerald suddenly is thrust into a home filled with abuse.

In her gutsy books about streetwise role models for teenage boys, Sharon Draper writes in a style that makes young readers feel present on the scene. Gerald, the main character, faces abuse, death and drugs in this suspense-filled novel. He survives, partly by growing close to Angel, his young stepsister. Gerald and Angel grow close as he strives to protect her from his abusive stepfather. Gerald's underlying commitment to being there for family, no matter what, makes him a positive character struggling with extraordinary challenges. Winner of the Newbery Award.

Keywords

African American, Role Models, Family Life, Fiction

Age Range:

Teenagers

Author: Sharon Mills Draper

Draper's first novel, *Tears of the Tiger*, received the first Coretta Scott King Genesis Award.

ISBN# 689818513 Date Published: Price: $ 4.99

Publisher: Aladdin Pages:

FROM THE NOTEBOOKS OF MELANIN SUN

A fourteen-year-old's life is shattered when his mother falls in love with a white woman.

Kirkus Reviews: "Mel's first reactions are predictable; except to say hurtful things, he clams up, retreating behind headphones and notebooks, rehearsing the common misconceptions about gays and agonizing over what will happen when his friends find out. Fortunately, Melanin Sun has inherited his mother's courage and intelligence, so after thinking hard about how central she is to what he truly values and trusts, he passes from rage to resentment to bewilderment, and, finally, acceptance. Melanin Sun's inner journey will leave readers moved and reassured." Winner of the 1996 Coretta Scott King Honor Book Award, winner of the Jane Addams Peace Award, 1996 Lambda Award, and ALA Best Book for Young Adults.

Keywords

African American, Gay and/or Lesbian, Family Life, Core Issues (Feelings), Fiction, Black Identity

Age Range:

Teenagers

Author: Jacqueline Woodson

Jacqueline Woodson is the author of *From The Notebooks of Melanin Sun; I Hadn't Meant To Tell You This;* and *The House You Pass On The Way.*

ISBN# 0590458817' Date Published: 1997 Price: $ 3.99

Publisher: Point Pages:

Rating

GOOD HAIR

"For colored girls who've considered weaves when the chemicals became too ruff."

Good Hair challenges Black women not to succumb to white ideas of beauty for themselves. It stresses that until women are convinced of their own inherent beauty, they can't be convincing to others. A combination of "how-to" beauty book and hilarious autobiography, this is a great reference book and a good read.

Keywords
African American, Hair, Racial/Ethnic Identity, Black Identity, Self-Esteem

Age Range:
Teenagers

Author: Lonice Bonner

Lonice Bonner is the author of *Plaited Glory* and *Good Hair.*

ISBN# 0-517-88151-9 Date Published: 1994 Price: $ 10.00
Publisher: Crown Pub Group Pages:

Rating

HOUSE OF DIES DREAR, THE

A Black family unravels secrets of their home, once a stop on the Underground Railroad.

"A huge, old house with secret tunnels, a cantankerous caretaker, and buried treasure is a dream-come-true for 13-year-old Thomas. The fact that it's reputedly haunted only adds to its appeal! As soon as his family moves in, Thomas senses something strange about the Civil War era house, which used to be a critical stop on the Underground Railroad.... He explores the hidden passageways in and under the house, piecing clues together in an increasingly dangerous quest for the truth about the past. Newbery medalist Virginia Hamilton creates a heart-pounding adventure with this absorbing classic for older readers." — Amazon books. An ALA Notable Children's Book

Keywords
Black Identity, Boy Focus, Cultural History, US History, Fiction, Race Relations

Age Range:
Teenagers

Author: Virginia Hamilton

ISBN# 20435207 Date Published: Price: $ 4.50
Publisher: Macmillan Pages:

I AM THE DARKER BROTHER

An anthology of modern poems by African Americans.

Adoff first published this collection of Black poetry in 1968 to present students of all racial and ethnic backgrounds with a more complete vision of American literature. In this edition, newly expanded to include 21 additional poets, 10 of them women, the poems are arranged by theme and include notes on the poems as well as brief biographies of the poets. A must-have book that belongs within easy reach of every African American child and that will be of interest to anyone conscious of racial issues.

Keywords
Poetry, African American, Racial/Ethnic Identity, Race Relations, Core Issues (Feelings)

Age Range:
Teenagers

Poet: Arnold Adoff

Arnold Adoff, the winner of the 1988 NCTE Award for Excellence in Poetry for Children, is the author of over 30 books.

ISBN# 689808690 Date Published: 1997 Price: $ 4.99
Publisher: Aladdin Pages:

NO TURNING BACK

"A can't-put-it-down account of an impoverished South African boy." –The Horn Book

To escape an abusive home, 12-year-old Sipho flees to the world of the malunde — or homeless boys — on the streets of Johannesburg. In a starred review, ALA Booklist called *No Turning Back* a story about "children anywhere who are on the edge." It's definitely about the hard stuff, like running away, drugs, etc. The Horn Book says it is "Charged with a rhythm that begins beating on the first page and carries through until the last." A 1998 Notable Children's Trade Book in Social Studies.

Keywords
Africa, Core Issues (Feelings), Grief and Loss, Boy Focus

Age Range:
Teenagers

Author: Beverley Naidoo

A white South African, Beverley Naidoo joined the active resistance to apartheid and was exiled to England. She now lives in Dorset, England.

ISBN# 64407497 Date Published: 1998 Price: $ 4.95
Publisher: Trophy Press Pages: 208

Rating

SARNY: A LIFE REMEMBERED

A former slave's journey into freedom.

This companion to the best-selling *Nightjohn* is the riveting saga of an African American woman after her release from slavery. Finding herself a free woman after the end of the Civil War, Sarny begins to search for her sold-away children and begins a new life, giving readers a panoramic view of America in a time of trial, tragedy and hoped-for change.

Keywords

African American, Racism, Black Identity, US History, Self-Esteem, Cultural History

Age Range:

Teenagers

Author: Gary Paulsen

Gary Paulsen is the author of *Sarny: A Life Remembered, The Tortilla Factory* and more.

ISBN# 385321953 *Date Published:* 1997 *Price:* $ 4.99

Publisher: Doubleday *Pages:* 224

Rating

SLAM!

Growing up isn't easy when you're Black in a new, mostly all-White school.

17-year-old Greg "Slam" Harris is in control on the court, but off the court he has trouble fitting in at his predominantly White high school. To make matters worse, his grandmother is dying. Slam struggles to separate the game on the basketball court from the game in life — where there is no ball and everyone is playing. In this Newbery Award winner story, Slam's stresses and many changes are portrayed with emotional honesty, free of stereotypes.

Keywords

African American, Self-Esteem, Sports, Fiction, Boy Focus, Friendship

Age Range:

Teenagers

Author: Walter Dean Myers

Walter Dean Myers is the author of *One More River To Cross; Brown Angels; Me, Mop, and the Moondance Kid s, Slam, Malcolm X , Hoops,* and many more.

ISBN# 590486683 *Date Published:* 1996 *Price:* $ 4.99

Publisher: Scholastic *Pages:* 272

TO BE A SLAVE

What it is like to be a slave, told by people who lived it.

The humiliation and ostracism of slavery is described in vivid and often painful detail by men and women who were once slaves themselves. Newbery Honor Book. ALA Notable Children's Book, School Library Journal Best Book of the Year, Lewis Carroll Shelf Award, Horn Book Fanfare Honor List, New York Times Outstanding Book of the Year, Library of Congress Book of the Year.

Keywords

African American, Cultural History, Race Relations, Racism, Black Identity, US History

Age Range:

Teenagers

Author: Julius Lester

Julius Lester is the author of *To Be A Slave; Sam and the Tigers; From Slave Ship To Freedom Road; What A Truly Cool World; Black Cowboy; Wild Horses,* and more.

ISBN# 590424602 *Date Published:* 1988 *Price:* $ 4.50

Publisher: Scholastic *Pages:*

WHERE BEAUTY TOUCHES ME

Natural hair care and beauty book for African Americans.

Step-by-step instructions for over sixty braided and natural hair styles for African American females. From washing baby's hair to caring for men's hair, this book covers complete hair care for African Americans.

Keywords

African American, Hair, Self-Esteem, Black Identity

Age Range:

Teenagers

Editor: Pamela Ferell"

Pamela Ferell is the author of *Where Beauty Touches Me* and *Let's Talk Hair.*

ISBN# 0939-183-01-3 *Date Published:* *Price:* $ 24.95

Publisher: Cornrows *Pages:* 129

Rating

AMERICAN EYES

Short stories that burn with conflicts and choices that occur when two cultures come together.

Books in Print: "What does it mean to Asian American adolescents growing up in a country that often regards them as aliens? This intriguing collection of short stories presents answers as individual as each writer's voice. The search for identity sometimes leads back to Asian roots: in one selection, an adopted person journeys to her native Korea to find her biological parents. For others, the battle takes place on the home front. In the darkly funny, surreal, and painful 'Knuckles,' a Chinese American girl stubbornly refuses to eat her mother's ethnic cooking. Immigrants from Japan, Vietnam, and the Philippines tell their stories as well, and each selection is firmly anchored in a particular time and place."

Keywords

Asian American, Fiction, Chinese American, Japanese American, Korean American, Vietnamese American

Age Range,

Teenagers

Editor: Lori Carlson

ISBN# 0-8050-3544-3 Date Published, Price, $ 4.50

Publisher, Henry Holt Pages, 160

Rating

BASEBALL SAVED US

A moving narrative about how baseball helped a boy endure injustice in an internment camp.

A Japanese American boy learns to play baseball when he and his family are forced to live in an internment camp during World War II, from 1942-45. "America is at war with Japan, and the government thinks that Japanese Americans can't be trusted. But it's wrong that we're in here. We're Americans too." The government said it could not tell who might be loyal to Japan. But none of these Japanese Americans or their children were ever proven to be dangerous to America during WWII., and in 1988, the U.S. government admitted that what it had done was wrong. Parents' Choice Award, Pick of the List: American Bookseller.

Keywords

Family Life, Sports, Cultural History, Race Relations, Self-Esteem, Japanese American

Age Range,

Teenagers

Author: Ken Mochizuki

Ken Mochizuki is the author of *Heroes and Passage to Freedom: The Sugihara Story*

ISBN# 1-880000-19-9 Date Published, Price, $ 5.95

Publisher, Lee & Low Books Pages,

CHILD OF THE OWL

Growing up Chinese-American in San Francisco.

"Combines chiseled fantasy with the anxiety of growing up poor and nonwhite," wrote Kirkus Reviews of this winner of the Boston Globe-Horn Book Award for Fiction. "Since I am Chinese American I could relate to this book very well. This is well written and dramatic. It made me cry when I was smiling," says Lauren Young.

Keywords

Asian, Chinese, Race Relations, Racial/Ethnic Identity, Racism, Core Issues (Feelings)

Age Range,

Teenagers

Author: Lawrence Yep

ISBN# 006440336X Date Published, 1999 Price, $ 4.95

Publisher, Apple Pages, 217

CHILDREN OF THE RIVER

A Cambodian teen struggles with the conflict between traditions and her love for an American.

Sundara fled Cambodia to escape the Khmer Rouge army when she was thirteen, leaving behind her parents, her brother and sister, and the boy she had loved since she was a child. In the safety of Oregon, she struggles to be a "good Cambodian girl." A good Cambodian girl never dates; she waits for her family to arrange her marriage to a Cambodian boy. Yet Sundara and Jonathan, an extraordinary American boy, are powerfully drawn to each other. Haunted by grief for her lost family, Sundara falls in love with Jonathan. Is her new life disloyal to her past?

Keywords

Asian American, Cambodia, Fiction, Racial/Ethnic Identity, Multicultural, Core Issues (Feelings)

Age Range,

Teenagers

Author: Linda Crew

ISBN# 440210224 Date Published, 1991 Price, $ 4.99

Publisher, Laurel Leaf Pages,

DRAGONWINGS

Rating 

Their dream was to fly!

A Chinese immigrant and his son build a flying machine in this unusual historical novel, unique in its perspective of the Chinese in America and its portrayal of early 20th-century San Francisco, including the earthquake, from an immigrant's view. Multiple awards.

Keywords

Asian American, Racial/Ethnic Identity, Self-Esteem, Chinese American, Cultural History, Fiction

Age Range:

Teenagers

Author: Lawrence Yep

ISBN# 0-06-44085-9 Date Published: Price: $ 4.95

Publisher: Harper Collins Pages: 256

FINDING MY VOICE

Rating

The only Asian in a small American high school, Ellen Sung must contend with racism.

Kirkus Reviews: "This portrait of a quietly sensitive teenager is filled with searing truths about day-to-day racism — those that don't make the evening news. Honestly rendered, and never didactic, the story allows readers first to flinch in recognition and then to look into their own hearts. A gently self-possessed work, told in economical language that veils its earnestness and depth."

Keywords

Asian American, Korean American, Family Life, Race Relations, Racial/Ethnic Identity, Fiction

Age Range:

Teenagers

Author: Marie Lee

Marie Lee is the author of *If It Hadn't Been For Yoon Jun* and *Finding My Voice*

ISBN# 440218969 Date Published: 1994 Price: $ 3.99

Publisher: Laurel Leaf Pages: 176

GROWING UP ASIAN AMERICAN

What is it like to grow up Asian in the US?

One of the few books addressing these issues. Thirty-two stories and essays on childhood, adolescence and coming of age. Asian American writers share their thoughts and feelings on growing up in America.

Keywords

Asian American, Family Life, Racial/Ethnic Identity

Age Range:

Teenagers

Editor: Maria Hong

ISBN# 380724189 Date Published: 1995 Price: $ 12.50

Publisher: Avon Pages:

LONG SEASON OF RAIN, THE

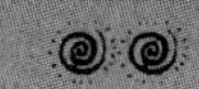

A Korean family's response to adoption.

From Booklist: "Set in Seoul, Korea, in 1969, the first-person narrative is true to 11-year-old Junehee's point of view, but it is her mother's story. Mother reaches the breaking point when her domineering husband and his mother refuse to allow her to adopt an orphan child she loves. At times there's too much local color and culture." Horn Book: "A clear-eyed view of societal restrictions and their effects on eleven-year-old Junehee's family. The presence of an orphan boy begins a breakdown of the family that is a prison for Junehee's mother, who stays only for her four daughters' sakes. Events clearly reflect a child's point of view."

Keywords

Korean, Family Life, Orphan, Asian, Adoption, Fiction

Age Range:

Teenagers

Author: Helen Kim

ISBN# 449704629 Date Published: 1997 Price: $ 4.50

Publisher: Fawcett Crest Pages: 239

RED SCARF GIRL

Rating 

Ji-Li Jiang's tale of losing her innocence through the Chinese Cultural Revolution.

Describing the feelings of a twelve-year-old girl who witnesses the losses and humiliations of her family, her nation and herself, Ji-Li Jiang's personal account of Mao's cultural revolution gives history a human face. "Ji-Li's deeply moving story should be on the shelf of every person's library," says the School Library Journal. "It's a very painful, very personal — therefore accessible — history. "Kirkus Reviews.

Keywords

Chinese, China, History, Family Life, Cultural History

Age Range,

Teenagers

Author: Ji-Li Jiang

Author: David Henry Hwang

ISBN# 64462080 Date Published, 1998 Price, $ 4.95

Publisher, Harper Trophy Pages, 258

SHABANU: DAUGHTER OF THE WIND

Rating 

Shabanu's struggle with identity.

Set against the backdrop of desert life in present day Pakistan, this book offers a passionate and deeply personal portrait of a young girl's struggle for identity in a culture that forbids even token expression of independence for women. 1990 Newbery Honor Book, ALA Notable Book, ALA Best Book for young adults, A Notable Children's Trade Book in the Field of Social Studies, Hornbook Fanfare Honor Book, IRA Teacher's Choice.

Keywords

Antiracist Strategies, Fiction, Core Issues (Feelings), Cultural History, Family Life, Racial/Ethnic Identity

Age Range,

Teenagers

Author: Suzanne Fisher Staples

ISBN# 679810307 Date Published, 1990 Price, $ 4.99

Publisher, Knopf Pages,

STAR FISHER, THE

Fifteen-year-old Joan Lee sees through two sets of eyes: Chinese and American.

Insights on belonging and assimilation, as depicted in the experiences of Yep's mother's Chinese family, who opened a West Virginia laundry in 1927. "Yep has shaped his family's stories into a rather old- fashioned novel of small-town prejudice bowing to good will and some humorously applied ingenuity."— Kirkus Reviews

Keywords

Asian American, Racial/Ethnic Identity, Self-Esteem, Chinese American, Cultural History, Fiction

Age Range,

Teenagers

Author: Lawrence Yep

ISBN# 140360034 Date Published, 1992 Price, $ 4.99

Publisher, Puffin Pages, 150

STELLA: ON THE EDGE OF POPULARITY

Stella struggles with fitting into traditional Korean culture at home and American culture at school.

Seventh grade is rough on Stella. She struggles with fitting in at home and school. Should she risk everything in order to be accepted? A story about how she finds her strength. Though the story line holds merit, the writing is uneven and fails to engage the reader; many children will not pursue it to the ending.

Keywords

Racial/Ethnic Identity, Race Relations, Self-Esteem, Fiction, Korean American, Girl Power

Age Range,

Teenagers

Author: Lauren Lee

ISBN# 1879965089 Date Published, Price, $ 10.95

Publisher, Polychrome Publishing Corp. Pages,

AMAZING HISPANIC AMERICAN HISTORY

Rating 

A Book of Answers for Kids (New York Public Library " Answer Books for Kids")

"From Columbus to Selena, from lima beans to 'Loisada,' Ochoa encompasses a diverse Hispanic American historical and cultural experience, using the question-and-answer format which caters to short attention spans. It makes browsing easy, and allows Ochoa to focus more closely on selected topics with frequent sidebars. In a vital, knowledgeable sweep through the history and immigration patterns of several regions and countries, including Spain, he takes as his major theme their distinctive characters. Not intended for sustained research, this has two bibliographies, one with web sites, to give readers a jump start on their studies." — Kirkus Associates

Keywords

Latino/a, Racial/Ethnic Identity, US History, Cultural History

Age Range:

Teenagers

Author: George Ochoa

ISBN# 047119204X *Date Published:* 1998 *Price:* $ 12.95

Publisher: Wiley *Pages:* 192

AN ISLAND LIKE YOU

Rating 

Twelve stories about kids caught between their Puerto Rican families and the American dream.

Booklist writes, "The contemporary teenage voices are candid, funny, weary, and irreverent. Cofer depicts a diverse neighborhood that's warm, vital, and nurturing, and that can be hell if you don't fit in. Some of the best stories are about those who try to leave." Horn Book finds that the stories "have universal resonance in the vitality, the brashness, the self-centered hopefulness, and the angst expressed by the teens as they tell of friendships, failed romances, and worries over work, family, and school."

Keywords

Intergenerational, Latino/a, Puerto Rico

Age Range:

Teenagers

Author: Judith Ortiz Cofer

Judith Ortiz Cofer is the author of *Silent Dancing: A Partial Remembrance of a Puerto Rican Childhood.*

ISBN# 014038068X *Date Published:* 1996 *Price:* $ 4.99

Publisher: Puffin *Pages:*

BASEBALL IN APRIL AND OTHER STORIES

The small events of daily life reveal big themes featuring Latino kids.

Eleven stories about Latino kids as they try out for Little League, perform in the school talent show, and go out on first dates. Horn Book says, "Gary Soto is an astute observer of the desires, fears, and foibles of children and teenagers going about the business of daily living. In these vignettes featuring Mexican American families, the character portrayals are gentle; the tone is quiet and somewhat bittersweet; and respect for family is a consistent value."

Keywords

Latino/a, Family Life, Core Issues (Feelings)

Age Range:

Teenagers

Author: Gary Soto

Gary Soto is an acclaimed poet and fiction writer. He is the author of *Living Up The Street; Jesse; Nerdlandia, Chato's Kitchen* and *Baseball in April.*

ISBN# 152057218 *Date Published:* 1990 *Price:* $ 6.00

Publisher: Harcourt Brace *Pages:* 137

HEART OF A JAGUAR

Life in a Mayan village was very different from our lives today.

From Booklist: "In this unusual offering, Talbert takes readers into a Mayan village during a death-inducing drought. Balam kills a jaguar, hoping the sacrifice will finally bring rain. But in a horrific final scene, it is not the heart of the jaguar that is offered to the gods, but the heart of Balam himself. Talbert pulls no punches. There is an opening scene of childbirth, another of penis- and tongue-piercing, and a graphic account of the final moment of Balam's life. The depth of Talbert's research into the late Mayan period is obvious, but readers will need a strong stomach for this one."

Keywords

Mexican, Cultural History

Age Range:

Teenagers

Author: Marc Talbert

Author: Felipe Davalos

ISBN# 689813325 *Date Published:* 1997 *Price:* $ 4.60

Publisher: Aladdin *Pages:*

I WANT TO BUY A VOWEL

Rating

A novel of illegal alienation.

"Alfredo Santayana, an illegal alien from Guatemala who is learning to speak English by watching TV commercials, is eager to start a new life in Waxahachie, a small Texas town. Even though he had so little in Guatemala, he has even less in the U.S. Enter Eva and Ana, two American girls who befriend him and who try to make sense out of immigration laws, religion, bad marriages, the Spanish language, and other important considerations in all of their lives. This is a satire of American life, especially of current U.S. immigration laws that, had they existed in the 1700s, would have certainly punished most ancestors of today's Americans." —Book Links

Keywords

Latino/a, Language, Guatemalan, Core Issues (Feelings)

Age Range.

Teenagers

Author: John Welter

ISBN# 1564412118X Date Published. 1996 Price. $ 18.95

Publisher. Algonquin Pages. 314

JESSE

Rating

Soto's story of a Mexican American boy during the height of the Vietnam War.

In 1968, 17-year-old Jesse faces the draft and poverty, while race and class prejudice limit him to field work. This engrossing story depicts his friendships, his questioning of Chavez's farm workers' movement, and his struggles to find himself and a meaningful life in spite of the limits he faces. Kirkus Reviews says, "The story smolders with an almost imperceptible uneasiness that grows toward the final chapters. The mere depiction of this teen's life, and his attempts to better himself, are a far greater indictment of racism and class distinction than any finger-pointing sermon could be. A satisfying and enlightening story."

Keywords

Latino/a, Core Issues (Feelings), Race Relations, Racism, Mexican American, Boy Focus

Age Range.

Teenagers

Author: Gary Soto

Gary Soto is an acclaimed poet and fiction writer. He is the author of *Living Up The Street; Jesse; Nerdlandia: Chato's Kitchen* and *Baseball in April.*

ISBN# 590528378 Date Published. 1996 Price. $ 4.99

Publisher. Point Pages. 216

JOURNEY FOR PEACE

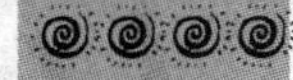

A young Mayan girl fights for her people.

Winner of the 1992 Nobel Peace Price, Rigoberta Menchú was a poor uneducated Mayan girl who became well known throughout the world as an advocate for human rights. Her family worked on a plantation run by a cruel, rich landowner who mistreated the Indians. When wealthy landowners tried to steal the villagers' land, Rigoberta decided to fight back.

Keywords

Biography, Role Models, Mexican, Self-Esteem, Cultural History, Girl Power

Age Range.

Teenagers

Author: Marlene Targ Brill

Illustrator: Rubén De Anda

ISBN# 525675248 Date Published. Price. $ 14.99

Publisher. Lodestar Pages.

JUANITA FIGHTS THE SCHOOL BOARD

Juanita is expelled for fighting, while the white girl who started it goes unpunished.

Johnny, the eldest daughter of Mexican farm workers, is expelled from high school, but with the help of a Latina psychologist and a civil rights attorney, she fights the discriminatory treatment and returns determined to graduate. A good topic, but an unappealing presentation. Kirkus Reviews concurs, saying "The narrative alternates between Juanita's and Ms. Martinez's voices — Juanita's present tense is particularly jarring — and reads like a real case history, with all the idiosyncrasies of actual speech and the irrelevancies of real life. Although the issues explored here are important ones, Velaquez's presentation is unengaging. Dry, repetitive, and all too realistic."

Keywords

Mexican, Latino/a, Fiction, Core Issues (Feelings), Race Relations, Racism

Age Range.

Teenagers

Author: Juanita Velasquez

ISBN# 1558851151" Date Published. 1994 Price. $ 7.95

Publisher. Arte Publico Press Pages. 149

Rating

LATINO VOICES

Writers of America series.

Booklist calls it "a thoughtful collection of Latino poetry, fiction, and excerpts from actual accounts of immigrants and settlers that offers a broad view of the Latino experience in the U.S. Chapter introductions provide insight into the authors' lives and their writings, which explore the themes of immigration, home and family, work, language, love, religion, and racial discrimination. Twenty-four writers from various backgrounds and countries are included. The selections are enjoyable as well as provocative. A glossary of Spanish terms follows each selection, and a list of sources and a bibliography are provided."

Keywords

Latino/a, Racial/Ethnic Identity, Role Models, Poetry, Fiction, Cultural History

Age Range:

Teenagers

Editor: Francis R. Aparicio

ISBN# 156294388X *Date Published:* 1994 *Price:* $ 23.90

Publisher: Millbrook Press *Pages:* 14443

Rating

PARROT IN THE OVEN: MI VIDA

The coming-of age of Manuel Hernandez.

His father says Manny is like the Mexican parrot who complains of the heat, not recognizing it is sitting in an oven. Manny wants to find out what it means to be a guy you have to respect. Growing up in the projects in Fresno, California, he lives with negativity, discrimination and a dysfunctional family. His growth into adulthood will not be easily forgotten, illuminated through a series of evocative first-person short stories. The reader, as witness, feels his yearning for what is out of reach, the confusion of seeing his family with new eyes, and his resiliency. Winner of the 1996 National Book Award for Young People's Fiction

Keywords

Latino/a, Core Issues (Feelings), Fiction

Age Range:

Teenagers

Author: Victor Martinez

ISBN# 64471861 *Date Published:* 1998 *Price:* $ 5.95

Publisher: HarperCollins *Pages:* 216

TOMMY STANDS ALONE

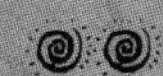

As far as we know, this is the only teen novel about a gay Latino.

Booklist writes, "Mexican-American Tomas is gay. Humiliated by his friends, he discovers that alcohol numbs his pain, and attempts suicide. The intervention of a caring Chicana therapist makes a difference. Though the topic is an important one, the writing is unfortunately dull."

Keywords

Gay and/or Lesbian, Latino/a, Fiction

Age Range:

Teenagers

Author: Gloria Velasquez

ISBN# 155885147X *Date Published:* 1995 *Price:* $ 9.95

Publisher: Arte Publico Press *Pages:* 135

TWENTIETH-CENTURY LATIN AMERICAN POETRY

A bilingual poetry anthology.

Book Links says, "This bilingual anthology attempts to include the major twentieth-century Latin American poets and their important works, which appear both in the original language (Spanish or Portuguese) and in English translations. The editor explains that he regrets not having included more works by what he calls the Hispanic Diaspora (Chicano poems, etc.) due to space limitations.... This is indeed a joyous encounter with some of the world's best poetry in the twentieth century, from Nobel laureates Gabriella Mistral, Pablo Neruda, and Octavio Paz to more experimental younger poets such as Raül Zurita and Marjorie Agosin."

Keywords

Poetry, Latino/a, Bilingual

Age Range:

Teenagers

Editor: Stephen Tapscott

ISBN# 292781407 *Date Published:* 1996 *Price:* $ 24.95

Publisher: University of Texas Press *Pages:* 418

Rating

COPING AS A BIRACIAL/ BIETHNIC TEEN

Part of a series on coping skills for teens.

Written in a down-to-earth easy-to-read style, the books in this series do a good job of presenting the basic issues to teens and of breaking through the sense of isolation likely to accompany being biracial/biethnic, normalizing the situation by offering accounts by other people sharing the same challenges.

Keywords

Core Issues (Feelings), Racial/Ethnic Identity, Multicultural, Multiracial Identity

Age Range:

Teenagers

Author: Renea D. Nash

Renea D. Nash is the author of *Coping as a Biracial/ Biethnic Teen* and *Everything You Need to Know About Being a Biracial/ Biethnic Child*

ISBN# 823918386 Date Published: 1995 Price: $ 17.95

Publisher: Rosen Pages: 122

Rating

EVERYTHING YOU NEED TO KNOW ABOUT BEING A BIRACIAL/BIETHNIC CHILD

What does it feel like to have more than one racial or ethnic heritage?

There are so few books available on this topic, it is wonderful to have this one. The primary message is that "discovering your identity is about becoming comfortable with all aspects of your heritage — racial, ethnic, and religious." Contents includes discovering your identity; this is who I am; the role of the parent; having pride; the best of both worlds; and it's a different world. Biracial or multiracial children will see that this book is specific to them, and all children will benefit from considering experiences unfamiliar to their own lives. The inclusion of photographs brings a greater sense of immediacy and realism to the text.

Keywords

Core Issues (Feelings), Multiracial Identity, Multicultural, Family Life

Age Range:

Teenagers

Author: Renea D. Nash

Renea D. Nash is the author of *Coping as a Biracial/ Biethnic Teen* and *Everything You Need to Know About Being a Biracial/ Biethnic Child*

ISBN# Date Published: 1995 Price: $ 17.95

Publisher: Rosen Pages:

HOUSE YOU PASS ON THE WAY, THE

For anyone who has ever felt different.

Thirteen-year-old Staggerlee used to be called Evangeline, but she has defiantly changed her name. She's always been different — set apart by the tragic deaths of her grandparents in an anti-civil rights bombing, by her parents' interracial marriage, and by her family's retreat from the world. This summer she has a new reason to feel set apart — her romantic longing for her girlfriend. From Kirkus Reviews: "(Staggerlee's cousin) Trout's visit may be a short one, but it's long enough for each to open up, find the courage to say the word gay — and to remember that they're only 14, too young to close off options."

Keywords

Multiracial Identity, Gay and/or Lesbian, Family Life, Friendship

Age Range:

Teenagers

Author: Jacqueline Woodson

Jacqueline Woodson is the author of From The Notebooks of Melanin Sun; I Hadn't Meant To Tell You This; and The House You Pass On The Way.

ISBN# 440227976 Date Published: 1997 Price: $ 4.50

Publisher: Bantam Pages: 99

NATIVE AMERICANS AND BLACK AMERICANS

When a book is the only one available, we are pleased it exists.

If Dramer had done a better job writing about this particularly fascinating topic for teens who are of both Native American and African American heritage, we would have been delighted. "Covering the history of this relationship, this sketchy survey is at its best when focusing on a little-known facet of American history — that some Native American tribes owned black slaves. Unfortunately, the remainder of the book is a series of very loosely related topics written in a plodding style littered with non sequiturs and dangling modifiers." — The Horn Book.

Keywords

Native American, African American, Race Relations, Racial/ Ethnic Identity, Racism

Age Range:

Teenagers

Author: Kim Dramer

ISBN# 791044629 Date Published: 1997 Price: $ 9.95

Publisher: Chelsea House Pages: 96

Rating

HALFBREED

Maria Campbell is Scottish, French, Cree, English, and Irish. This is her story.

"I write this for all of you, to tell you what it is like to be a Halfbreed woman in our country. I want to tell you about the joys and sorrows, the oppressing poverty, the frustration and the dreams.... I am not bitter.... I only want to say: this is what it was like, this is what it is still like." —Maria Campbell. This book, which has become a classic, speaks directly to the heart about challenges of racism.

Keywords

Multiracial Identity, Native American, Race Relations, Racial/ Ethnic Identity, Racism, Self-Esteem

Age Range:

Teenagers

Author: Maria Campbell

Maria Campbell is a Cree writer.

ISBN# 803263112 *Date Published:* 1982 *Price:* $ 7.95

Publisher: University of Nebraska Press *Pages:* 157

Rating

MOON DANCER

Fifteen-year-old Mira feels a connection to the women who preceded her.

"Fifteen-year-old Mira accompanies her sister Jenny, cousin Emily, and Emily's handsome friend Max on a backpacking trip into southern Utah's remote canyons. Led by descriptions in a pioneer woman's journal, the foursome are on a quest to find ancient rock art. Swept in by the rugged beauty of the natural environment and deeply touched by the images of women in the art, she falls in love for the first time with Max. Rostkowski's romantic plot is nicely entwined with the story of a young woman's growing awareness of self and of her connections to the archetypal feminine images she sees in the ancient art." — Booklist

Keywords

Native American, Core Issues (Feelings), Spiritual Meanings, Fiction

Age Range:

Teenagers

Author: Margaret Rostkowski

ISBN# 152001948 *Date Published:* 1995 *Price:* $ 5.00

Publisher: Athenaeum *Pages:* 260

NATIVE AMERICAN MEDICINE

An introduction to Native American medicine

"Bonvillain discusses Native American philosophies of healing, involving the physical,emotional, and spiritual harmony of the individual, brought about through chants and songs, herbal remedies, and numerous rituals. Offering personal accounts of native healers and witnesses to healings, as well as many color and black-and-white photographs and illustrations, this book also documents the integration of traditional healing and modern medicine." —The Horn Book

Keywords

Native American, Health, Rituals and traditions, Cultural History, Spiritual Meanings

Age Range:

Teenagers

Author: Nancy Bonvillain

ISBN# 791044645 *Date Published:* 1997 *Price:* $ 9.95

Publisher: Chelsea House *Pages:*

SONG OF THE BUFFALO BOY

Loi's mother is Vietnamese, her father an American GI. How Loi copes with bias.

"An Amerasian girl, an outcast in her village, dreams of the American soldier who appears with her mother in an old photo. Loi also dreams of Khai, the buffalo tender who returns her love but whose family considers her inferior. It's unfortunate that the issue of interracial children is not explored here in a cultural or historical context; rather, the author repeatedly reminds readers how beautiful Loi is because of her Caucasian freckles and curly hair—as if those features make her superior to those who ostracize her. That's the wrong message. In every other way, the story is vividly realized: effective and moving, from the people inhabiting these seldom-glimpsed lands to the genuine poignancy surrounding the plight of Amerasians." —Kirkus Reviews

Keywords

Vietnam, Multiracial Identity, Core Issues (Feelings), Cultural History, Fathers, Fiction

Age Range:

Teenagers

Author: Sherry Garland

Sherry Garland is the author of *Song of The Buffalo Boy* and *The Lotus Seed.*

ISBN# 152771077 *Date Published:* 1992 *Price:* $ 6.00

Publisher: Harcourt Brace *Pages:* 249

Rating

DANGER ZONE

When Jimmy's team encounters neo-Nazi threats, winning doesn't seem as important as staying alive.

Booklist: "When promoters pick an American High School Dream Team for a tournament in Italy, Doyle is offered a starting spot. The problem becomes persuading the talented African American inner-city kids who make up most of the team that he deserves the opportunity. The pace never lags, and Klass does a convincing job of capturing the feel of the game and depicting Doyle's attempts to be accepted by his teammates, as well as showing what happens when some terrorists add fear to the list of the team's opponents."

Keywords

Sports, Fiction, Race Relations, Racism, Boy Focus

Age Range:

Teenagers

Author: David Klass

ISBN# 590485911 Date Published: 1998 Price: $ 4.99

Publisher: Scholastic Pages:

Rating

GIRLS SPEAK OUT

Finding your true self.

Many girls lose self-esteem when they reach adolescence, and this interactive guide is designed to help them reverse that process and make positive changes. This handbook offers images of women and their roles throughout the ages and excerpts from works by Alice Walker and others.

Keywords

Girl Power, Multicultural, Self-Esteem

Age Range:

Teenagers

Editor: Andrea Johnston

ISBN# 590897969 Date Published: 1999 Price: $ 4.50

Publisher: Simon & Schuster Pages:

GO AND COME BACK

Seeing ourselves as others see us.

Alicia is a Peruvian teenager. When two American anthropologists come to her jungle village, we see their behavior through her eyes. Book Links says, "This is a wonderful opportunity to shift perspective and take a look at our culture as others see us, while exploring those differences that interfere with understanding, and the commonalities that bind us all."

Keywords

Multicultural, Peru, Race Relations, Racial/Ethnic Identity

Age Range:

Teenagers

Author: Joan Abelove

ISBN# 789424762 Date Published: 1999 Price: $ 16.95

Publisher: DK Publishing Pages: 177

GONE FROM HOME: SHORT TAKES

Twelve offbeat short stories filled with unexpected events and outrageous characters.

Starr, the prescreened baby sitter, shows up with a shaved head, wearing a T-shirt that says "Cook the Rich Slowly"; Sweetness, a ten year old, finds an abandoned baby and cares for it ("She didn't know what made people do what they did. Nobody in the world should do something so sick as to leave a little baby alone") only to commit her first armed robbery an hour after she drops the baby at the police station; Noel writes a suicide note that turns out to be a thank you note to a beauty parlor. "Johnson's unconventional humor burnishes each story so that the ordinary becomes something else entirely," says the Horn Book.

Keywords

Core Issues (Feelings), Multicultural, Fiction

Age Range:

Teenagers

Author: Angela Johnson

Angela Johnson is the author of *Mama Bird, Baby Bird; The Aunt In Our House; Julius, The Leaving Morning; Gone From Home; Heaven;* and more.

ISBN# 789424991 Date Published: 1999 Price: $ 15.95

Publisher: DK Publishing Pages: 104

Rating

HABIBI

A teen love story about an Arab-American girl and a Jewish boy.

In this award-winning first novel, a 14-year-old Arab American girl moves to Jerusalem and falls in love with a Jewish boy — challenging her family, culture, and tradition.

Keywords

Multicultural, Judaism, Arab, Fiction, Race Relations, Racism

Age Range:

Teenagers

Author: Naomi Shihab Nye

Naomi Shihab Nye is an acclaimed poet and the author of *This Tree Is Older Than You Are* and *Habibi*.

ISBN# 689825234 Date Published: 1999 Price: $ 4.99
Publisher: Aladdin Pages: 272

Rating

I HADN'T MEANT TO TELL YOU THIS

Sharing their differences, two girls – one White, one Black – find the strength to go on.

Jacqueline Woodson won a Coretta Scott King Honor for this story of friendship, racism, and loss. In a starred review, The Horn Book calls it a "haunting and beautifully poetic novel." The characters are complicated and the plot resists sugarcoating. Marie, a Black middle-class teen, was left by her mother on a "walkabout" from which Marie and her father know she'll never return. Lena, Marie's new friend, is White and poor. Her mother is dead and she tells Marie in secret that "My daddy does things to me." The sexual abuse is quietly told, spelled out in terms of the rage and helplessness that Lena feels. Racism and class prejudice on all sides is graphically confronted. Both the honesty and the hope are welcome here.

Keywords

Friendship, Race Relations, Racism, Fiction, Sexual Abuse, Core Issues (Feelings)

Age Range:

Teenagers

Author: Jacqueline Woodson

Jacqueline Woodson is the author of *From The Notebooks of Melanin Sun; I Hadn't Meant To Tell You This*, and *The House You Pass On The Way*.

ISBN# 440219604 Date Published: Price: $ 4.50
Publisher: Laurel Leaf Pages:

PEELING THE ONION

Who is Anna and who does she want to be?

Before the car accident, Anna knew who she was and what she looked like — a pretty, popular girl who loved karate. But now she's a stranger to her family, her friends, and even herself. Anna's body has betrayed her, and she knows it will never be the same. All the layers that made up the old Anna — her looks, her friends, her sport — have been peeled away, leaving her to face the question of who she really is and what she wants to be. This book should be of particular interest to teens struggling with complex challenges of identity as a result of adoption. An ALA Best Book for Young Adults.

Keywords

Core Issues (Feelings), Racial/Ethnic Identity, Fiction

Age Range:

Teenagers

Author: Wendy Orr

ISBN# 440227739 Date Published: 1999 Price: $ 4.50
Publisher: Dell Pages:

RESPECTING OUR DIFFERENCES

A guide to getting along in a changing world.

From Booklist: "More than simply a consciousness- raising exploration of prejudice today, this is an activist's approach to promoting cultural diversity. Duvall is neither preachy nor strident, touching briefly on everything from theories about race and 'speaking in stereotypes' to the current controversy over U.S. immigration.... The thought-provoking questions found in the book's 'Time Out' sections can be used by independent readers or as classroom discussion starters, and the anecdotal material, featuring young people who have experienced prejudice and are working singly or in groups to overcome it, will encourage young adults to act."

Keywords

Diversity, Antiracist Strategies, Family Life, Educational Issues

Age Range:

Teenagers

Author: Lynn Duvall

ISBN# 915793725 Date Published: 1994 Price: $ 12.95
Publisher: Free Spirit Pages: 208

Rating

STAY TRUE

Short stories for strong girls.

Featuring strong girl heroines, these stories explore coming-of-age themes with a mix of humor and seriousness. Authors contributing to this all-original collection include Norma Fox Mazer, Rita Williams Garcia, and M.E. Kerr.

Keywords

Multicultural, Girl Power, Role Models

Age Range.

Teenagers

Editor: Marilyn Singer

ISBN# 590360337 *Date Published.* 1999 *Price.* $ 4.99

Publisher. Scholastic *Pages.*

Rating

STORYTELLER'S BEADS, THE

Learning to trust an enemy.

"Set in Ethiopia during the revolution that followed the overthrow of Haile Selassie, this novel follows the stories of two girls from opposing cultural groups. Sahay, one of the Kemant people, hid in a cave while her parents were killed. To find safety, she must leave home and overcome her hatred of the Beta-Israel people, who are also fleeing and with whom she must travel. The trust that slowly grows between Sahay and Rahel, a blind young Beta-Israel girl, help readers understand that hatred and fear cause a blindness far more debilitating than loss of physical sight." —Book Links

Keywords

Africa, Multicultural, Race Relations, Fiction, Differently-abled, Girl Power

Age Range.

Teenagers

Author: Jane Kurtz

ISBN# 152010742 *Date Published.* 1999 *Price.* $ 15.00

Publisher. Harcourt Brace *Pages.* 154

WHAT ARE YOU?

Voices of mixed-race young people.

This collection of authentic writing conveys the emotional impact of being of mixed race in a time of identity politics. Through the lively voices of 45 young people, ages 14-26, speaking of the shame and pride that fill their own lives, this book helps us begin to understand how it feels to grow up outside traditional racial boundaries. Their views about the challenges of coming-of-age when the complexities of race are part of each milestone are honest, to-the-point, inspirational, and remarkably insightful. The more you read, the better you can see both the common issues they share and the unique human qualities of each writer. Includes extensive resource lists.

Keywords

Multicultural, Race Relations, Racial/Ethnic Identity, Racism, Multiracial

Age Range.

Teenagers

Editor: Pearl Gaskins

Pearl Fuyo Gaskins is an award-winning journalist whose articles frequently appear in *Scholastic Choices* magazine. She is of mixed racial heritage.

ISBN# 805059687 *Date Published.* 1999 *Price.*

Publisher. Henry Holt *Pages.* 192

WHO BELONGS HERE? AN AMERICAN STORY

What is life like for Nary, a Cambodian refugee, called a chink and a gook:

This award-winning book about immigration, racism, and tolerance helps children consider their own positions on these highly charged issues. Probing and plainspoken, it's filled with lively anecdotes. Best Multicultural Book, 1993; Publishers Weekly Off-the-Cuff award.

Keywords

Parenting, Racial/Ethnic Identity, Racism, Multicultural, Multiracial, US History

Age Range.

Teenagers

Author: Margy Burns Knight

Illustrator: Anne Sibley O'Brien

Margy Burns Knight also wrote *Welcoming Babies* and *Talking Walls*, illustrated by Anne Sibley O'Brien.

ISBN# 8844816797 *Date Published.* 1993 *Price.* $ 8.95

Publisher. Tilbury *Pages.*

Books for Adults

As for children, books can offer adults comfort, interest, information and insight. As in our children's section, our adult offerings reflect our desire to help you discover a wealth of books to illuminate and explore issues central to your life. We want books that directly and indirectly reflect the world's diversity of cultures, races, attitudes, family styles; that address issues specific to race and adoption; that provide guidance and affirmation; that articulate the sometimes-hard-to-say; and that, at all times, embrace the pleasures and recognize the challenges of life's complexities.

Adoption - Triad Views: This section contains books (fiction and nonfiction) for and about birth parents, adoptive parents, and adopted people, with a particular emphasis on the issues of adoption and the interrelationships among triad members. Additionally, the adoptive-parent section includes books on preparing to adopt and parenting after adoption, and offers books for birth parents considering, facing, and resolving a decision to create an adoption plan. This section also includes books for families with gay and/or Lesbian members, families with internationally-adopted members, single-parent families, transracial families, and families in open adoptions.

Professional Resources/System Reform: This section includes a wide range of nonfiction books addressing adoption systems and offering insight into potential changes in institutions and systems affecting adoption in the United States. Books on foster care, open records, search and reunion and social welfare are located in this section.

Race as an Issue: This section includes books (fiction and nonfiction) on racial identity, race relations, racism, ethnic cultural histories, and biography. We call this category "race as an issue" not because race is always an "issue" and not to suggest a belabored preoccupation, but because while race is sometimes just a part of daily life and experience, at other times it takes center stage, whether as part of interpersonal transactions or as a matter of interior development.

Rating

ADOPTEE COME OF AGE

Living within two families.

This is a Christian Life book, subtitled *Counseling and Pastoral Theology*. We were not able to review it in time for publication but wanted to let you know of its availability.

Keywords

Adopted Adult, Spiritual Meanings, Christianity

Age Range:

Adult

Author: Ronald J. Nydam

ISBN# 664256716 *Date Published:* 1999 *Price:* $ 20.95

Publisher: Westminster John Knox Press *Pages:* 192

Rating

BEING ADOPTED: THE LIFELONG SEARCH FOR SELF

The "Dr. Spock, T. Barry Brazelton, and Penelope Leach" of adoption books.

Emphasizing adoption issues as viewed "through the eyes of adopted people," this books offers a sensitive and intelligent guide to developmental perspectives, normality, individuality, search for self, and loss, illustrating common passages and probing complex issues. Without suggesting that adoption is an endless "wound," the authors do argue that adoption is "an issue that emerges, seems to be settled, and then reemerges at some later point along life's path." Excellent. A Pact bestseller.

Keywords

Adoption, Child Development, Core Issues (Feelings), Family Life, Adopted Adult, Adoptive Parent

Age Range:

Adult

Author: David M. Brodzinsky, Ph.D.

Author: Marshall D. Schechter, M.D.

Author: Robin Marantz Henig

David Brodzinsky is Associate Professor of Clinical and Developmental Psychology at Rutgers University. With Marshall Schechter, he is coeditor of *The Psychology of Adoption.*

ISBN# 0-385-41426-9 *Date Published:* 1993 *Price:* $ 14.00

Publisher: Doubleday *Pages:* 214

BEST OF PACT PRESS: BEING ADOPTED

From those who are living it!

Forty-eight-page collections of the best articles published in Pact Press from the perspective of people who have grown up adopted.

Keywords

Adopted Adult, Adopted Child

Age Range:

Adult

Editor: Beth Hall

Author: Gail Steinberg

Gail Steinberg and Beth Hall are Co-Directors and founder of Pact, An Adoption Alliance and each is also the parent of children adopted transracially.

ISBN# NA *Date Published:* 1998 *Price:* $ 10.00

Publisher: Pact Press *Pages:* 48

FOSTER CARE

An overview of the foster care system.

This introduction to foster care includes the history of the foster care system; why children enter care; life in foster homes; foster parents; caseworkers; laws; controversies; and alternatives.

Keywords

Foster Care

Age Range:

Adult

Author: Nancy Millichap Davies

ISBN# 0-531-11081-1 *Date Published:* 1994 *Price:* $ 22.70

Publisher: Franklyn-Watts *Pages:* 111

FREEDOM FROM THE INSIDE OUT

Rating 

A guide for the wounded self.

Natalie Goldrain is a domestic violence counselor, a hypnotherapist, and a visionary counselor who combines knowledge of parapsychology and alternative healing arts with her personal story of survival. She was abandoned by her parents at birth, spent a year in an orphanage, and was abused by her adoptive family. As a teen, she struggled with cancer. Her book tackles the why of suffering, touching on reincarnation and emphasizing healing by unconditional love. Our personal biases make it difficult for works about paraspychology and reincarnation to hold our interest, but for those who believe differently, this book makes an earnest attempt to make a difference.

Keywords

Grief and Loss, Adopted Adult, Spritual Meanings

Age Range,

Adult

Author: Natalie Goldrain

ISBN# 1891850075 Date Published, 1999 Price, $ 13.95

Publisher, Pages, 206

ITHAKA: A DAUGHTER'S MEMOIR OF BEING FOUND

Rating 

The voice on the phone said, "I think I'm your birth mother.'

Sarah had always known she was adopted but had never chosen to search for her birth family. Ithaka is an evenhanded description of what occurred after her birth parents found her when she was twenty-three years old. It took three years more before she felt ready to meet them and her three younger siblings. Without self indulgence, her diary reports her own shifting emotions along the way, painting a sensitive and respectful picture of her birth family and their motivations. *Ithaka* provides a clear sense of the challenges and growth which accompany the development of relationships after reunion, offering illuminating reading.

Keywords

Birth Mother, Adopted Adult, Adoption, Search and Reunion

Age Range,

Adult

Author: Sarah Saffian

ISBN# 046503618X Date Published, 1998 Price, $ 23.00

Publisher, Basic Books Pages, 308

JOURNEY OF THE ADOPTED SELF: A QUEST FOR WHOLENESS

Filled with moving stories, this book examines how separation and secrecy affect identity and attachment.

Asking why adopted adopted people feel alienated, unreal, invisible, unborn, this book offers psychological grounding for the deepest issues in adoption from the perspective of the adopted person. Lifton believes that only by restoring connection to the past can one move ahead with dignity and hope. The New York Times Review says, "'Inside every adopted person is an abandoned baby,' Lifton writes — not a rescued baby but an abandoned one. Shocked first by separation from the birth mother and later by learning 'that he both is and is not the child of his parents,' the child splits his psyche into 'the Forbidden Self and the Artificial Self.'"

Keywords

Adoption, Adoptive Parent, Core Issues (Feelings), Open Records, Search and Reunion

Age Range,

Adult

Author: Betty Jean Lifton

Betty Jean Lifton is a therapist in private practice and the author of *Tell Me A Real Adoption Story, Journey of the Adopted Self,* and *Lost and Found.*

ISBN# 465036759 Date Published, 1995 Price, $ 16.50

Publisher, Basic Books Pages, 328

LOST AND FOUND

If something has to be kept secret, there must be something wrong about it.

B.J. Lifton draws upon her own experience as an adopted person and on her extensive work with triad members to explore secrecy's harmful effects on children's identity.

Keywords

Adopted Adult, Adoption Reform, Adoption, Self-Esteem, Triad Issues, Core Issues (Feelings)

Age Range,

Adult

Author: Betty Jean Lifton

Betty Jean Lifton is a therapist in private practice and the author of *Tell Me A Real Adoption Story, Journey of the Adopted Self,* and *Lost and Found.*

ISBN# 0-06-097132-0 Date Published, Price, $ 12.00

Publisher, Harper Row Pages,

Rating

LOST BOY, THE

A foster child's search for the love of a family.

The Lost Boy is the harrowing but ultimately uplifting true story of a boy's journey through the foster-care system in search of a family to love. This is Dave Pelzer's long-awaited sequel to *A Child Called "It"* — a moving sequel and inspirational read for all.

Keywords

Foster Child, Foster Parent, Core Issues (Feelings)

Age Range:

Adult

Author: Dave Peltzer

ISBN# 1558745157 *Date Published:* 1997 *Price:* $ 10.95

Publisher: Health Communications *Pages:*

Rating

LOST DAUGHTERS (HARDSCRABBLE BOOKS)

Characters who aren't what they seem...

Just in case her daughter Lila finds her, Allie, her birthmother, is writing an account of her life for her daughter placed for adoption at birth; for her part, Lila is pregnant but uncertain about who's the baby's father. Both birthmother and adopted daughter have survived difficult childhoods in this quiet look at the issues of belonging within a family, the choices we make, and their impact on our lives.

Keywords

Adopted Adult, Adopted Child, Birth Parent, Fiction

Age Range:

Adult

Author: Laurie Alberts

ISBN# 874518989 *Date Published:* 1999 *Price:* $ 22.95

Publisher: University Press of New England *Pages:* 220

NOTHING GOOD EVER HAPPENS TO ME

A moving and honest retelling of the challenges involved in adopting an older child.

After six years of shuttling from one foster home to another, Leigh Ann comes to the Lindsay home with humor, good survival skills, and a host of problems. Through the next ten tumultuous years' efforts to legally adopt Leigh Ann, the Lindsays discover and rediscover the meaning of love, commitment, family, and identity. The author is unsparing when describing Leigh Ann's own frustration and depression and bold in her frankness when she writes of her inability to "fix the past" for her daughter. Ms. Lindsay brings a rare unflinching honesty to the story of her family's personal journey.

Keywords

Depression, Grief and Loss, Foster Care, Core Issues (Feelings), Foster Child, Attachment

Age Range:

Adult

Author: Caroline Lindsay

ISBN# 0-87868-601-0 *Date Published:* 1996 *Price:* $ 14.95

Publisher: Child Welfare League *Pages:* 126

OUTER SEARCH, INNER JOURNEY

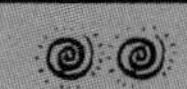

A German orphan, adopted by American parents, describes his lifelong quest for belonging.

Peter Dodds' account of his feelings about being "rescued" from a German orphanage at age three and adopted by American parents, and of his lifelong quest for wholeness. This exploration of a search for roots and of the parallel inner journey toward healing contributes to the understanding of the effects of international adoption with valuable insights to the core issues of transracial adoption as well. One of the first autobiographical accounts of growing up adopted to be written by a man, the anger of the writer is thought provoking.

Keywords

Adoption, Search and Reunion, Core Issues (Feelings), Biography, International Adoption, Adopted Adult

Age Range:

Adult

Author: Peter Dodds

Peter Dobbs was born in Germany and placed for adoption with American parents.

ISBN# 1-889702-24-2 *Date Published:* *Price:* $ 15.00

Publisher: Aphrodite *Pages:*

Rating

PANDORA'S HOPE

Prose and poems offer moving images and insights to the lifelong issues of adoption.

Clear-eyed poems and prose about being adopted, melding the challenges of contemporary life with humor, anger, compassion, and insight into the special issues of being adopted.

Keywords

Poetry, Adopted Adult, Core Issues (Feelings), Adoption, Triad Issues, Adoption

Age Range.

Adult

Author: Penny Partridge

Penny Callan Partridge, a poet who writes about adoption, is the author of *Pandora's Hope* and *New Legs*, among others.

ISBN# NA *Date Published.* *Price.* $ 10.00

Publisher. Self-published *Pages.*

Rating

SECOND CHOICE

A psychiatrist looks at his own adoption.

One of the few first-person adoption memoirs written by a male. Though the circumstances and details of Anderson's personal story are different, this book compares to Peter Dodd's *Outer Search, Inner Journey*, also written from a male perspective. "So much better than most of the adopted person and birth mother books that it is really in a different league," says Annette Baran, a leading adoption expert.

Keywords

Search and Reunion, Adoption, Adoption Reform, Social Welfare, Adopted Child

Age Range.

Adult

Author: Robert Anderson

ISBN# 0-9632648-4-2 *Date Published.* 1993 *Price.* $ 10.00

Publisher. Badger Hill Press *Pages.*

SOLDIER'S DAUGHTER NEVER CRIES, A

Channe has to learn how to live in a new culture .

This coming-of-age story of Channe Willis, a Parisienne growing up in the United States in the early 70s, provides a clear window into what it feels like to be suddenly thrust into a new way of life. This is good escapist reading with a romantic core; adoptive parents of internationally adopted children may be particularly interested in the ways Channe learns to deal with stereotypes.

Keywords

Parenting, Race Relations, Family Life, Fathers, Fiction, International Adoption

Age Range.

Adult

Author: Kaylie Jones

ISBN# 60977558 *Date Published.* 1998 *Price.* $ 12.00

Publisher. HarperCollins *Pages.* 188

TRUMPET

"The world runs on secrets.... Our secret was harmless. It did not hurt anybody.'

Millicent and Joss Moody's secret is exposed when Joss dies; only then does Coleman, the Moodys' adopted son, find out that his father Joss, a jazz great, was in fact a woman. Though the story starts with the question of gender and truth, it attempts to explore the deeper issues of connection and love.

Keywords

Adopted Adult

Age Range.

Adult

Author: Jackie Kay

ISBN# 375405097 *Date Published.* 1999 *Price.* $ 23.00

Publisher. Random House *Pages.* 288

ADOPTING AFTER INFERTILITY

Rating 

A guide to deciding if you should pursue adoption.

This is a landmark book for anyone considering adoption after infertility. The only title that we know of to address these issues in a comprehensive and supportive manner, this book is required reading for Pact families who have struggled with infertility issues. Part One (The Challenge) explores the losses that accompany infertility, suggesting ways people can learn to communicate about them and providing a step-by-step process for making any infertility-related decision. Part Two (The Commitment) explores adoption options and parent preparation. Part Three (Adoption through a Lifetime) explores adoptive parenting issues. A Pact bestseller.

Keywords
Adoption, Infertility, Required for Pact Families, Adoptive Parent, Grief and Loss, Core Issues (Feelings)
Age Range:
Adult
Author: Patricia Irwin Johnston

Patricia Irwin Johnston is the author of *Taking Charge of Infertility, Perspectives on a Grafted Tree, Understanding Infertility,* and *Launching A Baby's Adoption.*

ISBN# 0-944934-10-2 Date Published: 1992 Price: $ 14.00
Publisher: Perspectives Pages: 320

ADOPTING THE OLDER CHILD

Rating 

An important information source on adopting an older child.

Four case studies of different types of adoptions highlight issues that are normal for children joining a new family at an older age. One of the few books to address this topic and in our opinion, the best.

Keywords
Adoption, Attachment, Family Life, Special Needs, Adopting Older Child
Age Range:
Adult
Author: Claudia Jewett

Claudia Jewett is the author of *Adopting the Older Child* and *Helping Kids Cope with Separation and Loss.*

ISBN# 916782093 Date Published: 1979 Price: $ 12.95
Publisher: Harvard Pages: 320

ADOPTING YOUR CHILD

A book for prospective adoptive parents encouraging parents to become well-educated.

This thoughtful guide to decision-making for prospective adoptive parents is well written and thorough, detailing questions and concerns families all families should address. In addition, it is one of the few books available that includes accessible information particularly useful for stepparents who want to adopt, relatives who plan to adopt a child born to an extended family member, and Canadian citizens who wish to adopt in or through the United States. Recommended for anyone first looking at adoption issues and particularly for those needing specialized information in these areas.

Keywords
Adoption, Adoptive Parent, Canada, Extended Family, Stepparents
Age Range:
Adult
Author: Nancy Thalia Reynolds

ISBN# 889082952 Date Published: 1993 Price: $ 12.95
Publisher: Self Counsel Press Pages:

ADOPTION JOURNEYS

Parents tell their stories.

Carole Turner conducted interviews with eleven families, representing a range of adoption circumstances including transracial parents, gay and Lesbian parents, open adopters, and single adoptive parents. Though each chapter tells a unique story, the chapters are linked together by their shared expression of some of the adoption's underlying uncertainties and core issues. By offering the words of the parents themselves, this thought-provoking book of the parents presents a nuanced and realistic picture of some of the central issues of adoption today.

Keywords
Adoption, Adoptive Parent, Transracial Adoption, Gay and/or Lesbian, Open Adoption, Single Parent Families
Age Range:
Adult
Author: Carole S. Turner

ISBN# 935526536 Date Published: 1999 Price: $ 23.95
Publisher: McBooks Press Pages: 256

Rating

ADOPTION RESOURCE BOOK, THE

A comprehensive guide for prospective adoptive parents.

Kirkus Reviews says, "Gilman's optimistic outlook, her specific advice and cautions, and her extensive listings...gives child-seekers every possible advantage." Lois Melina, author of *Raising Adopted Children and Making Sense of Adoption* writes, "Lois Gilman has concisely compiled a wealth of essential information for prospective parents in a book that is not only readable but a valuable reference."

Keywords

Adoption, Adoptive Parent

Age Range.

Adult

Author: Lois Gilman

ISBN# 62733613 Date Published. 1990 Price. $ 14.95

Publisher. Adams Press Pages. 576

Rating

ADOPTION TODAY: OPTIONS AND OUTCOMES

Adoptive parents describe the adoption process.

Options and Outcomes is directed to prospective adopters. Candid interviews with adoptive parents, illustrated by photos of each child, detail how long it took to adopt, costs incurred, whether the child had special needs, and "how to" advice. It describes international and domestic adoptions of infants to teens, presented in catalog format without index. The goal is to reassure prospective parents that adoption "works." But the book implies that the process ends when the child comes home. And what about the child's needs? How can it feel to have one's private medical or emotional challenges and acquisition costs become public property? Not recommended.

Keywords

Adoption, Adoptive Parent, International Adoption, Special Needs

Age Range.

Adult

Editor: Cynthia V.N. Peck

Cynthia Peck is editor of *Roots and Wings*, a magazine about adoption; she is the educational director of Seedlings, Inc., a New Jersey adoption agency she helped found.

ISBN# 965996212 Date Published. 1997 Price. $ 15.95

Publisher. R&W Publications Pages. 94

AN EMPTY LAP

Sam and Jill don't agree. Their story is about working through relationship challenges and adopting.

Joe Treen was very clear about his indifference to having children. When Smolowe married Treen, she hoped to change his mind about children, only to discover seven years later that conception was impossible. Infertility treatment followed — and when that, too, failed,Smolowe decided to pursue adoption, despite Joe's warning that he might leave her. The rest of the book follows them through the process of international adoption and traces the effects of a child on their marriage. An *Empty Lap* is touching, but the book rarely transcends the focus on personal memoir, so news is thin.

Keywords

Adoptive Parent, Infertility, Adoption, International Adoption, Core Issues (Feelings)

Age Range.

Adult

Author: Jill Smolowe

Jill Smolowe is a senior writer at *Time Magazine*.

ISBN# 0-671004-3-79 Date Published. 1997 Price. $ 14.00

Publisher. Pocket Books Pages. 288

AND HANNAH WEPT

What is the Jewish perspective on infertility and adoption?

This book includes a review of how infertility is discussed in religious literature and conclusions to be drawn; strategies for dealing with infertility; a discussion of pregnancy loss from a Jewish perspective; the Jewish view of adoption; and techniques to help Jewish couples adopt. To our knowledge, this is the only book addressing these topics.

Keywords

Adoption, Grief and Loss, Judaism, Infertility, Core Issues (Feelings)

Age Range.

Adult

Author: Michael Gold

Michael Gold is the rabbi of Temple Beth Torah in Tamarac, Florida. An adoptive father, he also wrote *Does God Belong In The Bedroom?*

ISBN# 827604424 Date Published. 1992 Price. $ 17.95

Publisher. Jewish Publication Society Pages. 235

Rating

BEATING THE ADOPTION ODDS

A comprehensive guide to infant adoption

This book provides useful preparation for prospective adoptive parents, offering basic information on the many routes to adoption (independent, agency, international), strategies for a successful outcome, and resources throughout the United States. It is one of the few guides available for prospective adoptive parents who are single, older, Gay or Lesbian, low-income, physically disabled, have medical problems, have a large family, are foster parents, or are in the military. Though the chapter on transracial adoption does not discuss clearly enough the challenges for the child nor detail the depth of commitment necessary for transracial adoptive parents, it does provide a useful overview.

Keywords

Adoption, Adoptive Parent, Guidebook

Age Range:
Adult

Author: Cynthia Martin

Author: Linda Girard

ISBN# 156005220 Date Published: 1998 Price: $ 16.00
Publisher: Harcourt Brace Pages: 590

Rating

COMPLETE ADOPTION BOOK, THE

Information for prospective adoptive parents.

Written for prospective adoptive parents (particularly those seeking to adopt white infants), this is a reference guide to attorneys, agencies, support groups and Internet sites. Includes state-by-state legal requirements. Much of the general information offered seems to apply to white adopters exclusively.

Keywords

Adoption

Age Range:
Adult

Author: Laura Beauvais-Godwin

Author: Raymond Godwin

Laura Beauvais-Godwin and Raymond Godwin are the authors of *The Complete Adoption Book.*

ISBN# 1-55850-644-6 Date Published: Price: $ 15.95
Publisher: Adams Media Pages:

COMPLETE IDIOT'S GUIDE TO ADOPTION, THE

A resource guide for prospective parents.

For those who consider adoption, being evaluated as potential parents is an intimidating and confusing process. This guide explains what to expect, from deciding whether or not one is ready to adopt, to choosing an agency, to meeting with birth parents. The book also discusses how to arrange international adoptions and adoptions for "nontraditional families" (such as single parents and older parents). Finally, readers learn what to do after they take an adopted child home. Caveat: William Pierce is America's most powerful lobbyist for closed adoptions and sealed records, and his vies reflect his conservative adoption philosophy.

Keywords

Adoptive Parent, Adoption, Guidebook, Triad Issues

Age Range:
Adult

Author: Christine Adamec

Author: William Pierce

ISBN# 28621085 Date Published: 1998 Price: $ 18.95
Publisher: Macmillan Pages: 386

FOREVER PARENTS

If you are thinking about adopting an older child, read this book!

The story of the creation of a family through the adoption of four older children. Discusses feelings of the children and of the parents. Normalizes expectations of challenging behavior from the children. A balanced view of the complications and the rewards in this complex form of family making.

Keywords

Adoption, Parenting, Special Needs, Family Life, Attachment, Adopting Older Child

Age Range:
Adult

Author: James Kloeppel

Author: Darlene Kloeppel

ISBN# 0-9650374-1-6 Date Published: Price: $ 11.95
Publisher: Adele Enterprises Pages:

Rating

FOSTERING OR ADOPTING THE TROUBLED CHILD

A guide for parents and professionals.

Introductory information most useful for prospective foster parents considering children with special emotional needs. Chapters include "The Child," "The Team Concept," "Life Suddenly Changes," "Coping With Negative Behaviors," "Working With Birth Families," and "Eighteen and Beyond."

Keywords

Foster Child, Foster Parent, Special Needs

Age Range:

Adult

Author: Janet Glatz

ISBN# 1879418746 | Date Published: 1998 | Price: $ 13.95

Publisher: Biddle | Pages: 168

Rating

GETTING STARTED ON ADOPTION

Preparing the heart: How do prospective adoptive parents cope with the waiting process:

This booklet is a pep talk to keep your spirits up and dispel adoption despair: the worry that you will never be chosen, can't afford to adopt, will never have the joy of becoming a parent. It portrays adoption as a path of personal transformation and growth and shows how believing really can make it so.

Keywords

Adoption, Adoptive Parent, Core Issues (Feelings)

Age Range:

Adult

Author: Randolph Severson, Ph.D.

Considered the poet of the adoption movement, and a strong advocate of open adoption, Randolph Severson, Ph.D., is a psychotherapist concerned particularly with spiritual issues.

ISBN# | Date Published: 1997 | Price: $ 5.00

Publisher: Heart Words Center | Pages: 15

IS ADOPTION THE RIGHT CHOICE FOR YOU?

A manual for prospective parents considering adoption.

This manual contains reprints of selected articles from professional journals, the popular press, and adoption publications grouped under the following topics: Making the decision; Understanding the process; From the inside, looking out; What about open adoption?; An adoptive parent's perspective; A birth parent's perspective; An adopted person's perspective; and Thinking ahead.

Keywords

Adoption, Parenting, Placement

Age Range:

Adult

Editor: Pact Staff

ISBN# NA | Date Published: 1994 | Price: $ 8.00

Publisher: Pact Press | Pages: 52

MULTICULTURAL BABY NAMES

5000 African, Arabic, Asian, Hawaiian, Hispanic, Indian, and Native American names.

If you are looking for a name that comes from your child's cultural heritage, this book can help. Naming traditions of Africa, China, Hawaii, India, Islam, Japan, Korea, and Native Americans are discussed. You and your family can be inspired by these names and the positive values of sharing in naming customs that have been handed down for centuries. But a good portion of them are quite distinct and would appear unusual in the United States, and you might give some thought to enabling your children, by granting them a familiar name, to have some areas of life where they readily fit into the culture in which they are growing up.

Keywords

Multiracial, Multicultural, Racial/Ethnic Identity, Names

Age Range:

Adult

Author: M. J. Abadie

M. J. Abadie is the author of *Multicultural Baby Names* and *Diego.*

ISBN# 0-681-453-32-3 | Date Published: | Price: $ 4.95

Publisher: Longmeadow | Pages:

OUR CHILD: PREPARATION FOR PARENTING

Rating 

Basic preparation of prospective adoptive parents.

Handbook covers preparing family and friends; equipment needed; infertility; adoptive nursing; the layette; arrival announcements; baby books; employee benefit programs; insurance policies; wills; baby care; choosing your pediatrician; childproofing; understanding "telling"; adjustment to parenthood and more.

Keywords

Parenting, Adoption, Adoptive Parent

Age Range:

Adult

Author: Carol A. Hallenback

ISBN# 961187204 *Date Published:* 1986 *Price:* $ 24.95

Publisher: Our Child Press *Pages:* 230

OUR OWN

Rating

Adopting and parenting the older child.

This practical approach to older child adoption contains how-to-adopt information including self- assessment for prospective parents to see if they have what is needed to adopt and information about parenting issues. Including material from interviews with 20 adoptive families, Maskew deals with grief, difficult behavior, birth family contact, racism, dealing with schools , language difficulties, grade placement, problems around holidays, disabled and special-needs children, international adoption, medical diagnosis and contains an extensive bibliography.

Keywords

Adopting Older Child, Parenting, Special Needs, International Adoption

Age Range:

Adult

Author: Trish Maskew

ISBN# 966970128 *Date Published:* 1999 *Price:* $ 23.95

Publisher: Milkweed Editions *Pages:* 284

PARENTS AT LAST

Celebrating adoption and the new pathways to parenthood.

32 portraits of people who became parents through alternative means, including adoption, high-tech conception and birth, step-parenting, and foster parenting. As adoptive parents themselves, the authors effectively translate into words the emotional impact of becoming a family through extraordinary means. Parents speak candidly of the obstacles and rewards they encountered as they struggled with complex issues. Organized in four sections to reflect the process of family growth, *Parents at Last* carries the reader through the developmental milestones predictable for these families and will provide hope for those facing obstacles in their quest to become family.

Keywords

Adoption, Adoptive Parent

Age Range:

Adult

Editor: Cynthia V.N. Peck

Author: Wendy Wilkinson

Author: Helen Kolikow Garber

Cynthia Peck is editor of *Roots and Wings*, a magazine about adoption; she is the educational director of Seedlings, Inc., a New Jersey adoption agency she helped found.

ISBN# 060960290X *Date Published:* 1998 *Price:* $ 27.50

Publisher: Clarkson Potter *Pages:* 160

PROUD HERITAGE

11,001 names for your African American baby.

This, perhaps our all-time favorite of the naming books, offers an astonishing selection. While most baby books cover various ethnic names, they include only a brief and limited list. Now comes the first comprehensive mass-market paperback to compile thousands of names especially for African American babies. Although many parents like to choose an individualistic name for their children, we feel that adopted children in general, and transracially adopted children in particular, have more than their share of not fitting in, and that parents might consider the benefits of choosing a name that doesn't, once again, draw especial attention. This book provides a wealth of options. Strongly recommended.

Keywords

Racial/Ethnic Identity, African American, Names, Black Identity

Age Range:

Adult

Author: Elza Dinwiddie-Boyd

ISBN# 380773406 *Date Published:* 1994 *Price:* $ 5.99

Publisher: Avon *Pages:* 458

Rating

TILL THERE WAS YOU

An adoption expectancy journal, documenting stages of emotional pregnancy for waiting adoptive parents.

This book offers a map to the predictable changes occurring in each trimester of the anticipatory "pregnancy" of waiting adoptive parents. This well-intended journal offers reassurance to parents-to-be that they are not the first to feel as they do, and that they are not alone. Though it does raise real questions about racial identity and whether a child should be transracially adopted, the book's ready "yes" perhaps reflects a recognition of parents' great desire for a child more than their level of dis/comfort with issues in transracial adoption. Although it fails to address some issues thoroughly, this book is sure to be well received by its target audience.

Keywords

Infertility, Adoption, Adoptive Parent, Birth Parent, Core Issues (Feelings)

Age Range:

Adult

Author: Rebecca Lyn Gold

ISBN# 966532805 Date Published: 1998 Price: $ 22.95

Publisher: Pineapple Press Pages: 121

Rating

WANTING A CHILD

How important is it to become a parent when barriers get in the way?

This finely crafted anthology offers emotionally rich essays about yearning to become a parent, reprinted from magazines such as Harper's and The New Yorker. The desire for a child is "a craving," writes contributor Rita Gabis, "hammered out of the bones of things, of winter, frozen groundwater, the sudden naked appearance of spring." With the advent of high-stake and expensive solutions such as expensive medical intervention or international travel, readers who are aware that not everyone shares the economic privileges of middle-class, middle-aged America may wonder how people of modest means address their desire to parent.

Keywords

Adoption, Adoptive Parent, Infertility

Age Range:

Adult

Editor: Jill Bialosky

Editor: Helen Schulman

ISBN# 374525943 Date Published: 1999 Price: $ 13.00

Publisher: Farrar-Strauss Pages: 288

WE ARE FAMILY

Single African American parents and their families.

The first publication of the *African American Children's Book Series Featuring Adoptive Families.* Focuses on single parent adopting, redefining family strengths to include the extended family and friends.

Keywords

Family Life, African American, Single Parent Families, Friendship, Black Identity

Age Range:

Adult

Author: Marie W. Woolf

Author: JoAnne Nelson

ISBN# 0-3-43-3150-3 Date Published: 1997 Price: $ 17.95

Publisher: African American Pages:

WHOLE LIFE ADOPTION BOOK

Key points adoptive parents should be aware of throughout the life of the family.

This book presents information in abbreviated form rather than considered in any depth, making it particularly suitable to jump-start group discussions. The writing is clear and easy to read. Contents includes: Adoption: A labor of the heart (unique challenges adoptive parents face); Critical success factors; Developing a supportive environment; When a child comes home (attachment, strategies to ease the transition); Communicating about adoption (critical questions for parents and children, when and how to talk to children); Growing up adopted (giving children what they need, teens, transcultural adoption, search and reunion).

Keywords

Adoption, Child Development, Family Life, Parenting

Age Range:

Adult

Author: Jayne Schooler

ISBN# 0-89109-722-8-Q Date Published: 1992 Price: $ 12.00

Publisher: Pinon Press Pages: 219

10 PRINCIPLES OF SPIRITUAL PARENTING

Rating 

Nurturing your child's soul.

From the back cover: "By offering concrete ways to help children develop positive values, Mimi Doe and Marsha Walch support parents' efforts to counteract negative messages." Children who have joined their families through adoption may be especially responsive to developing a sense of connection to the universe at large and spiritual values in general. Given the comfort often expressed by people who actively embrace spiritual practices in their daily lives, it seems that finding ways to help your children have this comfort could only be a benefit.

Keywords

Parenting, Spiritual Meanings, Core Issues (Feelings)

Age Range:

Adult

Author: Mimi Doe

Author: Marsha Fayfield Walch

Mimi Doe is an award-winning T.V. producer. Her mother, Marsha Walch, Ph.D., is a psychotherapist who works in private and community health practice.

ISBN# 60952415 *Date Published:* 1999 *Price:* $ 13.00

Publisher: HarperCollins *Pages:* 378

ADOPTION AND THE JEWISH FAMILY

Rating 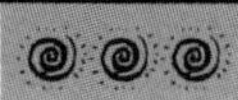

Challenges and benefits of being both adopted and Jewish.

Adoption and the Jewish Family is the first book to consider issues of particular interest to Jewish families. A range of special family circumstances is discussed (see keywords). Rosenberg's dedication to a comprehensive and evenhanded approach is evident in the exceptionally broad range of views culled from seemingly hundreds of interviews. Though the book is packed with useful on-topic information, it also overflows with readily-available general information not especially relevant to the Jewish context. The work would be improved by focusing on material relevant to raising an adopted child within the Jewish community while taking a position on central issues.

Keywords

Judaism, Sibling Issues, Gay and/or Lesbian, Single Parent Families, Transracial Adoption, Special Needs

Age Range:

Adult

Author: Shelley Kapnek Rosenberg

Shelley Kapnek Rosenberg, an adoptive parent, is a special-needs consultant in the Philadelphia Jewish community.

ISBN# 827606532 *Date Published:* 1998 *Price:* $ 19.95

Publisher: Jewish Publication Society *Pages:* 298

ADOPTION CHARMS AND RITUALS FOR HEALING

The poet of the adoption world speaks.

The goal is help your children know truly the depths of their parents' joy in adopting them while also learning of the ordeal through which their parents passed in order for the family to come to be. First published in 1991, this book pioneered a mythopoetic approach to family therapy based on the idea of 'family as culture' instead of system and reflects the work of the Adoptive Family Therapy Project, a five year interdisciplinary clinical research project. It blends Celtic poetry and story and vision with practical rituals, and includes the much-loved allegorical adoption story, "Fire on the Dream Cloud."

Keywords

Adoption, Triad Issues, Required for Pact Families, Core Issues (Feelings), Depression, Open Adoption

Age Range:

Adult

Author: Randolph Severson, Ph.D.

Considered the poet of the adoption movement, and a strong advocate of open adoption, Randolph Severson, Ph.D., is a psychotherapist concerned particularly with spiritual issues.

ISBN# *Date Published:* 1991 *Price:* $ 17.50

Publisher: Heart Words Center *Pages:* 150

ADOPTION LIFE CYCLE

Children and their families through the years. Practical advice on handling the issues.

This book examines the ways that adoption affects all members of the triad at each stage of their lives. It includes an outline of developmental tasks and offers practical advice for understanding the past and anticipating the future, discussing implications for clinical, social, and legal practice. Considers the myth of adoption as a perfect solution; developmental tasks of birth parents; adoptive parents; children growing up adopted and the interrelationship of roles.

Keywords

Adoption, Child Development, Triad Issues, Family Life

Age Range:

Adult

Author: Elinor B. Rosenberg

ISBN# 0-02-927055-3 *Date Published:* 1992 *Price:* $ 22.95

Publisher: Free Press *Pages:* 209

Rating

ADOPTION PHILOSOPHY AND EXPERIENCE

"Adoptive parenting is a spiritual vocation."

Randolph Severson is called the poet of the adoption movement; with moving text that encompasses the topic and many of the philosophical and practical roots in adoption's history and philosophy, this book is a good blend of the practical and beyond. Addresses the primal wound; open adoption; adoption loss; kinship; adoption politics; family preservation; sibling reunions; adoption ceremonies and more.

Keywords

Adoption, Open Adoption, Parenting, Placement, Spiritual Meanings, Social Welfare

Age Range:

Adult

Author: Randolph Severson, Ph.D.

Considered the poet of the adoption movement, and a strong advocate of open adoption, Randolph Severson, Ph.D., is a psychotherapist concerned particularly with spiritual issues.

ISBN# 1-880856-09-3 *Date Published:* 1994 *Price:* $ 22.50

Publisher: Heart Words Center *Pages:* 270

Rating

ALWAYS KISS ME GOOD NIGHT

A "what's important/what's not" guide to parenting, from kids aged six to twelve.

In the tradition of *Kids Say the Darndest Things* and *Really Important Stuff My Kids Have Taught Me*, this warm and funny book offers 147 truly wise parenting tips in the words and handwriting of kids who don't always know how to spell but always know what they need. If kids came with an instruction manual, this would be it — a clever and poignant collection of suggestions, observations and reminders to parents from the experts themselves. These one- or two-line requests will bring a smile to your face, a lump to your throat, and a renewed sense of confidence that you can give your kids the love and support they deserve.

Keywords

Parenting, Family Life, Adopted Child, Core Issues (Feelings)

Age Range:

Adult

Editor: J. S. Salt

ISBN# 051788738X *Date Published:* 1997 *Price:* $ 7.00

Publisher: Crown *Pages:* 128

AMERICAN FAMILIES

A multicultural overview of the variations and interactions among different, constantly changing families.

This insightful book is of special interest to adoptive families, which are often marginalized as not quite "real." Katha Pollitt, Associate Editor of *The Nation* writes, "A wide variety of family forms and values have worked — and not worked — for different people. Coontz demonstrates that the family-values debate is really a denial of diversity. Case studies describe a wide array of family forms and values, gender roles, and parenting practices that have prevailed in dissimilar situations. Paying special attention to class and ethnicity, as well as their impact on gender, sexuality, and personal identity, the contributors highlight the forces that affect the organization and internal dynamics of family life."

Keywords

Family Life, Multicultural

Age Range:

Adult

Editor: Stephanie Coontz

Editor: Maya Parson

Editor: Gabrielle Raley

Stephanie Coontz is a Professor at Evergreen State, WA. She is the author of *The Way We Really Are: Coming to Terms with America's Changing Families.*

ISBN# 415915740 *Date Published:* 1999 *Price:* $ 27.99

Publisher: Routledge *Pages:* 496

AND BABY MAKES FOUR

Welcoming a second child into the family.

"Funny, friendly, helpful advice," says Booklist. "Wagner raises the appropriate questions: Have I had enough time with my eldest? Won't a newborn shatter my firstborn's world? When will he understand why I decided to have another? Other subjects include planning a sibling strategy; understanding rivalry issues; the father's role; adopting a sibling; and managing two or more kids while sustaining your marriage. Wagner offers numerous references to appropriate books and websites, and her suggestions for the best books for new siblings are well worth the cost of admission." Note: Much of this book deals with handling the logistics of a pregnancy, though adoption is also covered.

Keywords

Family Life, Sibling Issues, Parenting

Age Range:

Adult

Author: Hilary Wagner

Hilary Wagner is the author of *The New Parent's Sourcebook*. She also writes for *Parenting, Parents, Child,* and *Babytalk* magazines.

ISBN# 380795051 *Date Published:* 1998 *Price:* $ 12.00

Publisher: Avon *Pages:* 205

Rating

ART OF FAMILY, THE

Rituals, imagination, and everyday spirituality.

Adoptive families must can be strengthened by placing special emphasis on developing a unique family identity. Here's help. Bria's strategies create a family culture in which we are more present — maybe not in every moment (we're tired enough!), but in key activities that can see us through the pace of life today to a strong, coherent, lived family life." An anthropologist with a sense of humor, Bria uses stories from diverse cultures to demonstrate how to assign special meaning to everyday events by incorporating rituals, imagination and spirituality for a richer family experience. Rather than a "formula" book, this is an invitation to families to create meaning for themselves.

Keywords

Family Life, Spiritual Meanings, Rituals and traditions

Age Range:

Adult

Author: Gina Bria

ISBN# 440507723 *Date Published:* 1998 *Price:* $ 12.95

Publisher: Dell *Pages:* 216

Rating

ATTACHMENT

"Attachment and Loss" Series, Volume 1

John Bowlby's classic psychological study of attachment. John Bowlby was one of the first to study attachment issues; his theories have had strong impact on the current generation of clinicians trying to help children with attachment issues. No one hoping to understand the body of work contributing to current theories can afford to miss this classic text.

Keywords

Attachment, Parenting, Child Development

Age Range:

Adult

Author: John Bowlby

ISBN# 465005438 *Date Published:* 1983 *Price:* $ 23.00

Publisher: Basic Books *Pages:*

BECOMING ATTACHED

An easy-to-understand book of great importance to adoptive parents.

Fresh views about the history of attachment theory and how contemporary thinking about bonding applies to the later lives of children.

Keywords

Attachment, Parenting, Child Development, Adoptive Parent

Age Range:

Adult

Author: Robert Karen

ISBN# 0-19-511501-5 *Date Published:* 1997 *Price:* $ 16.95

Publisher: OUP *Pages:* 512

BECOMING THE PARENT YOU WANT TO BE

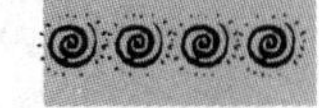

"If every parent could read this book, we'd have a much better world."

This book offers a developmental approach for both children and parents. Provides parents with energy to explore, experiment and grow along with their kids. Thought-provoking, challenging and enriching. Books in Print: "The authors examine both the needs of children and the feelings of parents. Dealing particularly well with the topic of kids who push limits, the authors suggest practical means for responding calmly and effectively to whining, nagging, biting, swearing and other potentially disruptive behaviors. They also offer suggestions for dealing with anger — both child's and parent's."

Keywords

Parenting, Child Development, Core Issues (Feelings)

Age Range:

Adult

Author: Laura Davis

Author: Janis Keyser

Laura Davis is the co-author of *The Courage to Heal and Allies in Healing.*

ISBN# 0-553-06750-8 *Date Published:* 1997 *Price:* $ 20.00

Publisher: Broadway Books *Pages:* 544

Rating

BEST OF PACT PRESS: ATTACHMENT

Practical, in-depth exploration.

Forty-eight-page collections of the best articles published in Pact Press concerning attachment.

Keywords

Adopted Child, Attachment, Parenting

Age Range:
Adult

Editor: Beth Hall

Author: Gail Steinberg

Gail Steinberg and Beth Hall are Co-Directors and founder of Pact, An Adoption Alliance and each is also the parent of children adopted transracially.

ISBN# NA *Date Published:* 1998 *Price:* $ 10.00

Publisher: Pact *Pages:* 48

Rating

BEST OF PACT PRESS: TALKING WITH KIDS ABOUT ADOPTION

Ideas for parents with children of all ages.

Forty-eight-page collections of the best articles published in Pact Press concerning how to talk about adoption with children of all ages.

Keywords

Adopted Child, Parenting, Core Issues (Feelings), Family Life, Triad Issues

Age Range:
Adult

Editor: Beth Hall

Author: Gail Steinberg

Gail Steinberg and Beth Hall are Co-Directors and founder of Pact, An Adoption Alliance and each is also the parent of children adopted transracially.

ISBN# NA *Date Published:* 1998 *Price:* $ 10.00

Publisher: Pact *Pages:* 48

BLACK PARENTING BOOK, THE

Caring for Black children in the first five years.

Written expressly for the parents of America's 3.6 million Black children under six, this book includes information on health, development, and cultural issues to help parents provide their children with racial pride and a sense of their heritage. Black kids are more at-risk than White kids in matters such as obesity, asthma, and loss of self-esteem. The authors raise and answer questions such as "How can I find a pediatrician who shares my values?" "Are all-Black preschools best?" and "Should I straighten my child's hair?" Advice about handling racist incidents, selecting a preschool, and support for spirituality and family traditions is included.

Keywords

Parenting, African American, Health, Child Development

Age Range:
Adult

Author: Anne C. Beal

Author: Linda Villarosa

Author: Allison Abner

Anne C. Beal is a pediatrician at Harvard Medical School. Linda Villarosa is an editor for the New York Times. Allison Abner is a journalist.

ISBN# 767901967 *Date Published:* 1998 *Price:* $ 20.00

Publisher: Broadway Books *Pages:* 416

BREASTFEEDING THE ADOPTED BABY

An optimistic and practical guide to adoptive breast feeding.

Written by an adoptive mother, this book is an extremely optimistic practical guide to breastfeeding for adoptive mothers. The author is convinced of the benefits and believes that the importance of the breastfeeding relationship stems from the direct contact and "bonding influence" more than from the production of milk. One of the few books to address this topic, it offers more thorough practical advice than any other we have seen. However, this book does not address the disappointment reported by many adoptive mothers who have attempted to breastfeed but found the process too frustrating for themselves and the baby.

Keywords

Adoption, Parenting, Breastfeeding, Skill Mastery, Attachment

Age Range:
Adult

Author: Debra Stewart Peterson

ISBN# 0-931722438 *Date Published:* 1994 *Price:* $ 8.95

Publisher: Corona *Pages:* 141

Rating

Rating

BROKEN CORD, THE: A FAMILY'S ONGOING STRUGGLE WITH FAS

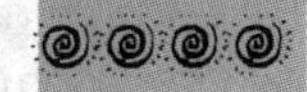

Intensely moving, this is Dorris' story of FAS and of love's limited power to heal.

One of the first to recognize an adoptive parent's struggle with self-blame over genetic factors, this book sheds new light on the truth of the power of expectations, blame, and guilt for adoptive parents. Books in Print writes, "Dorris adopted an Indian child in 1971 who, after batteries of tests and transfer from school to school, was finally diagnosed as suffering from FAS. To understand fully his son's condition, Dorris was compelled to 'systematically confront Native American history.' Dorris includes a wealth of scientific data, excellent treatments of alcohol's effects upon Native American culture and of the physiopathological aspects of FAS, and a very complete bibliography. Highly recommended."

Keywords

Special Needs, Depression, FAS/FAE, Native American, Parenting, Adoption

Age Range:

Adult

Author: Michael Dorris

Michael Dorris is an adoptive father and the author of *The Broken Cord, Morning Girl, The Window* and numerous others.

ISBN# 0-06-091682-6 Date Published: 1992 Price: $ 13.00

Publisher: Harper Collins Pages: 288

CHALLENGING CHILD, THE

Understanding and enjoying your child, by one of the leading child psychiatrists of our time.

According to this book, most challenging children are born with a personality that falls into one of five personality types: sensitive, self-absorbed, defiant, inattentive or active/aggressive. How about yours? Whatever your child's personality type, this book will help you turn challenges into assets, build on your child's strengths, and help your child master weaknesses with confidence and joy. A Pact bestseller.

Keywords

Parenting, Child Development

Age Range:

Adult

Author: Stanley Greenspan

ISBN# 0-201-62647-0 Date Published: Price: $ 13.00

Publisher: Addison-Wesley Pages:

CHILD'S JOURNEY THROUGH PLACEMENT, A

Understanding and supporting the child who has been placed in foster care or residential treatment.

This book provides help for parents (birth, foster, and adoptive) and professionals (therapists, social workers, pediatricians, volunteers, and child advocates) supporting children who have experienced out-of-home care. Includes chapters on attachment and separation; child development; separation and loss; minimizing the trauma of moves; case planning; behavior problems; and direct work with children.

Keywords

Adoption, Attachment, Parenting, Foster Care, Core Issues (Feelings), Special needs

Age Range:

Adult

Author: Vera Fahlberg

Vera Fahlberg is the author of *Residential Treatment* and *A Child's Journey Through Placement.*

ISBN# 0-944934-04–8 Date Published: Price: $ 20.00

Publisher: Perspectives Pages:

CHILDREN'S ADJUSTMENT TO ADOPTION

Developmental and clinical issues.

This book has not yet been released as we go to press. Please call for updated information.

Keywords

Adoption, Child Development, Core Issues (Feelings)

Age Range:

Adult

Author: David M. Brodzinsky, Ph.D.

Author: Anne Braff Brodzinsky

Daniel W. Smith

David Brodzinsky is Associate Professor of Clinical and Developmental Psychology at Rutgers University. With Marshall Schechter, he is coeditor of *The Psychology of Adoption.*

ISBN# 761905162 Date Published: 1998 Price: $ 18.95

Publisher: Sage Pages:

Rating

CREATING CEREMONIES

Innovative ways to meet adoption challenges.

This exploration of the use of ceremony in adoption situations provides easy-to-understand suggestions for using rituals in common (and not so common) family situations for families built through adoption. This well of good ideas is easy to dip into and encourages readers to think creatively about their own situations.

Keywords

Adoption, Family Life, Spiritual Meanings, Rituals and traditions

Age Range.

All ages

Author: Cheryl A Lieberman

Author: Rhea K. Bufferd

ISBN# 189194410X   Date Published. 1999   Price. $ 23.95

Publisher. Zeig Tucker & Co.   Pages.

Rating

DIALOGUES ABOUT ADOPTION

Parents and children talk about adoption

Real-life conversations between parents and their children to lend comfort and support to parents who want to know how other families have handled the normal developmental issues of adoption. This book is easy to read but does not compare well to *Talking With Children About Adoption* or *Flight of the Stork,* both of which address the child's psychological development on a deeper level.

Keywords

Adoption, Child Development, Parenting, Family Life

Age Range.

Adult

Author: Linda Bothun

Linda Bothun is the author of *Dialogues About Adoption* and *When Friends Ask About Adoption.*

ISBN# 0-9619559-1-0   Date Published. 1994   Price. $ 12.95

Publisher. Swan Publications   Pages. 216

FACILITATING DEVELOPMENTAL ATTACHMENT IN FOSTER & ADOPTED CHILDREN

The road to emotional recovery and behavioral change in foster and adopted children.

Children, especially those who have experienced abuse or neglect, need to feel connected to a caring adult in order to develop trust. Describing techniques based on the work of Milton Erickson, this book offers suggestions to help therapists working with children unable to form secure attachments. Dr. Daniel Hughes has based many of his interventions on the work of the Attachment Center in Evergreen, Colorado. Chapters include: integrative psychotherapy principles and goals, parental participation, therapeutic interventions, contract, holding, attachment sequences, confrontations, verbal directives, psychodrama, , stories and props (books, photos, stuffed animals, music, etc.), parenting principles and day-to-day tools.

Keywords

Attachment, Parenting, Child Development, Foster Care, Core Issues (Feelings), Grief and Loss

Age Range.

Adult

Author: Daniel A. Hughes

Daniel A. Hughes is the author of *Facilitating Developmental Attachment in Foster and Adopted Children* and *Building The Bonds of Attachment.*

ISBN# 765700387   Date Published. 1997   Price. $ 40.00

Publisher. Jason Aronson   Pages.

FIRST FEELINGS

Milestones in the Emotional Development of Your "Baby and Child

Recommended by Holly van Gulden, author of *Real Parents, Real Children* and an expert on adoption attachment, this book takes a long look at the six stages of emotional development of infants, provides help in observing your baby, and offers strategies to support your child's emotional development. You will learn how to take inventory of your own parenting style and how to develop positive patterns of interaction with your baby; how to stimulate your baby; what to do when baby is nasty (temper tantrums, aggressiveness, attacks on siblings), how to encourage curiosity and independence, and more. Easy to read and useful.

Keywords

Attachment, Child Development, Parenting, Adoptive Parent

Age Range.

Adult

Author: Stanley I. Greenspan, M.D.

Author: Nancy Thorndike Greenspan

Stanley I. Greenspan, M.D., is Clinical Professor of Psychiatry, Behavioral Sciences and Pediatrics at the George Washington University Medical School.

ISBN# 140119884   Date Published. 1994   Price. $ 12.95

Publisher. Penguin   Pages. 248

Rating

FLIGHT OF THE STORK

The best book about how children understand sex and family creation (including adoption).

1994 Pact Praise book award-winner. Books in Print writes, "Bernstein examines how children think differently from adults concerning sex and birth. Page after page of enlightening interviews take us deep into the minds of children three to 12 years old. The interviews demonstrate each child's level of mental development and also show how a child's thinking changes with age. This understanding of child development will help adults communicate better with children about the origin of families as well as the origin of babies. Also deals with assisted reproductive technology, donor insemination, and surrogacy. These valuable additions make the book essential even for libraries already owning the first edition."

Keywords

Adoption, Child Development, Parenting, Educational Issues

Age Range:
Adult

Author: Anne C. Bernstein, Ph.D.

Anne C. Bernstein, Ph.D., a practicing family psychologist, is the author of *Yours, Mine, and Ours: How Families Change When Remarried Parents Have A Child Together.*

ISBN# 0-944934-09-9 Date Published: 1994 Price: $ 14.95
Publisher: Perspectives Pages: 286

Rating

GOLDEN RULES

A useful and inspirational book to jump-start parents who want to model positive values.

Imparting the essential values of respect, honesty, fairness, responsibility, compassion, gratitude, friendship, peace, maturity and faith to help a child learn the difference between right and wrong and lead a happy life. Inspiriting and fun to read.

Keywords

Parenting, Core Issues (Feelings)

Age Range:
Adult

Author: Wayne Dosick

ISBN# 62512048 Date Published: Price: $ 12.00
Publisher: HarperCollins Pages:

HANDBOOK FOR SINGLE ADOPTIVE PARENTS

How to adopt, how to parent, and how other single people have successful adopted.

Practical information includes financing an adoption, medical guidance, laws affecting adoption, and resources. Includes questions single people have; domestic and international adoption; transracial adoption; adoption by gay, Lesbian, bisexual, and transgendered people; adoption costs, finding child care, choosing heath care, medical information; adopting a child with special needs, and case studies.

Keywords

Adoption, Adoptive Parent, Gay and/or Lesbian, Open Adoption, Transracial Adoption, Single Parent Families

Age Range:
Adult

Editor: Hope Marindin

ISBN# 963404512 Date Published: 1997 Price: $ 20.00
Publisher: Ntl. Council for Single Adoptive Parents Pages: 140

HELPING KIDS COPE WITH SEPARATION AND LOSS

This book should be on every adoptive parent's and every adoptive professional's shelf.

All adopted children suffer the loss of their birth parents. Claudia Jewett helps parents understand a child's reactions by detailing a child's emotions and behaviors. She offers direct and clear suggestions for how to talk to and with children about loss, and helps parents understand the ways other losses trigger reactions to the early losses the child has experienced through adoption.

Keywords

Adoption, Parenting, Grief and Loss, Core Issues (Feelings)

Age Range:
Adult

Author: Claudia Jewett

Claudia Jewett is the author of *Adopting the Older Child* and *Helping Kids Cope with Separation and Loss.*

ISBN# 1-55832-051-2 Date Published: Price: $ 12.95
Publisher: National Book Pages:

Rating

HOLDING TIME

No parent should be without this book.

Words can be meaningless when kids are hurt. This book teaches a technique to help kids trust that their parents will not let them hurt themselves or others and to get a clear message that the parent is strong enough to take care of them. A Pact bestseller.

Keywords

Parenting, Core Issues (Feelings), Skill Mastery, Attachment, Grief and Loss, Special Needs

Age Range.

Adult

Author: Martha G. Welch

ISBN# 0-671-68878-2 *Date Published.* 1989 *Price.* $ 11.00

Publisher. S&S Children's *Pages.*

Rating

HOW TO RAISE AN ADOPTED CHILD

The practical question-and-answer style covers questions from infancy to ten years.

Although its information is generally good, this book should be read with a critical eye, since almost everyone will be able to find something to disagree with in this comprehensive text. Includes issues relevant to adopting older and special-needs children, to single parenting, and to searching. Books in Print: "Positive and easy to read, this how-to manual offers special chapters on transracial and single-parent adoptions and adoptions of older and foreign-born children. There are end-of-chapter questions and answers and a list of resources keyed to parents of children with disabilities."

Keywords

Adoption, Child Development, Parenting, Special Needs, Transracial Adoption, Adopting Older Child

Age Range.

Adult

Author: Judith Schaffer

Author: Christina Lindstrom

ISBN# 0-452-26560-6 *Date Published.* 1990 *Price.* $ 12.95

Publisher. Dutton *Pages.* 320

I SWORE I'D NEVER DO THAT!

Recognizing family patterns and making wise parenting choices.

What parent hasn't felt a shock of recognition with the thought, "I sound just like my parents!"? To our surprise, we often hear the past echoing through the choices we make as parents. Explore the ways in which unresolved issues from our childhood regarding discipline, intimacy, and self-esteem prevent us from being the parents we want to be.

Keywords

Parenting, Adoptive Parent, Child Development, Family Life

Age Range.

Adult

Author: Elizabeth Fishel

The author of the best-selling *Sisters and The Men In Our Lives,* Elizabeth Fishel has written extensively on family issues for magazines nationwide.

ISBN# 0-94323369-0 *Date Published.* *Price.* $ 12.95

Publisher. Conari *Pages.*

IN PRAISE OF SINGLE PARENTS

For mothers and fathers embracing the challenges of raising children alone.

Alexander has created a helpful and moving account of the joys and challenges of parenting without a partner. Chapters cover the decision to become a single parent, dealing with perfectionism, guilt, finances, childcare, setting boundaries, helping the parent grow up and take care of personal needs, dating, and support. Recommended to all single parents.

Keywords

Parenting, Single Parent Families, Adoptive Parent

Age Range.

Adult

Author: Shoshana Alexander

ISBN# 039566991X *Date Published.* 1994 *Price.* $ 13.95

Publisher. Houghton Mifflin *Pages.* 404

Rating

KEYS TO PARENTING AN ADOPTED CHILD

Practical advice including blending adopted children into the family, answering children's questions and more.

Covers a multitude of adoption issues: adoption successes; raising well-adjusted children; attachment; developmental stages; blending families; school issues; issues for your child; transracial adoptions; international adoptions; adopting older children; special-risk issues; attention deficit; attachment disorders; substance exposure; sexual abuse. Also includes managing resources; securing subsidies; finding therapists; accessing birth records, and more.

Keywords

Adoption, Parenting, Child Development, Special Needs, Family Life, Adopting Older Child

Age Range:

Adult

Author: Kathy Lancaster

ISBN# 0-8120-9104-3 *Date Published:* 1996 *Price:* $ 6.95

Publisher: Barrons *Pages:* 196

Rating

LAUNCHING A BABY'S ADOPTION

Practical strategies for parents and professionals on welcoming a new adopted baby.

A clear and insightful look at the issues of infant adoption including the parent's history and past experiences with loss and expectations for the future, the child's genetic and prenatal heritage, naming, bonding, attachment, and birth parent contact. As always, reading Pat's writing feels as effortless as listening to a warm but very intelligent voice flow in your ear, chatting easily about the things that matter most. Important information for prospective and new parents launching into a new life experience.

Keywords

Adoption, Parenting, Child Development, Required for Pact Families, Adoptive Parent

Age Range:

Adult

Author: Patricia Irwin Johnston

Patricia Irwin Johnston is the author of *Taking Charge of Infertility, Perspectives on a Grafted Tree, Understanding Infertility* and *Launching A Baby's Adoption.*

ISBN# 0-944934-16-1 *Date Published:* 1997 *Price:* $ 15.00

Publisher: Perspectives *Pages:* 265

LETTER TO ADOPTIVE PARENTS ON OPEN ADOPTION, A

An introduction to open adoption delivered in a passionate, intriguing, and warmly convincing manner.

If you are considering adoption and are afraid of connection with the child's birth family, please do your child a favor and read this booklet.

Keywords

Adoption, Parenting, Open Adoption, Adoptive Parent, Triad Issues

Age Range:

Adult

Author: Randolph Severson, Ph.D.

Considered the poet of the adoption movement, and a strong advocate of open adoption, Randolph Severson, Ph.D., is a psychotherapist concerned particularly with spiritual issues.

ISBN# 1880856050 *Date Published:* 1991 *Price:* $ 6.50

Publisher: Heart Words Center *Pages:*

LIMITS OF HOPE, THE

An adoptive mother's discovery that love is not enough.

Nature and previous nurture cannot always be fixed by loving parents. Loux questions policies that do not prepare parents for high-risk children and suggests that some children might do better if raised in group homes. *The Limits of Hope* provokes questions that must be asked by every family considering adoption. Kirkus Reviews says, "The Louxs adopted three- and four-year-old white sisters. From early on, the girls were unable to integrate successfully. As adults, Margey turned to drug abuse and works as a prostitute. Dawn is trying to raise two developmentally disabled children. Their mother contends that her experiences in raising children, whose backgrounds were shielded from her, are far from unique."

Keywords

Adoptive Parent, Biography, Adoption, Adoption Reform, Family Life, Parenting

Age Range:

Adult

Author: Ann Kimble Loux

ISBN# 813917107 *Date Published:* 1997 *Price:* $ 24.95

Publisher: University Press of Virginia *Pages:* 280

Rating

LOST ART OF LISTENING, THE

"Listen with an intensity most people save for talking," advises Lily Tomlin.

These techniques, easily learned, offer a practical approach to identifying and harnessing the emotional triggers that generate anxiety, drive misunderstanding and conflict, and prevent us from hearing each other. Parents can strengthen connections with their children and provide greater support by learning to listen to how their children experience being adopted and how the issues of race affect their lives. This book describes the yearning to be understood, the real reasons people don't listen ("When is it my turn?"), the hidden assumptions that prejudice listening, techniques for getting through to each other (how to let go of your own needs and listen), and listening in context.

Keywords

Adoption, Core Issues (Feelings), Race Relations, Family Life, Parenting, Skill Mastery

Age Range,

Adult

Author: Michael P. Nichols, Ph.D.

ISBN# 1572301217 *Date Published,* 1996 *Price,* $ 14.95

Publisher, Guilford *Pages,* 251

Rating

MAKING SENSE OF ADOPTION

When to tell, what to tell, and how to tell your child about adoption.

Cues for talking with children about adoption. Includes chapters on how to begin; where did I come from?; why didn't they keep me?; what does being adopted say about me?; who am I?; I want to meet my birth parents; and why didn't you tell me? An adoption classic designed particularly for families with closed adoptions.

Keywords

Adoption, Parenting, Open Adoption, Child Development, Core Issues (Feelings), Triad Issues

Age Range,

Adult

Author: Lois Ruskai Melina

Lois Melina is author of *Raising Adopted Children* and co-author with Sharon Kaplan Roszia of *The Open Adoption Experience.*

ISBN# 60903190 *Date Published,* 1989 *Price,* $ 13.00

Publisher, HarperCollins *Pages,* 277

MEDITATIONS FOR ADOPTIVE PARENTS

Meditations for Adoptive Parents contains thirty days of Christian thoughts for adoptive parents.

A gift for adoptive parents in the style of the best-selling *Meditations for the New Mother*. Using her family experiences, the author weaves many threads into the fabric of these meditations on adoption. She includes advice about bonding to infants and older children, the stages in relinquishment and adoption, how "entitlement" happens, and more. For each day, there is a poem or story, a Bible quotation, an essay on the author's experiences, a prayer, and a prayer focus.

Keywords

Adoption, Adoptive Parent, Christianity, Spiritual Meanings, Adopting Older Child

Age Range,

Adult

Author: Yernell Klassen Miller

ISBN# 836136063 *Date Published,* 1992 *Price,* $ 7.99

Publisher, Herald Press *Pages,*

MOTHER DANCE, THE

How children change your life: seldom heard wisdom, stories and healing advice.

Written from her dual perspective as a psychologist and a mother, Lerner shines the spotlight on how a woman is changed when she become a mother. From birth to empty nest syndrome, Lerner chronicles her own experiences and shares them with readers. "Lerner writes with charm, precision and at times unbearable honesty about what motherhood is," writes Mary Pipher, Ph.D., author of *Reviving Ophelia* And Anne Lamott concurs: "I love *The Mother Dance.* It's wonderful — true, touching, practical, spiritual, sanity-saving, and I laughed out loud a number of times, with recognition, surprise and gratitude."

Keywords

Mothers, Family Life

Age Range,

Adult

Author: Harriet Lerner

Harriet Lerner is the author of *The Dance of Anger.*

ISBN# 60187689 *Date Published,* 1998 *Price,* $ 14.00

Publisher, HarperCollins *Pages,* 256

MOTHERS AND DAUGHTERS

Rating 

Searching for new connections.

Because the relationship between adoptive mothers and their daughters rests on their abilities to connect deeply with each other, Caron's interviews with mothers at mid-life and daughters making the transition to full adulthood has special resonance. As both age groups seek deeper connections to others and especially each other, they appear to deepen their acceptance of one another and to become closer. Readers seeking to understand the development of relationships within adoptive families will find many parallels to consider.

Keywords

Parenting, Child Development, Family Life, Core Issues (Feelings), Adoption, Triad Issues

Age Range:

Adult

Author: Ann Caron

ISBN# 080505149X *Date Published:* 1998 *Price:* $ 25.00

Publisher: Holt *Pages:* 288

OLDER CHILD ADOPTION

Rating 

Interviews with 30 families who adopted older children.

Case studies. Useful to parents of children who join adoptive families at older ages.

Keywords

Adopted Child, Adoption, Adoptive Parent, Family Life, Parenting, Self-Esteem

Age Range:

Adult

Author: Grace Robinson

ISBN# 824517075 *Date Published:* 1998 *Price:* $ 17.95

Publisher: Crossroads *Pages:* 229

PARENT AND CHILD

How to communicate with your child.

A developmental approach to parenting, though not adoption-specific. This book is out of print, but if you place an order we may be able to find you a used copy within 2-6 months. We will notify you and request your approval of the price and condition. We will also notify you if we are unable to locate this title within six months.

Keywords

Parenting, Adoptive Parent, Child Development

Age Range:

Adult

Author: Lawrence Kutner

ISBN# 0-380-71368-3 *Date Published:* 1992 *Price:* $ 10.00

Publisher: Avon *Pages:*

PARENTING AFTER ADOPTION

Treats adoption as an issue, not a problem.

Manual compiled by Pact for families parenting after adoption. Covers parenting strategies from infancy through teens. Treats adoption as an issue, not a problem. Contains a selection of articles of value reprinted from professional journals, the popular press, and adoption newsletters.

Keywords

Adoption, Adoptive Parent, Parenting, Child Development, Racial/Ethnic Identity, Required for Pact Families

Age Range:

Adult

Editor: Pact Staff

ISBN# NA *Date Published:* *Price:* $ 10.00

Publisher: Pact Press *Pages:*

Rating

PARENTING WITH LOVE AND LOGIC

Kids learn responsibility when they're given a task, allowed to make choices and to fail.

Offering techniques to teach your kids responsibility through practice, this is a recipe book of methods to take the power struggle out of parent-child interactions and to help kids grow stronger through positive experiences. Popular on the adoption circuit.

Keywords

Parenting, Special needs, Attachment, Adoptive Parent, Foster Care, Skill Mastery

Age Range.

Adult

Foster Cline

Author: Jim Fay

Foster Cline is the author of *Parenting with Love and Logic; Can This Child be Saved?* and many more.

ISBN# 891993117 *Date Published.* 1990 *Price.* $ 18.00

Publisher. Pinon Press *Pages.* 224

Rating

PATTY'S JOURNEY: FROM ORPHANAGE TO ADOPTION AND REUNION

Patty's Journey is one of a great many variations of the adoption journey.

Children who enter their family through adoption share certain core issues with others who have had to move from one family to another — but the circumstances of each journey are unique. Reading and talking about the many forms adoption takes is another useful way to talk about feelings without talking about your child's specific journey with a capital "A."

Keywords

Adoption, Search and Reunion, Foster Care, Family Life, Social Welfare, Foster Child

Age Range.

Adult

Author: Donna Norling

ISBN# 816628661 *Date Published.* 1996 *Price.* $ 14.95

Publisher. University of Minnesota Press *Pages.*

PRESERVING FAMILY MEMORIES

A guide to creating oral histories.

Families created or enlarged through adoption are scrutinized more closely by outsiders in today's world.... Is this a real family? Are those your real kids? That can't be your real mommy! To meet these challenges head on, it's important to make conscious effort to cultivate your family's awareness of the things that absolutely make us belong together: shared experiences, shared loved and shared history. With this book, you can learn to record family memories for your child. It teaches you how to create a video or audio tape that you and your child can treasure always, and includes techniques for interviewing family members, friends, and relatives for posterity.

Keywords

Family Life, Adoption, Cultural History, Memory Book

Age Range.

Adult

Author: Marc A. Seligman

ISBN# *Date Published.* 1997 *Price.* $ 9.95

Publisher. Tapestry *Pages.* 32

RAISING ADOPTED CHILDREN

This book should be on every adoptive parent's shelf.

This book explains the need to recognize that the job of being an adoptive parents brings with it some challenges different from those faced by "just parents," while it offers the essential basics of parenting an adopted child. Offers information on bonding and attachment; talking with children about adoption; sexuality and the adoptive family; adolescence; transracial adoptions; behavior problems and more. Well-organized, clear, and accessible. A classic.

Keywords

Adoption, Parenting, Triad Issues, Transracial Adoption

Age Range.

Adult

Author: Lois Ruskai Melina

Lois Melina is author of *Raising Adopted Children* and co-author with Sharon Kaplan Roszia of *The Open Adoption Experience.*

ISBN# 0-06-096039-6 *Date Published.* 1986 *Price.* $ 12.50

Publisher. HarperCollins *Pages.* 274

Rating 

Rating 

RAISING OUR CHILDREN'S CHILDREN

Explores the challenges and rewards faced by grandparents raising their grandchildren.

Grandparent/journalist Deborah Doucette-Dudman and family therapist Jeffrey LaCure explore the social, legal, and emotional issues faced by the more than three million grandparents in the US who are raising their grandchildren. The authors stress that the greatest challenge grandparents face is in finding support for the kinship family, without severing ties with the child's birth parents; they offer case studies on important elements: The "Bad" Parent; When Grandparents Don't Agree; Integrating the Birth Parent; Grandchildren Having their Say; Family Secrets; Healing the Wounds; What's in a Name?; Guardianship; Adoption; Letting Go.

Keywords

Intergenerational, Family Life, Extended Family, Social Welfare, Stepparents

Age Range:

Adult

Author: Deborah Doucette-Dudman

illustrated by Author: Jeffrey R. LaCure

Deborah Doucette-Dudman is a grandparent and journalist. Jeffrey La Cure is a family therapist and the author of *Adopted Like Me.*

ISBN# 1577490266 Date Published: 1997 Price: $ 12.95

Publisher: Fairview PR Pages: 256

RAISING YOUR SPIRITED CHILD

A lifesaver for parents of adopted children.

Children who are more intense, perceptive and persistent may also be less adaptable, have more energy, and exhibit more difficult behavior. This optimistic book offers support and practical advice to parents raising spirited children. The author advises "progress, not perfection." The engaging writing clearly presents practical skills for parenting. Highly recommended to parents of adopted children, many of whom act out their feelings about their core experiences by having difficulty with transitions, testing authority, fighting bedtime, and a range of behaviors discussed by the author. A Pact bestseller.

Keywords

Parenting, Special Needs, Child Development, Adoptive Parent

Age Range:

Adult

Author: Mary Sheedy Kurcinka

ISBN# 60923288 Date Published: Price: $ 12.00

Publisher: Harper Row Pages:

RAISING YOUR SPIRITED CHILD WORKBOOK

At last, a do-it-yourself way to access Mary Sheedy Kurcinka's work on raising spirited children.

The essential companion to *Raising Your Spirited Child*, this workbook brings readers right into Kurcinka's world-famous workshops. Through exercises, observations, and dialogue from actual groups, readers learn to identify the "triggers" that lead to tantrums and challenging behaviors.

Keywords

Adopted Child, Adoptive Parent, Child Development, Core Issues (Feelings), Family Life, Parenting

Age Range:

Adult

Author: Mary Sheedy Kurcinka

ISBN# 60952407 Date Published: 1998 Price: $ 14.00

Publisher: HarperCollins Pages: 208

READ TO YOUR BUNNY

Read to your bunny twenty minutes a day!

Rosemary Wells has created a book that celebrates reading through this intimate story and vibrant, bunny-filled pictures — the perfect gift book for new parents. Children who may feel different because of adoption or racial variety within their own family will find real support in being able to read about other children just like them who share their feelings. Parents of adopted children need to take special care to nurture a love of reading in their children. It can be an important strategy in countering a sense of isolation the child may come to feel. Start as soon as you can. This book points the way in a delightful manner.

Keywords

Adopted Child, Skill Mastery, Self-Esteem, Parenting

Age Range:

Adult

Author-Illustrator: Rosemary Wells

Rosemary Wells is the author of *Read To Your Bunny; Max's Bath; Max's Bedtime; Max's Toys;Max's Ride;* and *Max's Breakfast.*

ISBN# 590302841 Date Published: 1998 Price: $ 7.95

Publisher: Scholastic Pages: 32

REAL PARENTS, REAL CHILDREN

Rating 

A must-read book for adoptive parents.

While there are many must-reads in this catalog, we think van Gulden offers insights no adoptive parent can do without. Want to know what your kids are thinking/feeling about their adoption? Want great ideas about how to talk to them from infancy on? This is a book about some of adoptive life's essential moments, those instances when, in a split-second of time, you're called upon to tackle some central questions and problems. Holly van Gulden offers tools and insights you need to consider. Highly recommended. A Pact bestseller.

Keywords

Adoption, Parenting, Child Development, Required for Pact Families, Family Life, Adopted Child

Age Range

Adult

Author: Holly van Gulden

Holly van Gulden is Director of a treatment center for adoptive families in Minnesota. She is also an adoptive mother who grew up in a multiracial family expanded by adoption.

ISBN# 0-8245-1514-4 Date Published Price $ 14.95

Publisher Crossroad-Herder Pages

SECRET THOUGHTS OF AN ADOPTIVE MOTHER

Rating 

A new adoptive mother's thoughts on open adoption and parenting across racial lines.

This book generated some controversy when it first came out in hardcover. We appreciated its candor and well-polished style, but we were concerned that the author's "secret thoughts" actually served to reinforce negative stereotypes about triad members. In this revision, Jana doesn't flinch from describing her ambivalences (about her son's birth mother, for instance) but acknowledges that her reactions stem from fear and ignorance. She addresses the early complexities of transracial parenting in a way that is sure to ring true to many readers. "An eloquent, refreshingly honest memoir, both disturbing in its revelations and hilarious in its smashing of taboos." —San Francisco Chronicle

Keywords

Adoption, Adoptive Parent, Triad Issues, Transracial Adoption, Open Adoption, Core Issues (Feelings)

Age Range

Adult

Author: Jana Wolff

ISBN# 0-8362-2186-9 Date Published 1997 Price $ 16.95

Publisher Andrews & McMeel Pages 148

SIBLINGS WITHOUT RIVALRY

Tools for resolving sibling squabbles.

"My sister's first words were 'I'm telling mommy!' Our rivalry finally ended when I left home at 18." This helpful book expertly handles such topics as teaching parents to stop treating their children equally instead of uniquely; helping children express their angry feelings acceptably; motivating children to solve their own problems; and handling fighting. This best-selling book puts the reader right into the middle of a fictional workshop, sitting with other frustrated parents, asking questions and working out solutions. Uses action-oriented stories to show parents how to teach children to get along.

Keywords

Sibling Issues, Parenting, Family Life

Age Range

Adult

Author: Adelle Faber

Author: Elaine Mazlish

ISBN# 380705273 Date Published 1988 Price $ 12.00

Publisher Avon Pages 272

STORY OF DAVID, THE

A personal memoir that makes an argument for open adoption, told by an adoptive father.

Despite the idealized depiction of all three parents as essentially heroic and virtuous, the book relates the struggle to discover and develop the relationships in the triad and then to defend them against others who don't understand that openness is not the same as invasiveness. "Though the writing is often graceless, with a strong soapbox element, the story is still powerful," says Publishers Weekly.

Keywords

Adoptive Parent, Adoption, Triad Issues, Open Adoption, Birth Parent

Age Range

Adult

Author: Dion Howells

Author: Karen Wilson Pritchard

ISBN# 440224616 Date Published 1998 Price $ 8.95

Publisher Dell Pages 310

SUPPORTING AN ADOPTION

Rating: @@

Help for friends and relatives.

An easy-to-read booklet for friends and relatives of adoptive families to help them support the adoptive family and to educate families about the issues of adoption. Friends and relatives often don't have the opportunity to learn about adoption and may respond based on myths and stereotypes they have never consciously thought through. This simple booklet, short and to the point, addresses their need for information to help them become more sensitive to the needs of the child and the adoptive parents. Availability: This item usually ships within six weeks. Please note that items occasionally go out of print or publishers run out of stock. We will notify you within three weeks if we have trouble obtaining this book.

Keywords
Adoption, Family Life, Friendship, Extended Family, Core Issues (Feelings)

Age Range:
Adult

Author: Pat Holmes

Pat Holmes is the author of *Concepts in Adoption* and *Supporting An Adoption.*

ISBN# 961187212 *Date Published:* 1986 *Price:* $ 4.50

Publisher: Our Child Press *Pages:* 23

TALKING TO YOUR CHILD ABOUT ADOPTION

Rating: @@

Designed to acquaint families new to adoption issues.

Takes a developmental approach, beginning with infancy and progressing through teen years.

Keywords
Adoption, Adoptive Parent, Parenting, Child Development

Age Range:
Adult

Author: Patricia M. Dorner

Patricia Martinez Dorner is author of *Talking To Your Child About Adoption* and co-author of *Children of Open Adoption.*

ISBN# NA *Date Published:* *Price:* $ 5.00

Publisher: Schaefer *Pages:*

TALKING WITH YOUNG CHILDREN ABOUT ADOPTION

Rating: @@@

What does your child understand about adoption? A guide to gathering rather than imparting information.

This book is the best currently available to offer clear direction on how to listen rather than tell. Written entirely from the perspective of adoptive parents, some of the stories cited reflect an approach to birth parents which we find distressing. Though the author's point is to understand what children are thinking rather than to hand them a politically correct doctrine of adoption thinking, we still find it troubling that no discussion of these stories is included in the text. Despite this flaw, the book is extremely valuable in helping adoptive parents reshape their view of the purposes of talking with their children about their children's experiences of adoption. A Pact bestseller.

Keywords
Adopted Child, Adoption, Child Development, Core Issues (Feelings), Parenting, Birth Parent

Age Range:
Adult

Author: Mary Watkins, Ph.D.

Author: Susan Fisher, M.D.

Mary Watkins is the author of *Waking Dreams and Invisible Guests.*

ISBN# 0-300-06317-2 *Date Published:* 1993 *Price:* $ 15.00

Publisher: Yale University Press *Pages:* 257

TEN PRINCIPLES FOR SPIRITUAL PARENTING

Rating: @@@

Advice for parents of all faiths offering practical tools and conversation-starters.

This mother-daughter team offers 10 principles of spiritual parenting. This book respects both parents and children and is not overly simplistic. Adopted children in particular can benefit by having a strong sense of being supported by a spiritual and ethical universe. Suggestions include providing daily quiet time, downshifting into your child's rhythms rather than always imposing your own, and trying to avoid the competitive rush to sign up, join in, and push harder to give your child a leg up on other kids.

Keywords
Religion, Spiritual Meanings, Parenting, Family Life, Child Development, Core Issues (Feelings)

Age Range:
Adult

Author: Mimi Doe

Author: Marsha Fayfield Walch

Mimi Doe is an award-winning T.V. producer. Her mother, Marsha Walch, Ph.D., is a psychotherapist who works in private and community health practice.

ISBN# 60952415 *Date Published:* 1998 *Price:* $ 13.00

Publisher: Harper Row *Pages:* 272

Rating

THIS ISN'T WHAT I EXPECTED

A book on postpartum depression with implications for post-adoption depression.

This book brings valuable information about recognizing and recovering from depression and anxiety after the birth of a child, which the reader can apply to post-adoption depression.

Keywords

Adoptive Parent, Birth Parent, Adoption, Core Issues (Feelings), Depression

Age Range.

Adult

Author: Karen R. Kleiman, MSW

Author: Valerie D. Raskin, M.D.

ISBN# 0-553-37075–8 Date Published. 1994 Price. $ 10.95

Publisher. Bantam Pages. 298

Rating

TO BLESS HIM UNAWARE

This short essay offers guidance about talking with a child conceived by rape.

When a child is the product of rape, adopted parents often dread the moment their child wants to know about his or her own birth. This warm and supportive essay is a wonderful guide and support.

Keywords

Adoption, Core Issues (Feelings), Grief and Loss, Sexual Abuse

Age Range.

Adult

Author: Randolph Severson, Ph.D.

Considered the poet of the adoption movement, and a strong advocate of open adoption, Randolph Severson, Ph.D., is a psychotherapist concerned particularly with spiritual issues.

ISBN# 1-8808-5604-2 Date Published. Price. $ 6.00

Publisher. Heart Words Center Pages. 15

TO LOVE A CHILD

A reluctant father adopts a "forgotten" child.

This memoir tells the true story of one couple and how they came to adopt a "forgotten" child. After watching a TV program, Ted and Leslie Schwartz adopted three-year-old Raheem, born addicted to the same drug that killed his mother, and began their journey toward becoming a family.

Keywords

Adoption, Special Needs, Attachment, Adoptive Parent, Family Life, Transracial Adoption

Age Range.

Adult

Author: Ted Schwartz

ISBN# 882821369 Date Published. 1995 Price. $ 21.95

Publisher. New Horizon Pages.

TO LOVE A CHILD

A guide to adoption, foster parenting, and other ways to share your life with children.

For those interested in sharing their lives with children, this book examines alternatives to giving birth to a child, including mentoring and kinship care.

Keywords

Adoption, Foster Care, Friendship, Adoptive Parent, Extended Family, Stepparents

Age Range.

Adult

Author: Marianne Takas

Author: Edward Warner

ISBN# 0-201-55083-0 Date Published. 1992 Price. $ 12.95

Publisher. Addison-Wesley Pages. 225

TODDLER ADOPTION

Rating 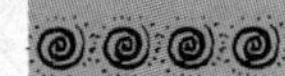

Practical, realistic and supportive advice for adoptive parents of children adopted between one and three.

Best's discussion of the factors that make adopting a toddler different from adopting either infants or older children with special needs is thorough, well grounded, and a good read. Substantiated by her study of what really happens when children join the family at a developmental stage typically centered on the need to be dependent and independent at once, this book presents an unflinching view of the challenges and the rewards for parents and children, a must for any parent of or prospective parent considering adoption of a toddler. We strongly recommend it.

Keywords

Cassette, Adoption, Parenting, Required for Pact Families, Special Needs, Adopting Older Child

Age Range:

Adult

Author: Mary Hopkins Best

ISBN# 0-944934-17-X *Date Published:* 1997 *Price:* $ 15.00

Publisher: Perspectives *Pages:*

TOMMY & ME: THE MAKING OF A DAD

Rating 

One man's views on becoming an adoptive father.

Along with his wife, Ben Stein, a 40-year-old television personality, adopted Tommy. Stein describes his son as his "angel boy" and himself as self-centered; we agree with the second categorization. Stein views life through an unexamined lens of privilege; he renders his wife invisible in the book; his skewed ideas about parenting ("Buy them whatever they want, whenever they want"); and his political diatribes (abortions are "chopping up babies") are shallow and simplistic. Though he claims his life has been changed by becoming a father, *Tommy & Me* does not seem to support that idea. Don't get this book.

Keywords

Adoptive Parent, Family Life, Fathers, Core Issues (Feelings)

Age Range:

Adult

Author: Benjamin Stein

Ben Stein is a television personality.

ISBN# 684838966 *Date Published:* 1998 *Price:* $ 23.00

Publisher: Simon & Schuster *Pages:* 224

TWENTY THINGS ADOPTED KIDS WISH THEIR ADOPTIVE PARENTS KNEW

Skills to help parents understand adoption through the eyes of their child!

This is a unique and perceptive treatment of the core issues of adoption from a child's perspective. Peek into children's unspoken emotions to understand what the adoption process means to your child. *Twenty Questions* will convince you that because there is no closure, the adopted child's loss is harder to resolve than a death — yet it's a loss adoptive parents are not responsible for. Eldridge says that "buried feelings caused by the loss of birth family must be identified and grieved or the child's ability to receive and give love will be diminished. The parental challenge is to learn the 20 unspoken feelings, create a nonjudgmental atmosphere for the child to grieve and cheer the child on."

Keywords

Adopted Child, Adoption, Core Issues (Feelings), Grief and Loss, Parenting

Age Range:

Adult

Author: Sherrie Eldridge

Sherrie Eldridge (adoptjewel@aol.com)

ISBN# 044050838X *Date Published:* *Price:* $ 11.95

Publisher: Dell *Pages:* 272

WAR AGAINST PARENTS, THE

A parents' bill of rights.

The crisis our children face today and what we must do about it. The publisher writes, "Sylvia Hewlett and Cornel West show how for 30 years big business, government, and the wider culture have waged a silent war against parents.... In calling for a Parents' Bill of Rights, the authors seek to unite America's 62 million parents behind an agenda that spans the divides of race, gender, and class.... Hewlett and West provide comfort and hope. There is not a parent among us who is not hungry for such healing."

Keywords

Social Welfare, Parenting, Family Life, Fathers, Mothers

Age Range:

Adult

Author: Cornel West, Ph.D.

Author: Sylvia Ann Hewlett

Cornel West, author of Race Matters, is Professor of Afro-American Studies and of the Philosophy of Religion at Harvard University.

ISBN# 0395891698' *Date Published:* 1998 *Price:* $ 14.00

Publisher: Houghton Mifflin *Pages:* 256

WHEN FRIENDS ASK ABOUT ADOPTION

Rating 

Simple ways to approach friends and family members who are not educated about adoption.

In supportive, encouraging language, Bothun demonstrates how to help others understand positive adoption language and develop supportive attitudes. A good gift book; though perhaps somewhat simplistic, it's a good way to prompt conversation about these issues.

Keywords

Adoption, Extended Family, Educational Issues

Age Range,

Adult

Author: Linda Bothun

Linda Bothun is the author of *Dialogues About Adoption* and *When Friends Ask About Adoption.*

ISBN# 0-9619559-0-2 Date Published, 1988 Price, $ 5.95

Publisher, Swan Publications Pages, 96

WHEN YOUR CHILD NEEDS HELP

Rating 

A parent's guide to assessing a child's emotional stress.

Could your child benefit from therapy? How do you choose a therapist? What kind of therapy would serve your family? What results can you expect? If your child is in emotional stress, you need to be able to identify resources that can help. This book is quite popular.

Keywords

Child Development, Parenting, Special Needs, Core Issues (Feelings)

Age Range,

Adult

Author: Norma Doft, Ph.D.

Author: Barbara Aria

ISBN# 517881691 Date Published, 1992 Price, $ 8.95

Publisher, Crown Pages, 224

WINNING FAMILY, THE

Increasing self-esteem in your children and yourself.

This book, which is highly recommended by *Parenting* magazine, *Mothering* magazine, American Families for Adoption, and others, focuses on the personal development of parents along with the growth of their children, offering a new, hopeful family model characterized by satisfaction. Chapters include listening skills; asking and refusing skills; the power of words; empowerment; self-talk; obsession with perfection; cultural barriers to self-esteem; the winning environment; extending your family and more.

Keywords

Parenting, Self-Esteem, Family Life

Age Range,

Adult

Author: Louise Hart

Dr. Louise Hart is author of *On The Wings of Self Esteem.*

ISBN# 0-89087-689-4 Date Published, 1989 Price, $ 12.95

Publisher, Celestial Arts Pages, 240

WONDERFUL WAYS TO LOVE A CHILD

Potent advice – includes more than 65 ways parents can put love into action.

Creative and easy-to-read suggestions to strengthen families. Offers more than 65 down-to-earth suggestions from the emotional and moral to the fun and frivolous to help you bring more love and laughter into your life.

Keywords

Parenting, Family Life

Age Range,

Adult

Author: Judy Ford

Judy Ford is a family therapist who works with children and families in a variety of settings.

ISBN# 943233895 Date Published, 1995 Price, $ 9.95

Publisher, Conari Pages, 137

Rating

ALL THE WAYS HOME

Parenting in the Lesbian and Gay Community

A collection of short fiction about gay and Lesbian families.

Keywords

Gay and/or Lesbian, Fiction

Age Range:

Adult

Editor: Jo Schneiderman

Editor: Cindy Rizzo

Editor: Lisa Schweig

ISBN# 934678650 *Date Published:* 1995 *Price:* $ 10.95

Publisher: New Victoria *Pages:* 211

Rating

GROWING UP IN A LESBIAN FAMILY

Effects of growing up in a Lesbian family through the eyes of grown children.

The book lays out the developmental effects of growing up in a same-sex household — and how children cope with prejudice. Confronting myths and stereotypes of Lesbian parenting through a series of in-depth interviews with grown children, these clear descriptions offer insight into family life, the child's awareness, integrating family with school communities, coping with prejudice, and psychological adjustment. The authors challenge common assumptions about the ways in which parents of any sexuality influence their children's development, presenting a longitudinal study of 25 children raised in Lesbian families.

Keywords

Gay and/or Lesbian, Parenting, Child Development, Family Life

Age Range:

Adult

Author: Susan Golombok, Ph.D.

Author: Fiona L. Tasker, Ph.D.

Susan Golombok is co-author of *Bottling it Up.*

ISBN# 1573201708 *Date Published:* 1997 *Price:* $ 18.95

Publisher: Guilford *Pages:* 200

I DWELL IN POSSIBILITY

One woman's account of life as a Black woman, a Southerner, and a Lesbian.

The publisher says, "This brave and lyrical memoir is a powerful social document as well as an account of emotional, psychological, and intellectual self-actualization over four decades — from McNaron's childhood encounters with segregation in Birmingham, Alabama; through her first days of teaching and her fear as a lesbian and an alcoholic, to her recovery and coming out." Kirkus Reviews writes that this book is so "engrossing and sensitive that it moves along at the swift pace of a well-written novel."

Keywords

African American, Biography, Cultural History, Diversity, Gay and/or Lesbian, Race Relations

Age Range:

Adult

Author: Toni McNaron

Toni McNaron is professor of English and women's studies at the University of Minnesota, MN and coeditor of *The New Lesbian Studies.*

ISBN# 1-55861-050-2 *Date Published:* *Price:* $ 12.95

Publisher: Oxford *Pages:* 216

ISSUES IN GAY AND LESBIAN ADOPTION

Proceedings of the Fourth Annual Peirce Warwick Adoption Symposium.

Extracts from the symposium presentations regarding dispelling myths and discussing policy-making.

Keywords

Gay and/or Lesbian, Adoption Reform, Social Welfare

Age Range:

Adult

Editor: Ann Sullivan

ISBN# 0-87868-598-7 *Date Published:* 1995 *Price:* $ 9.95

Publisher: CWLA *Pages:* 42

LESBIAN AND GAY PARENTING HANDBOOK

Rating 

An indispensable resource for Lesbians and gay men who are considering parenthood.

Parenting and Families Editor's Recommended Book: "Martin, a psychologist and Lesbian parent of two children, has compiled advice and information from almost 60 families and has drawn on her own experience. She touches on every aspect of gay and Lesbian parenting, and where she doesn't go into depth, she refers readers to further resources. Covers alternative insemination to surrogacy. It includes details on adoption, gay men making babies, co-parenting, and legal issues. Martin discusses family roles, dealing with anti-homosexual bias, dealing with family crises, and how to handle issues children may have about growing up with gay or Lesbian parents."

Keywords

Parenting, Gay and/or Lesbian, Family Life, Core Issues (Feelings), Fathers, Mothers

Age Range:

Adult

Author: April Martin, Ph.D.

ISBN# 60969296 | Date Published: 1993 | Price: $ 16.00

Publisher: HarperCollins | Pages: 416

LESBIAN PARENTING BOOK, THE

Rating 

A commonsense guide with a Lesbian twist.

Drawing on the real-life experiences of Lesbian families facing homophobia, dealing with school issues, and other issues, the authors present comprehensive information on each stage of parenthood and child development. Filled with humor.

Keywords

Adopted Child, Parenting, Blended Family, Child Development, Family Life, Gay and/or Lesbian

Age Range:

Adult

Author: D. Merilee Clunis, Ph.D.

ISBN# 1878067680 | Date Published: 1995 | Price: $ 16.00

Publisher: Seal Press | Pages: 378

RUBYFRUIT JUNGLE

Molly Bolt's coming of age story.

Molly Bolt is a young Lesbian who was adopted into her family. This engrossing novel describes her transition into adulthood.

Keywords

Gay and/or Lesbian, Adopted Adult, Fiction

Age Range:

Adult

Author: Rita Mae Brown

Rita Mae Brown was adopted into her family.

ISBN# 0-553-27886-X | Date Published: 1977 | Price: $ 6.50

Publisher: Bantam | Pages: 256

WE ARE FAMILY: QUEER PARENTS TELL THEIR STORIES

Testimonies of Lesbian and gay parents living in Britain.

Written by families in Britain, this book covers the issues of parenting in nontraditional families. Through interviews with gay and Lesbian parents from a wide range of circumstances, this book paints a detailed, emotional and enlightening picture. It shows how 'queers' often make excellent parents and provide a balanced and successful environment for raising children. This book reflects the most common ways in which non-heterosexuals form family units and become parents in the UK and suggests that problems these families face are in fact the problems of the heterosexual community which cannot accept alternative families.

Keywords

Gay and/or Lesbian, Family Life, Adoption, Parenting

Age Range:

Adult

Author: JoAnne Nelson

Author: Marie W. Woolf

ISBN# 0-614-22138-2 | Date Published: 1996 | Price: $ 17.95

Publisher: Cassell | Pages: 166

Rating

ADOPTING ALYOSHA

A single man finds a son in Russia.

The story of how a single father adopted a son in Russia. This book was not available for review in time for publication in this edition of the BookSource. If you would like updated information, please call Pact at 415 221-6957.

Keywords

Adopted Child, International Adoption, Fathers, Russia

Age Range:

Adult

Author: Robert Klose

ISBN# 1578061199 Date Published: 1999 Price: $ 22.00

Publisher: University Press of Mississippi Pages: 165

Rating

AN AMERICAN FACE

International adoption from Korea.

This book was not available for review in time for publication in this edition of the BookSource. If you would like updated information, please call Pact at 415 221-6957.

Keywords

Korean American, International Adoption, Transracial Adoption, Fiction

Age Range:

Adult

Author: Jan M. Czech

ISBN# 878687181 Date Published: 1999 Price: NYP

Publisher: Child Welfare League Pages:

COMPLETE GUIDE TO FOREIGN ADOPTION

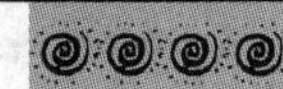

Closing the international adoption information gap.

McKelvey and Bascom offer an illuminating account about what to expect and how to prepare for international adoption. Without hysteria, the writers document their view that "every foreign adoption should be considered a special-needs adoption of a high-risk child," simultaneously encouraging and supporting adoption while insisting that children are served only by those with realistic understanding of their needs and histories. Though sometimes heartbreaking, this compelling book is filled with hope born of the resiliency of the human spirit. Required reading for every family adopting a child from another country.

Keywords

Adoption Reform, International Adoption, Russia, Romania, Special Needs, Asian

Age Range:

Adult

Author: Carole A. McKelvey, M.A.

Author: Barbara B Bascom, M.D.

Carole McKelvey, M.A. is an award-winning journalist and the co-author of *Adoption Crisis and High Risk.*

ISBN# 671546465 Date Published: 1997 Price: $ 14.00

Publisher: Pocket Books Pages: 364

EIGHT WAS NOT ENOUGH: THE UNLIKELY ADVENTURES OF AN ONLY CHILD

Life is to be spent, not saved.

At first glance, Jeannie Satre's life looks unremarkable: married, children, home in the suburbs, a minivan and occasional trips to the family cabin near Yosemite. But Jeannie and her husband have dedicated their lives to raising special children from around the world. Twin boys born to them were followed by girls from Korea, children from Mother Teresa's orphanage in India and then a girl from their home town! Traumas ranging from the children's hospitalizations, to facing her own adoption issues, and confronting serious breast cancer risk have kept Jeannie's life challenging and eventful, as she and her whole family have learned life lessons of love, perseverance and joy.

Keywords

Adoption, International Adoption, Health, Differently-abled

Age Range:

Adult

Author: Jeannie M. Satre

Jeannie Satre and her husband Neal are the parents of nine children who were adopted internationally and are orthopedically challenged.

ISBN# 965674959 Date Published: 1998 Price: $ 11.00

Publisher: Pages: 198

Rating

HOW TO ADOPT INTERNATIONALLY

A guide to agency-directed and independent international adoptions.

A step-by-step guide through the process of adopting internationally, including a compendium of adoption information for 88 child-placing countries and samples of almost every form and document an adoptive parent will need. This is a well-organized reference guide which covers choosing the right agency; the local home study; INS approval; finding a child to adopt; the adoption trip; meeting the child; emigration and immigration; health issues of internationally-adopted children; post-placement; re-adoption and citizenship; and parenting issues. A handy introduction to the many choices within international adoption, particularly useful to prospective parents.

Keywords

Adoption, International Adoption, Guidebook, Adoptive Parent

Age Range:

Adult

Author: Heino R. Erichsen, M.A.

Author: Jean-Nelson Erichsen

Jean-Nelson and Heino Erichsen are the authors of Butterflies In the Wind and How To Adopt Internationally.

ISBN# 940352125 *Date Published:* 1997 *Price:* $ 22.00

Publisher: Mesa House *Pages:* 280

Rating

INTERNATIONAL ADOPTION HANDBOOK, THE

How to make an overseas adoption work for you.

A step-by-step guide offers information and advice about international adoption, along with interviews with families who have adopted. Booklist calls it "heartfelt, simply stated, and specific...a godsend to harried international adopters." After a general discussion of who may adopt and what restrictions may apply, the book goes into the nitty-gritty of what the process entails: choosing where to adopt and how to go about it; using an agency or a facilitator; initiating the home study; assembling a dossier; working with the U.S. Immigration and Naturalization Service; knowing the types of expenses that can be anticipated, and so on. Includes Internet resource list.

Keywords

International Adoption, Guidebook, Adoption

Age Range:

Adult

Author: Myra Alperson

ISBN# 805045791 *Date Published:* 1997 *Price:* $ 14.95

Publisher: Henry Holt *Pages:* 224

INTERNATIONAL ADOPTION TRAVEL JOURNAL

A journal for recording adoption travel notes and memories.

Part of the internationally adopted child's personal history is the story of the parents' journey to bring him or her home, and we feel parents should record as many details of this journey as they can. This is the first travel journal we've seen to record this special journey and we are very glad it has become available. Ample blank space is provided for personal thoughts, particularly in the daily journal section. One caveat: A fully-bound journal rather than a spiral-binding might have promised greater hope that the book would stand up to a child's repeated readings.

Keywords

Adoption, International Adoption, Guidebook

Age Range:

Adult

Author: Mary E. Petertyl

ISBN# 965575306 *Date Published:* 1997 *Price:* $ 24.00

Publisher: Folio One *Pages:* 154

OUR CHILDREN FROM LATIN AMERICA

Making adoption part of your life.

A personal account of one family's decision to adopt children from Latin America, the stories of their process to adopt two children over time, and advice and direction regarding how to adopt from Latin America and how to parent after adoption. This book provides a thoughtful consideration of the key issues and should be of interest to any families considering similar journeys.

Keywords

Adoption, Latino/a, International Adoption, Family Life

Age Range:

Adult

Author: Laurel Strassberger

ISBN# 913292249 *Date Published:* 1992 *Price:* $ 14.00

Publisher: Tiresias Press *Pages:* 144

Rating

PASSAGE TO THE HEART, A

Writings from Families with Children from China

This collection of articles from FCC (Families with Children from China) newsletters has information for all pre-adoptive international adopters as well as those who are already parenting. The collection begins at the beginning — how it feels to prepare for a baby you have never seen in a country you may have never visited — to practical items of what to bring and how to greet your newly adopted child. It goes on to address connection, racial identity, birth parents and parenting. The writings are heartfelt and earnest explorations of the issues involved in parenting Chinese children as seen through adoptive parents' eyes. A worthwhile book.

Keywords
International Adoption, Cultural History, Transracial Adoption, Racial/Ethnic Identity, Asian, China
Age Range:
Adult

Editor: Amy Klatzkin

Amy Klatzkin is the adoptive mother of a daughter from China. Proceeds from the book will benefit the Amity Foundation and the Foundation for Chinese Orphanages.

ISBN# 0-9638472-2-8 *Date Published:* 1999 *Price:* $ 19.95
Publisher: Yeong & Yong *Pages:* 338

Rating

SALVADOR'S CHILDREN: A SONG FOR SURVIVAL

A journey toward family.

The story is dramatic and intense. A North American college professor adopts eight-year-old Maria de Jesus and quickly learns that language is not the only barrier between them. Maria, having lived through the death of her parents, disappearance of two siblings, and responsibility of taking care of her younger brothers, is mature beyond her years. Will her new mother understand her needs? This book explores connection, communication, and letting go of the fear of being unloved.

Keywords
International Adoption, Latino/a, El Salvador, Adoption, Family Life, Social Welfare
Age Range:
Adult

Author: Lea Marenn

Author: M.J. Marenn

ISBN# 814205933 *Date Published:* 1993 *Price:* $ 26.50
Publisher: Ohio State University *Pages:* 216

STRENGTH OF MERCY, THE

God sent the Beazelys to Romania and they obeyed.

Written from a Christian perspective, this is one family's story of adopting a child from Romania. There is an unfortunate overtone that implies self-congratulation on the part of the parents for saving a poor child, a tone which we find offensive and all too common.

Keywords
Biography, Romania, International Adoption, Adopted Child, Religion, Christianity
Age Range:
Adult

Author: Jan Beazely

ISBN# 1578561949 *Date Published:* 1999 *Price:* $ 8.95
Publisher: Waterbrook *Pages:* 140

TRAVELER'S GUIDE TO LATIN AMERICAN CUSTOMS AND MANNERS

How to act when you get there.

Provides travelers with specific guidelines on how to converse, dine, tip, drive, bargain, dress, make friends, and conduct business in South and Central America, including Mexico. Though not adoption-specific, it provides important information for prospective international adoptive parents.

Keywords
Latino/a, International Adoption, Manners, Guidebook, Central America, South America
Age Range:
Adult

Author: Elizabeth Devine

ISBN# 312023030 *Date Published:* 1999 *Price:* $ 14.95
Publisher: St. Martin *Pages:* 239

Rating

UNDERSTANDING MY CHILD'S KOREAN ORIGINS

For adoptive parents of Korean children

Positive identity-building for internationally adopted children respects the dual nature of their heritage. This book contains advice on how to build your child's pride and interest in his or her Korean heritage as well as information on how to help your child adjust to your family.

Keywords

Adoptive Parent, Korean American, International Adoption, Racial/Ethnic Identity, Family Life

Age Range:

Adult

Author: Hyun Han

ISBN# NYA Date Published: Price: $ 9.50

Publisher: self published Pages:

Rating

WEST MEETS EAST

Who are these families with middle-aged Caucasian parents and young Chinese daughters:

This book is about these new "American & Chinese" families that are being formed through international adoption. It was not available for review in time for publication in this edition of the BookSource. If you would like updated information, please call Pact at 415 221-6957.

Keywords

Chinese, Chinese American, Adopted Child, Adoptive Parent, International Adoption

Age Range:

Adult

Author: Richard C. Tessler

Author: Gail Gamache

Author: Liming Liu

Richard Tessler is a Professor of Sociology and Associate Director of the University of Massachusetts' Social and Demographic Research Institute.

ISBN# 897896580 Date Published: 1999 Price: $ 18.00

Publisher: Praeger Pages:

WITH EYES WIDE OPEN

A workbook for parents adopting international children over age one.

This book points out the developmental steps a child over age one is likely to have taken before joining an adoptive family: attaching to a care giver; experiencing pain and relief from pain; learning to recognize sounds; discovering his or her own body; and dividing the world into a place of trust or distrust. *With Eyes Wide Open* suggests that in order to form the missing connections, adoptive parents should revisit with their children these developmental milestones they've missed in their children's lives.

Keywords

Adoption, International Adoption, Child Development, Transracial Adoption, Toddler Adoption, Attachment

Age Range:

Adult

Author: Nancy Ward, MA, LCSW

Author/Photographer: Margaret Miller, M.A.

ISBN# NA Date Published: 1996 Price: $ 17.50

Publisher: Children's Home Society of Minnesota Pages: 155

WORLD OF LOVE, A

Adopting from Russia

Maggie Conroy's story recounts the trials and tribulations which beset the Conroy family when they decide to adopt a child from the former Soviet Union. International adopters will benefit from reading of the legal and medical battles that occurred during their struggle to adopt three youngsters from the former Soviet Union and Colombia — and the unique bonds that are forged in the process.

Keywords

Adoption, International Adoption, Russia, Guidebook

Age Range:

Adult

Author: Maggie Francis Conroy

ISBN# 1575661594 Date Published: 1997 Price: $ 23.00

Publisher: Kensington Pages: 230

ADOPTING AND ADVOCATING FOR THE SPECIAL NEEDS CHILD

Rating 

Bridges the gap between wanting to help a child and the special-needs adoption system.

This book offers practical and supportive ideas on how to get started, the issues of becoming a family, realities of having special needs in today's world, and support for hanging in when times are tough. "Completely frank and remarkably compassionate, this detailed, comprehensive guide to the issues, participants, process, and outcomes involved in adopting children who will require special support is an important, sorely needed addition to the current informational literature on adoption.... Tables, checklists, and frequent references to additional resources add value to their informed advice to prospective adoptive parents." — Booklist

Keywords
Adopted Child, Special needs, Adoption, Differently-abled, Family Life

Age Range:
Adult

Author: L. Anne Babb

Author: Rita Laws

ISBN# 897894898 | Date Published: 1997 | Price: $ 35.00
Publisher: Bergin & Garvey | Pages: 280

ADOPTING THE HURT CHILD

Rating 

An honest look at the challenges faced by families adopting children with difficult histories.

With the help of this book, families dealing with hurt children will realize that neither they nor their children are crazy nor alone. Chapters on waiting children; attachment difficulties; the toll of impermanence; dreams and realities; giving your child a history; therapy; when adoption fails; success stories; international adoption, and reflections from the trenches. Books in Print writes that this book "addresses various phases of the adoption process: early issues; age-specific problems as well as solutions; and clarification on issues of parenting or working with the abused or damaged child. It includes superior resources, readings, and index arrangements, and is recommended for all libraries."

Keywords
Adoption, Special Needs, Core Issues (Feelings), Parenting, Sexual Abuse, International Adoption

Age Range:
Adult

Author: Gregory C. Keck

Author: Regina M. Kupecky

ISBN# 0-89109-907-7 | Date Published: 1995 | Price: $ 20.00
Publisher: Pinon Press | Pages: 239

ADOPTING THE SEXUALLY ABUSED CHILD

Understanding the issues of sexual abuse prior to adoption.

As many as 75% of the children waiting to find permanent adoptive families are estimated to have experienced some form of sexual abuse. Anyone considering adoption of an older child should be well-educated about the issues and the outcomes of this experience. This anthology provides a reality check for prospective adoptive parents about the likely histories of older kids waiting to be adopted. Includes positive directions.

Keywords
Adoption, Sexual Abuse, Special Needs, Foster Child, Adopting Older Child

Age Range:
Adult

Author: Joan McNamara

Joan McNamara is the author of *Adopting the Sexually Abused Child, Sexually Reactive Children in Adoption* and *Foster Care* and more.

ISBN# NA | Date Published: | Price: $ 14.95
Publisher: self published | Pages: 203

ATTACHMENT, TRAUMA, AND HEALING

Understanding and treating attachment disorder in children and families.

Attachment, Trauma, and Healing examines the causes of RAD (reactive attachment disorder) and provides in-depth discussion on effective solutions — including attachment-focused assessment and diagnosis, specialized training and education for caregivers, the controversial "in arms" treatment for children and caregivers, and early intervention and prevention programs for high-risk families.

Keywords
Special Needs, Attachment, Health

Age Range:
Adult

Author: Terry M Levy

Author: Michael Orlans

ISBN# 878687092 | Date Published: 1998 | Price: $ 34.95
Publisher: Child Welfare League | Pages: 328

Rating

BEYOND RITALIN

Facts about medication and new ways to help adults with ADHD/ADD.

Facts about Strategies for Helping Children, Adolescents and Adults. Chapters include: Confusion and Controversy; Facts and Fallacies About Medication; How to Get an Accurate Diagnosis; What to Try Before You Try Medication; When Medication is Needed: Finding the Best Fit; Why On-Task in the Classroom is Not Enough; Solving Social Problems; Rechanneling the ADHD Mind: Learning Self-Control; Building Organization Skills; Cultivating Inner Calm; Alternative Treatments; ADHD Grown Up: From Disc Jockeys to Doctors.

Keywords

Special Needs, ADHD, Health, Child Development

Age Range.

Adult

Author: Robyn Freedman Spizman

Author: Marianne Daniels Garber, Ph.D.

Author: Stephen W. Garber, Ph.D.

Robyn Freedman Spizman has published sixty books and numerous articles on enhancing children's learning.

ISBN# 0-06-097725-6 *Date Published.* 1996 *Price.* $ 13.00

Publisher. Harper Collins, Random *Pages.* 272

Rating

BRUISED BEFORE BIRTH

A wealth of practical information and encouragement for parents of drug- or alcohol-exposed children.

What are the effects of prenatal substance abuse? What can you expect at each developmental stage? What will the future hold? How can you help your child to be the most he or she can be? Contents include: How substances used by mothers can affect unborn children; Roadblocks and decoders; Parenting is not for sissies; Some suggestions and tools for planning; Considering placement; Adopting a drug exposed infant; Under the influence; Adoption, abuse, and addictive behavior, and more. Availability: This item usually ships within six weeks. Please note that items occasionally go out of print or publishers run out of stock. We will notify you within three weeks if we have trouble obtaining this book.

Keywords

Special Needs, Parenting, FAS/FAE, Child Development, Health, Learning Difficulties

Age Range.

Adult

Author: Amy Bullock

Author: Joan McNamara

Author: Elizabeth Grimes

ISBN# NA *Date Published.* *Price.* $ 16.95

Publisher. self published *Pages.*

BUILDING THE BONDS OF ATTACHMENT

Awakening love in deeply troubled children.

Katie is one small girl in foster care who does not dare to love. Filled as it is with terror and rage, shame and depression, her story is used to illustrate the effects of abuse and neglect on our vulnerable children. The book also offers practical strategies for working with children who, like Katie, have reactive attachment disorders.

Keywords

Attachment, Special Needs, Foster Care

Age Range.

Adult

Author: Daniel A. Hughes

Daniel A. Hughes is the author of *Facilitating Developmental Attachment in Foster and Adopted Children* and *Building The Bonds of Attachment.*

ISBN# 765701685 *Date Published.* 1998 *Price.* $ 45.00

Publisher. Jason Aronson *Pages.*

CAN THIS CHILD BE SAVED?

Solutions for adoptive and foster families facing reactive attachment disorder.

Over 500,000 children live in foster homes in America. 40% of these children have behavioral, psychiatric, emotional and neurological disorders. They often become uncontrollable and forcefully reject those who want to help them. This book offers parents help and hope. Examining what causes children to act and react the way they do, and why conventional strategies and approaches often fail to reach them, it explores and validates parents' feelings, offering struggling families clearly detailed and easy to understand parenting techniques and therapeutic approaches that succeed with disturbed children.

Keywords

Adoptive Parent, Family Life, Foster Child, Foster Parent, Special Needs, Attachment

Age Range.

Adult

Author: Foster Cline

Author: Kathy Helding

Foster Cline is the author of *Parenting with Love and Logic; Can This Child be Saved?* and many more.

ISBN# 966892224 *Date Published.* 1999 *Price.* $ 24.95

Publisher. World Enterprises *Pages.* 359

Rating

CAN'T YOU SIT STILL?

Issues of adoption and Attention Deficit Hyperactivity Disorder.

ADHD is diagnosed four times more often in adopted children than in children raised in their birth families. This book, especially useful for adoptive parents, provides concrete, thought-provoking advice and a message of hope.

Keywords

Special Needs, ADHD, Parenting, Spiritual Meanings, Adoptive Parent

Age Range:

Adult

Author: Randolph Severson, Ph.D.

Considered the poet of the adoption movement, and a strong advocate of open adoption, Randolph Severson, Ph.D., is a psychotherapist concerned particularly with spiritual issues.

ISBN# Date Published: Price: $ 6.00

Publisher: Heart Words Center Pages: 70

Rating

CHANGED BY A CHILD

Companion notes for parents of a child with a disability.

Without sentimentality or sugar coating, Barbara Gill, the mother of a child with Down Syndrome, presents a collection of brief, empathetic essays drawn from real-life situations, addressing the inner needs of parents of children with disabilities, from grief to anger to fatigue to medical issues. There are three sections: "In the Beginning," "Rounding the Curves," and "Transformed."

Keywords

Special Needs, Differently-abled, Parenting, Core Issues (Feelings), Family Life, Health

Age Range:

Adult

Author: Barbara Gill

ISBN# 385482434 Date Published: 1998 Price: $ 10.00

Publisher: Doubleday Pages: 336

CHILDREN WITH PRENATAL ALCOHOL AND/OR OTHER DRUG EXPOSURE

Weighing the risks of adopting children prenatally exposed to drugs or alcohol.

Practical suggestions, recommendations and food for thought for prospective adoptive parents considering adopting a special-needs child.

Keywords

Adoption, Special Needs, FAS/FAE

Age Range:

Adult

Author: Susan Edelstein

ISBN# 878686304 Date Published: 1995 Price: $ 12.95

Publisher: Guilford Pages:

DANGEROUS LEGACY

Crack, alcohol, cocaine, opiates, tobacco, marijuana: What happens to baby when mom uses during pregnancy?

Crack, alcohol, cocaine, opiates, tobacco and marijuana: what are the consequences for baby when mother uses during pregnancy?

Keywords

Special Needs, FAS/FAE

Age Range:

Adult

Author: Ben Sonder

ISBN# 531111954 Date Published: 1994 Price: $ 24.00

Publisher: Franklyn-Watts Pages: 96

Rating

DON'T TOUCH MY HEART

Healing the pain of an unattached child.

Imagine being five years old and so consumed by rage you destroy everything you touch. A well-meaning family feels hurt, confused, and angered by a child's manipulative behavior and inability to return love after adoption. This book offers support and hope. Currently out of print but if you would like, we will attempt to find a copy for you. Please inquire.

Keywords

Adoption, Attachment, Core Issues (Feelings), Special Needs, Grief and Loss

Age Range.

Adult

Author: Lynda Gianforte Mansfield

Author: Ruth Nulton Moore

Christopher H. Waldmann and Lynda Gianforte Mansfield.

ISBN# 08910-98208 Date Published. Price. $ 10.00

Publisher. Pinon Press Pages.

Rating

DRIVEN TO DISTRACTION

Attention Deficit Disorder (ADD) is a neurological problem that resembles a lack of self-discipline.

This book discusses diagnosis, medication, behavior modification techniques, and the impact on other family members of living with someone who faces the challenges of ADD. "Hallowell and Ratey offer a fine addition to literature on ADD. The authors employ a broad, general definition of ADD ('high-energy, action-oriented, bottom-line, gotta-run type people') and continually emphasize the positive qualities of people with ADD. They explain how the American temperament helps create ADD-like symptoms. Best of all are the stories and case studies of myriad folks who have dealt successfully with their diagnosis. A state-by-state list of support groups are included in this excellent approach to an intriguing subject," says Books in Print.

Keywords

Special Needs, Differently-abled, ADHD

Age Range.

Adult

Author: Edward M. Hallowell, M.D.

Author: John J. Ratey, MD.

ISBN# 0-679-42177-7 Date Published. 1994 Price. $ 13.00

Publisher. Pantheon Pages. 319

EARLY INTERVENTION WITH HIGH RISK CHILDREN

Intervention techniques developed during the last 30 years by The Center for Preventive Psychiatry.

Sam is a foster child whose mother repeatedly breaks her promises to take him back. In order to love himself more, Sam must be helped to rely on his mother less. Many children live in circumstances that threaten their emotional and physical development. This book describes innovative intervention techniques affording the reader an opportunity to appreciate the depth of the children's dilemmas and the difficulties inherent in resolving them. The treatment provides relief to the children in the here and now, as well as follow-up data, including positive effects on IQ, family stability, and psychological functioning of individual children.

Keywords

Attachment, Core Issues (Feelings), Depression, Foster Child, Adopted Child, Special Needs

Age Range.

Adult

Author: Arthur Zelman

ISBN# 765700085 Date Published. 1996 Price. $ 60.00

Publisher. Jason Aronson Pages. 376

FANTASTIC ANTONE SUCCEEDS!

Experiences in educating children with fetal alcohol syndrome.

Contents Includes: How prenatal alcohol exposure affects children and their families, parental advocacy for alcohol-affected children, early intervention, teachers' techniques, mainstreaming children, stereotypes and realities, overcoming the cycle of failure and frustration and more.

Keywords

Special Needs, FAS/FAE, Differently-abled, Learning Difficulties, Educational Issues, Self-Esteem

Age Range.

Adult

Author: Judith S. Kleinfield

Judith Kleinfield is a professor of psychology.

ISBN# 091200665X Date Published. Price. $ 23.75

Publisher. U. of Alaska Press Pages. 369

Rating

FOSTERING CHANGES

Treating attachment-disordered foster children

If you're wondering why you just can't seem to break through to the emotionally disturbed child in your care, this book will provide clear explanations and practical suggestions. Written for professionals, this book is certainly useful for parents as well, providing a clear description of typical attachment difficulties and the history that often includes abuse, neglect, exploitation and abandonment. Availability: This item usually ships within six weeks. Please note that items occasionally go out of print or publishers run out of stock. We will notify you within three weeks if we have trouble obtaining this book.

Keywords

Foster Care, Attachment, Special needs, Adoption

Age Range:

Adult

Author: Richard Delaney

Dr. Rick Delaney, a practicing psychologist, is the author of *Fostering Changes; Troubled Transplants;* and *Long Journey Home.*

ISBN# 962984906 Date Published: 1991 Price: $ 13.95

Publisher: R.J. Delaney Pages: 94

Rating

HANDBOOK FOR TREATMENT OF ATTACHMENT-TRAUMA PROBLEMS IN CHILDREN

How to build attachment with children who have learned not to trust.

Clinical suggestions for adults caring for children experiencing the trauma of attachment problems. Methods for building the necessary ability to trust and to develop the security necessary to lasting normal relationships. For both parents and professionals.

Keywords

Attachment, Parenting, Special Needs

Age Range:

Adult

Author: Beverly James

ISBN# 29160057 Date Published: 1994 Price: $ 34.95

Publisher: Free Press Pages:

HEALING POWER OF THE FAMILY, THE

Overview of life with the disturbed foster or adopted child.

A user-friendly approach to helping disturbed foster and adopted children. Written in Dr. Delaney's usual straightforward and sometimes humorous style, this book puts "front-line" strategies in the hands of lay readers. He addresses telltale "survival behaviors" displayed by troubled, formerly abused children; the predictable, devastating impact of the disturbed child on the foster or adoptive family; and the unique family-based strategies which focus on curing disruptive behaviors while building bridges between child and family.

Keywords

Special Needs, Foster Care, Core Issues (Feelings), Grief and Loss, Adopted Child

Age Range:

Adult

Author: Richard Delaney

Dr. Rick Delaney, a practicing psychologist, is the author of *Fostering Changes; Troubled Transplants;* and *Long Journey Home.*

ISBN# 1885473168 Date Published: 1997 Price: $ 17.95

Publisher: Wood N Barnes Pages: 123

HELP FOR THE HOPELESS CHILD

Innovative and aggressive assessment and treatment strategies for the most difficult child.

Designed specifically for families that have struggled with an unmanageable child, this book focuses on clear and specific treatment strategies. Specialized sections of this book focus on dealing with the complexities of the internationally-adopted child who has survived years of institutionalization. "Children who have suffered extreme deprivation often arrive with a spectrum of problems that overwhelms most parents. Dr. Federici helps parents navigate through the complexities of medical and behavioral services for children with complex problems," writes Dana E. Johnson, M.D., Ph.D., Co-Director, International Adoption Clinic, The University of Minnesota Hospital

Keywords

Attachment, Special Needs, Core Issues (Feelings)

Age Range:

Adult

Author: Ronald S. Federici

Author: Cari Urgent

ISBN# 096671010X Date Published: 1998 Price: $ 29.95

Publisher: self published Pages: 212

Rating

INVISIBLE ROAD, THE

Suggestions to help parents deal with the challenges of attachment disorders.

A parent's approach for helping a child with an attachment disorder to navigate interactions with family members, friends, and the community. Addresses common problems encountered through the development process. Easy to read.

Keywords

Attachment, Special Needs, Child Development, Extended Family

Age Range.

Adult

Author: Janelle R.N. Peterson

ISBN# NA   Date Published. 1995   Price. $ 17.95
Publisher. self published   Pages. 70

Rating

IT'S NOBODY'S FAULT

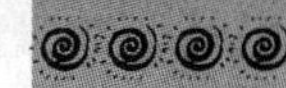

Get rid of the guilt: New hope and help for difficult children and their parents.

It's Nobody's Fault challenges parents being blamed when their children are hyperactive or don't behave in socially approved ways because of neurological disorders. This book is designed to support parents raising challenging children and provides suggestions for dealing with the outside community of professionals and other parents.

Keywords

Parenting, FAS/FAE, Differently-abled, Core Issues (Feelings), ADHD, Special Needs

Age Range.

Adult

Author: Harold S. Koplewicz

ISBN#   Date Published. 1996   Price. $ 15.00
Publisher. Random House   Pages. 303

MAYBE YOU KNOW MY KID

How do you parent a child with ADHD?

Mary Fowler's child has ADHD. This is her story of the challenges and the skills she developed in parenting. A very human approach to the issues based on personal experience.

Keywords

Self-Esteem, Special Needs, Child Development, ADHD

Age Range.

Adult

Author: Mary C. Fowler

ISBN# 1-55972-490-0   Date Published. 1993   Price. $ 14.95
Publisher. Carol Pub. Group   Pages. 240

NOBODY'S CHILDREN: ORPHANS OF THE HIV EPIDEMIC

The most useful book on this topic.

Contents includes Ch. 1. The Second Decade Ch. 2. The State of the Child Ch. 3. To Everything There Is a Season Ch. 4. Devices for Safekeeping Ch. 5. Angel Ch. 6. The Uncertainty of Knowing Ch. 7. Voices from the Past Ch. 8. The Mourning Dove Ch. 9. The Natural History of Affection Between Males Ch. 10. The First Time, the Only Time, Each Time Ch. 11. At Certain Hours It Haunts the House

Keywords

Adoption, Special needs, Orphan, AIDS/HIV

Age Range.

Adult

Author: Steven F. Dansky

ISBN# 1560239239   Date Published. 1997   Price. $ 14.95
Publisher. Harrington   Pages.

Rating

QUESTION OF DAVID, THE

A disabled mother's journey through adoption, family, and life.

In 1987, Neil and Denise Jacobson, both of whom have cerebral palsy, adopted a six-week-old infant. Readers will find new understanding into challenges both familiar and unfamiliar through Denise's insights as a woman with cerebral palsy embracing the difficulties and joys of motherhood for the first time. This inspiring book celebrates the aspects in each of us that are the same, as well as those that differ.

Keywords

Adoptive Parent, Special Needs

Age Range:

Adult

Author: Denise Sherer Jacobson

Denise Sherer Jacobson is a contributor to *The Adoption Reader.*

ISBN# 887392016 Date Published: 1997 Price: $ 14.95

Publisher: Creative Arts Book Company Pages: 272

Rating

REACHING OUT TO CHILDREN WITH FAS/FAE

Supportive and optimistic resources for children with FAS/FAE.

Approximately one in every 700 babies born in the U.S. has Fetal Alcohol Syndrome and one in every 350 demonstrates Fetal Alcohol Effects. This practical resource for teachers, counselors and parents prevents useful information on diagnosis, parenting, and teaching. Contents include: Diagnosis and prognosis: How to distinguish FAS and FAE; Confronting the cause; Parenting a child with FAS/FAE; Developmental stages; Educating doctors; counselors, and other helping professionals; Teaching the child with FAS/FAE; Techniques for helping children through adults; Behavior modification techniques; Support for parents and counselors with adolescents and adults with FAS/FAE.

Keywords

Special Needs, FAS/FAE

Age Range:

Adult

Author: Diane Davis

Diane Davis is a Chemical Dependency Counselor.

ISBN# 876288573 Date Published: 1994 Price: $ 27.95

Publisher: Ctr. for Applied Research in Ed. Pages: 192

RESIDENTIAL TREATMENT

A tapestry of many therapies

This book provides tools to help parents understand treatment options for children in need of out-of-home care. How to find and what to expect from out-of-home treatment for the seriously disturbed or unattached child. Vera Fahlberg brings a lifetime of experience from her successful work as a clinician seeking to make a difference in the lives of children who have been separated from their families. Her insights and methods for dealing with children with the most complex problems bear significant application to all children who have had to transfer from their first family and reconnect to new families or care givers.

Keywords

Triad Issues, Adoption, Foster Child, Adopted Child, Child Development, Attachment

Age Range:

Adult

Author: Vera Fahlberg

Vera Fahlberg is the author of *Residential Treatment* and *A Child's Journey Through Placement.*

ISBN# 10-944934-02-1 Date Published: Price: $ 24.95

Publisher: Perspectives Press Pages:

SEXUALLY REACTIVE CHILDREN IN ADOPTION AND FOSTER CARE

For parents of children whose behaviors reflect strong reactions to inappropriate sexual exposure.

This book points out how issues of abuse and attachment may be enmeshed for children moving from foster care into adoptive families. Dissociation and sexualized and/or sexually aggressive behaviors may become the child's defense mechanisms. Parents can learn effective responses to help their children cope with complex histories.

Keywords

Sexual Abuse, Special Needs, Child Development, Attachment, Foster Child, Core Issues (Feelings)

Age Range:

Adult

Author: Joan McNamara

Joan McNamara is the author of *Adopting the Sexually Abused Child, Sexually Reactive Children in Adoption* and *Foster Care* and more.

ISBN# 939561069 Date Published: 1994 Price: $ 14.95

Publisher: Univ. of So. Maine Pages: 147

Rating

SPECIAL NEEDS ADOPTIONS

Specialized recruitment, preparation, and post-placement supports for adoptive families of children with special needs.

This volume reports the results of a survey of 799 families who adopted children with "special needs." It assesses perceptions of social work services, parent-child relationships, family functioning, child behavior, school performance, and other aspects of adoptive family life. Rosenthal and Groze compare outcomes for different types of adoptions, including adoptions of children of different ages, adoptions by minority families, transracial adoptions, single-parent adoptions, adoptions by less-educated and less-wealthy families, adoptions by foster parents, adoptions of children with handicaps, and sibling group adoptions.

Keywords

Special Needs, Adoption

Age Range:

Adult

Author: James A Rosenthal

Author: Victor K. Groze

James A. Rosenthal is Associate Professor of Social Work at the University of Oklahoma, Norman.

ISBN# 275937909 Date Published: 1992 Price: $ 49.95

Publisher: Praeger Pages:

Rating

TAKING CHARGE OF ADHD

Become an empowered parent! How to help your child ...and yourself.

Bombarded with conflicting advice and worn down by the daily frustrations of caring for their child, most parents of children with ADHD end up exhausted, confused and feeling totally helpless. Forgetting that it's they who know their child best, they surrender control to others. These step-by-step suggestions to manage a child with ADHD in everyday situations provide valuable support. This reviewer is the parent of a child with ADHD who recommends this book as the most useful on the market on this topic.

Keywords

Special needs, ADHD, Parenting, Skill Mastery

Age Range:

Adult

Author: Russell A. Barkley

ISBN# 0-89862-099-6 Date Published: 1995 Price: $ 16.95

Publisher: Guilford Pages: 302

THE THINGS I WANT MOST

The extraordinary story of a boy's journey to a family of his own.

Portraying the unpredictability, frustration, and heartbreak of everyday life with an uncontrollable child scarred by abuse, The Things I Want Most is a testament to the strength it took to convince Mike he might get what he wanted most—a loving family. Booklist calls it "superbly written." Kirkus reviews says that "Despite the inevitable strain he places on the Miniters, they persevere, and gradually Mike begins ever so slowly to heal. Though he improves, he remains a challenged boy. In choosing honesty over hype, Miniter provides a clear picture of the children who need parents like himself. Candid and breathtakingly hopeful."

Keywords

Adopting Older Child, Foster Child, Attachment

Age Range:

Adult

Author: Richard F. Miniter

ISBN# 553379763 Date Published: 1998 Price: $ 12.95

Publisher: Bantam Pages: 288

TROUBLED TRANSPLANTS

Unconventional insights and strategies to help families dealing with disturbed foster and adopted children.

Based on a model of teamwork among the foster/adoptive family members, the birth family, the caseworker, mental health professional, teachers, and others connected to the child, this book covers the impact of a disturbed child on the family, symptoms of children who have suffered abuse, neglect, and exploitation and their typical views of the world, how family members can easily get pulled into the child's disturbed system and negative view, and concrete strategies to contain acting-out behaviors, increase the child's ability to communicate verbally, foster negotiation skills, and promote positive encounters with significant others.

Keywords

Parenting, Core Issues (Feelings), Adoption, Child Development, Foster Care, Attachment

Age Range:

Adult

Author: Richard Delaney

Author: Richard R. Kunstal

Dr. Rick Delaney, a practicing psychologist, is the author of *Fostering Changes; Troubled Transplants;* and *Long Journey Home.*

ISBN# 0-9395-611-4X Date Published: 1993 Price: $ 14.95

Publisher: U. of S. Maine Pages: 169

Rating

BEST OF PACT PRESS: BIRTH PARENTS

From those who are living it!

Forty-eight-page collections of the best articles published in Pact Press concerning birth parents.

Keywords

Adoption, Birth Parent, Triad Issues

Age Range:

Adult

Editor: Beth Hall

Author: Gail Steinberg

Gail Steinberg and Beth Hall are Co-Directors and founder of Pact, An Adoption Alliance and each is also the parent of children adopted transracially.

ISBN# NA *Date Published:* 1998 *Price:* $ 10.00

Publisher: Pact . *Pages:* 48

Rating

BIRTHMOTHER'S BOOK OF MEMORIES, A

Adopted children can find great benefit in this gift from their birth mothers.

A colorful fill-in-the-blanks book that provides room for a birth mother to describe in her own words her family, friends, traditions, childhood history and feelings about placement. The questions are thorough and sensitive, and the presentation is attractive, stimulating, and durable. Once complete, it makes a wonderful gift to a child from his birth mother. A Pact bestseller.

Keywords

Adoption, Birth Parent, Mothers, Memory Book

Age Range:

Adult

Author: Brenda Romanchik

ISBN# 0-964-103524 *Date Published:* *Price:* $ 19.95

Publisher: R-Squared *Pages:* 60

BIRTHMOTHERS

Great reading for anyone interested in the birth parent experience.

70 women tell their stories of placing a baby into adoption; they include discovery of the pregnancy; birth and separation from the baby; relinquishment; later impact; raising other children; search; reunion; and more. Highly readable and informative. A Pact bestseller.

Keywords

Adoption, Grief and Loss, Birth Parent, Triad Issues, Core Issues (Feelings)

Age Range:

Adult

Editor: Merry Jones

ISBN# 1-556523009 *Date Published:* *Price:* $ 14.95

Publisher: Chicago Review Press *Pages:*

BLOODTIES

Not recommended. Missy places her baby for adoption; the next day, Missy is found dead.

Killing off birth mothers who change their minds seems to be an unfortunately popular theme in contemporary fiction! An exercise in adoptism, likely to offend. "Reporter Jack McMorrow sticks his head above the tree line long enough to contract for an article on kids having kids, then homes in on one particular high-school kid — Missy Hewett, a success story of sorts who puts her baby up for adoption. Having second thoughts about the adoption...the day after she phones Jack [she is] found dead." —Kirkus Reviews. See Fresh Kills for a very similar theme.

Keywords

Adoption, Birth Parent, Fiction

Age Range:

Adult

Author: Gerry Boyle

ISBN# 425151824 *Date Published:* 1996 *Price:* $ 5.99

Publisher: Berkeley Publishing Group *Pages:*

Rating

DEAR BIRTHMOTHER, THANK YOU FOR OUR BABY

Helps to reveal openness as not "dangerous" while clarifying the role of a birth mother.

A collection of actual letters between adoptive parents and birth parents, and letters written by birth parents to their children, advocating for the benefits of openness and demonstrating, through the included letters, the ways in which initial — even though limited — openness provides the opportunity for increasing comfort and trust between birth parents and adoptive parents, to the benefit of the children loved by them all. Recommended by the Child Welfare League of America.

Keywords

Adoption, Triad Issues, Birth Parent, Open Adoption, Adoptive Parent

Age Range,

Adult

Author: Kathleen Silber

Kathleen Silber is the co-author of *Children of Open Adoption* and a pioneer and spokesperson for open adoption.

ISBN# 0-931722-19-5 Date Published, 1991 Price, $ 10.95

Publisher, Corona Pages, 193

Rating

FATHERS FAILING AND HEALING

An expanded version of dear birth father.

This book presents ways a father can heal when he feels he has in some way failed his child. Useful after placement, divorce, or other forms of separation. "Begin by looking yourself in the mirror and saying, I'm a father now. I've brought a new life into the world." Advice from fathers who are not parenting their children. "And even if I can't take care of this baby, it doesn't change the fact that I am the father."

Keywords

Fathers, Family Life, Core Issues (Feelings), Spiritual Meanings, Grief and Loss

Age Range,

Adult

Author: Randolph Severson, Ph.D.

Considered the poet of the adoption movement, and a strong advocate of open adoption, Randolph Severson, Ph.D., is a psychotherapist concerned particularly with spiritual issues.

ISBN# Date Published, 1997 Price, $ 5.00

Publisher, Heart Words Center Pages, 40

GIVEN IN LOVE

For mothers who are choosing an adoption plan.

A supportive booklet in easy-to-read format for prospective birth mothers, covering decision making, contact with baby, naming, saying good-bye, grief, anger, and where to find support. Nicely done.

Keywords

Placement, Parenting, Adoption, Birth Parent, Core Issues (Feelings)

Age Range,

Adult

Author: Maureen Connelley

Maureen Connelley is the author of *All Babies and Given In Love.*

ISBN# 56123-010-3 Date Published, Price, $ 2.95

Publisher, Centering Corp. Pages,

GIVING AWAY SIMONE

A penetrating account from a birth mother's perspective of the experience of reconnecting after adoption.

Waldron's path after reunion with the daughter she placed for adoption includes "both straightways and detours, flowers and weeds." This is an insightful look at mother-daughter relationships, whether connected by genetics or adoption.

Keywords

Adoption, Triad, Birth Parent, Search and Reunion, Parenting, Core Issues (Feelings)

Age Range,

Adult

Author: Jan Waldron

Jan L. Waldron was an editor of *New Hampshire Profiles* magazine; she is a freelance writer and editor.

ISBN# 385485999 Date Published, 1997 Price, $ 12.95

Publisher, Random House Pages, 240

Rating

HEALING THE HOLE IN A HEART

One birth mother's journey into the adoption triangle

Healing the Hole is a guide to making adjustments and building relationships, offering the reader a series of techniques, exercises, and resources; written with humor and affection, it provides reunion survival tactics to help manage the shift from the mania and exuberance of first contact to a love-filled friendship developed over time.

Keywords

Birth Parent, Adopted Adult, Search and Reunion, Core Issues (Feelings), Triad Issues

Age Range:

Adult

Author: Nancy Mac Isaac

ISBN# 967249902 *Date Published:* 1999 *Price:* $ 19.95

Publisher: Mac Isaac Enterprises *Pages:* 346

Rating

I WISH FOR YOU A BEAUTIFUL LIFE

Letters written to their children by Korean birth mothers of the Ae Ran Won agency

At the Ae Ran Won agency in Korea, each birth mother is encouraged to write a letter to her child at the time of placement. *I Wish For You A Beautiful Life* is a collection of letters from voices not often heard, providing a window into the birth mothers' innermost emotions at a very difficult time in their lives. What thoughts are typical? Hope that the children will have a positive life, sadness over personal losses, love for the children, and a level of guilt that sheds new light on what it is like to be a birth mother in Korea. This book is not intended for children.

Keywords

Adoption, Adopted Child, Birth Parent, Placement, International Adoption, Korean American

Age Range:

Adult

Editor: Sharon Mathis

Sharon Mathis is the author of *Running Girl; I Wish for You;* and *The Hundred Penny Box*

ISBN# 0-9638472-3-6 *Date Published:* 1998 *Price:* $ 18.95

Publisher: Yeong & Yong *Pages:*

JOURNEY OF ADOPTION, THE

Assistance for birth mothers after adoption placements from a Christian point of view.

Written to help a young birth mother think about her adoption experiences, including the pregnancy, birth, and adoption plan, this book examines how her relationships with those close to her may change as a result of the adoption, suggesting ways to make a lifeline of her adoption experience. The final chapter helps her explore whether or not she needs to do further grief work. This workbook, which expresses a Christian perspective, is written for use after the adoption experience, and can be useful to older birth mothers who placed a child in adoption years before.

Keywords

Birth Parent, Placement, Christianity, Grief and Loss, Extended Family

Age Range:

Adult

Author: Anne Pierson

ISBN# NA *Date Published:* 1997 *Price:* $ 5.00

Publisher: Loving and Caring *Pages:*

KID, THE

What happened after my boyfriend and I decided to go get pregnant: an adoption story.

This book is a new release. We were not able to review it in time for this publication but wanted you to know about it. Call 415-221-6957 for updated information.

Keywords

Adoption, Birth Parent

Age Range:

Adult

Author: Dan Savage

ISBN# 525945253 *Date Published:* 1999 *Price:* $ 22.95

Publisher: Dutton *Pages:* 240

Rating

OTHER MOTHER, THE

One woman's story of search and reunion.

Carol was forced by her parents to place her son for adoption in 1966. The nuns at the Catholic home for unwed mothers promised she would forget and go on with her life. But 17 years of longing for her firstborn son sent Carol on a quest to find him. This book tells of her personal journey toward reunion and what happened after she met her son and his adoptive family twenty years later.

Keywords

Birth Parent, Search and Reunion, Core Issues (Feelings), Mothers, Placement, Triad Issues

Age Range:

Adult

Author: Carol Schaeffer

ISBN# 0-939149-75-3 Date Published: 1991 Price: $ 12.95

Publisher: Soho Pages:

Rating

OUT OF THE SHADOWS: BIRTHFATHERS' STORIES

Birth fathers' stories.

Interviews with fathers who are not parenting their children: their reasons, feelings, wishes, advice, and reality. Currently out of print but if you would like, we will attempt to find a copy for you. Please inquire.

Keywords

Birth Parent, Fathers, Parenting, Placement, Social Welfare, Adoption Reform

Age Range:

Adult

Author: Mary Martin Mason

Mary Margaret Mason is the author of *Out of the Shadows*, a book of interviews with birth fathers.

ISBN# 0-964259-1-1 Date Published: Price: $ 14.95

Publisher: O.J. Howard Pages: 272

PARENTS, PREGNANT TEENS AND THE ADOPTION OPTION

Focuses on the problems and needs of the parents of teens facing too-early pregnancy.

Helps parents to cope with the shock of a child's too-early pregnancy; understand how much their daughter or son needs their support; and deal with the inevitable grieving they and their daughter or son will experience after placing a baby through adoption.

Keywords

Birth Parent, Extended Family, Placement, Adoption, Triad Issues

Age Range:

Adult

Author: Jeanne Lindsay

Author: Catherine Monserrat, Ph.D.

Jeanne Lindsay is the author of *Adoption Awareness* and *Open Adoption: A Caring Option.*

ISBN# 0-930934-28-8 Date Published: Price: $ 8.95

Publisher: Morning Glory Pages: 208

SAYING GOODBYE TO A BABY, VOLUME 1

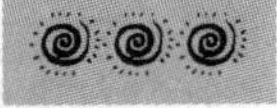

A book about loss and grief in adoption for birth parents.

Written by a social worker who is also a birth mother, this book describes a framework for grief after placement, along with intervention techniques to assist in the process. Useful resource to help break the isolation and invisibility that are too common for birth parents.

Keywords

Placement, Grief and Loss, Birth Parent, Grief and Loss

Age Range:

Adult

Author: Patricia Roles, MSW

Patricia Roles is a counselor who placed a child for adoption.

ISBN# 0-87868-387-9 Date Published: Price: $ 12.95

Publisher: Child Welfare League Pages:

Rating

SAYING GOODBYE TO A BABY, VOLUME 2

A counselor's guide to birth parent loss and grief in adoption.

Written by a social worker who is also a birth mother, this book describes a framework for grief after placement along with intervention techniques to assist in the process. Useful resource for counselors to help break the isolation and invisibility that are too common for birth parents.

Keywords

Educational Issues, Birth Parent, Placement, Grief and Loss

Age Range:

Adult

Author: Patricia Roles, MSW

Patricia Roles is a counselor who placed a child for adoption.

ISBN# 0-87868-393-3 *Date Published:* 1990 *Price:* $ 10.95

Publisher: Child Welfare League *Pages:* 36

Rating

SHADOW TRAIN

A Journey Between Relinquishment and Reunion

Annette Baran, a leading adoption expert, calls this book "an important contribution. Its importance is primarily in its being written by a family therapist who understands systems theory. Taylor gives us her own story and shows how the events reverberated in the lives of all involved. That's what makes *Shadow Train* so interesting and different from other birthmother books." "*Shadow Train* outlines the emotional experience of rebuilding a relationship after a nineteen-year separation and the pain which must be overcome by the author and her daughter in building their relationship." —Reuben Pannor

Keywords

Adopted Adult, Birth Mother, Birth Parent, Extended Family, Search and Reunion, Core Issues (Feelings)

Age Range:

Adult

Author: Patricia E. Taylor

Patricia E. Taylor is a family therapist.

ISBN# 614132924 *Date Published:* 1995 *Price:* $ 18.95

Publisher: Gateway Press *Pages:* 335

SHATTERED DREAMS, LONELY CHOICES

What are your choices if you cannot care for a baby born with special needs?

Sometimes the reason a birth parent entrusts a child to another family is an inability to parent a child born with a disability. This book explores the choices available to parents of a baby born with special needs and serves as a resource to professionals.

Keywords

Placement, Special Needs, Depression, Birth Parent, Core Issues (Feelings)

Age Range:

Adult

Author: Joanne Finnegan

ISBN# 897892860 *Date Published:* 1993 *Price:* $ 22.95

Publisher: Bergin & Garvey *Pages:* 184

SOUL CONNECTION

A New Age memoir of search and spiritual process.

The author says "*Soul Connection* explores the possibility that losses may be part of a Higher Plan to help us grow and lead us to serve others. A deeper look at how adoption effects people and at healing through expanded spiritual understanding." Ms. Hughes believes souls exist before birth, that reincarnation and astrology are facts, and that all that happens is preordained and occurs to teach us lessons. She states that adoptees know and choose their fate before birth, in order to learn and teach some cosmic lesson. We are among the many who will find her ideas insupportable, at best, and her writing style infuriating.

Keywords

Adoption, Birth Parent, Spiritual Meanings, Search and Reunion

Age Range:

Adult

Author: Ann H Hughes

ISBN# 961405325 *Date Published:* 1999 *Price:*

Publisher: self published *Pages:* 272

Rating

THIRD CHOICE, THE

Finally! An intelligent guide for adults facing the complexities of placing a child for adoption.

There are few books in print for or about birth mothers that reflect a belief in the benefits of openness. This is the first book not directed primarily at teens that accurately details the predictable emotional steps in the journey of placement, from the initial decision through common events beyond the first year. What an illuminating addition! Written in a warm, conversational tone and filled with the personal thoughts and feelings of those who have been there, this book is engaging, respectful, and realistic. It is sure to provide answers and comfort to anyone facing the complex challenges inherent in the placement process. Required reading for Pact families.

Keywords

Open Adoption, Birth Parent, Core Issues (Feelings), Triad Issues, Placement, Required for Pact Families

Age Range:

Adult

Author: Gail Mosconi

Author: Leslie Foge

Gail Mosconi and Leslie Foge are co-authors of *The Third Choice*.

ISBN# 0-88739-297-5 Date Published: 1998 Price: $ 14.50

Publisher: Creative Arts Book Company Pages: 143

Rating

TORN FROM THE HEART

Memoir of a birth mother's search for her adopted daughter.

"Books like Jurgens' will not only change the image of the birth mother, but will also change the image of adoptive parents," says Lois Melina. "This moving story presents an example of the struggles of young mothers to heal from the profound loss of babies lost to them through adoption." — Kenneth W. Watson.

Keywords

Triad Issues, Birth Parent, Search and Reunion, Grief and Loss, Adoption

Age Range:

Adult

Author: Louise Jurgens

ISBN# 0-944031-44-7 Date Published: 1992 Price: $ 12.95

Publisher: Avon Pages: 213

WAITING TO FORGET

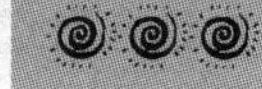

How does placing one child for adoption affect the way you parent your second?

Margaret Moorman was compelled at age 15 to place her child in adoption. For the ensuing years, she buried her feelings about her loss. At age 40, pregnant again, she realized how the issues had affected her and wrote this remarkable book. In it, she explores questions about secrecy, responsibility, parenthood, and love. This is the only book we know of to address this important topic from the vantage point of a second pregnancy. *The New York Times* says, "Moorman has effectively made the connection between the personal and the political."

Keywords

Biography, Birth Parent, Parenting, Core Issues (Feelings), Grief and Loss

Age Range:

Adult

Author: Margaret Moorman

ISBN# 393317838 Date Published: 1998 Price: $ 13.00

Publisher: Norton Pages: 216

WITH COURAGE AND LOVE

A birth mother's journal, a place to record feelings both during pregnancy and after.

A soft-cover journal with space to write a poem and letters, personal goals for the future, pockets for photos, and more. It is both attractive and inexpensive, but not very durable.

Keywords

Birth Parent, Memory Book, Core Issues (Feelings)

Age Range:

Adult

Author: Janet Sieff

ISBN# NA Date Published: Price: $ 5.10

Publisher: Centering Corp. Pages:

Rating

ADOPTION READER, THE

30 women touched by adoption explore their experiences.

Compelling, emotional, and sometimes controversial, these essays cover the gamut of adoption experiences: open adoption, international adoption, Lesbian families, single parents, biracial identity, search and reunion, special needs children, open records, foster parenting and more. Enlightening, sometimes provocative, often deeply touching, these essays together offer a multivocal narrative of the interrelated experiences of being a woman in any part of the adoption triad.

Keywords
Adoption, Adoptive Parent, Adopted Adult, Birth Parent, Triad Issues, Core Issues (Feelings)

Age Range:
Adult

Editor: Susan Wadia-Ells

Susan Wadia-Ells, a writer and longtime feminist, educator and activist, is co-director of The Wise Ones Conference Group.

ISBN# 1-878067-65-6 | Date Published: 1995 | Price: $ 15.95
Publisher: Seal Press | Pages: 285

Rating

ADOPTION TRIANGLE

A classic in the field, encouraging understanding of adoption as a lifelong process.

Sealed or opened records: how they affect adopted people, birth parents, and adoptive parents. This is one of the most important books in the history of adoption reform, calling attention to the problems created by sealed records and advocating for positive change. Anyone with an interest in the movement for open records must study this work, which is as responsible for the development of the adoption reform movement as any other work.

Keywords
Adoption, Open Records, Birth Parent, Adoptive Parent, Social Welfare, Triad Issues

Age Range:
Adult

Author: Arthur D. Sorosky
Author: Annette Barran
Author: Reuben Pannor

ISBN# 0-931722-59-4 | Date Published: 1989 | Price: $ 9.95
Publisher: Corona | Pages: 236

ADOPTION WISDOM

A guide to the issues and feelings of adoption.

General information on the issues and feelings of adoption in a question-and-answer format. Includes chapters on adoption awareness; the basic truths of adoption; search and reunion; and an ideal adoption.

Keywords
Triad Issues, Adopted Adult, Adoptive Parent, Birth Parent, Adoption, Core Issues (Feelings)

Age Range:
Adult

Author: Marlou Russell, Ph.D.

Marlou Russell is an adopted adult and a therapist in private practice in Southern California.

ISBN# 1-888511-12-5 | Date Published: 1996 | Price: $ 14.95
Publisher: Broken Branch | Pages: 195

ADOPTION WITHOUT FEAR

Positive views of open adoption.

This book offers first-person narratives from seventeen sets of adoptive parents sharing their experiences with open adoption. Contents include Vander-Haagen: Love is doubled, not divided; Dombroski: They had selected us; Spry: An extraordinary moment; Vander-Kolk: That crazy 'open adoption' outfit; Cottrell: Love and trust for one another; Lundy: No one can possess another; Joslin: A sense of completeness for everyone; Bohnhorst: A lock of Brendan's hair; Swander: I felt the pain and exhaustion; Olson: A lot of hurting, crying, and waiting; Jonn: The good-byes are not forever; Thomas: A whole different perspective; Ehle: Love is patient, and more.

Keywords
Birth Parent, Adoptive Parent, Placement, Adopted Adult, Open Adoption, Core Issues (Feelings)

Age Range:
Adult

Editor: James L. Gritter

James L. Gritter, M.S.W., is Child Welfare Supervisor for Community, Family and Children Services in Traverse City, MI.

ISBN# 3172213 | Date Published: 1988 | Price: $ 8.95
Publisher: Corona | Pages: 176

Rating 

BEST OF PACT PRESS: OPEN ADOPTION

The Joys and challenges.

Forty-eight-page collections of the best articles published in Pact Press concerning connections between children, birth parents, and adoptive parents.

Keywords

Birth Mother, Birth Parent, Adopted Adult, Adopted Child, Adoptive Parent, Open Adoption

Age Range.

Adult

Editor: Beth Hall

Author: Gail Steinberg

Gail Steinberg and Beth Hall are Co-Directors and founder of Pact, An Adoption Alliance and each is also the parent of children adopted transracially.

ISBN# NA Date Published. 1998 Price. $ 10.00
Publisher. Pact Pages. 48

Rating 

DESIGNING RITUALS OF ADOPTION

Rituals, both religious and secular, to enhance the passages of adoption.

Full of information about celebration and mourning — both secular and religious — to mark and heighten the experiences of adoption for all who are touched by it.

Keywords

Adoption, Core Issues (Feelings), Triad Issues, Spiritual Meanings

Age Range.

Adult

Author: Mary Martin Mason

Mary Margaret Mason is also the author of *Out of the Shadows*, a book of interviews with birth fathers.

ISBN# 0-9646259-0-3 Date Published. 1995 Price. $ 12.95
Publisher. Resources for Adoptive Parents Pages. 91

FAMILIES AND ADOPTION

An anthology of contemporary adoption articles.

A blend of personal adoption experiences and research studies, *Families and Adoption* explores how all parties involved can work together to improve placement decisions, ensure that a woman is confident in her decision to relinquish her child, and help families select the most appropriate adoption arrangement.

Keywords

Adoption, Family Life, Adoption Reform, Triad Issues

Age Range.

Adult

Editor: Harriet E. Gross

Editor: Marvin B. Sussman

ISBN# 789003228 Date Published. 1997 Price. $ 45.00
Publisher. Haworth Pages.

FAMILY OF ADOPTION, THE

Your child needs you to read this book.

An expert by training as well as an adopted person acutely sensitive to the core issues of adoption, Joyce Maguire Pavao offers one of the clearest voices in the world of adoption, alert to the deeper truths that may otherwise go unnoticed. Reading her book is like listening to a wise friend; she links her personal experience with the knowledge gleaned from many disciplines, creating that elusive "ah ha" experience. If you do not know her work, we envy you the first read. We regret that her "Family Garden" and "Normative Development Stages for Adopted People" models are not described; we've been waiting for them, but then this is just book one. Write on, Joyce, please.

Keywords

Adopted Child, Triad Issues, Adoption, Adoption Reform, Adoptive Parent, Birth Parent

Age Range.

Adult

Author: Joyce Maguire Pavao

ISBN# 807028010 Date Published. 1998 Price. $ 14.00
Publisher. Beacon Pages. 138

Rating

GHOST AT HEART'S EDGE, A

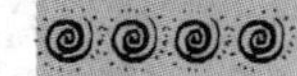

An anthology of stories and poems on adoption.

A thoughtful and moving collection of poems and stories that dismantles adoption myths by showing people touched by adoption in all their complexity. Poignant short pieces are arranged in sections which represent the adoption process: the period before adoption takes place, the transition period when the child moves from one family to another, how adoption affects childhood, identity issues for those who grow up adopted, and search and reunion between birth relatives. This wonderful collection resonates some of the deepest truths of the adoption experience from the points of view of all who are affected: adopted people, birth parents and adoptive parents.

Keywords
Adoption, Adopted Adult, Adopted Child, Birth Parent, Triad Issues

Age Range:
Adult

Editor: Susan Ito

Author: Tina Cervin

ISBN# NYA *Date Published:* 1999 *Price:*
Publisher: *Pages:*

Rating

GRIEF RECOVERY HANDBOOK, THE

"The most sensible, accessible and authentic plan for recovery from loss I have ever encountered."

Co-founders of the Grief Recovery Institute present their step-by-step recovery program for recovering from loss, both current and past. This very useful book suggests specific actions to help grievers work through their losses and create a richer, fuller life. This updated edition incorporates improvements in technique and contains twenty percent new material. This book has been especially useful for birth parents facing the emotional impact of placement and adoptive parents when a child is removed from the home.

Keywords
Grief and Loss, Core Issues (Feelings), Birth Parent

Age Range:
Adult

Author: John W. James

Author: Russell Friedman

ISBN# 60952733 *Date Published:* 1997 *Price:* $ 13.00
Publisher: Harper Row *Pages:* 208

HOW TO SURVIVE THE LOSS OF A CHILD

Filling the emptiness and rebuilding your life.

The author of *Grief: The Morning After*, who is also a bereaved parent, provides a compassionate book meant to help grieving parents recognize their emotions and realize they are not alone, in this understanding and empathetic guide that helps them rebuild their lives and go on without guilt.

Keywords
Grief and Loss, Core Issues (Feelings), Birth Parent

Age Range:
Adult

Author: Catherine Sanders

ISBN# 1559581646 *Date Published:* 1992 *Price:* $ 14.00
Publisher: Prima Publishing *Pages:* 246

KINSHIP WITH STRANGERS

How does our culture's understanding of birth, biology, and blood affect people who experience adoption?

Judith Modell examines the way people experience the opening of records, the acknowledgment of a birth and a legal parent, and the blending of families that are related only through a child. "Surrender" is the dominant motif for birth parents, while "love at first sight" may capture an adoptive parent's sense of parenthood. For the adopted person, "telling" is central — the moment when one learns one is not "like everyone else." This insightful analysis reveals the perplexing complexities of discussions of adoption. This book is currently on back order from the publisher. We do not have a reprint date, but we expect to be able to ship it to you within 5 weeks.

Keywords
Adoption, Core Issues (Feelings), Triad Issues, Extended Family, Adoptive Parent, Birth Parent

Age Range:
Adult

Author: Judith S. Modell

ISBN# 520081188 *Date Published:* 1994 *Price:* $ 40.00
Publisher: Univ. California Press *Pages:*

Rating

NECESSARY LOSSES

The illusions, dependencies, and impossible expectations we have to give up to grow.

This is the only book we know of that examines loss as a necessary experience for personal growth. *Necessary Losses* takes readers through the typical moments of loss throughout life — from maternal separation to shifting friendships, from divorce to aging. First published in 1986, this life-affirming, life-changing, and timeless book is filled with insights into how we must all adjust to the changes that are an inevitable part of life. Since adoption is built in part on loss, everyone touched by adoption will gain something from the author's focus.

Keywords

Adoption, Core Issues (Feelings), Grief and Loss, Triad Issues

Age Range:

Adult

Author: Judith Viorst

Judith Viorst is the author of *Alexander and the Terrible, Horrible, No Good, Very Bad Day;* and *Necessary Losses,* among many others.

ISBN# 684844958 Date Published: 1998 Price: $ 14.00
Publisher: Fireside Pages: 448

Rating

NEW LEGS

Seven Core Adoption Poems.

We invited Penny Callan Partridge to write a poem for Pact Press on one of the core issues of adoption (loss, rejection, guilt and shame, grief, identity, intimacy, and control as developed by Sharon Kaplan Roszia and Deborah Silverstein). Penny responded with a great poem on grief, going on to create poems about the six remaining issues. A treat for anyone with any level of interest in how adoption touches real people. Thank you again, Penny.

Keywords

Poetry, Adopted Adult, Adoption, Triad Issues, Core Issues (Feelings)

Age Range:

Adult

Author: Penny Partridge

Penny Callan Partridge, a poet who writes about adoption, is the author of *Pandora's Hope* and *New Legs,* among others.

ISBN# NA Date Published: 1999 Price: $ 10.00
Publisher: Self-published Pages: 20

PERSPECTIVES ON A GRAFTED TREE

A rare book that speaks to the emotional truth of adoption.

In this collection of poetry by and for those touched by adoption, the works of 65 writers explore a rich world of feelings. The poems deal with a unique blend of gains and losses, happiness and pain that are part of the emotional spectrum. A good gift item.

Keywords

Core Issues (Feelings), Adoption, Poetry, Grief and Loss

Age Range:

Adult

Author: Patricia Irwin Johnston

Patricia Irwin Johnston is the author of *Taking Charge of Infertility, Perspectives on a Grafted Tree, Understanding Infertility,* and *Launching A Baby's Adoption.*

ISBN# 0-9609504-0-0 Date Published: 1982 Price: $ 14.95
Publisher: Perspectives Pages: 144

PRIMAL WOUND, THE

Suggests that any child separated from birth parents suffers a psychological wound.

Nancy Verrier believes that the separation issues that occur for adopted people have lifelong effects which need to be healed. Her book has been embraced by adopted adults, many of whom call it their bible, as well as challenged by many adoptive and birth parents, who find her point of view unsupported. Whether or not you agree, all triad members will benefit by becoming familiar with the idea of the primal wound and with the information presented about perinatal psychology.

Keywords

Adoption, Adoption Reform, Triad Issues, Core Issues (Feelings), Self-Esteem, Grief and Loss

Age Range:

Adult

Author: Nancy N. Verrier

ISBN# 0-9636480-0-4 Date Published: 1993 Price: $ 14.95
Publisher: N. Verrier Pages: 252

Rating

SHARED FATE

A classic, this book sent shock waves through the world of adoption in 1964.

Shared Fate is a groundbreaking classic examination of the mystiques surrounding adoption. Originally written in 1964 and revised in 1986, this book still stands the test of time. Kirk helps us understand how adoptive families are different and then goes further to show how difference can be an asset. This book is required for Pact families. Currently out of print but if you would like, we will attempt to find a copy for you. Please inquire.

Keywords

Adoption, Social Welfare, Required for Pact Families, Parenting

Age Range:

Adult

Author: David H. Kirk

ISBN# 0-914539-00-0 Date Published: Price: $ 13.50

Publisher: Ben-Simon Pages:

Rating

STORIES OF ADOPTION

A rare opportunity to share the inner feelings of triad members who experience reunions.

Eric Blau has captured a special human story in each of his photographs, and the individual stories speak an emotional truth about how adoption affects people's lives. Annette Baran, a leader adoption educator, writes, "The pages within this extraordinarily moving volume offer, in photographic image and personal reflection, a rare opportunity for the reader to share the inner feelings of adopted people, birth parents, and adoptive parents." Highly recommended. A Pact bestseller.

Keywords

Adoption, Triad Issues, Biography, Adopted Adult, Birth Parent, Adoptive Parent

Age Range:

Adult

Author: Eric Blau

ISBN# 0-939165-17-1 Date Published: 1992 Price: $ 16.95

Publisher: New Sage Pages: 132

TOUCHED BY ADOPTION

Autobiographical sketches by birth parents, adopted persons, and adoptive parents.

Writers from Canada and the United States share their personal adoption stories in a collection that strives to balance positive and negative experiences and emotions. Though none of the respondents is a professional writer, the reader cannot help but respect the intensity of the raw emotions that are so candidly shared. However, the writing is uneven, and the overall collection tends to be redundant.

Keywords

Adopted Adult, Adoption, Adoptive Parent, Birth Parent, Birth Mother, Triad Issues

Age Range:

Adult

Author: Blair Matthews

ISBN# 968234011 Date Published: 1998 Price: $ 13.95

Publisher: Playing With Words Pages: 107

TRAIL OF SECRETS

A psychologist, haunted by the kidnapping of her baby 23 years ago, decides to adopt.

Eileen Goudge sets the stage for a story rich with drama and family secrets. From Booklist: "Skyler, an astonishingly beautiful and wealthy equestrienne who was adopted by her parents, finds herself pregnant — by New York City policeman Tony Salvatore. Is she ready to raise a child? Skyler decides to give the baby up for adoption and Tony introduces her to psychiatrist Ellie Nightingale, who has been trying to adopt. Skyler delivers the baby, changes her mind, finds out that she was kidnapped from her birth mother (who, it turns out, is Ellie) and realizes she truly loves Tony. Ultimately, everybody goes home happy, ensuring this book will be popular among fans of romance novels."

Keywords

Adoption, Fiction, Birth Parent

Age Range:

Adult

Author: Eileen Goudge

ISBN# 451187741 Date Published: 1997 Price: $ 6.99

Publisher: Dutton Pages:

Rating

Rating

WHAT IS WRITTEN ON THE HEART

Another look at the "primal wound."

In a clear and interesting fashion, Marcy Wineman Axness presents information on the connection between adopted children and their birth parents. Her goal appears to be to educate adoptive parents about the importance of validating and supporting their children's birth bonds in ways that enhance ongoing intimate relationships, both within the adoptive family and in the larger world .

Keywords
Adopted Adult, Adopted Child, Core Issues (Feelings), Adoption Reform, Open Adoption, Search and Reunion

Age Range:
Adult

Author: Marcy Wineman Axness

Marcy Wineman Axness is an adult adopted person.

ISBN# NA *Date Published:* 1998 *Price:* $ 11.95
Publisher: Self-published *Pages:* 45

CHILD OF MY HEART

Rating 

Celebrating adoption.

Child of My Heart includes brief memoir-like contributions from a wide range of adoptive parents and adopted people, both famous and unknown, from Michelle Pfeiffer, Rosie O'Donnell, Dave Thomas, Pearl S. Buck, Robert Fulghum, and others, revealing the frustrations and the ultimate fulfillments of the adoption experience.

Keywords

Adoption, Adopted Child, Adoptive Parent

Age Range:

Adult

Author: Barbara Alpert

ISBN# 425169014 *Date Published:* 1999 *Price:* $ 12.00

Publisher: Berkley Pub. Group *Pages:* 192

CHILDREN OF OPEN ADOPTION

Rating 

What is the effect of open adoptions on the children?

Using a developmental approach, the authors present evidence to support their thesis that openness in adoption benefits infants through teens. Discusses infant bonding and entitlement; grief in preschoolers; when to share difficult information with school-agers; inconsistent contact; when one child has connection to birth family and a sibling does not; and the teen years.

Keywords

Adoption, Open Adoption, Child Development, Parenting

Age Range:

Adult

Author: Kathleen Silber

Author: Patricia M. Dorner

Kathleen Silber is the co-author of *Children of Open Adoption* and a pioneer and spokesperson for open adoption.

ISBN# 0-931722-78-0 *Date Published:* 1989 *Price:* $ 9.95

Publisher: Corona *Pages:* 190

EYES THAT SHINE

Essays on open adoption.

Lively in conception, fresh and vivid in style, these essays ground the practice of open adoption in a traditional psychological-philosophic framework. Includes the philosophy of open adoption; where grief and joy divides; thoughts on a placement ceremony; opening a closed adoption.

Keywords

Parenting, Open Adoption, Adoption, Triad Issues

Age Range:

Adult

Author: Randolph Severson, Ph.D.

Considered the poet of the adoption movement, and a strong advocate of open adoption, Randolph Severson, Ph.D., is a psychotherapist concerned particularly with spiritual issues.

ISBN# 1880856085 *Date Published:* 1991 *Price:* $ 6.00

Publisher: Heart Words Center *Pages:* 35

OPEN ADOPTION: A CARING OPTION

Developing trust in open adoption.

Discusses how, in open adoption, birth parents take responsibility for planning their child's future. Both positive and negative views are presented and risks and problems are dealt with honestly.

Keywords

Adoption, Open Adoption, Birth Parent, Placement, Triad Issues

Age Range:

Adult

Author: Jeanne Lindsay

Author: Catherine Monserrat, Ph.D.

Jeanne Lindsay is the author of *Adoption Awareness* and *Open Adoption: A Caring Option.*

ISBN# 0-930934-23-7 *Date Published:* 1987 *Price:* $ 9.95

Publisher: Morning Glory *Pages:* 256

OPEN ADOPTION BOOK, THE

Rating 

A guide to making adoption work for you.

In an open adoption, the birth parents and adoptive parents are in charge of all phases of the process. This book answers common questions about open adoption and uses personal stories to illustrate how relationships work. Written by the director of an agency that specializes in open adoptions, this book suggests that open adoption is a faster process than other forms of adoption.

Keywords
Adoption, Adoptive Parent, Birth Parent, Triad Issues, Open Adoption

Age Range:
Adult

Author: Bruce Rappaport, Ph.D.

ISBN# 28621700 | Date Published: 1998 | Price: $ 13.95
Publisher: Macmillan | Pages: 224

OPEN ADOPTION EXPERIENCE, THE

Rating 

The first definitive book on open adoption.

This book covers all the bases, from theory to reality. It addresses both the easy and the challenging realities of living an open adoption. The many personal stories make the book believable and useful for all kinds of situations. It is sometimes a bit dense, but it makes for a perfect reference manual for many issues of open adoptions, from starting an open relationship to managing the ongoing issues of relationship as they develop over the years.

Keywords
Open Adoption, Parenting, Required for Pact Families, Adoption, Triad Issues

Age Range:
Adult

Author: Lois Ruskai Melina

Author: Sharon Kaplan Roszia

Lois Melina is author of *Raising Adopted Children* and co-author with Sharon Kaplan Roszia of *The Open Adoption Experience.*

ISBN# 60969571 | Date Published: 1993 | Price: $ 14.00
Publisher: HarperCollins | Pages: 389

PAINFUL LESSONS, LOVING BONDS

The heart of open adoption

Marcy Wineman Axness believes that open adoption is the best way to support adopted children. In this book, she presents basic information on the values and philosophy of openness in a clear and comprehensible way, informed by her own experiences as an adopted person. *Painful Lessons, Loving Bonds* reframes ideas originally presented by Jim Gritter, Randolph Severson, Nancy Verrier, and others.

Keywords
Adopted Adult, Adopted Child, Core Issues (Feelings), Adoption Reform, Open Adoption, Search and Reunion

Age Range:
Adult

Author: Marcy Wineman Axness

Marcy Wineman Axness is an adult adopted person.

ISBN# | Date Published: 1998 | Price: $ 9.95
Publisher: Self-published | Pages: 32

SPIRIT OF OPEN ADOPTION, THE

A spiritual journey that explores one agency's change from closed to open adoptions in 1980.

Viewing adoptive families as resources for birth families facing unplanned pregnancies, this book defines excellence in adoption by the replacement of fear, pain and shame with honor, respect, and reverence of each participant for one another. Open adoption is seen as a model built on candor, commitment, community, and cooperation. Gritter expresses deep concern about for-profit adoption services and about the lack of true excellence in services available. The book also traces the reasons for opening contact and the effects on the people whose lives are directly touched.

Keywords
Open Adoption, Adoption Reform, Adoption, Social Welfare, Spiritual Meanings

Age Range:
Adult

Editor: James L. Gritter

James L. Gritter, M.S.W., is Child Welfare Supervisor for Community, Family and Children Services in Traverse City, MI.

ISBN# 0-87868-637-1 | Date Published: 1997 | Price: $ 18.95
Publisher: CWLA | Pages: 315

Rating

ADOPTION REUNIONS

What happens after a search is completed? Firsthand experiences of triad members and birth siblings.

A book for adopted people, birth parents, and adoptive parents on all phases of the getting to know each other after the separation and reunion process. Anecdotal in style, the author clearly values the process of search and reunion and explores the complexities of developing relationships after birth-family reunions. Particularly interesting are the discussions of how this process affects siblings — brothers and sisters by adoption and brothers and sisters by birth. Some of the transitions between sections are awkward, but despite this limitation, this book valuably covers new ground.

Keywords
Adoption, Search and Reunion, Family Life, Triad Issues, Sibling Issues

Age Range:
Adult

Author: Michelle McColm

ISBN# 0-929005-41-4 *Date Published:* 1993 *Price:* $ 15.95
Publisher: LPC InBook *Pages:* 175

Rating

ADOPTION SEARCHES MADE EASIER

A private detective provides tools to make search easier.

Searching for birth relatives is challenging. This book brings practical skills based on experience.

Keywords
Search and Reunion, Adopted Adult, Birth Parent, Adoptive Parent, Family Life

Age Range:
Adult

Author: Joseph J. Culligan

Joseph J. Culligan is a private detective.

ISBN# 1572961007 *Date Published:* 1996 *Price:* $ 34.95
Publisher: Fla Inc. *Pages:* 757

BIRTHRIGHT

What happens when you search for birth relatives and how to do it.

This book is filled with stories...direct quotes from adoptive parents, birth parents, and adopted people who have experienced search and reunion. Includes guidelines for beginning a search.

Keywords
Birth Parent, Adopted Adult, Search and Reunion, Core Issues (Feelings), Triad Issues

Age Range:
Adult

Author: Jean A. Strauss

ISBN# 0-14-051295-0 *Date Published:* 1993 *Price:* $ 12.95
Publisher: Viking *Pages:* 288

COURAGEOUS BLESSING

When your child starts a search for birth relatives, how will you handle it?

Though adoptive parents are not usually direct participants in search and reunion, they may have strong and conflicting or troubling feelings about it. This book responds to adoptive parents' concerns about why adopted people search, how they will feel, seeking support, etc.

Keywords
Search and Reunion, Adoptive Parent, Adoption, Triad Issues, Birth Parent, Core Issues (Feelings)

Age Range:
Adult

Author: Carol L. Demuth

ISBN# 1-884319-0205 *Date Published:* *Price:* $ 6.00
Publisher: Aries *Pages:*

Rating

HOW TO FIND ALMOST ANYONE, ANYWHERE

Instructions for searching for birth family members on the Internet.

Clear, intelligent and user-friendly directions for conducting adoption searches for birth parents, adopted people, or siblings. Includes examples and advice for what to do after the person is located, along with a particularly useful reference section of website addresses. A most helpful guide for anyone starting a search who is computer literate, it also includes snail-mail addresses and directions that will assist people not using the Internet.

Keywords

Birth Parent, Birth Mother, Adopted Adult, Search and Reunion, Guidebook

Age Range:

Adult

Author: Norma Tillman

ISBN# 1558536574 Date Published: 1998 Price: $ 14.95

Publisher: Routledge Hill Press Pages: 238

Rating

HOW TO OPEN AN ADOPTION

A guide toward opening adoptions for adoptive parents, birth parents of minors and professionals.

Adopted children shouldn't have to wait until they are 18 years old to have their questions answered. Contact between birth parents and their adopted children allows the children to ask their questions directly and receive answers from the source. This book covers the benefits of opening adoptions; the issues raised if the request is initiated by adoptive parents or birth parents; professional help; preparation for contact; the first visit; the role of commitment of all the adults; when there is inequality among adoptive siblings; reopening open adoptions and more.

Keywords

Open Adoption, Adoption Reform, Open Records, Search and Reunion

Age Range:

Adult

Author: Patricia M. Dorner

Patricia Martinez Dorner is author of *Talking To Your Child About Adoption* and co-author of *Children of Open Adoption.*

ISBN# AVAIL. 9/30/97 Date Published: 1997 Price: $ 9.95

Publisher: R-Squared Pages:

JUST ANOTHER HEARTBEAT

A fictional account of search and reunion.

"When the phone rings for 37-year-old Jesse Bartlett, it shatters her life. It's her grown daughter, Gwen, whom Jesse gave up for adoption. An extended flashback tells Jesse's struggles: teen pregnancy in 1972 and the heart-wrenching parting from her baby, her own mother's distant disapproval, the secret she keeps from her husband. As Part One ends back in the present, Jesse picks up the phone. Part Two belongs to Gwen, always wondering about the birth mother who abandoned her. With sweeping emotion and suspense, *Just Another Heartbeat* moves quickly, never losing track of its goal of reunion." — Sara Jameson, The Daily Courier.

Keywords

Adopted Adult, Search and Reunion, Birth Mother, Family Life, Adoption, Fiction

Age Range:

Adult

Author: Susan D. Clayton-Goldner

ISBN# 965894002 Date Published: 1997 Price: $ 12.95

Publisher: Ballard Ave. Press Pages: 250

LOOKING FOR LOST BIRD

A Jewish woman discovers her Navajo roots.

Melanson was raised in a Jewish home, only to learn she'd been born Navajo and taken off the reservation against her mother's wishes. "Who am I?" she asks. "Even as I learned to weave Navajo rugs, I looked for ways to intertwine my Jewish faith with the Navajo. I was exploring identity and the meaning of family, measuring the ties of upbringing against the tug of blood. What I found is faith, in all its forms." Publishers Weekly said, "The present from which she looks back keeps moving forward as Melanson writes about integrating the person she had been with the person she is becoming."

Keywords

Search and Reunion, Judaism, Native American, Core Issues (Feelings), Transracial Adoption, Racial/Ethnic Identity

Age Range:

Adult

Author: Yvette Melanson

ISBN# 380976013 Date Published: 1999 Price: $ 22.00

Publisher: Avon Pages:

MAY THE CIRCLE BE UNBROKEN

Rating 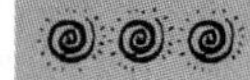

An Intimate Journey into the Heart of Adoption

May the Circle Be Unbroken is a plea to open adoption records. At age 19, Franklin relinquished her son for adoption. Twenty-seven years later, they were reunited and faced the challenges of building a new relationship. Franklin uses her own history to explore the emotional, practical, and legal terrain of adoption from the 1960s to the present. "I had given up my child and had to find a way to not believe I was a terrible person," she writes, advocating that the secrecy and silence cloaking traditional adoptions must be countered by open records.

Keywords

Adopted Adult, Adoption Reform, Adoptive Parent, Birth Parent, Search and Reunion, Open Records

Age Range:

Adult

Author: Lynn Franklin

Author: Elizabeth Ferber

ISBN# 517707551 Date Published: 1998 Price: $ 24.00
Publisher: Harmony Books Pages: 228

REUNION

Rating 

A year in letters between a birthmother and the daughter she couldn't keep

After decades of separation, 26-year-old adopted person Katie Hern writes to her birth mother, Ellen McGarry Carlson. Written over a course of one year, this book follows the women's progress — from elation to understanding to accepting — and their efforts to create an honest relationship. After several months, mother and daughter finally meet face-to-face in an emotional and exhilarating reunion.

Keywords

Adopted Adult, Birth Parent, Search and Reunion

Age Range:

Adult

Author: Katie Hern

Author: Ellen McGarry Carlson

ISBN# 1580050301 Date Published: 1999 Price: $ 16.95
Publisher: Seal Press Pages: 250

SEARCH: A HANDBOOK FOR ADOPTEES AND BIRTH PARENTS

Internet and other search sources

Book News: "A detailed step-by-step process for unearthing adoption information through sealed adoption records, government data, and reference resources. New to this edition is a listing of online services for networking with other searchers, and a 'Search Resources and Services' chapter."

Keywords

Adopted Adult, Birth Parent, Search and Reunion, Guidebook

Age Range:

Adult

Author: Jayne Askin

ISBN# 1573561150 Date Published: 1998 Price: $ 24.50
Publisher: Onyx Press Pages: 352

SEARCHING FOR A PIECE OF MY SOUL

How to find a missing family member or loved one.

A guide to both the emotional and practical aspects of search. The first book to guide people through both the physical and emotional process of finding a long-lost relative or loved one includes the author's own experience of searching for her father, as well as the experience of dozens of others who have also searched for family members.

Keywords

Adopted Adult, Adoptive Parent, Birth Parent, Search and Reunion, Fathers

Age Range:

Adult

Author: Tammy L. Kling

ISBN# 809230631 Date Published: 1997 Price: $ 12.95
Publisher: NTC-Contemporary Pages: 224

Rating

SHADOW MOTHERS

Stories of adoption and reunion.

This book answers the question, "What if I find her/him or I am found — then what?" It helps readers come to recognize that they are not alone in their birth history or in their search, that there are many birth parents and their children in America and that many are involved in search and reunion. Highlighting the variety of their stories, it also reveals the important common bonds, for all searchers, of pain and joy. With each book purchased, Linda McKay also offers the flyer, "Top Ten Ways to Help Ensure a Happy Reunion and Relationship," free upon request.

Keywords

Search and Reunion, Birth Mother, Birth Parent, Adopted Adult, Core Issues (Feelings)

Age Range:

Adult

Author: Linda Back McKay

ISBN# 878391290 *Date Published:* 1998 *Price:* $ 14.95

Publisher: North Star Pr of St Cloud *Pages:* 168

Rating

SIBLING REUNIONS

A letter to those who have been contacted as previously-separated members in the adoption triad.

This small book explores in depth the issues involved in the reunion process for siblings. Chapters include anger; first meetings; getting to know each other; family matters; and loss and forgiveness.

Keywords

Search and Reunion, Sibling Issues, Adoption, Triad Issues, Core Issues (Feelings), Grief and Loss

Age Range:

Adult

Author: Randolph Severson, Ph.D.

Considered the poet of the adoption movement, and a strong advocate of open adoption, Randolph Severson, Ph.D., is a psychotherapist concerned particularly with spiritual issues.

ISBN# *Date Published:* *Price:* $ 6.50

Publisher: Heart Words Center *Pages:* 35

SOUL CONNECTION

Memoir of a birthmother's healing journey.

Soul Connection is about healing through expanded awareness — and about using spiritual alignment to create miracles. The journey begins in 1966, when a young unmarried woman must surrender her baby to adoption. Afterwards, she stumbles along a healing path that transforms her understanding of life, eventually putting this new knowledge to the test in 1989 when she undertakes a search for her birth daughter using spiritual process. A memoir of inner and outer discovery.

Keywords

Birth Parent, Search and Reunion, Core Issues (Feelings), Spiritual Meanings

Age Range:

Adult

Author: Ann H. Hughes

Ann H. Hughes is a student of astrology and Science of the Mind. Director of Gateway Press, she is an adoption reform activist.

ISBN# 961405325 *Date Published:* 1999 *Price:* $ 14.95

Publisher: Gateway Press *Pages:* 272

TOGETHER AGAIN

True stories of birth parents and adopted children reunited.

True stories of reunited families from the files of a large search organization.

Keywords

Adoption, Search and Reunion

Age Range:

Adult

Author: Carolyn Campbell

ISBN# 425164543 *Date Published:* 1999 *Price:* $ 6.99

Publisher: Berkley Pub. Group *Pages:* 342

Rating

ADOPTION, RACE, AND IDENTITY

Rita J. Simon and Howard Altstein have conducted longitudinal research on transracial adoptive families.

This volume examines the placement of nonwhite (predominantly Black) adopted people with white parents. In addition to reviewing recent court decisions involving race as a factor in child custody, Simon and Altstein examine research including adoption policy and practice as carried out by some adoption agencies. The work is almost exclusively devoted to responses to questions about the experiences of families. The authors conclude that the majority of families and their adopted children are well integrated into society and that the adopted people now, as adults, do not see themselves as any less "Black" than their intraracially-raised peers.

Keywords

Adoption, Transracial Adoption, Family Life, Racial/Ethnic Identity

Age Range:

Adult

Author: Rita J. Simon

Author: Howard Altstein

Rita J. Simon and Howard Altstein are the authors of *The Case for Transracial Adoption* and numerous other research studies concerning transracial adoption.

ISBN# 275937488 Date Published: 1992 Price: $ 55.00

Publisher: Praeger Pages:

Rating

AN INSIDER'S GUIDE TO TRANSRACIAL ADOPTION

A comprehensive manual for adoptive and foster parents raising children across racial lines.

This manual addresses the predictable issues in transracial adoption. Sections cover the challenges transracial families face, how racial identity develops for people of color and White people, how to make connections to your child's racial or ethnic community, special issues concerning identity, White identity, not knowing your child's birth culture, birth parents, extended families, siblings, blended families, single parent families, only-child families, international families, gay and Lesbian families, Jewish families, families of children with special needs and sections on how to recognize and support the racial or ethnic development of infants, preschoolers, school-age kids, and teens.

Keywords

Adoptive Parent, Foster Care, Transracial Adoption, Child Development, Core Issues (Feelings), Family Life

Age Range:

Adult

Author: Gail Steinberg

Author: Beth Hall

Gail Steinberg and Beth Hall are Co-Directors and founder of Pact, An Adoption Alliance and each is also the parent of children adopted transracially-.

ISBN# NA Date Published: 1998 Price: $ 22.95

Publisher: Pact Press Pages: 431

ARE THOSE KIDS YOURS?

This classic book deals optimistically with the basic issues of international adoption.

Books in Print says, "As the adoptive mother of two Korean girls, Register has considered some practical and ethical issues involved in cross-cultural adoption: are the parents in the wealthier nations 'entitled' to raise children left homeless in other parts of the world by poverty or social stigma? Do adoptive parents have a responsibility to their children's birth countries or to other disadvantaged children and their families? What does it mean to 'own' a child, anyway, and who can ultimately make that claim? Register addresses these and other issues and shows how they are played out in the actual, day-to-day experience of her own and other adoptive families."

Keywords

Adoption, Adoptive Parent, Family Life, International Adoption, Parenting, Transracial Adoption

Age Range:

Adult

Author: Cheri Register

ISBN# 0-02-925750-6 Date Published: 1990 Price: $ 24.95

Publisher: Free Press Pages: 250

BELOW THE SURFACE

Helping pre-adoptive parents decide for themselves if transracial adoption is the right choice for them.

Below the Surface will provide feedback to anyone considering adoption across racial or cultural lines, offering insight into adjustments parents will want to make to support a child from a heritage different from their own. Families get a chance to quiz themselves in four areas: personality, attitude, lifestyle, and knowledge, and to determine their Transracial Adoption Suitability Index. These materials have been Federally approved for MEPA training. Designed as a user-friendly learning tool, the material does not debate transracial adoption; instead it gives potential parents real tools to decide whether this choice suits them.

Keywords

Transracial Adoption, Adoptive Parent

Age Range:

Adult

Author: Beth Hall

Author: Gail Steinberg

Gail Steinberg and Beth Hall are Co-Directors and founder of Pact, An Adoption Alliance and each is also the parent of children adopted transracially.

ISBN# NA Date Published: 1998 Price: $ 5.00

Publisher: Pact Press Pages: 32

Rating

BUTTERFLIES IN THE WIND

Memoir about two Spanish/Indian children with white parents.

This personal history of one family's experiences with transracial international adoption tells the story of Tatiana and Rosana, adopted 20 years ago from Columbia by the Erichsens. Availability: This item usually ships within six weeks. Please note that items occasionally go out of print or publishers run out of stock; we will notify you within three weeks if we have trouble obtaining this book.

Keywords

Adoption, Parenting, Transracial Adoption, Family Life, International Adoption, Biography

Age Range.

Adult

Author: Jean-Nelson Erichsen

Author: Heino Erichsen

Jean-Nelson and Heino Erichsen are the authors of *Butterflies In the Wind* and *How To Adopt Internationally.*

ISBN# 935366199 Date Published. 1992 Price. $ 18.00

Publisher. Los Ninos Pages. 358

Rating

CASE FOR TRANSRACIAL ADOPTION, THE

A useful guide to research and study on transracial adoption.

Simon and Altstein have done longitudinal research on transracial adoption for the past quarter century. This is a summary and continuation of their work and that of others in the field of adoption, as it relates to the question of transracial adoption. They believe that transracial adoption has not been shown empirically to harm children and is therefore a legitimate placement option for children. The book reviews research on the subject through 1991. One of the few books to address this topic.

Keywords

Adoption, Transracial Adoption, Child Development

Age Range.

Adult

Author: Rita J. Simon

Author: Howard Altstein

Author: Marygold S. Melli

Rita J. Simon and Howard Altstein are the authors of *The Case for Transracial Adoption* and numerous other research studies concerning transracial adoption.

ISBN# 1-879383-20-9 Date Published. 1993 Price. $ 17.50

Publisher. American University Press Pages. 124

GIFT CHILDREN

The experiences of white parents watching their African American daughters grow.

Learning to care for his daughters in a nearly all-white community posed challenges for the author. "As I began comprehending what lay ahead, I felt myself losing whatever remaining shreds of paternal responsibility I possessed.... Were my daughters doomed to gravitate to the Other America of their biological parents? Were my grandchildren predestined to lives of poverty in the nation's black underclass?" If Bates believes that being Black is the same as being part of the underclass, perhaps he ought to pay some attention to the difference between race and class. Bates states that he and his family have "moved beyond" adoption and "achieved assimilation." Was that his daughters' goal?

Keywords

Transracial Adoption, Adoption, Adoptive Parent, African American, Black Identity, Family Life

Age Range.

Adult

Author: J. Douglass Bates

ISBN# 395633141 Date Published. 1993 Price. $ 21.95

Publisher. Ticknor & Fields Pages. 270

LOSING ISAIAH

A novel about baby Isaiah, whose two mothers both love him and want custody.

Should Margaret, a white woman who with her husband adopted Isaiah, retain legal custody of him? Or should Selma, the Black birth mother who has gotten off drugs and is building a new life for herself? *Losing Isaiah* touches on many current adoption issues such as the rights of adoptive versus birth parents and whether Black children should be adopted by white parents. It was made into a major motion picture now available on video.

Keywords

Transracial Adoption, Adoption, Fiction, Triad Issues

Age Range.

Adult

Author: Seth J. Margolis

ISBN# 515115398 Date Published. 1993 Price. $ 5.95

Publisher. Jove Pubns Pages. 392

Rating

RAISING HEALTHY MULTIRACIAL ADOPTIVE FAMILIES

A question and answer guide for transracial families.

A clear and concise set of common questions and good answers for transracial families put together by the Adoptive Parents Association of British Columbia.

Keywords

Transracial Adoption

Age Range:
Adult

Editor: Harriet Fancott

ISBN# NA | Date Published: 1999 | Price: $ 11.50
Publisher: APABC | Pages: 72

Rating

TRANSRACIAL ADOPTION

Manual for families parenting across racial lines.

A hard look at the debate and far beyond to provide practical advice for transracial families. Covers international and domestic adoptions. This manual consists of reprints from professional journals, the general press, and a range of adoption publications. Six subject areas are addressed: "Entering the debate; Deciding to adopt: are you ready to become a family of color?; Reality testing: Facing racism, facing adoptism; Building racial identity; Biracial identity; and Solutions and resources." Provides an overview for parents considering transracial adoption and direction for adoptive parents already raising a family. One of the few books to address this topic.

Keywords

Transracial Adoption, Parenting, Adoption, Racial/Ethnic Identity

Age Range:
Adult

Editor: Pact Staff

ISBN# NA | Date Published: 1995 | Price: $ 12.00
Publisher: Pact Press | Pages: 138

TRANSRACIAL ADOPTION AND FOSTER CARE

Practice issues for professionals.

Joe Crumbley is one of the adoption world's clearest thinkers about transracial placements. Informed by his expertise as a clinician and his experience as a Black American, he has created an important book for anyone interested in identity development. This book describes specific ways practitioners can work with transracial families to ensure that children develop positive racial and cultural identities, as well as how ideas for how professionals can better serve these families. Dr. Crumbley also addresses such concerns as cultural competence and recruitment of minority adoptive and foster parents. Case studies and "myths" of transracial adoption provide valuable background information for child welfare professionals.

Keywords

Transracial Adoption

Age Range:
Adult

Author: Joseph Crumbley

Joseph Crumbley is a clinician in private practice specializing in adoption and foster care issues.

ISBN# 878687173 | Date Published: 1999 | Price: $ 18.95
Publisher: Child Welfare League | Pages:

TRANSRACIAL ADOPTIVE PARENTING

A dialogue about transracial adoption between two leading experts.

Leora Haskett-Neal is Executive Director of the Association of Black Social Workers' Child Adoption Service and Al Stumpf is Director of Foster Care and Adoption Training at NYS Child Welfare Institute. Their debate offers useful information for those who are interested in getting beyond the question of whether or not transracial adoption is in a child's best interest. Considers the development of partnerships between communities of color and transracial families to support the child's connection to his or her racial heritage.

Keywords

Transracial Adoption, African American, Social Welfare, Adoption Reform, Adoptive Parent, Antiracist Strategies

Age Range:
Adult

Author: Lorna Neal

Author: Al Stumph

ISBN# NA | Date Published: 1993 | Price: $ 6.00
Publisher: Haskett-Neal | Pages: 21

Rating

AMERICA IS ME

170 fresh questions and answers on black american history.

While it's a tall order to create a general reference that's both comprehensive and detailed, this account manages to balance the need for contextual information with the need for specificity for a nonacademic audience. Its thorough and accurate research and engaging tone make this an ideal reference source, particularly valuable to those parents who may not have encountered much Black American history in their education and want to rectify that error in teaching their children. "America is Me is as fine an introduction to African American history and culture as I have seen.... It belongs in every American's personal library," says Arnold Rampersad, Chair, African American Studies, Princeton University.

Keywords

African American, Cultural History, Educational Issues, Black Identity, US History, African American

Age Range.

All ages

Author: Kennell Jackson

Kennell Jackson is an associate professor of history at Stanford University, where he teaches courses in both African and Black American history.

ISBN# 0-06-092785-2 *Date Published.* 1997 *Price.* $ 14.00

Publisher. HarperCollins *Pages.* 446

Rating

BABY MEMORIES

A journal for your baby's first year of life, designed for African American babies.

Finally, there is an attractive and reasonably priced baby book that reflects African American heritage! This is a well-designed memory book with pages for baby's photos, records of height, weight, teeth, and developmental milestones. In addition, it includes appealing pictures of babies, quotations from African American heroes, and the seven principles of Kwanzaa. However, it provides no place to recognize that a baby may have joined her family through adoption, and it exclusively depicts same-race and heterosexual parents.

Keywords

Adopted Child, Parenting, Memory Book, African American

Age Range.

Adult

Author: Annye Nichols

Author: Candi Nichols

ISBN# 0-9654914-04 *Date Published.* 1997 *Price.* $ 12.95

Publisher. Nichols & Nichols Publishers *Pages.* 64

BASIC BLACK

Tips on Black etiquette that Emily Post doesn't address: how to confront racism effectively.

An exploration of Black traditions, cultural issues and guidelines in managing social relations. In addition to the Emily Post territory regarding civil social behavior (setting the table; sending invitations), it offers Black Americans essential advice on how to stay alive as well as on issues regarding race, comportment and self-esteem — "If your waiter is rude or indifferent, ask for the manager and explain the problem. Some black diners have gotten excellent results simply by asking pointblank, 'Does your restaurant not want black clients? We're getting that impression from your staff, but we thought we should check with you directly.'"

Keywords

Racial/Ethnic Identity, African American, Cultural History, Black Identity, Manners

Age Range.

Adult

Author: Karen Grigsby Bates

Author: Karen Elyse Hudson

Karen Grigsby Bates is a contributing columnist to the LA Times and a commentator for NPR.

ISBN# 0-385-48434-8 *Date Published.* 1996 *Price.* $ 24.95

Publisher. Doubleday *Pages.* 473

BEATING THE ODDS

How young African American men can achieve academic success.

Hrabowski leads a trio of University of Maryland scholars who interviewed 50 Black families with sons who are among the top two percent of African American males in SAT scores and grades. The authors endorse child-focused love; strong limit-setting and discipline; continually high expectations; open, consistent, and strong communication; positive racial identity and positive male identity; and full use of community resources as values that create success. The book is academic in style, targeted for educational professionals but useful for all parents of Black children facing the obstacles inherent in American education today.

Keywords

African American, Educational Issues, Black Identity, Boy Focus, Parenting, Self-Esteem

Age Range.

Adult

Author: Freeman A. Hrabowski

ISBN# *Date Published.* 1998 *Price.* $ 17.50

Publisher. Oxford Paperbacks *Pages.* 240

Rating

BELOVED BABY

A memory book for Black babies.

Beloved Baby is especially designed for the African American infant. It does not reflect adoption experiences but does provide parents with a way to capture their babies' accomplishments. Color illustrations.

Keywords

Memory Book, African American, Black Identity

Age Range:

Adult

Author: Michaela Angela Davis

Lesley Ehlers

ISBN# 671522698 Date Published: 1995 Price: $ 18.00

Publisher: Pocket Books Pages:

Rating

BLACK CHILDREN

Ways of improving the effectiveness of educational programs geared to Black children.

Offers a range of ideas for effectively choosing and negotiating with your children's schools and discusses barriers and supports for children. Hale-Benson is a pioneer in giving content to new categories for understanding the cultural, linguistic and intellectual behaviors of Black children. She brings together ideas and research which can be used to build a foundation for an alternative education process for Black children. Deserves a place in the library of parents of any African American child.

Keywords

Educational Issues, African American, Self-Esteem, Core Issues (Feelings), Racial/Ethnic Identity, Black Identity

Age Range:

Adult

Author: Janice Hale-Benson

Janice Hale-Benson is author of *Black Children, Their Roots, Culture and Learning Style.*

ISBN# 0-8018-3383-3 Date Published: 1996 Price: $ 14.95

Publisher: John Hopkins University Press Pages: 240

BLACK HISTORY FOR BEGINNERS

An easy-access resource, reference, and curiosity- generator.

Keep a copy close at hand and think about sending one to friends and extended family members who would like to educate themselves. Easy to read.

Keywords

African American, Racial/Ethnic Identity, Self-Esteem, Cultural History, Black Identity

Age Range:

Adult

Author: Denise Dennis

Author: Susan Willmarth

ISBN# 0-86316-068-9 Date Published: 1984 Price: $ 9.95

Publisher: Writers and Readers Pages: 192

BLACK, JEWISH AND INTERRACIAL

How do children of interracial parents – one Jewish, one Black – think about personal identity?

This question is at the heart of Katya Gibel Azoulay's *Black, Jewish and Interracial.* Motivated by her own experience as the child of a Jewish mother and Jamaican father, Gibel Azoulay blends historical, theoretical, and personal perspectives to explore the possibilities and meanings that arise when Black and Jewish identities merge. Comparing the issues for transracial adoptive families when children of color are adopted by Jewish families is both interesting and useful.

Keywords

African American, Black Identity, Judaism, Race Relations, Racial/Ethnic Identity, Religion

Age Range:

Adult

Author: Katya Gibel Azoulay

ISBN# 822319713 Date Published: 1997 Price: $ 15.95

Publisher: Duke University Press Pages: 224

Rating

BLACK ON WHITE

Black writers are among America's keenest observers of white behavior. 50 writers explain whiteness.

Particularly useful for white parents of children of color to help build understanding of the role of whiteness within racial inequality. "Historian Roediger, author of *The Wages of Whiteness,* has been at the forefront of the study of what it means to be white, the latest approach to understanding racial divisiveness. In this anthology of works by 50 African American writers of the last two centuries, Roediger presents eloquent perspectives on white people and 'whiteness' as a 'system of terror.' Roediger includes works that examine everything from issues of gender and race to aesthetics and the myth that to be American is to be white."— Booklist.

Keywords

Race Relations, Racial/Ethnic Identity, Racism, Transracial Adoption, Black Identity, White Identity

Age Range.

Adult

Editor: David R. Roediger

ISBN# 805241469 Date Published. 1998 Price. $ 14.00

Publisher. Shocken Pages. 320

Rating

BLUEST EYE, THE

The Bluest Eye was the first novel written by Toni Morrison.

From the 1993 Nobel Prize winner came a first novel "so charged with pain and wonder that it becomes poetry," said the *New York Times*. It is the story of eleven-year-old Pecola Breedlove — a Black girl in America who prays, with unforeseen consequences, for her eyes to turn blue: so that she will be beautiful, so that people will look at her, so that her world will be different. This is the story of the nightmare at the heart of her yearning and the tragedy of its fulfillment.

Keywords

African American, Core Issues (Feelings), Racial/Ethnic Identity, Fiction, Black Identity, Race Relations

Age Range.

Adult

Author: Toni Morrison

ISBN# 452273056 Date Published. 1994 Price. $ 10.95

Publisher. Dutton Pages.

BOYS TO MEN

Maps for the Journey. Important reading for parents of African American boys.

Emmy Award-winning actor Greg Alan-Williams offers a path toward manhood for young men and a constructive approach for parents who want to open a dialogue with their growing sons.

Keywords

African American, Black Identity, Self-Esteem, Parenting, Core Issues (Feelings), Family Life

Age Range.

Adult

Author: Greg Alan-Williams

ISBN# 038548688X Date Published. 1997 Price. $ 10.95

Publisher. Doubleday Pages. 224

CHILDREN OF THE DREAM

The psychology of Black success built on the premise that success is possible.

Black readers who are tired of depictions of African Americans as lacking ambition and ability can take heart in these stories of self-made successes who realized their dreams in spite of racism's challenges, and other readers should be encouraged to consider and discuss this upbeat and realistic collection of complex personal stories of people overcoming obstacles, including politics, power plays and their own self-doubts. Contents include: Black success in America: a progress report; From separate to equal; To be young, gifted, and qualified; Getting mad, getting even; Success and the Black woman; Success and the Black man; and How we have overcome. Inspiring reading. Highly

Keywords

recommended. A Pact bestseller.

Age Range.

African American, Self-Esteem, Black Identity, Cultural History, Role Models, Race Relations *Author:*

Adult

Author: Audrey Edwards

Craig K. Polite

ISBN# Date Published. Audrey Price. Edwards

Publisher. has been an editor at *Essence*, the *New York Times* Pages. and other

Rating

CLIMBING JACOB'S LADDER

Traces Black family history from ancient Africa, through slavery and Reconstruction.

"Billingsley challenges the worth of studies of dysfunctional Black families and argues that the breakdown of the African American family is overstated and its causes misunderstood. He points out that female-headed households as well as new family structures are also appearing in white society and represent adaptations to a changing economic environment; Black families — the most economically vulnerable in our society — simply feel the impact of structural change first. His discussion is dry, his profiles too general, and his writing often awkward. Still... he frames an intelligent approach for addressing the social and economic trauma of Black America." — Kirkus Reviews.

Keywords

African American, Cultural History, Race Relations, Black Identity, US History, Social Welfare

Age Range:

Adult

Author: Pauls Giddings

671677098

ISBN# 1992 Date Published: $ 14.00 Price: Touchstone

Publisher: 446 Pages:

Rating

COMPLEX, THE

The politics of skin color among African Americans.

Wilson is a white professor; Hall is a Black professor , and Russell is a Black scriptwriter and poet. Their discussion of intraracial color attitudes is informative, historically-informed, and accessible without being simplistic. This book examines how differences in color and features play an ongoing role in socioeconomic status, family relationships, friendships, romances, and professional lives of African Americans. The heritage of slavery (in which those with dark skin were assigned to the fields and those with light skin to the house), centuries of white racism, the "one-drop rule" of racial identity, and other factors have all contributed to the color complex and its legacy of prejudice within the Black community.

Keywords

African American, Racial/Ethnic Identity, Black Identity, Racism

Age Range:

Adult

Author: Kathy Russell

Author: Midge Wilson, Ph.D.

Author: Ronald Hall, Ph.D.

ISBN# 385471610 Date Published: 1993 Price: $ 12.95

Publisher: Anchor Pages:

COLOR OF WATER, THE

A New York Times Bestseller, a Black man's tribute to his complicated white mother.

James McBride's mother was a rabbi's daughter, born in Poland and raised in the South, who fled to Harlem, married a Black man, founded a Baptist church, and put twelve children through college. She taught her children that only two things really mattered: school and church. A complex story in which race, religion, and identity surface but are subordinate to the central message: that determination and responsibility are essential to success.

Keywords

Racial/Ethnic Identity, Race Relations, African American, Biography, Mothers, Multiracial Identity

Age Range:

Adult

Author: James McBride

ISBN# 1-57322-589-9 Date Published: 1996 Price: $ 12.00

Publisher: Riverhead Books Pages: 291

COMPLETE GUIDE TO AFRICAN AMERICAN BABY NAMES, THE

Our favorite baby name guide for African American kids lists American, African, and Muslim names.

This, a favorite baby name book, is easy to use and includes good scholarship and lots of stories about famous people and their names. The author writes, "Every name included celebrates the name of a real person and the traditions, creativity, spirituality, families, history, and lives behind those names. Each name becomes a symbol of 'being' after it is attached to a living person; it becomes an instrument for honoring the life behind the name. This book recognizes that each name is a vehicle for exploring and understanding American history and African heritage, because each name is a medium for expressing the culture that passes down from one generation to the next."

Keywords

Names, African American, Parenting, Black Identity, Self-Esteem

Age Range:

Adult

Author: Linda Wolfe Keister

ISBN# 45190823 Date Published: 1998 Price: $ 6.99

Publisher: Mass Market Paperback Pages: 400

Rating

COUNTERING THE CONSPIRACY TO DESTROY BLACK BOYS

Is your Black son a member of an endangered species?

Kunjufu believes that Black boys are an endangered species. Chapters on Fourth Grade Failure Syndrome and Counter Conspiracy Strategies should be of interest to anyone raising a Black son, whether or not you come to agree with his ideas.

Keywords

African American, Educational Issues, Racism, Racial/Ethnic Identity, Black Identity

Age Range:

Adult

Author: Jawanza Kunjufu

Jawanza Kunjufu is the author of many books about African American education including *Developing Positive Self-Images* and *Discipline in Black Children.*

ISBN# 0-913543-00-4 Date Published: Price: $ 4.95

Publisher: African American Images Pages:

Rating

DAUGHTERS OF AFRICA

An international anthology of writings by women of African descent.

The Washington Post Book World calls it "a stunning wealth of writing...discovering and uncovering the silent, forgotten, and underrated voices of Black women."

Keywords

African American, Africa, Fiction, Cultural History

Age Range:

Adult

Editor: Margaret Busby

ISBN# 345382684 Date Published: 1999 Price: $ 21.00

Publisher: Ballentine Pages:

DEVELOPING POSITIVE SELF IMAGE AND DISCIPLINE IN BLACK CHILDREN

Expect your child to succeed.

Jawanza Kunjufu is a well-known educator, lecturer, and advocate for the education of Black children. This book addresses the need to have high expectations of children. Chapters include The Politics of Educating Black Children; Developing Positive Self-Images and Self Esteem, A Relevant Curriculum; Developing Self Discipline; Parenting; Children are the Reward of Life; and From Theory To Practice.

Keywords

African American, Educational Issues, Self-Esteem, Racial/Ethnic Identity, Black Identity

Age Range:

Adult

Author: Jawanza Kunjufu

Jawanza Kunjufu is the author of many books about African American education including *Developing Positive Self-Images* and *Discipline in Black Children.*

ISBN# 913543012 Date Published: Price: $ 7.95

Publisher: African American Pages:

DIFFERENT AND WONDERFUL

Raising Black children in a race-conscious society. An important book for all parents.

This direct and clear book offers a positive and realistic approach toward preparing African American children to become positive, productive and self-respecting. Chapters focus on modeling, racial identification, sexuality, day-care and family relations. A Pact bestseller.

Keywords

African American, Child Development, Required for Pact Families, Black Identity, Race Relations, Family Life

Age Range:

Adult

Author: Darlene Hopson, Ph.D.

Author: Derek S. Hopson, Ph.D.

Darlene and Derek S. Hopson are the authors of *Raising the Rainbow Generation, Juba This and Juba That,* and *Different and Wonderful.*

ISBN# 0-671-75518-8 Date Published: 1992 Price: $ 10.00

Publisher: Simon & Schuster Pages:

Rating

DON'T BELIEVE THE HYPE

Fighting cultural misinformation about African Americans.

Filled with facts for fighting stereotypes and information to show the real picture on jobs, education, social welfare, crime, politics, and affirmative action, this is an important reference. Books in Print writes that each chapter "examines the reality behind frequently asked questions and frequently- held myths. For example, Chideya disputes the idea that most welfare mothers are Black, have lots of children and no desire to work by citing figures on the ratio of Black and white women on welfare, the average number of children each recipient has and their efforts in finding and keeping work. She uses this formula to tackle affirmative action, the armed forces, drugs, gangs, violence, sex, family values, politics and other issues."

Keywords

Race Relations, Black Identity, Racism, African American, Self-Esteem, Cultural History

Age Range:

Adult

Author: Farai Chideya

Farai Chideya is the author of *Don't Believe The Hype* and *The Color of Our Future.*

ISBN# 0-452-27096-0 *Date Published:* 1994 *Price:* $ 11.95

Publisher: Plume Books *Pages:* 256

Rating

DR. CARL ROBINSON'S BASIC BABY CARE

Advice from an African American pediatrician.

In this book, written for new parents about children during their first year, Dr. Robinson addresses health issues for African American infants.

Keywords

Parenting, Family Life, Mothers, Fathers, Health, African American

Age Range:

Adult

Author: Carl Robinson, Dr.

ISBN# 1572241055 *Date Published:* 1998 *Price:* $ 10.95

Publisher: New Harbinger *Pages:*

DREAMKEEPERS, THE

What do successful teachers of African American children do? How do we learn from them?

Quality education remains an elusive dream for most African American children. In this invaluable, eye-opening book, Gloria Ladson-Billings explores the notion of culturally-relevant teaching. She profiles eight terrific teachers, whose approaches to teaching affirm and strengthen cultural identity are full of hope for all children. Written in three voices — as an African American researcher, a teacher, and a parent — this book is a mixture of scholarship and storytelling. Includes: A dream deferred; Does culture matter?; Seeing color; Seeing culture; We are family; The tree of knowledge; Culturally relevant teaching; and Making dreams into reality.

Keywords

Racial/Ethnic Identity, Self-Esteem, Educational Issues, African American, Black Identity

Age Range:

Adult

Author: Gloria Ladson-Billings

Gloria Ladson-Billings is a professor of education at the University of Wisconsin, Madison.

ISBN# 0-7879-0338-8 *Date Published:* 1994 *Price:* $ 16.00

Publisher: Jossey-Bass *Pages:* 187

EMPOWERING AFRICAN AMERICAN MALES TO SUCCEED

A ten-step approach for parents and teachers:"Teacher/Parent Workbook

Mychal Wynn outlines ten building blocks for working with Black males. From encouraging cultural understanding to tips on developing an empowered consciousness, this book outlines strategies and exercises for grades kindergarten through 12.

Keywords

African American, Black Identity, Educational Issues, Self-Esteem, Skill Mastery, Parenting

Age Range:

Adult

Author: Michael Wynn

ISBN# 1880463024 *Date Published:* 1996 *Price:* $ 9.95

Publisher: Rising Son *Pages:* 143

Rating

FACE FORWARD

Sharing a desire to give back to the Black community and be seen accurately.

A Black Studies Editor's Recommended Book: "An incident on a San Francisco street made Julian C. R. Okwu realize there were white people who saw him not as a man, but as a Black man who was a potential source of trouble because of the color of his skin. 'I wanted to introduce the world to another idea of young African American men,' he writes, explaining the reason for this powerful and important book." Midwest Book Review: "This collection of positive role models should be in the homes of any Black family struggling to impart positive images to younger generations."

Keywords

African American, Black Identity, Core Issues (Feelings), Biography, Gay and/or Lesbian, Self-Esteem

Age Range:

Adult

Author: Julian C.R. Okwu

ISBN# 811812154 *Date Published:* 1997 *Price:* $ 19.95

Publisher: Chronicle Books *Pages:* 160

Rating

FAST FORWARD

Young African American men in a critical age.

This collection of forty positive role models should be in the home of any family struggling to impart positive images of Black men to younger generations. Portraits in black and white blend with interviews with young men between the ages of 18 and 32. What they have in common is a desire to give back to the Black community and to be seen for who they are.

Keywords

African American, Race Relations, Racial/Ethnic Identity, Role Models, Self-Esteem, Black Identity

Age Range:

Adult

Author: Julia Okay

ISBN# 811812154 *Date Published:* 1997 *Price:* $ 19.95

Publisher: Chronicle Books *Pages:* 160

FUTURE OF THE RACE, THE

African American intellectuals address the dreams, fears, aspirations, and responsibilities of the Black community.

Reviews, Books in Print: "Gates and West explore the challenge of W.E.B. DuBois' famous essay 'The Talented Tenth' and consider the future of African American society in light of it. Gates and West are noted African American intellectuals on the faculty of Harvard. Examines the responsibility of the successful and talented Black middle and upper classes to uplift the impoverished. While Gates writes of the sense of guilt and attachment of Black intellectuals to the lower class, West challenges the naiveté of DuBois' belief in empowerment through education. The text includes DuBois' 'The Talented Tenth' and, reprinted for the first time, his 1948 critique of it. Highly recommended."

Keywords

African American, Racial/Ethnic Identity, Race Relations, Racism, Black Identity

Age Range:

Adult

Author: Henry Louis Gates, Jr., Ph.D.

Author: Cornel West, Ph.D.

Henry Louis Gates, Jr. is the chair of Harvard's African American studies department. Gates is the author of *Thirteen Ways of Looking At A Black Man, The Future of the Race* and more.

ISBN# 0-679-76378-3 *Date Published:* 1996 *Price:* $ 12.00

Publisher: Knopf *Pages:* 176

GOOD HEALTH FOR AFRICAN AMERICAN KIDS

The first health guide for African American children.

Addressing the sometimes unique health concerns of African American children, this long-needed book includes up-to-date information on diseases that significantly affect them. Covers allergies and handling milk intolerance, food and environmental sensitivities, and stress in the lives of children. HIV and AIDS, asthma, diabetes, heart disease, high blood pressure, sickle-cell disease, and common childhood ailments are discussed. The bad news is that Black Americans are more likely than any other group to die sooner and of a more major disease. The positive message of this self help book is that by incorporating healthy diet and lifestyle, African American kids can improve their chances to live long and healthy lives.

Keywords

African American, Health, Parenting, Black Identity, AIDS/HIV

Age Range:

Adult

Author: Josleen Wilson

ISBN# 517882698 *Date Published:* 1996 *Price:* $ 10.00

Publisher: Crown *Pages:* 423

GUIDE MY FEET

Rating 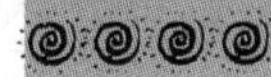

Meditations on loving and working for children. An inspirational pick-me-up for anyone who loves children!

Written by the country's most influential child advocate, Miriam Wright Edelman's *Guide My Feet* offers an inspiring collection of prayers and meditations for parents and children caught in a world in which values and communities are under siege. A Pact bestseller.

Keywords

African American, Parenting, Black Identity, Spiritual Meanings

Age Range:
Adult

Author: Marian Wright Edelman

Marian Wright Edelman is the founding director of The Children's Defense Fund.

ISBN# 60977116 *Date Published:* 1996 *Price:* $ 10.00
Publisher: Harper Row *Pages:*

HAIR RAISING

Rating 

Beauty, culture and African American women.

Chapters include: Nappy by Nature: Afros, Hot combs, and Black pride; Beauty, Race, and Black pride; Advertising Contradictions; Gender, Hair, and African American Women's Magazines; Broadening Representational Boundaries; and In Search of Connections. African American children will see that this book is specific to them, and all children will be able to appreciate the self-affirming values of the culture.

Keywords

Hair, African American, Black Identity, Self-Esteem

Age Range:
Adult

Author: Noliwe M. Rooks

ISBN# 813523125 *Date Published:* 1996 *Price:* $ 15.95
Publisher: Rutgers University Press *Pages:*

HOW TO BE

Contemporary etiquette for African Americans.

Cole's guide, reflecting on the history and culture of the African American community, treats good manners as a tool for empowerment. Addressing the kinds of questions that are rarely discussed in public, Cole's answers are a mixture of equal parts Emily Post, Oprah, and Lao-Tsu. Knowing good manners and how to behave appropriately is a form of protective armor that will be especially useful to children who have no ethnic role models within their family circle, and children who join their families through adoption may have particularly sensitivity to feeling connected to the larger community. Interesting information for all parents of African American children.

Keywords
Adoptive Parent, Antiracist Strategies, African American, Central America, Cultural History, Racial/Ethnic Identity, Manners

Age Range:
Adult

Author: Harriet Cole

Harriet Cole, a former fashion editor of *Essence Magazine*, is the author of *Jumping the Broom.*

ISBN# 684826453 *Date Published:* 1999 *Price:* $ 26.00
Publisher: Simon & Schuster *Pages:* 352

I DREAM A WORLD

Beautiful and inspiring photo essays of Black heroines, women who believed in themselves.

This outstanding book truly deserves a place on every family's coffee table — not just to be shown off but to be lingered over and learned from. "Documents the achievements of 75 black women — from 'unsung heroine' Priscilla L. Williams ("I had fourteen children. Seven of them was my sister's") to former Congresswoman Shirley Chisholm — in the arts, politics, business, academia, athletics and other fields. Photographs by Pulitzer Prize winner Lanker are often striking, quietly revealing pride of character.... The book functions as art, history, literature, or social commentary. Amazingly beautiful and moving, this book cannot be treated adequately on paper; go quickly and purchase copies for your library and yourself," says Books in Print.

Keywords
African American, Biography, Racial/Ethnic Identity, Role Models, Girl Power, Black Identity

Age Range:
Adult

Photographer: Brian Lanker

ISBN# 1-55670-092-X *Date Published:* 1989 *Price:* $ 24.95
Publisher: Stewart Tabori & Chang *Pages:* 160

Rating

I'M CHOCOLATE, YOU'RE VANILLA

What Black children know about race and what we can teach them

Marguerite A. Wright believes that young Black and biracial children are unable to understand racial prejudice; in fact, she believes they are developmentally incapable of understanding the concept of race. She coaches parents to keep their children "innocent" of the harshness of racism as long as possible and not to be concerned about reflecting race when choosing dolls, books, etc. because "childhood isn't about being politically correct." We have very mixed feelings about her positions, which often contradict one another, and we disagree with her assertions that young children benefit when their parents try to emphasize "colorblindness."

Keywords

Family Life, Parenting, African American, Race Relations, Racial/Ethnic Identity, Black Identity

Age Range.

Adult

Author: Marguerite A. Wright

ISBN# 787941964 *Date Published.* 1998 *Price.* $ 22.00

Publisher. Jossey-Bass *Pages.* 256

Rating

I'VE KNOWN RIVERS

Interviews over a period of years with six extraordinary African American men and women.

Kirkus Reviews: "In extended conversations with the author, [these men and women] detail their experiences: the often riveting events that have molded their feelings about race; their attempts to negotiate the crossing between black and white society; the lives they have created for themselves, both personally and professionally. A few themes recur. One is the cultural obsession with skin color among middle-class blacks, and a caste system favoring lighter complexions. Another theme is intense empathy for less fortunate African Americans. All six claim to understand the rage that surfaced in L.A. in 1992 — seeing the riots as symptomatic of racism. Lawrence-Lightfoot brings her formidable storytelling gifts to their lives."

Keywords

African American, Cultural History, Biography, US History, Race Relations, Role Models

Age Range.

Adult

Author: Sara Lawrence-Lightfoot

Sara Lawrence-Lightfoot is a winner of the MacArthur Prize Award, a Harvard professor and the author of *Balm In Gilead.*

ISBN# 140249702 *Date Published.* 1995 *Price.* $ 14.95

Publisher. Penguin *Pages.*

IF I CAN COOK/YOU KNOW GOD CAN

A delicious, thought-provoking celebration of Black culture through food.

Always a lively thinker, in this book Shange turns her focus to what we eat — why food is prepared the way it is, why traditional dishes may be made in different ways in different states, communities, or families. This peek through the richness of her thoughts illuminates culturally authentic details of African American experience, at the same time presenting an overview of how politics, relationships, and the state of the world influence what (and who) comes to the table. Recipes add to the flavor of her informed commentaries. This is a delightful book for anyone interested in an insider's view of African American culture.

Keywords

African American, Cultural History, Family Life, Racial/Ethnic Identity, Food, Festivals

Age Range.

Adult

Author: Ntozake Shange

Ntozake Shange is the author of *For Colored Girls Who Have Considered Suicide When the Rainbow Is Enuf.*

ISBN# 807072419 *Date Published.* 1999 *Price.* $ 12.00

Publisher. Beacon *Pages.* 128

JOY AND CHALLENGE OF RAISING AFRICAN AMERICAN CHILDREN

"Be there" is the message.

Emma Talbott tells parents they must shape up themselves if they expect their children to grow into healthy, mature adults. Talbott's lessons range from parents' involvement with their children's education and schools to what parents can do at home to enhance the identity and self-esteem of the child. After a brief look at African American history in the U.S., Talbott turns her attention to ways that families can nurture their children with respect to that history. Her strongest message is that great rewards are reaped when parents place value on education and are directly involved in their child's education both in and outside the classroom.

Keywords

Parenting, Family Life, African American, Black Identity, Educational Issues, Self-Esteem

Age Range.

Adult

Author: Emma McElvaney Talbott

Emma McElvaney Talbott teaches undergraduate courses in language arts and writes book reviews and editorials for the Louisville Courier-Journal.

ISBN# 1881320790 *Date Published.* 1996 *Price.* $ 15.95

Publisher. Black Belt Comm *Pages.* 191

LEST WE FORGET

Rating 

The Passage from Africa to Slavery and Emancipation.

Based on the Black Holocaust Exhibit, *Lest We Forget* is history brought to life by Velma Maia Thomas, curator. This stunning, interactive work brings Black history of slavery in the United States alive. We can touch and hold the experience of our ancestors through images of slave cargo, maps and insurance papers, replicated receipts for the sale of a slave woman, advertisements for the return of runaway slaves, and marks on the back of a slave from bullwhips. We can read the moving words of slaves themselves. This work allows us to know a period of US history which is the legacy of all Americans, not just African Americans.

Keywords

African American, Cultural History, Black Identity, Civil Rights, US History, Race Relations

Age Range:

Adult

Author: Velma Maia Thomas

Velma Maia Thomas is also the author of *Industrial Ecology and Global Changes* and *Passages.*

ISBN# 609600303 *Date Published:* 1997 *Price:* $ 29.95

Publisher: Crown *Pages:* 32

LET'S TALK HAIR

Rating 

Every woman's personal consultation for healthy growing hair

Hair care and positive self image for African Americans. This book takes a natural approach to hair care and also includes information about history and cultural values involved with hair.

Keywords

Hair, Health, African American, Racial/Ethnic Identity, Cultural History, Black Identity

Age Range:

Adult

Editor: Pamela Ferell"

Pamela Ferell is the author of *Where Beauty Touches Me* and *Let's Talk Hair.*

ISBN# 939183021 *Date Published:* 1996 *Price:* $ 24.95

Publisher: Cornrows *Pages:*

LIFE ON THE COLOR LINE

A memoir about biracial identity, by a man who hadn't known of his Black heritage.

The true story of a white boy who discovered he was Black when his parents divorced and he came to know his father's family for the first time. A compelling drama of a man straddling two worlds and two heritages, this book is ultimately a testament of triumph.

Keywords

Multiracial, Race Relations, Racial/Ethnic Identity, African American, Black Identity

Age Range:

Adult

Author: Gregory Howard Williams

ISBN# 545938508 *Date Published:* 1995 *Price:* $ 13.95

Publisher: Dutton *Pages:* 285

MAKES ME WANNA HOLLER

How young Black men try to maintain self-respect by going against the white "system."

Nathan McCall was a smart kid from a caring family in a suburban working-class neighborhood who ended up in prison for armed robbery at age twenty. In prison, he transformed himself through disciplined reading, study, and thought; upon his release after three years, he went back to school and began a career in journalism. In the newsrooms, he found himself facing hidden prejudice and racism, even among those who seemed to be liberals.

Keywords

African American, Biography, Race Relations, Racism, Black Identity, Self-Esteem

Age Range:

Adult

Author: Nathan McCall

Nathan McCall is a former Washington Post reporter and author of *What's Going On* and *Makes Me Wanna Holler.*

ISBN# 0-679-41268-9 *Date Published:* 1994 *Price:* $ 13.00

Publisher: Random House *Pages:* 404

Rating

MEASURE OF OUR SUCCESS

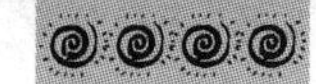

An inspirational book by America's premier advocate for children.

Marian Wright Edelman is a powerful role model. In this inspiring book, written for her own children, she details the lessons for life she hopes to pass along to the next generation. Beautifully written and highly recommended.

Keywords
African American, Parenting, Racial/Ethnic Identity, Black Identity, Spiritual Meanings

Age Range:
Adult

Author: Marian Wright Edelman

Marian Wright Edelman is the founding director of The Children's Defense Fund.

ISBN# 60975466 *Date Published:* 1992 *Price:* $ 10.00
Publisher: HarperCollins *Pages:* 97

Rating

MY FIRST WHITE FRIEND

Patricia Raybon decided she had to "stop hating (white people) to start living."

These essays, while episodic, are packed with powerful moments. Through God and the writings of Gandhi and Martin Luther King, Raybon frees herself from the hatred for white people that had kept her a slave to her anger and her past. But forgiveness, she stresses, is a process, a matter of degree. Kirkus Reviews writes: "This isn't the usual attack-the- bad-guy stuff. For most of her life Raybon, a journalist and commentator on National Public Radio's Weekend Edition, saw that 'white people every day did something hateful' — and she hated them. Here she traces the origins of her hatred, focusing on how lessons of hate, not love, were taught in daily life."

Keywords
African American, Antiracist Strategies, Black Identity, Race Relations, Racial/Ethnic Identity, Racism

Age Range:
Adult

Author: Patricia Raybon

Patricia Raybon is a journalist and commentator for National Public Radio.

ISBN# 140244360 *Date Published:* 1997 *Price:* $ 11.95
Publisher: Penguin *Pages:* 256

MY SOUL LOOKS BACK, LESS I FORGET

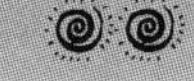

A collection of quotations by people of color.

A compelling record of a much-overlooked literary and cultural tradition, with over 7,000 quotations on 450 subjects. Voted a Best Reference Source of 1993 by Library Journal.

Keywords
African American, Racial/Ethnic Identity, Cultural History, Black Identity, Proverbs

Age Range:
Adult

Editor: Dorothy W. Riley

ISBN# 0-06-272057-0 *Date Published:* 1994 *Price:* $ 14.00
Publisher: HarperCollins *Pages:* 512

NAPPY

How American beauty standards affected an author as a measure of self worth.

Particularly engrossing for white parents of Black daughters. "HAIR IS A BIG DEAL. Whether we admit it or not, hairstyle (or lack of) is another one of our intercultural racisms. And corporate America ain't down with hairstyles that represent freedom and any attachment to the Motherland. The author sucked me into the story from page one, and I look forward to devouring her future projects. Miss Gibson, keep pen to paper." — Eric Jerome Dickey, author of *Sister, Sister; Friends and Lovers*; and *Milk In My Coffee.*

Keywords
African American, Racial/Ethnic Identity, Self-Esteem, Hair, Black Identity, Girl Power

Age Range:
Adult

Author: Aliona L. Gibson

ISBN# 863163297 *Date Published:* 1997 *Price:* $ 10.00
Publisher: Writers and Readers *Pages:*

Rating

NOTES OF A WHITE BLACK WOMAN

A positive vision of the way life could be.

From Booklist: "As a Black woman with a light complexion, Scales-Trent knows firsthand just how absurd and capricious society's imposed boundaries of race, color, and ethnicity can be. These stunningly powerful essays call upon experiences utterly personal yet distinctly universal; they examine flawed constructs that have evolved to set people apart from one another — fundamental notions about how a person is supposed to look or act based upon arbitrary groupings. With a goal no less compelling than building what she terms 'a new kind of community,' Scales-Trent proves to be a teacher of remarkable humanity and great clarity of thought."

Keywords
White Identity, Black Identity, Race Relations, Racial/Ethnic Identity, Racism, Antiracist Strategies

Age Range:
Adult

Author: Judy Scales-Trent

ISBN# 027101430X *Date Published:* 1995 *Price:* $ 19.50
Publisher: Pennsylvania Un. Press *Pages:*

Rating

QUARRY, THE

Would Donald's mixed-race heritage change his destiny?

Donald Glover was a star of the Harlem Renaissance, whose looks made him the "quarry" of women, while his adoptive Black parents are determined that he become a leader of the Black people. His story depicts the conflicts within this heritage. From Kirkus Reviews: "This novel (completed in 1928) argues against both passing as white, and black separatism. When his white adoptive parents discover his black blood and reject him, light-skinned Donald commits himself to the uplift of his race. This formulaic novel seldom transcends its obvious plot devices. However meritorious, it is strictly for scholars and literary historians."

Keywords
Transracial Adoption, Race Relations, Racial/Ethnic Identity, History, Fiction

Age Range:
Adult

Author: Charles Waddell Chesnutt

Author: Dean McWilliams

Charles Waddell Chesnutt was the first African American writer to find success during the Harlem Renaissance.

ISBN# 691059969 *Date Published:* 1999 *Price:* $ 39.50
Publisher: Princeton University Press *Pages:* 288

RACE MATTERS

"[A] compelling blend of philosophy, sociology and political commentary." –The New Republic""

"As moving as any of the sermons of the Rev. Martin Luther King, as profound as W.E.B. DuBois's *The Souls of Black Folk,* as exhilarating in their offering of liberation as James Baldwin's early essays," writes the Washington Post Book World. And Marian Wright Edelman says, "Cornel West is one of the most authentic, brilliant, prophetic and healing voices in America today. We ignore his truth in *Race Matters* at our personal and national peril."

Keywords
African American, Race Relations, Racial/Ethnic Identity, Racism, Black Identity, Social Welfare

Age Range:
Adult

Author: Cornel West, Ph.D.

Cornel West, author of *Race Matters*, is Professor of Afro-American Studies and of the Philosophy of Religion at Harvard University.

ISBN# 0-679-74986-1 *Date Published:* 1993 *Price:* $ 11.00
Publisher: Beacon *Pages:* 159

RACISM 101

Essays by Nikki Giovanni

Blunt, funny, angry, and personal, the author addresses the inequities in higher education; the legacy of the 1960s; Spike Lee; W.E.B. DuBois; gardening; Toni Morrison; Star Trek; affirmative action; space exploration; JFK and much more.

Keywords
African American, Racism, Racial/Ethnic Identity, Race Relations, Black Identity

Age Range:
Adult

Poet: Nikki Giovanni

Nikki Giovanni is the author of *Genie in the Jar* and *Racism 101.*

ISBN# 0-688-04332-1 *Date Published:* 1994 *Price:* $ 11.00
Publisher: Morrow *Pages:* 203

Rating

RAGE OF A PRIVILEGED CLASS, THE

This could be a great teaching tool, perhaps a bridge to understanding.

Without screeching, this book invites readers to share the startling experiences of middle class Blacks. Bears witness to the experiences, largely invisible to outsiders, of those who have gained material success at a huge cost to psychic well-being. Enlightening.

Keywords
African American, Race Relations, Racial/Ethnic Identity, Racism, Black Identity

Age Range.
Adult

Author: Ellis Cose

ISBN# 0-06-018239-3 *Date Published.* 1993 *Price.* $ 20.00
Publisher. HarperCollins *Pages.* 176

Rating

RAISING BLACK CHILDREN

African American experts provide answers to 1000 questions about the challenges Black children face daily.

Two leading African American psychiatrists confront the educational, social and emotional issues facing Black children. Along with the traditional demands of parenthood, Black parents face an even more challenging task — fighting the negative messages of racism while teaching their children to succeed in a white-dominated culture. This guide to raising African American children focuses on such problems as building self-esteem, helping children cope with racism, teaching children to excel in school, and more.

Keywords
Parenting, African American, Child Development, Racial/Ethnic Identity, Self-Esteem, Black Identity

Age Range.
Adult

Author: James P. Comer

Author: Alvin F. Poussaint

James P. Comer, M.D., a Professor of Psychiatry at the Yale Child Study Center, is a regular columnist for *Parent's* magazine.

ISBN# 452268397 *Date Published.* *Price.* $ 14.95
Publisher. Penguin *Pages.* 435

RAISING THE RAINBOW GENERATION

Teaching your children to Be successful.

Essential reading for parents whose children will be targets of racism, and important for everyone involved in the lives of children growing up in a culturally-diverse America. Filled with concrete, age-appropriate examples, *Raising the Rainbow Generation* shows how to combat bias and negative attitudes. Currently out of print but if you would like, we will attempt to find a copy for you. Please inquire.

Keywords
Race Relations, Racial/Ethnic Identity, Racism, Self-Esteem, Parenting

Age Range.
Adult

Author: Darlene Hopson, Ph.D.

Author: Derek S. Hopson, Ph.D.

Darlene and Derek S. Hopson are the authors of *Raising the Rainbow Generation, Juba This and Juba That,* and *Different and Wonderful.*

ISBN# 0-671-79806-5 *Date Published.* 1993 *Price.* $ 10.00
Publisher. Simon & Schuster *Pages.* 205

REACHING UP FOR MANHOOD

Transforming the lives of boys in America.

Kirkus Reviews: "Raised in the South Bronx, Canada is now president of the Rheedlen Centers for organizations employing and guiding urban kids. But in this slender volume of home truths, he seems to squander the opportunity to really enlighten readers with his specific experience, opting instead for therapeutic homilies on often familiar themes."

Keywords
Black Identity, Boy Focus, Core Issues (Feelings), Cultural History, Parenting, Fathers

Age Range.
Adult

Author: Geoffrey Canada

ISBN# 807023167 *Date Published.* 1997 *Price.* $ 10.00
Publisher. Beacon *Pages.* 176

Rating

RESTORING HOPE

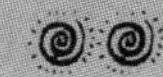

A new book of essays from the author of Race Matters.

In this book, Harvard professor Cornel West issues a wake-up call for ideas for inspiring and reinvigorating Black America. Actor-singer Harry Belafonte talks about his influences; politician Bill Bradley urges each of us to confront race in our daily lives; and trumpeter and composer Wynton Marsalis discusses both music and the need to rebuild Black communities. But Kirkus Reviews writes, "Disappointing. The problem, as is usually the case with conversations, is that the quality of thought varies greatly. There are moving moments but too often the things said are unsurprising and without much impact. A mixed bag, best for West's typically salty and precise comments throughout."

Keywords
African American, Cultural History, Race Relations, Black Identity, Self-Esteem
Age Range:
Adult
Author: Cornel West, Ph.D.

Cornel West, author of *Race Matters*, is Professor of Afro-American Studies and of the Philosophy of Religion at Harvard University.

ISBN# 807009423 Date Published: 1997 Price: $ 14.00
Publisher: Beacon Pages: 256

Rating

RESTORING THE VILLAGE

Coping strategies to build strong families.

Discusses the four stages of a relationship and asks why African American females lead the world in teen pregnancy and why more fathers do not remain in the home with their children.

Keywords
African American, Social Welfare, Family Life, Black Identity
Age Range:
Adult
Author: Jawanza Kunjufu

Jawanza Kunjufu is the author of many books about African American education including *Developing Positive Self-Images* and *Discipline in Black Children.*

ISBN# 913543470 Date Published: 1997 Price: $ 19.95
Publisher: African American Pages:

SHADES OF BLACK

Diversity in African American identity. Exploring the relationship between group identity and self-esteem.

Though dry, this scholarly book is worth the effort. While reexamining earlier studies of Black identity, Cross also presents results indicating that the racial identity of transracially-adopted children may be more Black-oriented that that of their peers being raised in Black homes. "Presents the results of close reading of the original data from the literature on Black identity from 1939-67. Almost without exception, the [original] scholars are in error: They drew conclusions about adult identity from research among preschool-aged children and they used measures that assessed racial identity but interpreted their findings as if they had also measured elements of personality such as self-esteem and self-hatred." —The Chronicles of Higher Education.

Keywords
Racial/Ethnic Identity, African American, Transracial Adoption, Self-Esteem, Black Identity
Age Range:
Adult
Author: William E. Cross

William E. Cross, Jr. is a psychologist and Associate Professor in the African Studies and Research Center of Cornell University.

ISBN# 0-87722-949-X Date Published: 1991 Price: $ 19.95
Publisher: Temple University Press Pages: 272

SHINING THREAD OF HOPE, A

A history of Black women in America.

A Shining Thread of Hope moves Black women from the fringes of history, comprehensively examining their impact on American life from colonial America to the years of antebellum slavery to the arts renaissance of the 1970s and '80s. More than a story of struggle, Black women's history is a story of hope. This book details the strength and courage of Black women as individuals and as a collective force for positive change. An important book for all American families. "Meticulously researched and told with lucid intelligence and power." —Ann Douglas, Columbia Univ.

Keywords
African American, US History, Role Models, Black Identity, Biography, Cultural History
Age Range:
Adult
Author: Darlene Clark Hine
Kathleen Thompson

Darlene Clark Hine is an expert of the intersection of race, class and gender in America. Kathleen Thompson is editor of the *Encyclopedia of Black Women.*

ISBN# 076790110X Date Published: 1998 Price: $ 14.96
Publisher: Broadway Books Pages: 355

Rating

SHOWING MY COLOR

Impolitic essays on race and identity.

Reflecting on changes in the racial landscape since the 1960s and drawing on a depth of personal experiences, a Pulitzer Prize-winning Chicago Tribune columnist reconnects the abstract political debates about Black conservatives, affirmative action, and the "race card" to the people for whom these words mean more than votes. "*Showing My Color* is an important statement on the most pressing social problem confronting Americans today. Page bridges the color line with solid arguments and compassion." —Manning Marable, author of *Beyond Black and White.*

Keywords

Racial/Ethnic Identity, Race Relations, Social Welfare, US History, Cultural History

Age Range.

Adult

Author: Clarence Page

ISBN# 60928018 Date Published. 1996 Price. $ 14.00
Publisher. HarperCollins Pages. 306

Rating

SPEAK MY NAME

An anthology of essays by notable Black American men about mass images of Black men.

Giving voice to Americans who are usually silenced, marginalized, emasculated or vilified by American pop culture, legal inequities and institutionalized racism, this important anthology offers 27 essays by Black American men writing on the construction of Black maleness in America and on their experiences as Black men in America. Arranged in five sections, these powerful essays, including works written expressly for this anthology by Amiri Baraka, John Edgar Wideman, and Henry Louis Gates, Jr., offer "a series of extended solos that develop toward visions of [Black] masculinity as a struggle for hope," says the editor. Especially important reading for those who are on the outside looking in at Black maleness.

Keywords

African American, Civil Rights, Cultural History, Racial/Ethnic Identity, Race Relations, Black Identity

Age Range.

Adult

Editor: Don Belton

Don Belton, author of *Almost Midnight*, teaches at Macalester College and is a former reporter at *Newsweek*.

ISBN# 0-8070-0937-7 Date Published. 1995 Price. $ 16.00
Publisher. Beacon Press Pages. 272

SUGAR IN THE RAW

First-person stories about growing up African American and female in the US today.

A transracially-adopted author presents interviews with young women about race. Subjects represent a range of experiences: biracial identity; Gay and Lesbian lives; transracially-adopted, and more. Interesting reading for everyone concerned with African American identity. Books in Print writes, "Rebecca Carroll profiles 15 girls, ages 11-20. They speak eloquently for the generation of young women coming of age in a complex world. Carroll writes in her introduction, 'many Black girls don't know that individual accountability is not a myth or a crime: it is what makes it possible for us to live together on the planet as human beings.' Her work is enabling and enlightening."

Keywords

African American, Self-Esteem, Black Identity, Transracial Adoption, Gay and/or Lesbian, Biracial

Age Range.

Adult

Author: Rebecca Carroll

Author: Ntozake Shange

ISBN# 0-517-88497-6 Date Published. 1997 Price. $ 12.00
Publisher. Random House Pages.

TESTIMONY

Young African Americans on self-discovery and Black identity.

Young experts recount their ideas and experiences on family and friends, love, education, art, Black identity, and revolution.

Keywords

Race Relations, Racial/Ethnic Identity, Racism, Self-Esteem, African American, Black Identity

Age Range.

Adult

Author: Natasha Tarpley

Natasha Tarpley is the author of *I Love My Hair* and *Testimony*.

ISBN# 0-8070-0929-6 Date Published. 1995 Price. $ 16.00
Publisher. Beacon Press Pages. 272

Rating

THIRTEEN WAYS OF LOOKING AT A BLACK MAN

What does it mean to be Black and male in 20th century America?

The idea of the unitary "Black man" is as illusory as the creature conjured up by Wallace Stevens in his poem, "Thirteen Ways of Looking at a Blackbird," says Henry Louis Gates, Jr. With these eight essays, most of which originally appeared in *The New Yorker*, he takes a close look at some of the most extraordinary figures of our time.

Keywords

Black Identity, Race Relations, Racial/Ethnic Identity, Role Models, Biography, Cultural History

Age Range:

Adult

Author: Henry Louis Gates, Jr., Ph.D.

Henry Louis Gates, Jr. is the chair of Harvard's African American studies department. Gates is the author of *Thirteen Ways of Looking At A Black Man, The Future of the Race* and more.

ISBN# 679776664 Date Published: 1998 Price: $ 12.00
Publisher: Vintage Pages: 256

Rating

UNBANK THE FIRE

How should early-childhood education be adjusted to meet the learning styles of African American youngsters?

Janice Hale-Benson, the author of *Black Children,* believes that simple adjustments in educational approaches will create a better fit to the needs of African American children. In this book, she analyzes the historical context of upward mobility, discusses the cultural milieu that provides the framework for African American values and behavior, and describes an early-childhood education program.

Keywords

African American, Educational Issues, Black Identity, Child Development, Cultural History

Age Range:

Adult

Author: Janice Hale

ISBN# 801848229 Date Published: 1994 Price: $ 14.95
Publisher: Johns Hopkins University Press Pages: 235

WHAT THE BLUES IS ALL ABOUT

Black women overcoming stress and depression.

A highly accessible self-help book filled with personal stories, useful for parents of African American girls. Focussing on the common elements of depression for Black women, *What The Blues Is All About* offers strategies for prevention and treatment. Content includes: How stereotypes contribute to depression; race and stress; self-esteem and relationships; family secrets and shame and more.

Keywords

Health, African American, Girl Power, Self-Esteem, Depression

Age Range:

Adult

Author: Angela Mitchell

Author: Kennise Herring

ISBN# 399523766 Date Published: 1998 Price: $ 12.95
Publisher: Penguin Pages: 238

YO, LITTLE BROTHER

Basic rules of survival for young African American males.

Why are there more African American males in prison than in college? Why does an African American male have a greater life expectancy in Africa than America? This book answers these questions, offering readers advice about how to keep the African American male alive, sane, prospering, and developing his full potential.

Keywords

African American, Core Issues (Feelings), Black Identity, Racism, Self-Esteem

Age Range:

Adult

Author: Anthony C. Davis

Author: Jeffrey W. Jackson

ISBN# 913543586 Date Published: 1998 Price: $ 14.95
Publisher: African American Pages: 120

Rating

ABOUT FACE

An examination of race in fashion and theater and its effect on popular culture.

A provocatively genre-bending text, *About Face* considers how representations in fashion and theater industries affect popular culture. From the runways of Paris to the Broadway stage, from a Commes des Garçons fashion show to Miss Saigon, from glossy magazine layouts to local college protests, *About Face* examines performances of "race," specifically the ways that representations of Asia reverberate in Asian and Asian American lives. Kondo examines the use of race, gender, nationality and sexuality stereotypes in this insightful book that brings together essays, vignettes, and interviews with playwright David Henry Hwang and designer Rei Kawakubo.

Keywords

Asian American, Race Relations, Racial/Ethnic Identity

Age Range:
Adult

Author: Dorinne Kondo

Dorinne Kondo, an anthropologist and feminist scholar, is the author of *Crafting Selves: Power, Gender, and Discourses of Identity in a Japanese Workplace.*

ISBN# 415911419 *Date Published:* 1997 *Price:* $ 18.99
Publisher: Routledge *Pages:* 224

Rating

ASIAN AMERICAN WOMEN WRITERS

Whether born in America or transplanted, these Asian American women have much to tell us.

These writings of Asian American women reflect the complexities of their authors' cultures, the stories set in places as disparate as Japanese internment camps in Arizona, flamboyant Manila under Marcos, and the Chinatowns of California. These writings reflect the ambiguities of their authors' identities and the tensions of a female consciousness caught between cultures. The variety of voices in these stories — from Wong's polite autobiographical "she" to Yamamoto's "double telling" to the "splinters" in Kingston's voice and Hagedorn's polyvocalism — tell of the richness of writing by Asian American women thus far.

Keywords

Asian American, Multiracial, History, Asian

Age Range:
Adult

Editor: Harold Bloom

ISBN# 791044912 *Date Published:* 1997 *Price:* $ 16.95
Publisher: Chelsea House *Pages:*

ASIAN AMERICANS

Personality patterns, identity, and mental health.

"Covers recent research on issues facing Asian Americans with respect to personality, ethnic identity, and mental health. Presents a demographic and historical profile of Asian American populations, and discusses cultural values, racism, general family characteristics, and differences in personality between Asian- and Euro-Americans. Examines sources of stress due to factors such as minority status, cultural conflicts, and reviews studies on rates and common manifestations of mental disorders," said Book News. Midwest Book Review said it "deserves a wider audience than just health professionals."

Keywords

Asian American, Race Relations, Racial/Ethnic Identity, Health, Cultural History

Age Range:
Adult

Author: Laura Uba

ISBN# 898623723 *Date Published:* 1995 *Price:* $ 36.00
Publisher: Guilford *Pages:* 302

CHARLIE CHAN IS DEAD

An inthology of contemporary asian american fiction.

As Hagedorn wrote in her introduction, for too long White America has seen Asian Americans as Charlie Chan. Her anthology shatters myths of the "model minority," featuring selections from some of the most talented Asian American writers today, including Meena Alexander, Hisaye Yamamoto, Peter Bacho, Cynthia Kadohata, Amy Tan, Gish Jen, Maxine Hong Kingston, Bharati Mukherjee, and many others. "A generous and varied sampling here...usually focused on personal life rather than on culture and history," said Kirkus Reviews.

Keywords

Asian American, Family Life, Fiction

Age Range:
Adult

Editor: Jessica Tarahata Hagedorn

ISBN# 140231110 *Date Published:* 1993 *Price:* $ 15.95
Publisher: Penguin *Pages:* 569

Rating

CLAIMING AMERICA

Constructing Chinese American identities during the exclusion era.

A collection of essays that recovers the experiences of individuals who staked their claim to Chinese American identity. The first section of the book focuses on the incoming immigrants. The second section looks at their children, who deeply felt the contradictions between Chinese and American culture but attempted to find a balance between the two.

Keywords

Asian American, Cultural History, US History, Core Issues (Feelings), Chinese American, Racial/Ethnic Identity

Age Range:

Adult

Editor: Kevin Scott Wong

Editor: Sucheng Chan

ISBN# 1566395763 *Date Published:* 1998 *Price:* $ 19.95

Publisher: Temple University Press *Pages:* 256

Rating

EVERYTHING YOU NEED TO KNOW ABOUT ASIAN AMERICAN HISTORY

A question-and-answer approach to Asian American history and culture.

How did the U.S. get involved in Vietnam? Why do Filipinos have Spanish names? What is the origin of the fortune cookie? Most Americans are woefully uninformed about their country's history, and most standard history books provide very little information on the rich history of Asian American peoples. This text helps fill that void, with a lively question-and-answer format that documents the dramatic impact of Chinese, Japanese, Vietnamese, Korean, Indian, and Pacific Island cultures on American society.

Keywords

Asian American, Race Relations, Racial/Ethnic Identity, US History, Cultural History

Age Range:

Adult

Author: Lan Cao

Author: Himilce Novas

ISBN# 452273153 *Date Published:* 1996 *Price:* $ 13.95

Publisher: Plume Books *Pages:* 366

FALLING LEAVES

The memoir of an unwanted Chinese daughter.

Adeline Yen Mah's stepmother was the wicked witch of the East. This is Adeline's memoir of growing up in China and Hong Kong, a chronicle of emotional abuse set in a world where girls were worth little. Resilient and resourceful, Adeline survived. As the Washington Post said, her story is "at once heartbreaking and heartening." Amy Tan, author of *The Joy Luck Club* calls it "riveting. Poignant proof of the human will to endure." *The New York Times Book Review* added "It's hard not to admire her [Mah's] persistence and perseverance." Though families who have adopted daughters from China may be especially interested in Mah's views, this book is a bestseller, winning universal interest.

Keywords

China, Chinese American, Core Issues (Feelings), Adopted Adult, Role Models

Age Range:

Adult

Author: Adeline Yen Mah

ISBN# 767903579 *Date Published:* 1999 *Price:* $ 10.00

Publisher: Broadway Books *Pages:* 278

FILIPINO AMERICANS

Footsteps to America

This book looks at the history, experiences, and contributions of Filipinos who have emigrated to America, including those who have come as a result of turmoil in their homeland. Discusses the reasons for Filipino immigration to the United States and the conditions they have found here, using case studies to describe the lifestyles of Filipino Americans.

Keywords

Filipino American, Multicultural

Age Range:

Adult

Author: Alexandra Bandon

ISBN# 27681432 *Date Published:* 1993 *Price:* $ 22.00

Publisher: Abingdon *Pages:* 112

Rating

FOREVER FOREIGNERS OR HONORARY WHITES

Multigenerational Asian Americans.

Asian Americans repeatedly express a sense of being treated as if nonwhite equals non-American, no matter if they were born here. The stigma of being labeled a foreigner — even if one is American-born — has helped make Asian Americans targets for hate crimes and media-based stereotypes. This book takes a deeper look at these issues.

Keywords

Asian American, Race Relations, Racial/Ethnic Identity, Racism

Age Range.

Adult

Author: Mia Tuan

ISBN# 813526248 *Date Published.* *Price.* $ 18.00

Publisher. Rutgers University Press *Pages.* 192

Rating

GROWING UP AMERICAN

How Vietnamese children adapt to life in the United States.

Contents includes support and control, language and adaptation, experiences in adaptation to American schools, bicultural conflicts and gender role changes, and insiders and outsiders.

Keywords

Asian, Vietnam, Multicultural, Asian American

Age Range.

Adult

Author: Min Zhou

Author: Carl L. Bankston III

ISBN# 871549948 *Date Published.* 1998 *Price.* $ 34.95

Publisher. Russel Sage Foundation *Pages.*

INTERETHNIC COMPANION TO ASIAN AMERICAN LITERATURE, AM

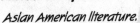

Asian American literature.

This volume provides a survey of literature by North American writers of Asian descent, both by national origins (Chinese, Filipino, Japanese, Korean, South Asian, Vietnamese) and by shared concerns. It was the first of its kind in terms of breadth and depth of coverage.

Keywords

Asian American, Racial/Ethnic Identity

Age Range.

Adult

Editor: King-Kok Cheung

ISBN# 521447909 *Date Published.* 1996 *Price.* $ 22.95

Publisher. Cambridge Univ. Press *Pages.* 414

INTO THE FIRE

Asian American prose.

"This collection of Asian American prose spans the globe in scope and content, gathering the works of Asian prose writers from around the world and examining a range of social and ethnic issues. These are all literary and revealing works which use family stories, Asian American images and ideas, and personal insights to explain and explore uniquely Asian experiences," wrote Midwest Book Review.

Keywords

Asian American, Family Life, Fiction

Age Range.

Adult

Editor: Sylvia Watanabe

Editor: Carol Bruchac

ISBN# *Date Published.* *Price.*

Publisher. *Pages.*

Rating

MAY YOU BE THE MOTHER OF A HUNDRED SONS

Women's lives in India.

Acclaimed journalist Elisabeth Bumiller presents a revealing look at the women of India. From horrific practices such "bride burnings," sterilization camps, and arranged marriages, to vital women struggling to succeed, Bumiller "zeros in on women and ends up illuminating a whole world," as *Newsweek* explained.

Keywords

Cultural History, India, Racial/Ethnic Identity, Self-Esteem, Family Life

Age Range:

Adult

Author: Elisabeth Bumiller

ISBN# 449906140 *Date Published:* 1991 *Price:* $ 12.00

Publisher: Fawcett Bk. Group *Pages:* 307

Rating

ORIENTALS

Asian Americans in Popular Culture

Why did certain images of Asian Americans emerge? Lee identifies six stereotypes and explains how each developed during a period of history when a shift in relationships between classes occurred alongside a cultural crisis. Describing the stereotypes — the pollutant, the coolie, the deviant, the yellow peril, the model minority, and the gook — Lee explains the emergence of each image. An interesting book for anyone trying to understand the development of Asian American identity.

Keywords

Asian American, Race Relations, Racial/Ethnic Identity, Racism

Age Range:

Adult

Author: Robert C. Lee

ISBN# 1566396581 *Date Published:* 1999 *Price:* $ 27.95

Publisher: Temple University Press *Pages:* 256

RACE, RIGHTS, AND THE ASIAN AMERICAN EXPERIENCE

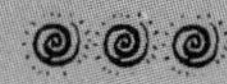

How Asian Americans are affected by civil rights laws.

Ancheta's concern is the law's insensitivity to Asian Americans regarding immigration, affirmative action, and hate crimes. He suggests expanding hate-crime protection to include immigration status and argues that protections for Asian Americans ought not be contingent on protections granted to African Americans. Using examples involving racist landlords, discriminatory employment practices, and anti-Asian racial taunts and stereotypes, he also suggests that Asian Americans have contributed to the eradication of racial segregation by setting important legal precedents in cases concerning the Fourteenth Amendment.

Keywords

Asian American, Race Relations, Racial/Ethnic Identity, Racism, Civil Rights

Age Range:

Adult

Author: Angelo N. Ancheta

Angelo Ancheta is a civil rights attorney.

ISBN# 813524644 *Date Published:* 1998 *Price:* $ 18.00

Publisher: Rutgers University Press *Pages:* 224

SEEDS FROM A SILENT TREE

A collection of poetry, fiction, and personal narratives written exclusively by Korean adopted people.

Explores issues of adoption, identity, race, and sexuality. Born in one culture, raised in another, assigned new names and families, thirty men and women write of their complex experiences.

Keywords

Adoption, Adopted Child, International Adoption, Korean American, Family Life, Racial/Ethnic Identity

Age Range:

Adult

Editor: Tonya Bishoff

Editor: Jo Rankin

ISBN# NA *Date Published:* 1998 *Price:* $ 15.00

Publisher: Pandal Press *Pages:*

Rating

TRAVELERS' GUIDE TO ASIAN CUSTOMS AND MANNERS, THE

How to converse, dress, make friends, and behave while in Asia.

A useful preparatory guide to mores, customs, and manners for anyone traveling in Asia or going to an Asian country to adopt a child.

Keywords

Guidebook, Asian, Manners, Asia

Age Range.

Adult

Author: Nancy L. Braganti

Author: Elizabeth Devine

ISBN# 312816103 Date Published. 1987 Price. $ 13.95
Publisher. St. Martin Pages. 315

Rating

TWO LANDS, ONE HEART

A second-generation story about adoption and racial identity for a Vietnamese American boy.

A Vietnamese American boy's mother, aunt and uncle were adopted and raised by white American families; his dad is a white American. This is the story of reconnecting to the rest of the family in Vietnam and of their return visit and reunion. The only book I know of to address the issues of adoption from the point of view of the grown children of adopted adults.

Keywords

Racial/Ethnic Identity, Adoption, Self-Esteem, International Adoption, Vietnam, Search and Reunion

Age Range.

Adult

Author: Jeremy Schmidt

ISBN# 802783570 Date Published. 1995 Price. $ 15.95
Publisher. Walker & Co. Pages. 44

WILD SWAN: THREE DAUGHTERS OF CHINA

Inspiring stories of three strong Chinese women and the resiliency of the human spirit.

A real page-turner, this nonfiction account is hard to put down; we particularly recommend it for parents of Chinese daughters. Chang's grandmother was a warlord's concubine. Her mother rose to a prominent position in the Communist Party before being denounced during the Cultural Revolution, and Chang herself worked for Mao until doubts crept in regarding his policies. Kirkus Reviews calls it "an exceptional tribute to three generations of courageous and articulate Chinese women.... A valuable historical perspective on the impact of Mao on traditional Chinese culture and character — as well as an unusual window on the female experience in the modern world."

Keywords

China, Asian, Girl Power, Family Life, Cultural History, Core Issues (Feelings)

Age Range.

Adult

Author: Jung Chang

ISBN# 385425473 Date Published. 1992 Price. $ 15.95
Publisher. Anchor World Views Pages. 524

WOMAN WARRIOR, THE: MEMOIRS OF A GIRLHOOD AMONG GHOSTS

Growing up Chinese American in Stockton, CA.

Kingston's account of the conflict between the two worlds she grew up in (the China of her mother's talk stories and her own life running a laundromat in a small California town) may be an excellent source for non-Chinese people who want to understand how some Chinese people view them, providing a peek — both informative and unsettling — through the barrier of race. Adoptive parents of Chinese children will be afforded a mirror to help them see themselves as they are viewed by many members of their child's cultural community.

Keywords

Chinese American, Family Life, Race Relations, Racial/Ethnic Identity

Age Range.

Adult

Author: Maxine Hong Kingston

ISBN# 679721886 Date Published. 1989 Price. $ 11.00
Publisher. Vintage Pages. 209

Rating

AMERICANOS

Appreciate the diversity within the Latino community.... This book shows it.

"The book captures the beauty of the culture that is never seen, not even by ourselves," Olmos writes, asserting, "The face of America should include us." This spirited bilingual book depicts a broad range of Latino life in the United States. "Latinos come in all colors, races, and creeds. This book is about understanding that we're all different — that's what makes us all the same. We're like thumbprints." Photographs compiled from the amazing work of 32 Latino photographers and 18 writers captures the beauty and grace of Latinos in the United States, making Americanos as colorful as the culture itself.

Keywords

Latino/a, Bilingual

Age Range:

Adult

Editor: Edward James Olmos

Edward James Olmos is a movie and TV actor known for his activism on behalf of Latinos.

ISBN# 316649090 *Date Published:* 1999 *Price:* $ 25.00

Publisher: Little Brown *Pages:* 160

Rating

CHOLOS & SURFERS

A Latino family album.

In this powerful collection that transcends race, Jack Lopez has crafted a series of essays that speak as much to the human condition as to the Latino condition. For Lopez, as one critic has pointed out, surfing is a powerful metaphor for staying alive and being true to yourself in a society in which identities are so easily washed away.

Keywords

Latino/a, Racial/Ethnic Identity, Family Life, Cultural History

Age Range:

Adult

Author: Jack Lopez

ISBN# 884964299 *Date Published:* 1998 *Price:* $ 15.95

Publisher: Capra Press *Pages:* 270

CURRENTS FROM THE DANCING RIVER

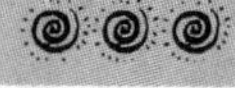

Contemporary Latino Fiction, Nonfiction, and Poetry.

Currents from the Dancing River brings together 135 works of accomplished contemporary writers along with some talented newcomers. Its variety of style and content offers the most realistic possible portrait of what "Latino" might mean. Includes work from Orlando Ramirez, Omar S. Castanaeda, Virgil Suarez, Enriqué Fernandez, Gary Soto, and many others. Booklist calls it a "profound collection...deeply satisfying."

Keywords

Poetry, Fiction, Latino/a

Age Range:

Adult

Editor: Ray Gonzalez

ISBN# 156001306 *Date Published:* 1994 *Price:* $ 15.95

Publisher: Harvest Books *Pages:*

EL CORO

A chorus of Latino and Latina poets.

A rich collection of poetry that celebrates the experiences of contemporary Latinos and Latinas. Among the poets represented are former farm workers and gang members, a practicing physician, a former tenant lawyer, a professional chef, a Vietnam veteran, professional writers, and more. Named by the Gustavus Myers Center as one of the Outstanding Books for Human Rights published in 1997.

Keywords

Poetry, Latino/a, Bilingual

Age Range:

Adult

Editor: Martin Espada

ISBN# 1558491112 *Date Published:* 1997 *Price:* $ 13.95

Publisher: University of Massachusetts Press *Pages:* 128

Rating

EMPRESS OF THE SPLENDID SEASON

The love life of a cleaning lady.

Oscar Hijuelos's novel chronicles the decline and fall of the dreams of Lydia España, a beautiful Cuban émigré. When her husband, who treated her as an empress, has a heart attack, she has to confront the gap between her sense of self-importance and her invisibility in the world. *The NY Times Book Review* says, "This is a tender novel but it isn't the pivotal crises of Lydia's life that make it so. This quality comes from the struggle between her instinct for self-invention and her inability to invent a suitable self." For people touched by adoption, the challenge of self-invention can be transformative and Lydia's story may be particularly engrossing.

Keywords

Latino/a, Core Issues (Feelings), Family Life, Fiction

Age Range,

Adult

Author: Oscar Hijuelos

Oscar Hijuelos won the Pulitzer Prize for his novel *The Mambo Kings Play Songs oj Love.*

ISBN# 60928700 *Date Published,* 1999 *Price,* $ 13.00

Publisher, Harper Flamingo *Pages,* 3442

Rating

ETHNIC IDENTITY

Review of research approaches to study the development oi ethnic identity in Latino children.

Covers acculturation and the development and socialization of Mexican Americans. Describes roles of social and behavioral scientists in government and effects of government policies. One of the few books to address this topic.

Keywords

Race Relations, Latino/a, Self-Esteem, Racial/Ethnic Identity, Mexican American

Age Range,

Adult

Editor: George P. Knight

ISBN# 791413020 *Date Published,* 1993 *Price,* $ 24.95

Publisher, State Univ. of New York Press *Pages,*

FIRE IN OUR SOULS, THE

Quotations of wisdom and inspiration by Latino Americans

From Carlos Fuentes to Gloria Estefan, this book features hundreds of quotations from famous Latin Americans. Words of wisdom, inspiration, and humor from artists, actors, political leaders, musicians, and writers are categorized by themes such as Culture, Identity, Family, Art, Hollywood, and Literature. This collection provides a compelling view of Latino American culture.

Keywords

Latino/a, Cultural History, Role Models

Age Range,

Adult

Editor: Rosie Gonzales

Editor: Edward James Olmos

ISBN# 452276845 *Date Published,* 1996 *Price,* $ 10.95

Publisher, Plume Books *Pages,*

HISPANIC 100, THE

Latino men and women who have most influenced Americar thought and culture.

Booknews, Inc. says this book "celebrates the lives of 100 Americans of Latino or Hispanic ancestry who have made outstanding contributions in fields including science, education, government, labor relations, and entertainment." It includes short biographies of individuals including Cesar Chavez, Joan Baez, Anthony Quinn, and George Santayana.

Keywords

Latino/a, Role Models, Racial/Ethnic Identity, Cultural History, Role Models

Age Range,

Adult

Author: Himilce Novas

Himilce Novas is the coauthor of *Everything You Need To Know About Asian History.*

ISBN# 806516518 *Date Published,* 1995 *Price,* $ 24.95

Publisher, Citadel *Pages,* 495

Rating

HISPANIC NATION

Culture, politics, and the constructing of identity.

"Hispanic Nation explores factors, from media and culture to local and national politics, drawing 'Hispanics' to involve themselves in shaping the meaning, agenda, and place of Hispanics at the political table of those who share this identity. The statistical fiction that lumps 'persons of Spanish-Hispanic origin or descent' into a single category is the basis for a key identity shift: a shift with important consequences for all Americans because, in merging their separate national backgrounds into a new identity, Hispanic Americans are inevitably challenging rigid black-and-white definitions of what it means to be an American." — Booklist

Keywords

Latino/a, Racial/Ethnic Identity, China, Cultural History

Age Range:

Adult

Author: Geoffrey E. Fox

ISBN# 816517991 Date Published: Price: $ 17.95

Publisher: Univ. of Arizona Press Pages: 264

Rating

HOUSE ON MANGO STREET, THE

Esperanza grows up in the barrio and yearns to leave.

"Esperanza's childhood is described in a series of vignettes. Each story centers on a detail of her childhood: a greasy cold rice sandwich, a pregnant friend, a mean boy, how the clouds looked, something she heard a drunk say, her fear of nuns. Esperanza's friends, family, and neighbors wander in and out of her stories; through them all Esperanza sees, learns, loves, and dreams of the house she will someday have — her own house — not on Mango Street," wrote Jesse Larsen in 500 Great Books for Women.

Keywords

Mexican American, Latino/a, Fiction, Friendship

Age Range:

Adult

Author: Sandra Cisneros

Sandra Cisneros is the award winning Mexican American author of *The House on Mango Street* and *Hair Pelitos.*

ISBN# 679734775 Date Published: 1991 Price: $ 9.95

Publisher: Vintage Pages: 110

LATINO CULTURAL CITIZENSHIP

Claiming identity, space, and rights.

Based on ethnographic work in Latino centers in San Antonio, Los Angeles, New York, San Jose, and Watsonville, California, this study looks at the process of Latino "cultural citizenship." Chapters detail acts of cultural affirmation in various community activities and concerns, illuminating the ways in which these communities use cultural expression to gain political rights while maintaining a vibrant local identity. Understanding how cultural identity is defined is of particular importance for adoptive parents of Latino children.

Keywords

Latino/a, Racial/Ethnic Identity, Race Relations, Cultural History, Transracial Adoption

Age Range:

Adult

Editor: William V. Flores

Editor: Rina Benmayor

ISBN# 807046353 Date Published: Price: $ 15.00

Publisher: Ballentine Pages: 322

LATINO STUDIES READER

Culture, economy, and society.

Growing faster than any other ethnic group, Latinos are predicted to become the largest ethnic-minority group by the year 2009. Conventional theories of 'race' and 'race relations,' with its exclusive Black/White focus, present serious theoretical problems as applied to Latinos. Instead, Darder and Torres use class analyses employing social, scientific and theoretical concepts to explore issues addressed by Latinos in America.

Keywords

Latino/a, Race Relations, Racial/Ethnic Identity

Age Range:

Adult

Editor: Antonio Darder

Editor: Rodolfo D. Torres

ISBN# 1557869871 Date Published: 1998 Price: $ 29.95

Publisher: Blackwell Pages: 448

PAPER DANCE

Rating

55 Latino poets.

Booklist says, "This vibrant anthology of the work of Latino/a poets living in the U.S. is a celebration of social, cultural, and private interfaces. Their poems examine the complex and ever-evolving relationships between tradition and change, Spanish and English, rural and urban, private and public, female and male, young and old, past and present, native and immigrant, dream and reality, love and despair, joy and anger, art and life. A poetry collection would usually be described as a chorus of voices, but the editors were right to choose dance for their title. These poems do dance in a dazzling array of tempos and moods."

Keywords

Poetry, Latino/a, Racial/Ethnic Identity

Age Range.

Adult

Editor: Victor Hernandez Cruz

Editor: Leroy Quintana

Editor: Virgil Suarez

ISBN# 892552018 Date Published. 1994 Price. $ 14.00
Publisher. Persea Books Pages. 242

QUINCEAÑERA!

Rating

The essential guide to planning the perfect sweet fifteen celebration.

One of the most beautiful and significant rituals in the Latino community, the quinceañera is a special birthday party, an all-day cultural event that begins a Latina's passage into womanhood at age 15. This comprehensive guide is designed to help with all the details of this important day, from making spiritual and religious preparations to choosing the court of honor to selecting appropriate clothing, food, and music, including what music to play for waltzing with Papi. Historical anecdotes and cultural traditions drawn from Mexican, Cuban, Puerto Rican, and Central and South American customs are included.

Keywords

Latino/a, Festivals, Family Life, Girl Power, Cultural History, Central America

Age Range.

Adult

Author: Michele Salcedo

ISBN# 805044655 Date Published. 1997 Price. $ 25.00
Publisher. Henry Holt Pages. 208

RAISING NUESTROS NIÑOS

Bringing up Latino children in a bicultural world.

Rodriguez shares her experiences of raising Latino children from infancy through preadolescence. She encourages parents to strengthen the foundations of family, marriage, and the community.

Keywords

Latino/a, Child Development, Adoptive Parent, Family Life, Race Relations, Racial/Ethnic Identity

Age Range.

Adult

Author: Gloria Rodriguez

Gloria Rodriguez is the founder of Avarice, a family education and support program based in San Antonio, Texas.

ISBN# 684839695 Date Published. 1999 Price. $ 13.00
Publisher. Fireside Pages. 400

THIRTY MILLION STRONG

Reclaiming the Hispanic image in American culture.

In this controversial and lively book, Nicolás Kanellos chronicles and analyzes the changing images of Hispanics in the United States from the age of exploration and conquest to the present, reclaiming the Hispanic role in American history and culture. Part history, part manifesto, this book challenges our notions of the Hispanic peoples, giving us a perspective into the great contributions this group has made to American society.

Keywords

Latino/a, US History, Cultural History

Age Range.

Adult

Author: Nicholas Kanellos

ISBN# 1555912656 Date Published. 1998 Price. $ 19.95
Publisher. Fulcrum Pub. Pages. 176

Rating

AMERICAN MIXED RACE

The culture of microdiversity.

This collection of articles on the subject of microracial life was written primarily for an academic audience rather than for the general public. This is dense reading but worth the effort for anyone with a strong commitment to this topic.

Keywords

Multiracial, Race Relations, Racial/Ethnic Identity

Age Range:

Adult

Author: Naomi Zack

ISBN# 847680134 *Date Published:* 1995 *Price:* $ 31.95

Publisher: Rowman & Littlefield *Pages:* 379

Rating

AS WE ARE NOW

New writers offer original treatments of an important subject.

A "mixblood," according to editor W.S. Penn, recognizes that his or her identity comes from the tension and interplay of all his or her ancestral relationships. These first-person narratives cross racial, national, and disciplinary boundaries in a refreshingly experimental approach to writing culture. Their authors call on varied cultural and aesthetic traditions — mostly oral — to address some aspect of race and identity about which they feel passionate. Mixblood Native American, Mestizo/a, and African American writers focus their discussion on the questions their people ask and the way in which they ask them, clearly merging the singular "I" with the communal "we."

Keywords

Native American, Multiracial Identity, Black Identity, Racial/ Ethnic Identity, Race Relations

Age Range:

Adult

Editor: William S. Penn

W. S. Penn, Professor of English at Michigan State University, is the author of *The Telling of the World* (1996), *All My Sins Are Relatives* (1995), and *The Absence of Angels* (1994).

ISBN# 520210735 *Date Published:* 1998 *Price:* $ 16.95

Publisher: Univ. of CA *Pages:* 282

BEST OF PACT PRESS: BIRACIAL IDENTITY

Dual heritage, dual loyalties.

Forty-eight-page collections of the best articles published in Pact Press concerning biracial identity.

Keywords

Adopted Child, Racial/Ethnic Identity, Multiracial, Multiracial Identity

Age Range:

Adult

Editor: Beth Hall

Author: Gail Steinberg

Gail Steinberg and Beth Hall are Co-Directors and founder of Pact, An Adoption Alliance and each is also the parent of children adopted transracially.

ISBN# NA *Date Published:* 1998 *Price:* $ 10.00

Publisher: Pact *Pages:* 48

BETWEEN CULTURES

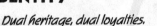

Developing identity in a world of diversity: Crossing cultural borders.

Exercises and examples illustrating the experiences of people who routinely cross cultural borders. Discusses culture, ethnicity and race; bilingualism; and archetypes and metaphors that can help develop identity.

Keywords

Diversity, Race Relations, Racial/Ethnic Identity, Transracial Adoption, International Adoption

Age Range:

Adult

Author: Charles Schaefer

Author: Jacqueline Howell Wasilewski

Charles Schaefer is a child psychologist.

ISBN# 844233056 *Date Published:* 1996 *Price:* $ 21.95

Publisher: Ntc Business Books *Pages:*

BLACK, WHITE, OTHER

Rating

Biracial Americans talk about race and identity.

This book, the first to explore the lives of adults with Black-white heritage and to present their unique view on race in America, presents a series of interviews with biracial adults.

Keywords

Multiracial Identity, Racial/Ethnic Identity, White Identity

Age Range.

Adult

Author: Lise Funderburg

ISBN# 0-688-11824-0 Date Published. Price. $ 15.00

Publisher. Morrow & Co. Pages.

CAUCASIA

Rating

Exploring the internal cultural tug of war of a multiracial family.

The New York Times Book Review says that "Senna superbly illustrates the emotional toll that politics and race take on one especially gutsy young girl's development as she makes her way through the parallel limbos between black and white and between girl and young woman." *The Boston Globe* calls it "a stunning debut. When their family breaks up, Birdie's father and sister move to Brazil to find racial equality, while Birdie and her mother take on new identities and move to a small New Hampshire town. Birdie tries to fit in but she wants both her white and black heritage to count. Her search for her sister leads to a search for her own identity."

Keywords

African American, Fiction, Multiracial, Race Relations, Racial/Ethnic Identity, Judaism

Age Range.

Adult

Author: Darcy Senna

Caucasia is Darcy Senna's first novel.

ISBN# 1573220914 Date Published. 1998 Price. $ 12.95

Publisher. Putnam-Paperstar Pages. 353

CROSSING THE COLOR LINE

Insights of a white mother of Black children exploring race, parenting, and culture.

A collection of essays by the Caucasian mother of a biracial child. She describes his encounters with racism, his identity both as African American and biracial, and her experience as an outsider to racial difference. "A combination of literary analysis, autobiography, and ethnography housed in a Black feminist framework.... Reddy's greatest insights come from her experiences within an interracial family, and these serve to reinforce her indictment of the ways schools teach and perpetuate racism.... Refreshing," says Contemporary Sociology.

Keywords

Transracial Adoption, Parenting, Multiracial Identity, Race Relations, Racial/Ethnic Identity, White Identity

Age Range.

Adult

Editor: Maureen T. Reddy

Maureen T. Reddy is author of *Mother Journeys: Feminists Write About Mothering* and *Sisters In Crime: Feminists and the Crime Novel.*

ISBN# 813523745 Date Published. 1997 Price. $ 16.95

Publisher. Rutgers University Press Pages. 193

HALF AND HALF

Writers of multicultural heritages provide firsthand accounts on growing up biracial and bicultural.

This work presents personal essays from seventeen writers, including Julia Alvarez, Indira Ganesan, James McBride, David Mura and Lori Tsang, on the experience of being biracial and bicultural in the United States today. Through its range of distinctive voices, this anthology reveals the constancy of the human concern to find the place that feels right, and the challenge of addressing and incorporating dual ethnic identities in the context of America's social and racial climate. This outstanding work offers food for thought for all readers, but in particular for those interested in transracial families or multiethnic identity.

Keywords

Family Life, Multiracial Identity, Transracial Adoption, Racial/Ethnic Identity, Core Issues (Feelings)

Age Range.

Adult

Editor: Claudine C. O'Hearn

ISBN# 375700110 Date Published. 1998 Price. $ 12.00

Publisher. Pantheon Pages. 224

Rating

HOW DID YOU GET TO BE MEXICAN?

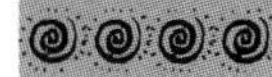

A White/Brown man's search for identity.

This is the first book to focus on the experiences of being mixed race Anglo/Latino in America. Johnson's mother denied her Mexican ancestry and claimed to be Spanish. Johnson's candid view of his own life on the color line and his development of racial identity addresses issues of assimilation for minority groups, anti-immigration policies, and being of mixed race in a time of identity politics. Though dry, the book's issues ring true; this is an important read for anyone interested in identity issues.

Keywords
Mexican American, Race Relations, Racial/Ethnic Identity, Biracial
Age Range:
Adult
Author: Kevin Johnson

ISBN# 1566396506 *Date Published:* 1999 *Price:* $ 27.95
Publisher: Temple University Press *Pages:* 256

Rating

MISCEGENATION BLUES

Voices of multiracial women.

A collection of writings by over 40 multiethnic women from a broad range of cultures. The writing skills and style vary, but this collection is interesting for anyone thinking about the complex issues of multiracial identity. Its immediacy springs from the thoughts conveyed by the real experts in this field — women who are themselves living the experience. Themes explored in depth include the development of racial identity, loyalty, and belonging. The moving and poignant essays are grouped within several chapters: Location, identity, paradox; But you don't look like a...; Objectification and exoticization; Betrayals, hard truths; and Return to Self and Culture.

Keywords
Biracial, Transracial Adoption, Multiracial Identity, Multicultural, Core Issues (Feelings), Black Identity
Age Range:
Adult
Editor: Carol Camper

ISBN# 092081395X *Date Published:* 1994 *Price:* $ 16.95
Publisher: Sister Vision *Pages:*

MIXED MATCHES

How to create successful interracial, interethnic, and interfaith relationships. Informative and practical.

Psychotherapist Joel Crohn has written this book to assist cross-cultural couples in negotiating their differences. Many multiracial adoptive families will find very useful some of the material and practical advice on how families can confront prejudice and stereotypes, deal with extended family members, create a family identity, and help children achieve a sense of identity in a multiracial family.

Keywords
Multiracial, Transracial Adoption, Parenting, International Adoption, Multicultural, Family Life
Age Range:
Adult
Author: Joel Crohn

ISBN# 0-449-90961-1 *Date Published:* 1995 *Price:* $ 12.00
Publisher: Fawcett Columbine *Pages:* 327

MULTI-AMERICA

Essays on cultural wars and cultural peace.

Speaking out on a broad variety of issues — including assimilation, racial conflicts between minorities, the gay rights movement, and stereotyping — this collection of essays by non-Anglo writers takes readers far beyond the issues of Black vs. white, introducing the authentic voices of Rainbow America in all their diverse, angry, proud, celebratory glory.

Keywords
Social Welfare, Latino/a, Gay and/or Lesbian, Race Relations, Multiracial, Racial/Ethnic Identity
Age Range:
Adult
Editor: Ishmael Reed

ISBN# 014025912- *Date Published:* 1998 *Price:* $ 14.95
Publisher: Penguin *Pages:* 496

MULTICULTURAL VOICES IN CONTEMPORARY LITERATURE

Rating 

The lives and works of 39 authors and illustrators from 2c different cultures.

Includes an assessment plan for multicultural programs, a calendar of multicultural events, and a chapter on evaluating children's books for bias. Includes Latino, Native American, African American, Asian, Jewish and white authors.

Keywords
Educational Issues, Antiracist Strategies, Multicultural, Multiracial, Diversity

Age Range.
Adult

Author: Frances Ann Day

ISBN# 435088262 Date Published. Price. $26.00
Publisher. Heineman Pages. 244

MULTIRACIAL EXPERIENCE, THE

Rating 

Essays on multiracial identity from some of the clearest thinkers of our times.

A rare collection of 24 stimulating essays on multiracial issues. Booknews writes, "For the first time in US history...the number of biracial babies is increasing at a faster rate than the number of single-race babies. Practical ideas for incorporating multiracial thinking into human rights, identity, blending and flexibility, gender, education, and the future." Includes "Transracial Adoptions: In Whose Best Interest?" by Ruth G. McRoy; "LatiNegra: Mental Health Issues of African Latinas," by Lilian Comas-Diaz; "Race as Process," by Teresa Kay Williams; "Without a Template: The Biracial Korean/White Experience," by Brian Chol Soo Standen; "Multicultural Education," by Francis Wardle and more.

Keywords
Multiracial, Race Relations, Racial/Ethnic Identity, Racism, Transracial Adoption, Multicultural

Age Range.
Adult

Author: Maria Root

ISBN# 803970595 Date Published. 1996 Price. $32.00
Publisher. Sage Pages.

NEW COLORED PEOPLE, THE

The mixed-race movement in America.

In recent years, dramatic increases in racial intermarriage have given birth to a generation of mixed-race children. Some have lobbied to add the category "multiracial" to official racial classifications, including the United States census. Since a nonracial society is one of the stated goals of the multiracialists, Spencer suggests that the undoing of racial classification will come not by initiating a new classification — which will only give Americans the impression that mixed-race people can be neatly classified — but by our increased recognition that there are millions of people who simply defy simple classification. *The New York Times Book Review* called it a "thought-provoking, if not always persuasive, book."

Keywords
African American, Antiracist Strategies, Multiracial Identity

Age Range.
Adult

Author: Hadley Irwin

Hadley Irwin is the pen name of Lee Hadley and Annabelle Irwin who teach English at Iowa State University.

ISBN# 814780717 Date Published. 1997 Price. $25.95
Publisher. New York University Press Pages. 216

RACE AND MIXED RACE

A challenge to all racial classifications.

This book argues that Black and White designations are themselves racist. Tracing the history of racial designations in the United States, Naomi Zack uses philosophical methods of inquiry to criticize the logic of American racial categories. She discusses why racial identity is a matter of importance; examines the treatment of mixed race in law, society, and literature; and addresses philosophical questions.

Keywords
Race Relations, Racial/Ethnic Identity, Social Welfare, Multiracial

Age Range.
Adult

Author: Naomi Zack

ISBN# 1566392659 Date Published. 1995 Price. $22.95
Publisher. Temple University Press Pages.

Rating

10 LITTLE WHITEPEOPLE

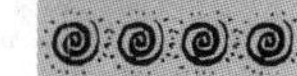

Hilarious approach to a serious subject. Demonstrates what's wrong with many "multicultural" children's books.

Bookmark says that "teachers looking for picture books that cut across the curriculum will find this a good way to combine a unit on white people with counting." The Five Porcupines says, "Hurray! At long last, primary school educators and lovers of children's literature have an accurate Caucasian American book written for primary children." And *The San Francisco Chronicle* asks, "Who would have thought there could be a new twist in counting books? [A] book guaranteed to pique interest."

Keywords

Adopted Adult, Native American, Multicultural, Multiracial, Race Relations, Racism

Age Range:

Adult

Author: Beverly Slapin

Illustrator: Annie Esposito

Beverly Slapin is a director of Oyate Books.

ISBN# Date Published: Price: $ 5.00

Publisher: Oyate Pages:

Rating

AFRICANS AND NATIVE AMERICANS

A history of interrelationships between Native Americans and African Americans in the United States.

What are Loros, Pardos, Mestizos, Mulattos, Half-Breeds, and Zambos? An exploration of the link between Native Americans and African Americans and the responses of the Anglo population over time.

Keywords

African American, Native American, Multiracial, Multiracial Identity, US History, Black Identity

Age Range:

Adult

Author: Jack E. Forbes

ISBN# 025206321X Date Published: 1993 Price: $ 15.95

Publisher: University of Illinois Pages: 344

AMERICAN INDIAN MYTHS AND LEGENDS

160 tales from 80 tribal groups to offer a panorama of Native American myths.

This book combines unpublished tales related by living storytellers with the best of folklore sources, creating a collection of myths and legends representing native American tribes across the country. This collection of tales preserved through oral history — either from the mouths of storytellers or from documents which first recorded their words — presents a comprehensive overview of Native spiritual philosophy. Though each chapter opens with an overview provided by Erdoes and Ortiz, the stories themselves are untrammeled by editorial revision.

Keywords

Native American, Spiritual Meanings, Folk tales and Legends, Cultural History

Age Range:

Adult

Editor: Richard Erdoes

Editor: Alfonso Ortiz

ISBN# 394740181 Date Published: 1985 Price: $ 18.00

Publisher: Pantheon Pages:

GARDENS IN THE DUNES : A NOVEL

"Unquestionably the best fiction yet from Silko," says Kirkus Review.

Gardens in the Dunes begins at a hidden garden on the California-Arizona border. But Silko covers ground that moves between two opposed worlds — the timeless, "traditional" world of Native American peoples and the elaborate, stylized world of White upper-class culture. Indigo is an Indian girl orphaned by an act of White brutality and adopted by a proper Victorian family. Her fascination with the world of privilege never eclipses her faith in the culture of her own people or her desire to return home to what remains of her tribe and her family. A major novel by perhaps the best-known of Native American writers today.

Keywords

Adoption, Native American, Family Life, History, Fiction

Age Range:

Adult

Author: Leslie Marmon Silko

Leslie Marmon Silko is the author of *Almanac of the Dead; The Man Made of Words; Garden In The Dunes;* and *Yellow Woman.*

ISBN# 684863324 Date Published: 1999 Price: $ 14.00

Publisher: Touchstone Pages: 304

Rating

HOW TO TELL THE DIFFERENCE

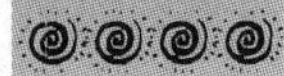

A guide to evaluating children's books for anti-Indian bias.

This important guide provides assessment questions to ask about children's books about children of color. Though focused for Native Americans, the questions are adaptable to books for children of any race: Is this book truthful? respectful? Would anything embarrass or hurt a child? Would anything foster stereotypic thinking? Is attention paid to accurate design and color and is the language respectful? Do people look all alike or just like whites with brown faces? Do characters use language skillfully? Are they portrayed as successful by their own standards? Is the history distorted?

Keywords

Native American, Educational Issues, Antiracist Strategies, Race Relations

Age Range:

Adult

Author: Beverly Slapin

Beverly Slapin is a director of Oyate Books.

ISBN# 963517550 Date Published: 1995 Price: $ 8.95

Publisher: Oyate Pages: 36

Rating

LIES MY TEACHER TOLD ME

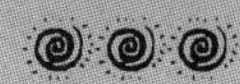

A critique of the blind patriotism and misinformation of high school history texts.

Loewen suggests a more honest approach to US history, complete with information most of us never learned in school. Of particular interest to parents of children of color. Winner of the 1996 American Book Award and the Oliver Cromwell Cox Award for Distinguished Antiracist Scholarship. Publisher's Weekly: "Sure to please liberals and infuriate conservatives. In condemning the way history is taught, he indicts everyone involved in the enterprise: authors, publishers, adoption committees, parents and teachers."

Keywords

African American, Native American, Race Relations, Racism, Educational Issues, US History

Age Range:

Adult

Author: James W. Loewen

ISBN# 684818868 Date Published: 1996 Price: $ 14.00

Publisher: Simon & Schuster Pages: 384

OFF THE RESERVATION

Reflections on Boundary-Busting, Border-Crossing Loose Canons

Off the Reservation gives us the best of Allen's political essays, literary criticism, and personal reflections. Section One explores the boundary between Native American cultures and Western civilization, contrasting proprietorship, literacy, individualism, and "rape culture" with the communal and spiritual connection to the earth that characterizes native societies. Section Two reviews contemporary Native American literature, including the work of N. Scott Momaday, Leslie Marmon Silko, and Mary Tallmountain.

Keywords

Native American, Racial/Ethnic Identity, Cultural History, Race Relations

Age Range:

Adult

Author: Paula Gunn Allen

ISBN# 080704640X Date Published: 1998 Price: $ 25.00

Publisher: Beacon Pages: 262

YELLOW WOMAN AND A BEAUTY OF THE SPIRIT

22 essays on Native American life today

"There is no one writing in America who more deserves our attention and respect."—Larry McMurtry. From Booklist: "Silko's essays are like songs; their harmonies are autobiographical, their melodies topical. The source is a controlled blend of pride in Pueblo heritage and anger over the perpetuation of injustice against Native Americans." And Kirkus Reviews writes, "Silko is best when recounting stories that demonstrate the strong spiritual relationship of the people to the land, as in the tale of Yellow Woman, who agrees to go away with a buffalo spirit so that her tribe will always have food."

Keywords

Native American, Cultural History

Age Range:

Adult

Author: Leslie Marmon Silko

Leslie Marmon Silko is the author of *Almanac of the Dead; The Man Made of Words; Garden In The Dunes;* and *Yellow Woman.*

ISBN# 684827077 Date Published: 1999 Price: $ 11.00

Publisher: Touchstone Pages: 208

ANTI-BIAS CURRICULUM

Rating 

A guide to helping children from two to five years old learn to value diversity.

This classic work on teaching young children to be multiculturally competent, first printed in 1989, is used to model curriculum in schools throughout the nation. Includes: creating an anti-bias environment; working with 2-year-olds; learning about differences and similarities of race, disabilities, gender, and culture; learning to resist stereotyping; activism with young children; holiday activities; working with parents. Includes resources.

Keywords

Core Issues (Feelings), Educational Issues, Multiracial, Race Relations, Racism, Diversity

Age Range:

Adult

Author: Louise Derman-Sparks

Louise Derman-Sparks is the author of *Anti-Bias Curriculum* and *Teaching/Learning Anti Racism*

ISBN# 0-935989-20-X Date Published: 1989 Price: $ 12.00

Publisher: Natl. Assn. Child Ed Pages: 149

ASSIMILATION BLUES

Rating 

A significant contribution to the way we think about families, Black-white relations, and social change.

Children of Black families who grow up in white communities share many issues with children of color who grow up with white parents. Beverly Daniel Tatum offers a fresh look at an interesting population.

Keywords

African American, Black Identity, Race Relations, Racial/Ethnic Identity, Racism, Transracial Adoption

Age Range:

Adult

Author: Beverly Daniel Tatum, Ph.D.

Beverly Daniel Tatum is a professor at Mount Holyoke College and a psychologist in private practice.

ISBN# 963214624 Date Published: 1992 Price: $ 12.95

Publisher: Hazel-Maxwell Pages:

BEST OF PACT PRESS: RACIAL IDENTITY

Building pride and connection.

Forty-eight-page collections of the best articles published in Pact Press concerning the development and support of racial identity in adopted children.

Keywords

Adopted Adult, Adopted Child, Racial/Ethnic Identity, Child Development

Age Range:

Adult

Editor: Beth Hall

Author: Gail Steinberg

Gail Steinberg and Beth Hall are Co-Directors and founder of Pact, An Adoption Alliance and each is also the parent of children adopted transracially.

ISBN# NA Date Published: 1998 Price: $ 10.00

Publisher: Pact Pages: 48

BEYOND THE WHITENESS OF WHITENESS

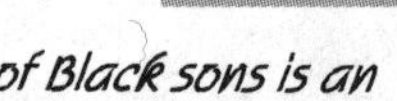

This moving memoir by a white mother of Black sons is an important contribution.

A mother's recognition of white economic, social, and moral complicity in the power structure of racism. From the book jacket: "'I am Black,' Jane Lazarre's son tells her. 'I have a Jewish mother but I am not "biracial." The term is meaningless to me.' She understands, she says — but he tells her, gently, that he doesn't think so, that she can't understand because she is white. This book is her memoir of learning to look into the nature of whiteness in a way that passionately informs the connections between herself and her family." This book is fabulous; clear-eyed, thoughtful and clearly written. Essential reading for white parents of children of color. A Pact bestseller.

Keywords

Transracial Adoption, Multiracial Identity, Core Issues (Feelings), White Identity, Racial/Ethnic Identity, Racism

Age Range:

Adult

Author: Jane Lazarre, Ph.D.

ISBN# 822330444 Date Published: 1996 Price: $ 12.95

Publisher: Duke University Pages: 140

BREAKING DOWN WALLS

Rating 

A model for reconciliation in an age of racial strife.

Offering insights and tools for races to work together, this book, though based on Christianity, provides information about bridging cultural differences that are useful for parents of children of color, regardless of religious beliefs. Contains eight principles of racial reconciliation to encourage action to cross barriers of race and class: Commitment to relationship, intentionality, sincerity, interdependence, sacrifice, empowerment, and call. Chapters 16 and 17 are titled "For Black Christians Only" and "For White Christians Only" — unfortunately excluding everyone else.

Keywords
Race Relations, Religion, Christianity, Social Welfare, Antiracist Strategies

Age Range
Adult

Author: Raleigh Washington
Author: Glen Kehrein

ISBN# 802426425 Date Published 1996 Price $ 11.99
Publisher Moody Press Pages

BRIDGE OVER THE RACIAL DIVIDE

Rating 

Rising inequality and coalition politics

One of the country's most influential sociologists focuses on the rising inequality in American society and the need for a progressive, multiracial political coalition to combat it. He reveals an American society that highlights racial differences rather than commonalities, making it difficult for Americans to appreciate the potential for mutual political support across racial lines. He advocates a cross-race, class-based alliance of working- and middle-class Americans to pursue policies that will benefit them rather than the rich. Using theoretical arguments and case studies, Wilson examines how a broad-based political constituency can be created, sustained, and energized.

Keywords
System Reform, African American, Antiracist Strategies

Age Range
Adult

Author: William Julius Wilson

William Julius Wilson, a MacArthur Prize Fellow, is a Professor at Harvard University. He is past president of the American Sociological Association.

ISBN# 520222261 Date Published 1999 Price $ 19.95
Publisher University of CA Pages 149

BY THE COLOR OF OUR SKIN

Intersection is not integration: the illusion of integration and the reality of race in America

The most troubling, thought-provoking assertion of the book is that the ideal of integration, while laudable in the abstract, "ironically helps us avoid a real reckoning on race," says Publishers Weekly. "The U.S. has created a grand illusion of imminent integration. The media have produced a 'virtual integration,' which many Whites not only accept but prefer to the real thing. To achieve real integration requires hard work, risk, social engineering, sacrifice, etc., " says Booklist.

Keywords
Race Relations, Racism, Cultural History

Age Range
Adult

Author: Leonard Steinhorn
Author: Barbara Diggs-Brown

Leonard Steinhorn and Barbara Diggs-Brown both teach communication at American University.

ISBN# 525943595 Date Published 1999 Price $ 23.95
Publisher Dutton Pages 299

CELEBRATING DIVERSITY

A multicultural resource for secondary-school curriculum planners.

This collection of writing, designed to build self-esteem and critical thinking skills, celebrates the diverse people and events that shape our world and offers student-centered activities to promote critical thinking skills. Includes 75 activities, presented in a logical developmental sequence that moves from the celebration of the self (via activities involving names, languages, family patterns and customs) to appreciating differences and diversity. Each activity's clear directions make it easy to use in group situations.

Keywords
Diversity, Multicultural, Multiracial, Educational Issues, Self-Esteem

Age Range
Adult

Author: Frank B. Siccone

Dr. Siccone is co-author of *101 Ways To Develop Student Self-Esteem and Responsibility.*

ISBN# 827362099 Date Published 1995 Price $ 39.95
Publisher Delmar Pages

Rating

CHALLENGING RACISM AND SEXISM

1996 Outstanding Book – The Gustavus Myers Center for the Study of Human Rights.

From the publisher: "The first collection to examine race and gender together, in an effort to uncover the social underpinnings of hatred based on difference. This volume challenges arguments that such traits as intelligence or aggression are genetically determined. Global in scope, with perspectives from a range of disciplines, this volume's topics include racism and sexism in psychotherapy and myths and realities regarding school performance of Asian and Asian-American school children."

Keywords

Antiracist Strategies, Cultural History, Diversity, Race Relations, Social Welfare

Age Range:

Adult

Author-Illustrator: Betty Rosoff

Illustrated by Author: Ethel Tobach

Betty Rosoff is professor emerita of biology at Stern College; Ethel Tobach worked as a comparative psychologist at the American Museum of Natural History.

ISBN# 1-55861-090-1 Date Published: 1996 Price: $ 14.95
Publisher: Oxford University Pages: 350

Rating

CHILDREN OF COLOR

Psychological interventions with children of color.

Traditional and innovative intervention strategies and techniques for helping children cope with the effects of discrimination. Deals with a broad range of Asian, Latino, African, and other heritages.

Keywords

Multicultural, Racial/Ethnic Identity, Racism, Educational Issues, Family Life, Multiracial

Age Range:

Adult

Author: Jewelle Taylor Gibbs

Author: Larke Nahme Huang

Jewelle Taylor Gibbs is a professor in the School of Social Welfare, University of California, Berkeley. Larke Nahme Huang is an assistant professor, School of Social Welfare, UC-Berkeley.

ISBN# 1-55542-156-3 Date Published: 1989 Price: $ 28.95
Publisher: Jossey-Bass Pages: 423

COLOR OF OUR FUTURE, THE

Our Multiracial Future.

By 2050, there will be more non-White than White Americans, and most will be Asian and Latino. Chideya interviews young people (Black, White, Latino, Asian, Native American, and multiracial) about how they deal with race in their own lives, exploring how their views will determine our future. "We do not obey the laws of race. We make them," she writes. "Now is the time for us to choose wisely what we will preserve about our racial history, and what destructive divisions we need to leave behind." Chideya's style is reminiscent of Studs Terkel with a touch of Jonathan Kozol. An interesting read.

Keywords

US History, Cultural History, Multicultural, Multiracial

Age Range:

Adult

Author: Farai Chideya

Farai Chideya is the author of *Don't Believe The Hype* and *The Color of Our Future.*

ISBN# 688165303 Date Published: 1999 Price: $ 23.00
Publisher: Morrow Pages: 288

COUNSELING FOR RACIAL UNDERSTANDING

For anyone concerned with prejudice and how it affects the perpetrators and the targets.

This very practical guide also provides the groundwork for understanding the insidious and institutional nature of prejudice. The book rests on the premise that we all have prejudices and that recognition is the first step toward change.

Keywords

Race Relations, Educational Issues, Diversity, Antiracist Strategies

Age Range:

Adult

Author: Brenda Bryant

ISBN# 1556201265 Date Published: Price: $ 17.95
Publisher: publication canceled Pages:

Rating

COUNTRY OF STRANGERS, A: BLACKS AND WHITES IN AMERICA

An intelligent, penetrating and intriguing look at how Black and white Americans perceive each other.

Shipler's book "is an effort to make black and white people less foreign to one another. I'd recommend picking up a copy of this book as a kind of cultural guide to the all-time most frequent pitfalls in listening, speaking and acting across the racial divide," wrote Patricia Williams in her New York Times review; "Unlike other examples of this genre, such as Studs Terkel's excellent Race: The American Obsession, which assembled interviews from people of all races, Shipler's book maintains a more studied gaze from one side of the fence to the other... even as it notes how full of holes the fence is ."

Keywords
African American, Race Relations, Black Identity, Diversity, Racism, White Identity

Age Range:
Adult

Author: David Shipler

David Shipler, a Pulitzer-prize winning author, wrote *Arab and Jew: Wounded Spirits in a Promised Land.*

ISBN# 0-679-73454-6 Date Published: 1997 Price: $ 15.00
Publisher: Knopf Pages: 640

Rating

DISPLACING WHITENESS

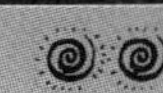

Essays in social and cultural criticism.

Displacing Whiteness describes how whiteness is lived, engaged, appropriated, and theorized in a range of geographical locations and historical moments. An important topic, but unfortunately not easily accessible in this account.

Keywords
Racial/Ethnic Identity, Racism, White Identity

Age Range:
Adult

Editor: Ruth Frankenberg

ISBN# 822320215 Date Published: 1997 Price: $ 17.95
Publisher: Duke University Press Pages: 352

DIVIDED SISTERS

Bridging the gap between Black women and White women.

Based on interviews, cultural literature, and extensive research, this book examines relations between Black and White women as children, as adults, at school, at work and at home in an effort to show the realities and challenges of what is too frequently an unbreachable cultural divide. The authors discover that the concerns and frustrations of Black and White women are often different, and that these differences are frequently not communicated. In addition, peer pressure, economic and historical inequality, real or perceived racism, and fear play a role in dividing rather than uniting women.

Keywords
African American, Antiracist Strategies, Race Relations, Black Identity, White Identity, Social Welfare

Age Range:
Adult

Author: Midge Wilson, Ph.D.

Author: Kathy Russell

Midge Wilson teaches psychology and women's studies at DePaul University. She and Kathy Russell are authors of *The Color Complex.*

ISBN# 385473621 Date Published: 1997 Price: $ 14.00
Publisher: Anchor Pages: 352

DIVIDED TO THE VEIN

An autobiography about racism and privilege in the family.

Midwest Book Review: "The author's father was a pampered Black child, his mother an idealistic girl from a large poor white farming family: he himself grew up in the 1950s and 60s. His mixed family background and his later search for ethnic identity as an adult are the subject of an autobiography which reflects on the powers of racial heritage and identity."

Keywords
Race Relations, Racial/Ethnic Identity, Intergenerational, Multiracial Identity, Biography, Cultural History

Age Range:
Adult

Author: Scott Minerbrook

ISBN# 151931070 Date Published: 1996 Price: $ 24.00
Publisher: Harcourt Brace Pages:

Rating

END OF RACISM, THE

D'Sousa, a man with controversial views, presents his ideas on how to end racism.

D'Sousa condemns "destructive elements" embraced by Black male youths that serve to alienate them from society, while he defends "rational discrimination" (the notion that everyday racism perpetrated by whites against Blacks is "rational"), and offers his vision for a multiracial society. Topics include The Origins of Racism Slavery; Liberal Antiracism Race Merchants: How Civil Rights Became a Profession; Race and the IQ Debate and more. This book presents lots of invitations to debate. We disagree with many of his opinions but feel readers should become familiar with them.

Keywords

Racism, Antiracist Strategies, Race Relations, Black Identity, Diversity, Cultural History

Age Range:

Adult

Author: Dinesh D'Sousa

ISBN# 684825244 Date Published: 1996 Price: $ 16.00

Publisher: Free Press Pages: 724

Rating

EVERYDAY ACTS AGAINST RACISM

Stories to inspire action offer ways of anticipating, resisting and undermining racism in American society.

A white mom of a Black daughter takes on discrimination at school; a Latina mom helps her biracial son celebrate his heritage; a White mom of Latina children examines the need for crossing cultural divides; a Japanese American woman reflects on her dual heritage as she prepares to raise her biracial son; a Black college professor takes race questions beyond the classroom, and more. The essays are shaped into three sections -Starting Points, Reading and Teaching, and Connections — which help establish the connections among these diverse but related experiences and perspectives, offering models and insights for application in other lives and circumstances.

Keywords

Social Welfare, Self-Esteem, Racism, Race Relations, Racial/ Ethnic Identity, Antiracist Strategies

Age Range:

Adult

Editor: Maureen T. Reddy

Maureen T. Reddy is author of *Mother Journeys: Feminists Write About Mothering* and *Sisters In Crime: Feminists and the Crime Novel.*

ISBN# 1-878067-85-0 Date Published: 1996 Price: $ 15.95

Publisher: Seal Press Pages: 270

FORTY WAYS TO RAISE A NONRACIST CHILD

"The only way is to raise our children differently than we were raised ourselves."

The majority of books on parenting don't mention racism, as if it weren't a major factor affecting child development. This book, which addresses children of white, Black, Asian, Latino and Native American origins, offers practical information keyed to a child's age and developmental level. The authors, one white and one Black, found they had to work through their own differing attitudes on the material to create this book. In doing so, they came to realize that their experience of collaborating on this project was in fact a model for breaking down prejudice. A clearly written, useful book.

Keywords

Social Welfare, Racial/Ethnic Identity, Race Relations, Racism, Parenting, Antiracist Strategies

Age Range:

Adult

Author: Barbara Mathias

ISBN# 62733222 Date Published: 1996 Price: $ 10.00

Publisher: Harper Row Pages: 152

GUNS, GERMS AND STEEL

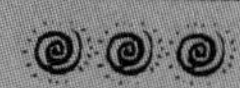

The antidote to The Bell Curve! *Here's a non-racist answer to why white people prosper.*

Think big. Think biogeography. This book brings a new angle to the question of how humanity developed. Here, at last, is a history that includes all the world's peoples. A major advance in our understanding of human societies, *Guns, Germs, and Steel* chronicles the way that the modern world, and its inequalities, came to be. The NY Times calls this "an artful, informative and delightful book." The Washington Post says that it's "a volume no one should leave college without reading." And as Paul R. Ehrlich points out, "The book demolishes the grounds for racist theories of history. After reading the first two pages, you won't be able to put it down."

Keywords

Racism, Race Relations, Cultural History, Educational Issues

Age Range:

Adult

Author: Jared Diamond

Jared Diamond is a MacArthur fellow and UCLA evolutionary biologist. He is the author of *The Third Chimpanzee.*

ISBN# 393317552 Date Published: 1998 Price: $ 14.95

Publisher: W.W. Norton Pages: 480

Rating

HOW YOUNG CHILDREN PERCEIVE RACE

An academic study confirming that children are aware of race at very young ages.

From Booknews: "Holmes examines children's conceptions of race and ethnicity and explores how these factors influence their social relationships. This study approaches children in the classroom setting and provides a real 'child's eye view.'"

Keywords

African American, Racial/Ethnic Identity, Black Identity, Educational Issues, Race Relations

Age Range.

Adult

Author: Robyn M. Holmes

ISBN# 803971095 *Date Published.* 1995 *Price.* $ 25.50

Publisher. Sage *Pages.*

Rating

IN THE SHADOW OF RACE

Growing up as a multiethnic, multicultural, and "multiracial" American.

Arboleda's heritage is Filipino Chinese, African American, Native American, and German-Danish. What's more, he was born in Brooklyn and grew up in Japan: for once, it's not just black and white. As a multicultural and multiethnic American, he presents his challenges in coming to terms with personal, family, and social identity. Topics include the social construction of race; racial separatism vs. diversity; racial, ethnic, and cultural identity development; politics of racial categorization; "mixed race" peoples; cultural identity vs. identity of heritage; the concept of a "cultural home"; and changing identities within cultures.

Keywords

Multicultural, Multiracial Identity, Racial/Ethnic Identity, Race Relations

Age Range.

Adult

Author: Teja Arboleda

ISBN# 805825754 *Date Published.* 1998 *Price.* $ 24.50

Publisher. Erlbaum, Lawrence Assoc. *Pages.* 280

LIGHT IN THEIR EYES, THE

Creating multicultural learning communities

Sonia Nieto makes student-learning the primary objective of multicultural education. Nieto draws on a host of research in learning styles, multiple intelligences, and cognitive theories to portray the way students learn. She then takes us beyond individual learners to discuss the social context of learning, educational equity, the influence of culture on learning, and critical pedagogy. Centering on multicultural education as a transformative process, the text includes many reflections of teachers who have undergone this process and whose experiences will be invaluable to other teachers.

Keywords

Multicultural, Educational Issues, Antiracist Strategies

Age Range.

Adult

Author: Sonia Nieto

Sonia Nieto is a Professor at the University of Massachusetts at Amherst. She is a leading theorist in multicultural education and author of *Affirming Diversity.*

ISBN# 807737828 *Date Published.* 1999 *Price.* $ 22.95

Publisher. Teachers College Press *Pages.* 224

LIVING WITH RACISM

"One step from suicide" or how it feels to be middle-class and African American.

Despite the prevalent white view that racism is diminishing, this study exposes the relentlessness of the racism faced by middle-class Black Americans every day: A man is refused service in a restaurant; a woman is harassed while shopping; a little girl is taunted in a public pool by white children. These are everyday incidents similar to those encountered by millions of African Americans. The authors argue that in the cumulative effect, these episodes are experienced not as separate incidents, but as a process demanding their constant vigilance and shaping their personal, professional, and psychological lives.

Keywords

Racial/Ethnic Identity, Race Relations, Racism, Black Identity

Age Range.

Adult

Author: Joe Feagin

Author: Mel Sikes

ISBN# 807009253 *Date Published.* 1995 *Price.* $ 14.00

Publisher. Beacon Press *Pages.*

Rating

MORAL ANIMAL, THE

Why we are the way we are. A forget- everything- you- used-to-know book.

Questions about sex, siblings, status and society. Wright uses examples from the life of Charles Darwin to unveil the genetic strategies behind everything from sexual preferences to office politics — and their implications for moral codes and public policies. He argues that we don't have to engage in certain behaviors just because we possess certain traits, but that we are better off knowing where our seemingly irresistible impulses come from. Reading this book may challenge your ideas about how to parent your child of color in a society where a desire for status and a capacity for guilt come with the territory.

Keywords

Child Development, Social Welfare, Parenting

Age Range:

Adult

Author: Robert Wright

Robert Wright is an editor for the *New Republic.*

ISBN# 679763996 *Date Published:* 1995 *Price:* $ 14.00

Publisher: Vintage Books *Pages:*

Rating

MULTICULTURAL MANNERS

New rules of etiquette for today's multicultural society.

Includes the dos and don'ts of successful business and social interaction with people from different cultures. Appropriate etiquette regarding body language, food, child rearing, clothing, word choices, colors, entertaining, romance, and gift giving. Detailed tips for avoiding embarrassment at work, in the classroom, at meals, at weddings, and at funerals. Important religious rules and traditions.

Keywords

Multicultural, Race Relations, Manners

Age Range:

Adult

Author: Norine Dresser

Norine Dresser writes the "Multicultural Manners" column for the *Los Angeles Times.*

ISBN# 0-471-11819-2-51495 *Date Published:* 1996 *Price:* $ 14.95

Publisher: John Willey *Pages:* 285

MULTICULTURAL/MULTIRACIAL PSYCHOLOGY

Perspectives in personality and mental health.

Dr. Ramirez addresses contemporary conditions in which distinctions between groups are blurred. The center of the mestizo (or "mixed") world view is a belief in the importance of integrating diversity. It explores the relationship between traditionalism/modernism and cognitive styles, and offers a method for multicultural assessment and psychotherapy that promotes the development of pluralistic perspectives and lifestyles. Though densely written, this book presents interesting material not readily available in the commercial press.

Keywords

Multicultural, Race Relations, Health, Multiracial Identity, Diversity

Age Range:

Adult

Author: Manuel Ramirez

ISBN# 765700735 *Date Published:* 1997 *Price:* $ 55.00

Publisher: Jason Aronson *Pages:*

OFF WHITE: READINGS ON RACE, POWER, AND SOCIETY

Essays on white identity, challenging racism.

Includes: "Whiteness and 'Black Underachievement'"; ""White Experimenters, White Blood, and Other White Conditions: Locating the Psychologist's Race"; "Behind Blue Eyes: Whiteness and Contemporary U.S. Racial Politics"; "Multicultural Performances in a Progressive School"; "Whiteness in Teacher Education"; "Does White Racism Necessarily Mean Antiblackness?"; "Is White a Race?"; "Loss of Privilege Inside White Working-Class Masculinity in the 1990s"; ""Television Talk Shows and Representations of Whiteness"; "Double Binds of Whiteness" and more.

Keywords

Race Relations, Racial/Ethnic Identity, Racism, White Identity

Age Range:

Adult

Editor: Michelle Fine

ISBN# 415913020 *Date Published:* 1996 *Price:* $ 24.99

Publisher: Routledge *Pages:* 448

Rating

PRIVILEGE REVEALED

How Invisible preference undermines America

Filled with penetrating images about the challenges that come with an understanding that race matters alongside the goal that it should not, *Privilege Revealed* reveals the complexity of race in all our lives. Of particular interest to adoptive parents is chapter five, "The implications of making comparisons between racism and other isms," which starts with a story about Tony Grillo, an Afro-Cuban woman who comes down with cancer. "Cancer became the first filter through which I see the world. It used to be race, but now it is cancer," she says. A terrific blend of clear theory and compelling stories, this is a read-it-from-cover-to cover book that belongs in every home library.

Keywords

Antiracist Strategies, Cultural History, Race Relations, Racial/Ethnic Identity, Racism

Age Range.

Adult

Author: Stephanie Wildman

ISBN# 841793037 Date Published. 1996 Price. $ 19.00

Publisher. New York University Press Pages. 240

Rating

RACE AND IQ

Race and IQ is the definitive response to The Bell Curve.

A lucid exploration of the concepts and misconceptions about race and intelligence.

Keywords

Race Relations, Racial/Ethnic Identity, Racism, Educational Issues

Age Range.

Adult

Author: Ashley Montague

ISBN# 195102207 Date Published. 1998 Price. $ 35.00

Publisher. Oxford University Press Pages. 400

RACE IN THE MIND OF AMERICA

Breaking the vicious circle between blacks and whites

Wachtel presents racial tension as a "vicious circle" provoking negative responses that feed existing biases. For example, anticipation of discrimination can create antisocial behavior; anticipation of antisocial behavior can create discrimination. But these learned actions and reactions are changeable; understanding this "vicious circle" is step one. As part of this larger concern, Wachtel addresses other issues, such as race in academic failure; affirmative action; racial stereotypes; and our inability to talk honestly about race. Wachtel believes that racial indifference is more challenging than racism itself. Kirkus Reviews calls it "Sophisticated reading for anyone with more than a casual interest in race."

Keywords

Race Relations, Racism

Age Range.

Adult

Author: Paul L. Wachtel

Paul Wachtel, a psychotherapist and director of the Colin Powell Center for Policy Studies at the City College of New York, wrote *The Poverty of Affluence.*

ISBN# 415920000 Date Published. 1999 Price. $ 24.99

Publisher. Routledge Pages. 3352

RACE MANNERS

Navigating the minefield between Black and White Americans.

A startling wake-up call to Black and White interaction, sure to change your thinking. Jacobs, an African American, explains that he wanted to write a book "that people could use, a book that would help each of us pick our way through the minefield of racial booby traps many of us encounter each and every day; [that would] lay bare everyday racial behavior and help make sense of it." Using concrete examples, he points out and then challenges our everyday assumptions about race and racial difference. His arguments are reasonable, understandable, and penetrating. This book really does provide an important contribution to our times.

Keywords

African American, Antiracist Strategies, Race Relations, Racial/Ethnic Identity, Racism, Manners

Age Range.

Adult

Author: Bruce A. Jacobs

Bruce A. Jacobs is the author of *Race Manners*

ISBN# 1559704535 Date Published. 1999 Price. $ 22.95

Publisher. Arcade Pages. 256

RACIST MIND, THE

Rating

Professor Raphael S. Ezekiel, who grew up Jewish in segregated East Texas, talks with Neo-Nazis.

Midwest Book Review: "Plagued by a fear of the federal government, which they believe to be a tool of a satanic Jewish conspiracy, white militants create a climate that nurtures hatred, fear, and acts of violence. 'Praise God for AIDS,' they cry at their rallies. Full of animosity and ignorance, they call for the deportation of Blacks, Hispanics, and Asians, and extermination of Jews, Communists, and gays. Ezekiel paints a chillingly gripping portrait of the racist mindset. This analysis takes us behind the swastikas to a place all of us need to go." Though painful, this account of hatred and fear may help readers grapple with the reality of racism and other forms of prejudice in America.

Keywords

Racism, Cultural History, US History

Age Range:

Adult

Author: Raphael Ezekiel

Raphael Ezekiel, a senior research scientist at the Harvard School of Public Health, is a leading scholar of racism in the US.

ISBN# 140234497 *Date Published:* 1996 *Price:* $ 12.95

Publisher: Penguin *Pages:*

SKIN DEEP

Rating

Writers explore relationships between Black and white women, questions of identity, and competition.

From Booklist: "Girlfriend, you don't want to miss the probing questions and answers in this fascinating, volume. The writers are brave, disconcerting, moving, funny, and challenging as they struggle to gaze squarely at the ways American women have penetrated — and failed to penetrate — the barriers of race. This is scary territory: a landscape littered with betrayals and failures of understanding, but illuminated by precious victories and by the editors' hope that we can 'both see and see beyond race,' that if we 'address our differences [now]... the issue of race in our children's generation will be, in fact, skin deep."

Keywords

African American, Antiracist Strategies, Black Identity, Friendship, Race Relations, Racial/Ethnic Identity

Age Range:

Adult

Editor: Marita Golden

Author: Susan Shreve

ISBN# 385474105 *Date Published:* 1996 *Price:* $ 14.00

Publisher: Anchor *Pages:*

SOMETIMES THERE IS NO OTHER SIDE

Chicanos and the myth of equality.

Acuña tells how colleges and the courts use concepts like truth and objectivity to subjugate minorities. He argues that these institutions base their moral authority on the myth of objective "facts," when what they claim as truth is really no more than shared misperceptions, such as the myth that the United States is a colorblind society. Should people of color support an educational system that withholds the knowledge needed to confront societal problems?

Keywords

Latino/a, Race Relations, Racism, Cultural History

Age Range:

Adult

Author: Rodolfo Acuña

ISBN# 268017638 *Date Published:* 1998 *Price:* $ 18.00

Publisher: University of Notre Dame Press *Pages:*

TEACHING/LEARNING ANTI RACISM

A developmental approach to working with children and creating antiracist consciousness.

This new book is a guide for teachers, trainers, and anyone interested in fighting racism by Louise Derman-Sparks, who also wrote *Anti-Bias Curriculum* for young children. This book is full of excellent ideas but because the presentation is formal and academic, it can be a challenging read. Contents include: The Dynamics of Racism; The Individual, Racism, and Anti-Racism; Beginning Explorations of Racism; Exposing the Contradictions; Transformation to an Understanding of Self and Society; Anti-Racism as a New Beginning; Making the Course Your Own.

Keywords

Racism, Racial/Ethnic Identity, Self-Esteem, Educational Issues, Race Relations, Social Welfare

Age Range:

Adult

Author: Louise Derman-Sparks

Author: Carol Brunson Phillips

Louise Derman-Sparks is the author of *Anti-Bias Curriculum* and *Teaching/Learning Anti Racism*

ISBN# 807736376 *Date Published:* 1998 *Price:* $ 17.95

Publisher: Teachers College Press *Pages:*

Rating

UPROOTING RACISM

How White people can work for racial justice and learn how to become allies.

A book for White people about addressing one's own racism. Includes: "I'm not racist"; the dynamics of racism; being allies; the effects of history; fighting institutional racism; multicultural competence.

Keywords

Race Relations, Racial/Ethnic Identity, Racism, White Identity

Age Range.

Adult

Author: Paul Kivel

ISBN# 0-86571-338-3 Date Published. Price. $ 16.95

Publisher. New Society Publishers Pages.

Rating

WAKE UP, LITTLE SUSIE

Single pregnancy and race.

A highly readable history of the difference in services provided to African American women facing unplanned pregnancies compared to white women in the United States. An exceptionally clear statement of the effects of racism on women and children in crisis. Highly recommended.

Keywords

Adoption, Birth Parent, Black Identity, Placement, Social Welfare, Racism

Age Range.

Adult

Author: Rickie Solinger

ISBN# 0-415-90448-X Date Published. 1992 Price. $ 19.95

Publisher. Routledge Pages. 324

WE CAN ALL GET ALONG

50 steps that put the power to change racism into your hands.

All positive change starts with one person who cares; Rosa Parks took a small step and made a difference. This is an extremely practical book that encourages readers to investigate and be convinced by the facts rather than accept assumptions or "expert opinions." Good ideas with real suggestions for making a difference, as well as an extensive bibliography, are included.

Keywords

Race Relations, Multiracial, Parenting, Racial/Ethnic Identity, Educational Issues, Antiracist Strategies

Age Range.

Adult

Author: Clyde Ford

ISBN# 0-440-50570-4 Date Published. Price. $ 9.95

Publisher. Doubleday Pages.

WE CAN'T TEACH WHAT WE DON'T KNOW

White teachers, multiracial schools.

With lively stories and compelling analysis, Gary Howard takes his readers of a journey toward change. From his 25 years of experience as a multicultural educator, he looks deeply into the mirror of his own racial identity to discover what it means to be culturally competent White teachers in racially diverse schools. Inspired by his collaboration with students and colleagues from many cultures, *We Can't Teach What We Don't Know* offers an innovative vision for educators.

Keywords

Multicultural, Educational Issues, Racial/Ethnic Identity

Age Range.

Adult

Author: Gary R. Howard

Gary R. Howard is founding President of the REACH Center for Multicultural Education in Seattle, Washington.

ISBN# 080773800X Date Published. 1999 Price. $ 20.95

Publisher. Teachers College Press Pages. 160

WHAT'S GOING ON

Rating 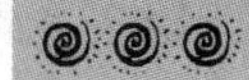

A strong collection of essays on the politics of race.

Kirkus Reviews writes, "In 'The Problem with Babies,' a white toddler who tries to engage McCall in play in a fast-food restaurant leads McCall to the conclusion that babies 'don't give a damn about the racial boundaries.' In other pieces, McCall meditates on his son, as he condemns intraracial violence that he states is destroying the African-American community; he writes of his daughter and confesses to having committed sexual assaults as a young man, not realizing that he wasn't entitled to women's favors by virtue of being male. This surprisingly and often disarmingly confessional tone brings cohesion to these essays. McCall knows his own faults and those of the community he defends and of which he is part."

Keywords

African American, Cultural History, Race Relations, Black Identity, Racism, US History

Age Range:

Adult

Author: Nathan McCall

Nathan McCall is a former *Washington Post* reporter and author of *What's Going On* and *Makes Me Wanna Holler.*

ISBN# 679455892 *Date Published:* 1998 *Price:* $ 11.00

Publisher: Random House *Pages:* 217

WHITE AWARENESS

Rating 

A handbook for antiracism training.

This text views white racism as a white problem that must be solved by whites. Details a step-by-step training program that involves defining racism; confronting the reality of racism; dealing with feelings; exploring cultural values of racism; confronting one's own racism; and developing action strategies. Filled with exercises.

Keywords

Educational Issues, Racial/Ethnic Identity, Racism, Core Issues (Feelings), Antiracist Strategies, White Identity

Age Range:

Adult

Author: Judith H. Katz

ISBN# 0-8061-1466-5 *Date Published:* 1950 *Price:* $ 14.95

Publisher: U. Oklahoma *Pages:* 211

WHY ARE ALL THE BLACK KIDS SITTING TOGETHER IN THE CAFETERIA?

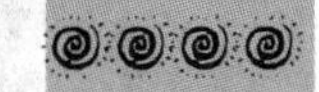

A psychologist explains the development of racial identity.

In high schools and colleges daily, young people can be observed segregating themselves by race. Integrating racial identity is a different process for people of color and white people in this society. Beverly Daniel Tatum explains this tendency as a way of affirming racial identity and outlines the process of developing racial pride through a series of predictable stages. A fascinating and clearly presented map of steps toward integration of racial identity, this book affirms the need to understand the process and to talk about it. Includes chapters on understanding Black, white, Latino, American Indian and Asian Pacific American identity. Highly recommended.

Keywords

Black Identity, Educational Issues, Multiracial, Race Relations, Racial/Ethnic Identity, Required for Pact Families

Age Range:

Adult

Author: Beverly Daniel Tatum, Ph.D.

Beverly Daniel Tatum is a professor at Mount Holyoke College and a psychologist in private practice.

ISBN# 046509127X *Date Published:* 1997 *Price:* $ 13.00

Publisher: Basic Books *Pages:* 270

WOMEN OF COLOR AND THE MULTICULTURAL CURRICULUM

Transforming the college classroom (with a segment on Puerto Rican Studies).

From the publisher: "This volume provides a guide to multicultural curricular change especially with respect to women of color. Section One highlights the actual process of faculty transformation as it occurred at UCLA and George Washington University during curricular projects. Section Two contains 37 transformed undergraduate syllabi, with brief essays describing professors' encounters with the new texts. Section Three is an interdisciplinary guide to teaching about Puerto Rican women inside and outside Puerto Rico."

Keywords

Antiracist Strategies, African American, Cultural History, Educational Issues, Multicultural, Puerto Rico

Age Range:

Adult

Editor: Liza Fiol-Matta

Editor: Miriam K. Chamberlain

Liza Fiol-Matta is assistant professor of English at LaGuardia Community College, CUNY. Miriam Chamberlain is Founding President of the National Council for Research on Women.

ISBN# 1-55861-083-9 *Date Published:* 1997 *Price:* $ 18.95

Publisher: Oxford University *Pages:* 390

Rating

ADOPTION AWARENESS

What should I do now? How to help young adults facing unplanned pregnancies.

This guide's goal is to help teens facing untimely pregnancies to make better decisions; it endorses adoption as a legitimate option — but not the only one, a position we share. Contents includes: creating a climate for adoption; encouraging conscious decision making; why teens don't consider adoption; agency services; private adoption; openness in adoption; family support; birth fathers; alternatives groups; the church's role; hospital staff; the grieving process; transition support; and responsibility.

Keywords
Adoption, Core Issues (Feelings), Birth Parent, Placement, Triad Issues

Age Range:
Adult

Author: Jeanne Lindsay

Jeanne Lindsay is the author of *Adoption Awareness* and *Open Adoption: A Caring Option.*

ISBN# 0-930934-32-6 Date Published: 1989 Price: $ 9.95
Publisher: Morning Glory Press Pages: 284

Rating

ADOPTION RESOURCES FOR MENTAL HEALTH PROFESSIONALS

Strategies of children who have survived repeated loss or contact with people they have trusted.

Intended as a handy reference to clinicians regarding children and adoption experiences, this guide is also useful for parents willing to take a deeper look at the psychological issues that can emerge after separation from birth family. Covers grief issues; holding therapy; anger and anxiety; mother-infant attachment; the severely disturbed child; disruptions; threatened families; post-placement services; developmental approach to separation-loss; transracial adoption; identity formation; sexually-abused children; enhancing attachment; adoption and divorce; identity crisis; prevention techniques; discipline issues for difficult children, and more.

Keywords
Adoption, Attachment, Grief and Loss, Self-Esteem, Special Needs

Age Range:
Adult

Author: Pamela V. Grabe

ISBN# 0-88738-7-934 Date Published: 1989 Price: $ 29.95
Publisher: Transaction Pages: 400

CONCEPTS IN ADOPTION

Examines differences between professionals and parents in their views on adoption.

Both professionals and adoptive parents have serious concerns as to the other's awareness of kids' needs after adoption. This book aids both groups in the challenging task of tackling the impasse along with post-placement dynamics, perceptions of trauma, effective parenting, identity and self-esteem.

Keywords
Adoption, Child Development, Core Issues (Feelings), Adoption Reform

Age Range:
Adult

Author: Pat Holmes

Pat Holmes is the author of *Concepts in Adoption* and *Supporting An Adoption.*

ISBN# 0911872-2-0 Date Published: Price: $ 8.00
Publisher: Our Child Press Pages:

COUNSELING WITH HEART AND SOUL

An introduction to counseling by Randolph Severson, a rare voice in adoption.

Speaking for higher values in all adoption encounters, he supports his ideas with compelling stories, literary and biblical references and an ongoing concern for integrity. We have not yet read this book but feel confident, based on the important body of his previous work, that it will present fresh information and be worth your while. From the publisher: "The author describes an 'art' of counseling rooted in a fundamentally spiritual approach to life's meaning. [Topics include] Relationship, Feeling, Process, Dialogue, Virtue, Healing; What a Christian world view might mean.... Counseling as a spiritual path that can heal the heart."

Keywords
Adoption, Adoption Reform, Core Issues (Feelings), Spiritual Meanings, Christianity

Age Range:
Adult

Author: Randolph Severson, Ph.D.

Considered the poet of the adoption movement, and a strong advocate of open adoption, Randolph Severson, Ph.D., is a psychotherapist concerned particularly with spiritual issues.

ISBN# Date Published: 1997 Price: $ 5.00
Publisher: Heart Words Center Pages: 40

Rating

PSYCHOLOGY OF ADOPTION, THE

Adoption research results covering adjustment, clinical issues, and social policy and casework issues in adoption.

While recent work has shown that adopted children are more vulnerable to psychological problems and that the rate of referral of adopted children to mental-health facilities is far above that of the general population, the basis for these problems remains unclear and controversial. In this book, theoretical, empirical, clinical, and social policy issues offer new insights into the problems facing parents of adopted children, and especially the children themselves.

Keywords

Adoption, Social Welfare, Open Adoption, Family Life

Age Range:

Adult

Author: David M. Brodzinsky, Ph.D.
Marshall D. Schechter, M.D.

David Brodzinsky is Associate Professor of Clinical and Developmental Psychology at Rutgers University. With Marshall Schechter, he is coeditor of *The Psychology of Adoption.*

ISBN# 0-19-508273-7 Date Published: 1994 Price: $ 35.00
Publisher: Oxford U. Press Pages: 416

Rating

SPIRITUAL EXISTENTIAL COUNSELING

A manual for counselors

This approach to adoptive counseling based on Catholic Existentialism views human existence as fundamentally 'spiritual,' or oriented toward Truth, Goodness, and Beauty. Persuasive rather than didactic, it focuses on therapy as conversation.

Keywords

Self-Esteem, Family Life, Core Issues (Feelings), Spiritual Meanings, Christianity

Age Range:

Adult

Author: Randolph Severson, Ph.D.

Considered the poet of the adoption movement, and a strong advocate of open adoption, Randolph Severson, Ph.D., is a psychotherapist concerned particularly with spiritual issues.

ISBN# Date Published: 1997 Price: $ 15.00
Publisher: Heart Words Center Pages: 140

WHEN LOVE IS NOT ENOUGH

How mental health professionals can help special-needs adoptive families.

This book, addressing the complex emotional issues and needs of the entire family of a special-needs child, focuses on helping professionals work to prepare families for adoption and to maximize adjustment after adoption of special-needs children.

Keywords

Special Needs, Adoption, Differently-abled, Family Life, Parenting

Age Range:

Adult

Author: Marilyn Sandmaier

ISBN# 8878683461 Date Published: 1988 Price: $ 9.95
Publisher: Child Welfare League Pages:

Rating

ADOPTION: A REFERENCE HANDBOOK

A guide to US adoption history and leaders.

This volume explores current adoption issues in the United States. Offering a chronological account, it documents the milestones in adoption history, along with a collection of biographical sketches of individuals who have profoundly affected child-welfare and adoption philosophies and practices. Readers will also find a selection of facts and figures as well as a discussion of important Federal legislation and policies, a summary of significant litigation, and a directory of organizations, associations, and government agencies. A detailed listing of print and electronic resources is included.

Keywords

Adoption, Adoption Reform, Social Welfare

Age Range:

Adult

Author: Kathleen Lathrop

Kathleen Lathrop is the author of *Adoption: A Reference Handbook* and *My Angel Goes Home.*

ISBN# 874368987 Date Published: 1998 Price: $ 45.00

Publisher: Abc-Clio Pages:

Rating

ADOPTION AND THE FAMILY SYSTEM

Uses family systems theory to consider practical strategies for families connected through adoption.

Employing a clean, clear-thinking writing style, Reitz and Watson look at adoption issues as interactions of family systems (birth families and adoptive families) over generations. Each individual is seen as a member of a larger system, influenced by and influencing the others over time. This book is a clear distillation of strategies for understanding the larger picture. Intended to provide an overview to professionals, this is a great book for anyone who wants to understand the broader and deeper issues of adoption. It is an exceptionally comprehensive, sensitively written, all-around superior guide, certainly one of the best on the market. Currently out of print but if you would like, we will attempt to find a copy for you. Please inquire.

Keywords

Adoption, Family Life, Placement, Required for Pact Families, Social Welfare, Triad Issues

Age Range:

Adult

Author: Kenneth W. Watson

Author: Miriam Reitz, Ph.D., LCSW

Kenneth Watson has been a contributor to the field of social work for 35 years. He is nationally recognized as an adoption expert.

ISBN# 0-89862-797-4 Date Published: 1992 Price: $ 34.00

Publisher: Guilford Pages: 340

ADOPTIVE KINSHIP

A consideration of the place of adoptive kinship in interpersonal relationships and in society.

The writings of H. David Kirk should not be missed. A follow-up book to Shared Fate, this book speaks out against many of the institutions in adoption which try to deny adoption, expecting adoptive families to be like families formed by birth. With this book, Kirk became a leader of the adoption reform movement. His honesty and compassion as an adoptive parent make this book timeless and well worth reading. Discusses differences between genetically-linked families and adoptive families and the importance of acknowledging differences and problems in adoption practice and their effect on adoptive families.

Keywords

Adoption, Fiction, Multiracial , Family Life, Adoption Reform, Triad Issues

Age Range:

Adult

Author: David H. Kirk

ISBN# 0-914359-01-9 Date Published: Price: $ 17.50

Publisher: Ben-Simon Pages:

ANNOTATED GUIDE TO ADOPTION RESEARCH

Access to current adoption research made easy.

Published in conjunction with The Evan B. Donaldson Adoption Institute, the *Annotated Guide to Adoption Research* presents approximately 850 abstracts of qualitative and quantitative adoption research conducted and/or published between 1986 and 1997. The guide encompasses clinical and nonclinical samples, case studies, longitudinal studies, epidemiological studies, grounded theory, experimental research, and single-subject research.

Keywords

Adoption, Social Welfare, Research

Age Range:

Adult

Author: Deborah Martin

Deborah Martin is Director of Information at the Evan B. Donaldson Institute.

ISBN# 878687084 Date Published: 1998 Price: $ 24.95

Publisher: Child Welfare League Pages: 368

Rating

AS IF KIDS MATTERED

Part exposé, part suggestions for change with the goal of recruiting more adoptive parents.

This book combs through the controversies in the adoption cosmos and promotes adoption as just another way to build a family. It advocates passionately for older child adoptions and for newer types of adopters: low-income, age 40 plus, single, fost-adopters, common law, gay and Lesbian, differently-abled, etc.

Keywords

Adoption, Adoption Reform, Foster Care, Gay and/or Lesbian, Special Needs, Social Welfare

Age Range:

Adult

Author: Marlene Webber

Marlene Webber is an adoption advocate who lives and works in Canada.

ISBN# 1550139312 Date Published: 1997 Price: $ 15.95

Publisher: Key Porter Pages:

Rating

CHILD DEVELOPMENT

A practitioner's guide.

This much-needed resource fills a crucial gap, focusing on how practitioners can apply the latest developmental knowledge to assessment and intervention with children and families. The book begins with a theoretical framework for understanding the transactions between individual development and the child's wider environments, examining the crucial roles of attachment and parenting and the ecology of risk and protective factors.

Keywords

Child Development, Social Welfare

Age Range:

Adult

Author: Douglas Davies

Douglas Davies, MSW, Ph.D., is Associate Professor at the School of Social Work, University of Michigan.

ISBN# Date Published: 1999 Price: $ 35.00

Publisher: Guilford Pages: 412

CLINICAL AND PRACTICE ISSUES IN ADOPTION

Bridging the gap between adoptees placed as infants and as older children.

Explores the similarities and differences between adopted people placed as infants and as older children. For the first time, the significant overlap between the two populations is reviewed along with strategies for interventions that can be used when working with adopted people regardless of their age at placement. Unfortunately, we did not find this book shedding any new light on an area in which clearer understanding would be particularly welcomed by prospective adoptive parents and workers alike.

Keywords

Adopted Child, Child Development, Adopting Older Child

Age Range:

Adult

Author: Victor Groza

Author: Karen Rosenberg

ISBN# 275958167 Date Published: 1998 Price: $ 55.00

Publisher: Praeger Pages:

FAMILY BONDS: ADOPTION AND THE POLITICS OF PARENTING

An adoptive mother's call for justice for adoptive parents.

Bartholet's book questions current thinking, challenging the legal system, the bureaucracies, and the social attitudes which hinder the adoption process, but it focuses exclusively on the needs of the adoptive parent. Her personal experiences with adopting take up a large part of the book. Though this book received a lot of positive publicity, we find that the writer fails to understand racial identity issues and appears to be saying that love is all you need in parenting across racial lines. We do not agree.

Keywords

Adoption, Transracial Adoption, Single Parent Families, International Adoption, Infertility, Adoption Reform

Age Range:

Adult

Author: Elizabeth Bartholet

Elizabeth Bartholet is a single adoptive parent and a professor at Harvard University.

ISBN# 395700647 Date Published: 1994 Price: $ 10.95

Publisher: Houghton Mifflin Pages: 352

MEDIATING PERMANENCY OUTCOMES

Rating 

Practice Manual

This manual addresses issues such as a child's needs, looking at options, counseling, a cooperative adoption, and letting go.

Keywords

Adoption, Adoption Reform, Birth Parent, Social Welfare

Age Range:
Adult

Author: Jean Etter
Illustrator: Tom Tierney

ISBN# 878686002 *Date Published:* 1997 *Price:* $ 34.95
Publisher: Child Welfare League *Pages:*

NEIGHBORHOOD OF THE HEART

Rating 

Fostering and the future of children.

Collects images and stories about the meaning of family and social service, whose defining characteristics here become the warmth of the fire and courage of the heart. Evocative and stirring.

Keywords

Foster Care, Social Welfare, Core Issues (Feelings)

Age Range:
Adult

Author: Randolph Severson, Ph.D.

Considered the poet of the adoption movement, and a strong advocate of open adoption, Randolph Severson, Ph.D., is a psychotherapist concerned particularly with spiritual issues.

ISBN# 188856069 *Date Published:* 1992 *Price:* $ 6.00
Publisher: Heart Words Center *Pages:*

PATTERNS OF ADOPTION

Nature, nurture, and psycho-social development.

Contents include nature and nurture, outcome studies of children adopted as babies, genetic and environmental influences on development, outcome studies of older children placed for adoption, pre- and post-placement environmental effects on development, heredity, environment and adoption outcomes. The second half of the book focuses on attachment patterns in adoption and includes chapters on secure, anxious, angry, avoidant and non-attached patterns.

Keywords

Adoption, Adoption Reform, Child Development

Age Range:
Adult

Author: David Howe

ISBN# 632041498 *Date Published:* 1998 *Price:* $ 29.95
Publisher: Blackwell Science Inc. *Pages:* 224

REALITIES OF ADOPTION

A review of changes in adoption practices over the last ten years.

This book looks at contemporary adoption practices, warts and all, offering an overview rather than an in-depth discussion of each topic. Chapters include Adoption, the contemporary scene; A personal note; Entitlement; The telling process; Open adoption: boon or bane?; Research in adoption; Research in open adoption; Psychological development of the latency-aged child; The adopted adolescent; Transracial adoption: Success or failure?; The birth parents; Child advocacy: My role in the baby Jessica case; and more.

Keywords

Adoption, Birth Parent, Adoption Reform

Age Range:
Adult

Author: Jerome Smith

ISBN# 1568330901 *Date Published:* 1997 *Price:* $ 14.95
Publisher: Madison Books *Pages:* 158

Rating

THEY CAGE THE ANIMALS AT NIGHT

A never-give-up story of a foster child's triumph over seemingly unbeatable odds.

Jennings Michael Burch writes of his childhood growing up in various institutions and foster homes. Jennings' mother placed him in an orphanage without telling him when she would be back. This was the first of many moves. Through all of his childhood transitions, he held on to the one constant thing in his life: his stuffed dog. He learned to survive, and he learned to love. This honest and spellbinding book evokes anger that any child should have to live through the sorry state of our out-of-home care system.

Keywords

Adoption, Attachment, Boy Focus, Core Issues (Feelings), Foster Child, Social Welfare

Age Range:

Adult

Author: Jennings Michael Burch

ISBN# 451159411 *Date Published:* 1998 *Price:* $ 4.99

Publisher: New American *Pages:*

Rating

TRAINER'S GUIDE FOR TRANSRACIAL ADOPTION

Advice on how to use materials in An Insider's Guide to Transracial Adoption.

This manual includes advice on how to use the materials and how to establish topic priorities, along with exercises for pre- and post-placement families. Step-by-step instructions for workshop planning include goals, trainer preparation, agendas and handouts. Modules for twelve individual workshops as well as all-day sessions are described.

Keywords

Transracial Adoption, Guidebook

Age Range:

Adult

Author: Gail Steinberg

Author: Beth Hall

Gail Steinberg and Beth Hall are Co-Directors and founder of Pact, An Adoption Alliance and each is also the parent of children adopted transracially-.

ISBN# *Date Published:* 1998 *Price:* $ 10.00

Publisher: Pact Press *Pages:* 40

UNDERSTANDING DIVERSE FAMILIES

What practitioners need to know about adoption, gay and Lesbian families, and multiracial families.

In-depth examination of adoptive, gay and Lesbian, and multiracial families. Each is considered first in a sociocultural context, then from a developmental perspective, and finally with an eye to treatment implication. Also addresses families that are single-parent by choice.

Keywords

Parenting, Adoption, Transracial Adoption, Gay and/or Lesbian, Multiracial, Single Parent Families

Age Range:

Adult

Author: Barbara F. Okun, Ph.D.

Barbara Okun is a professor at Northeastern University and teaches at Harvard Medical School.

ISBN# 1572300566 *Date Published:* 1996 *Price:* $ 31.50

Publisher: Guilford *Pages:* 376

ADOPTION AND DISCLOSURE

Rating

Overview of the legal developments around disclosure of health and background information in adoption.

Reviews of major court decisions and statutory laws regarding disclosure and requirements for professionals in disclosing non-identifying information. One of the few books to address this topic.

Keywords

Adoption, Social Welfare, Adoption Reform, Open Records, System Reform

Age Range.

Adult

Author: Madelyn DeWoody

ISBN# 878685774 | Date Published. 1994 | Price. $ 12.95

Publisher. Child Welfare League | Pages.

ADOPTION AND FOSTER CARE

Rating

Understanding foster systems.

Describes how placement systems work and reveals the feelings of young people who find homes through adoption and foster care.

Keywords

Foster Care, Social Welfare, Adoption

Age Range.

Adult

Author: Kathleen Gay

Kathleen Gay is also the author of Adoption and Foster Care and numerous other books for young people.

ISBN# 894902393 | Date Published. 1990 | Price. $ 18.95

Publisher. Enslowe | Pages. 128

ADOPTION AND THE CARE OF CHILDREN

The British and American Experience.

Arguing that the state cannot serve as a good parent, Morgan advocates for the removal of obstacles which make it hard for children to be placed in permanent adoptive families and hard for prospective adoptive parents to receive placements. Of particular interest is the chapter on transracial adoption, "Colour Blind," which, citing both American and British research, supports the claim that children in such families are "more likely to acquire an accurate, self-confident and positive" racial identity than those in same-race placements, while at the same time noting that the disproportionate number of Black children in the system is rooted in the racism of white social workers who do not appreciate the strengths of Black families.

Keywords

Adoption, Adoption Reform, Transracial Adoption

Age Range.

Adult

Author: Patricia Morgan

ISBN# 255364342 | Date Published. 1998 | Price. $ 18.00

Publisher. IEA | Pages. 210

ADOPTION, IDENTITY, AND KINSHIP

Argues that controversies about open adoption records stem from adoptism.

Questions are examined from a sociologist's perspective. Covers the Origins of Sealed Records; Controversy; Adoption Research: Trends and Perspectives; Debating Sealed Records: The Social Construction of Search Narratives; Adoption in Popular Culture: Similar Yet Different; and Adoption in Context. Controversial because of its dependence on the idea that genetically linked families are normal and those connected by adoption are not.

Keywords

Search and Reunion, Social Welfare, Open Records, Extended Family, Adoption Reform, Family Life

Age Range.

Adult

Author: Katarina Wegar

Wegar is an assistant professor of sociology at Old Dominion University.

ISBN# 0300067593" | Date Published. 1997 | Price. $ 22.50

Publisher. Yale University Press | Pages. 169

Rating

EXPLORING ADOPTIVE FAMILY LIFE

The collected adoption papers of H. David Kirk.

Exploring Adoptive Family Life is a collection of research papers and writings by H. David Kirk, one of the premier thinkers in the field of adoption in the last thirty years. This book picks up where *Shared Fate* left off. Because of the academic style, this is not an easy read — but it's worthwhile.

Keywords

Adoption, Family Life, Child Development

Age Range:

Adult

Author: H. David Kirk

H. David Kirk has applied his academic excellence to adoption theory in *Adoptive Kinship, Exploring Adoptive Family Life, Shared Fate,* and *Looking Back, Looking Forward.*

ISBN# 914539-03-5 Date Published: Price: $ 17.50

Publisher: Ben-Simon Pages:

Rating

FAMILY MATTERS

The history of sealed adoption records in the US.

Mining a vast range of sources, Carp discovers that openness, not secrecy, has been the norm in adoption for most of US history. *Family Matters* offers surprising insights into Americans' complex feelings about biological kinship versus socially constructed families; the stigma of adoption, and suspect psychoanalytic concepts such as 'genealogical bewilderment' and bogus medical terms, such as 'adopted child syndrome' that paint all parties to adoption as psychologically damaged. Useful, though he prefers passive registries to active search.

Keywords

Adoption, Adoption Reform, Social Welfare, Open Adoption, Adopted Adult, Family Life

Age Range:

Adult

Author: E. Wayne Carp

ISBN# 674796683 Date Published: 1998 Price: $ 27.95

Publisher: Harvard Pages:

GHOSTS FROM THE NURSERY

Evidence that violent behavior is linked to abuse in the first three years of life.

Outlining case histories of "children who kill" along with the latest in brain development research, *Ghosts from the Nursery* demonstrates the poisonous effect of neglect, abuse, trauma, injury, and toxicity in the first thirty-three months of life, making a convincing case for a revolution in our beliefs about the care of babies. Important implications for children in foster care and adoptive families. Includes Prenatal Exposure to Drugs and Malnutrition; Adverse Experiences in the Womb and at Birth; The Role of Temperament; The Impact of Trauma; and The Impact of Early Emotional Deprivation.

Keywords

Family Life, Parenting, Pregnancy, Special Needs, Social Welfare, Sexual Abuse

Age Range:

Adult

Author: Meredith S. Wiley

Author: Robin Karr-Morse

Author: T. Berry Brazelton

ISBN# 871137038 Date Published: 1998 Price: $ 15.00

Publisher: Atlantic Monthly Pr Pages: 256

LOOKING BACK, LOOKING FORWARD

"No single twentieth-century thinker has had a greater impact on the professional practice of adoption."

H. David Kirk, whose Shared Fate theory is a cornerstone of positive adoption thought, has strong views about where adoption practice has come from and where it is going. This provocative essay pulls no punches.

Keywords

Social Welfare, Adoption, Adoption Reform, Triad Issues

Age Range:

Adult

Author: David H. Kirk

ISBN# 0-944934-14-5 Date Published: 1995 Price: $ 5.00

Publisher: Perspectives Pages:

Rating

NOBODY'S CHILDREN

Abuse and Neglect, Foster Drift, and the"Adoption Alternative

Despite her professional stature and the platform it allows her, we do not hold Bartholet's work on adoption in high esteem. Though she claims to write in the best interest of children, we feel she serves not the children but those adults hoping to adopt, by advocating adoption as a first choice rather than encouraging real effort to resolve challenges within birth families, and by arguing against the benefits of race-matching and cultural competence in families who adopt children of color. Kirkus Reviews says "Bartholet's writing lacks emotional power...[and] appeals not to the heart, but to the head."

Keywords

Adoption, Adoption Reform

Age Range,

Adult

Author: Elizabeth Bartholet

Elizabeth Bartholet is a single adoptive parent and a professor at Harvard University.

ISBN# 807023183 *Date Published,* 1999 *Price,* $ 28.50

Publisher, Beacon *Pages,* 320

Rating

ORPHANS OF THE LIVING, THE

How America cares for its abused and neglected children.

Toth traveled to foster-care homes, orphanages, and juvenile detention centers to record the moving and heroic voices of youngsters trying to survive in an overburdened system.

Keywords

Adoption Reform, Foster Parent, Biography, Core Issues (Feelings), Social Welfare, Foster Child

Age Range,

Adult

Author: Jennifer Toth

ISBN# 156005832 *Date Published,* 1998 *Price,* $ 13.00

Publisher, Harvard *Pages,* 320

RELATIVES RAISING CHILDREN

Kinship care is the full-time parenting of children by relatives.

Information on how to support families where relatives are raising children. Covers common clinical issues, intervention strategies, policy and program recommendations.

Keywords

Adoption, Family Life, Social Welfare, Foster Care, Foster Parent, Parenting

Age Range,

Adult

Author: Joseph Crumbley

Author: Robert L. Little

Joseph Crumbley is a clinician in private practice specializing in adoption and foster care issues.

ISBN# 878686843 *Date Published,* 1997 *Price,* $ 16.95

Publisher, Child Welfare League *Pages,* 1224

SOUL OF FAMILY PRESERVATION, THE

This book puts a human face on the drama of securing a child's fate.

Explores the spiritual and psychological motivations behind teen pregnancies, examines the losses entailed in the separation of the child from the family of origin, and includes a plea to social work to recover its commitment to those who are struggling with nearly impossible choices.

Keywords

Adoption, Family Life, Adoption Reform, Spiritual Meanings, Core Issues (Feelings), Social Welfare

Age Range,

Adult

Author: Randolph Severson, Ph.D.

Considered the poet of the adoption movement, and a strong advocate of open adoption, Randolph Severson, Ph.D., is a psychotherapist concerned particularly with spiritual issues.

ISBN# *Date Published,* 1997 *Price,* $ 10.50

Publisher, Heart Words Center *Pages,* 100

Rating

WITHIN ME, WITHOUT ME

Personal stories from birth mothers in New Zealand on the agony of closed adoptions.

Birth mothers advocate for open adoption in New Zealand.

Keywords

Open Records, Birth Parent, Biography, Adoption Reform

Age Range:

Adult

Editor: Suc Wells

ISBN# 1-85727-042-8 Date Published: 1994 Price: $ 8.95

Publisher: Scarlett Press Pages: 205

Rating

WRONGFUL ADOPTION

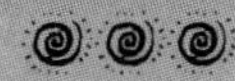

Law, Policy & Practice

A review of the history of disclosure in adoption. What are the key issues regarding full and accurate information to prospective parents about a child's physical, emotional and developmental history? How has the legal system responded to cases of inadequate disclosure? What are the indications for best practices to serve the interests of a child?

Keywords

Adoption, Adoption Reform, Social Welfare

Age Range:

All ages

Author: Madclyn Frcundlich

Author: Lisa Pcterson

Madelyn Freundlich is a Director of the Evan B. Donaldson Adoption Institute in New York City.

ISBN# 878687378 Date Published: 1998 Price: $ 18.95

Publisher: Child Welfare League Pages:

Books For All Ages On Race and Adoption

Some of life's best pleasures just don't fit into any predetermined category; this truth is likely to be particularly familiar to those whose lives are touched directly by issues of adoption and race. Many of our families, many of our experiences, many of our concerns just refuse simple labels. So it is with the books in this section. Sometimes, a book comes along that captures everyone lucky enough to stumble across it. Maybe it's the intensity of the language, or the brilliance of the illustrations, or the power of its imagery, or the astonishing combination of expressive factors, as when, for example, the defiant declaration of Maya Angelou's poem "Life Doesn't Frighten Me" gives vocal expression to the dramatic dream-world paintings of Jean-Michel Basquiat; or when Walter Dean Myers' poems find perfect visual complement in Myers' collection of antique photographs of Black children, each of the faces — like each of the poems — simultaneously glorious, unique and universal.

So we encourage you to devote some open-minded browsing time to the books in this section; with books, as in life, sometimes the greatest pleasure can be discovered in stories and people and styles and identities that demand their own unique definition, that inhabit their own self-created place.

Rating

Rating

11TH COMMANDMENT, THE

Ways we worship. Wisdom from our children.

What would you write if you were asked to create the eleventh commandment? This picture book was written and illustrated in full color by children from all faiths and backgrounds. It provides a chance for readers to explore their views about God in a multicultural context.

Keywords

Spiritual Meanings, Multicultural, Transracial Adoption

Age Range.

All ages

Author: Jewish Lights Staff

ISBN# 1-879045-46-X Date Published. 1996 Price. $ 16.95

Publisher. Jewish Lights Pages. 48

AFRICAN AMERICAN FIRSTS

Celebrations of the achievements of African Americans in the United States.

Famous, little-known, and unsung triumphs of Blacks in America are represented in a question and answer format with photographs illuminating these stories of 419 hard-won triumphs of men and women who dared to succeed, stories that belong in the library of every family raising an African American child.

Keywords

African American, Self-Esteem, Cultural History, Role Models, Racial/Ethnic Identity, Black Identity

Age Range.

All ages

Author: S. Kramer

ISBN# 0-99632476-1-1 Date Published. Price. $ 14.95

Publisher. Pinto Press Pages.

ALL NIGHT, ALL DAY

A Child's First Book of African-American Spirituals.'

Ashley Bryan, one of America's most renowned storyteller-anthologizers, presents an inspiring introduction to African-American spirituals. Kirkus Reviews writes, "Bryan's resplendent paintings fill textless double spreads that alternate with the unembellished pages of music. A truly beautiful book, worthy of the wonderful music it showcases." The Horn Book writes, "A splendid new collection. An exuberance of warm color and great variety in pattern and design distinguish the illustrations; Bryan's use of a clear, strong yellow adds radiance to a wholly gratifying book." Winner of the Coretta Scott King Award for 1992.

Keywords

African American, Music and Dance, Black Identity, Self-Esteem, Poetry, Cultural History

Age Range.

All ages

Author Illustrator: Ashley Bryan

Ashley Bryan is an award winning author and illustrator. He lives in Maine.

ISBN# 689316623 Date Published. 1991 Price. $ 16.00

Publisher. Athenaeum Pages. 48

ALL THE COLORS OF THE EARTH

"Children come in all the colors of the earth.'

Reveals in verse the truth that, despite outward differences, children everywhere are essentially the same and all are lovable. Everyone is present and represented — the children come in all the colors of love. The clear oil paint-on-canvas illustrations and the simple, flowing language make this a great read-aloud favorite. A Pact best seller.

Keywords

Multiracial, Multicultural, Race Relations, Self-Esteem, Poetry, Diversity

Age Range.

All ages

Author-Illustrator: Sheila Hamanaka

Sheila Hamanaka is also the author/illustrator of *Peace Crane* and *The Journey*.

ISBN# 0-688-11131-9 Date Published. 1994 Price. $ 16.00

Publisher. Morrow Pages. 36

ASHANTI FESTIVAL

Rating

Stories of children abound the world from Highlights for Children.

Here are sixteen stories that feature characters from many countries and cultures. Among the stories of excitement, adventure and friendship are "Ashanti Festival" by Lynda Pavlik; "Like An Antelope" by Lee Ebler; "On the Bog" by Patrick L. Sullivan; and "A Gypsy Fortune" by S. Jones Rogan.

Keywords

Diversity, Multicultural, Fiction

Age Range:

All ages

Author: Highlights Staff

ISBN# *Date Published:* 1993 *Price:* $ 3.95

Publisher: Highlights *Pages:* 96

BETWEEN EARTH AND SKY

Rating

Legends and illuminating paintings of ten Native American sacred places.

Through the guidance of his uncle Old Bear and the retelling of various Native American legends, Little Turtle learns that everything, whether living or inanimate, has its place and should be considered sacred and given respect. Books in Print: "More than a guide to places sacred to Native Americans, this reverent book prompts readers to look within themselves to find the hallowed ground that 'sets our spirits on the right path.' While visiting ancestral land, a Native American man shares with his nephew 10 legends of sacred places. Locker's traditional oil paintings, alternating between ethereal illuminations and atmospheric veils, capture the natural splendor of their subjects while retaining the hushed quality of the text."

Keywords

Folk tales and Legends, Self-Esteem, Native American, Spiritual Meanings

Age Range:

All ages

Author: Joseph Bruchac

Joseph Bruchac is the author of *A Boy Called Slow; Between Earth* and Sky; *The First Strawberries* and more.

ISBN# 0-15-200042-9 *Date Published:* *Price:* $ 16.00

Publisher: Harcourt Brace *Pages:* 32

BLACK LIGHT, THE AFRICAN AMERICAN HERO

Add this book to your family reference library.

Profiles of African American heroes serve as role models to building a solid sense of self-worth in your child. Add this book to your family reference library.

Keywords

African American, Cultural History, Self-Esteem, Racial/Ethnic Identity, Biography, Role Models

Age Range:

All ages

Author: Paul C. Harrison

ISBN# 1-56025-060-7 *Date Published:* 1992 *Price:* $ 14.95

Publisher: Thunders Mouth *Pages:* 196

BURY MY BONES BUT KEEP MY WORDS

Each one tell one, read aloud and pass- it-on stories from Africa.

An excellent collection of stories to be read or told aloud. African storytellers have shared eerie, humorous, and spellbinding tales for generations. Tony Fairman heard these stories firsthand, and his retellings bring Africa to vivid life. "Deliciously lively writing... Fresh, funny, and almost audible," says Kirkus Reviews in a pointered review. A NCSS/CBC Notable Children's Trade Book in the Field of Social Studies.

Keywords

Africa, Cultural History, Fiction, Folk tales and Legends, Racial/ Ethnic Identity, Black Identity

Age Range:

All ages

Author-Illustrator: Tony Fairman

Author: Meshack Asar

ISBN# 140368892 *Date Published:* 1994 *Price:* $ 4.99

Publisher: Puffin *Pages:*

Rating

CELEBRATIONS!

Favorite festivals of children around the world from the creators of Children Just Like Me.

Photographs of children in more than 30 countries show their favorite holidays and traditions. Readers will enjoy learning about the rituals, holiday foods, and festivities of other children as they discuss them with the authors, a teacher and a photographer. Interviews with youngsters from all walks of life reveal their diverse cultural backgrounds and universal similarities. For all ages. Over 500 color photos.

Keywords
Multicultural, Multiracial, Festivals, Diversity, Cultural History, Holidays and Celebrations

Age Range.
All ages

Author-Photographer: Barnabas Kindersley

Author: Anabel Kindersley

ISBN# 0-7894-2027-9 | Date Published. 1997 | Price. $ 17.95

Publisher. Dorling Kindersley | Pages. 79

Rating

CELEBRATIONS OF LIGHT

A year of holidays around the world.

Each of the twelve festivals described is from a different culture, yet all celebrate the gift of light. Demonstrating our deep commonalities while respecting our unique differences, the book is a clear statement of appreciation for diversity. The Cubist-influenced illustrations add much to the descriptions of New Year in Brazil, China and Taiwan; Lanterns in Sierra Leone; Candlemas in Luxembourg; Buddha's Birthday in Korea; Bon Matsure in Japan, Diwali in India; Loy Krathong in Thailand; Chanukah in Israel; Luciadagen in Sweden; Christmas in the United States and Mexico, and Kwanzaa in the United States.

Keywords
Multicultural, Multiracial, Holidays and Celebrations, Festivals

Age Range.
All ages

Author: Nancy Luenn

ISBN# 68931986 | Date Published. 1998 | Price. $ 16.00

Publisher. Athenaeum | Pages. 32

CHINESE PROVERBS

Centuries of Chinese wisdom. Each illustrated proverb is accompanied by its corresponding Chinese character.

Becoming familiar with the wisdom of one's heritage is important to building positive racial identity. Every child adopted from China needs access to the great thoughts the Chinese have contributed to the world and can take personal pride in their connections to this rich tradition. This little book is quite useful for the library of children born in China.

Keywords
Bilingual, China, Chinese, Cultural History, International Adoption, Proverbs

Age Range.
All ages

Author: Ruthanne Lum McCunn

ISBN# 811800830 | Date Published. 1992 | Price. $ 7.95

Publisher. Chronicle Books | Pages. 58

COOL MELONS TURN TO FROGS

The life and poems of Issa.

An inspiring introduction to the life and Haiku poetry of Issa, an eighteenth-century Japanese poet. This collection of some of his best loved poems illustrated by Kazuko Stones' watercolors reflect the challenges of his life. Issa's mother died when he was three, his stepmother mistreated him, and when the boy was fourteen, his father reluctantly abandoned him. *Cool Melons* tells the story of Issa's growth from a sad child to a recognized poet, while also explaining how Haiku poetry is made. Children who are sensitive to personal loss will be touched and inspired by Issa's story.

Keywords
Poetry, Japanese, Core Issues (Feelings)

Age Range.
All ages

Author: Floyd Cooper

Author: Kazuko Stone

Floyd Cooper is the author of *Coming Home; Cool Melons Turn To Frogs* and more.

ISBN# 188000717 | Date Published. 1998 | Price. $ 16.95

Publisher. Lee & Low Books | Pages. 60

COOL SALSA

Rating

Bilingual poems on growing up Latino in the United States.

Growing up Latino in the United States sometimes means speaking two languages and learning the rules of two cultures. These poems celebrate the trials and triumphs that come with the experience. Contains selections by Sandra Cisneros, Martin Espada, Gary Soto and Ed Vega. Bilingual in Spanish and English.

Keywords

Bilingual, Latino/a, Racial/Ethnic Identity, Poetry, Multicultural

Age Range:

All ages

Editor: Lori Carlson

ISBN# 044070436X   Date Published: 1995   Price: $ 4.50

Publisher: Mass Market Paperback   Pages: 118

DID YOU HEAR WIND SING YOUR NAME?

Rating

An Oneida Song of Spring

This book invites the reader to join the Oneida Indians of New York and Wisconsin as they give thanks for each small sign of Spring — tasting the first strawberries, smelling the sacred cedar, feeling the warmth of the sun and hearing the wind singing your name. It is a pleasure to partake of this jewel of a celebration. Vibrant illustrations.

Keywords

Native American, Spiritual Meanings, Cultural History, Festivals

Age Range:

All ages

Author: Sandra De Coteau Orie

Author: Christopher Canyon

ISBN# 802774587   Date Published: 1996   Price: $ 6.95

Publisher: Walker & Co.   Pages: 32

ENCYCLOPEDIA OF AFRICAN-AMERICAN HERITAGE

Covers contributions of Africans from all sectors.

An easy-to-use compilation of the rich cultural heritage of African Americans illustrated by over 100 photographs. This book, which offers a history not often covered in school curriculums, belongs in the home library of any family raising American children.

Keywords

African American, Cultural History, Self-Esteem, Role Models, Educational Issues, Black Identity

Age Range:

All ages

Author: Susan Altman

Susan Altman is the author of *Extraordinary Black Americans* and *Followers of the North Star.*

ISBN# 816038244   Date Published: 1998   Price: $ 18.95

Publisher: Facts on File   Pages:

EYES THAT SEE DO NOT GROW OLD

Proverbs of Mexico, Central and South America

Zona presents the reflections on life, the sage advice, and the eye-opening observations expressed in common Latino sayings and proverbs from Mexico, Central America, and South America. While highlighting the values and traditions of individual cultures, these wise sayings also remind readers of the universality of human behavior and beliefs, fears and hopes. Children of Latino heritage should have this wisdom in their home libraries.

Keywords

Mexico, Latino/a, South America, Central America, Poetry, Proverbs

Age Range:

All ages

Editor: Guy A. Zona

ISBN# 684800187   Date Published: 1996   Price: $ 9.00

Publisher: Touchstone   Pages:

Rating

FESTIVALS TOGETHER

Join in the multicultural celebrations! Learn the meanings and experience the fun of age-old traditions.

"Through festivals, music and stories, we discover the universal and the unique." One of the best resources we've seen for multicultural celebrations, filled with tales, recipes, music, and craft projects for sharing throughout the seasons. A great reference for families who value diversity.

Keywords

Festivals, Holidays and Celebrations, Multicultural, Diversity

Age Range:

All ages

Author: Diana Carey

Author: Judy Large

Illustrators: Cornelie Morris / Sylvia Mehta

ISBN# 1869890469 *Date Published:* *Price:* $ 19.95
Publisher: Gryhs *Pages:*

Rating

FOR EVERY SEASON

A complete guide to African American celebrations, traditional to contemporary.

Eklof reviews the ceremonies of ancient Africa and America that surround four major passages of the human experience: naming ceremonies, holidays, weddings and family reunions. African-inspired traditions are a growing part of Black culture and are especially interesting to young people trying to build the culture into their daily lives.

Keywords

African American, Cultural History, Games and Activities, Festivals, Holidays and Celebrations, Black Identity

Age Range:

All ages

Author: Barbara J. Eklof

ISBN# " *Date Published:* 1997 *Price:* $ 25.00
Publisher: HarperCollins *Pages:*

GIVING THANKS

A traditional Iroquois celebration of the beauty and spirit of Mother Earth.

This is Chief Swamp's adaptation for children of the Mohawk Thanksgiving address, which acknowledges and thanks all aspects of creation. This story projects positive images children will identify with. Native American children will see that this book is specific to them, and all children will be able to appreciate the self-affirming values of the culture. "The Thanksgiving Address...possesses the haunting internal repetition and rhythm that mark many of the world's most affecting prayers," says Horn Book Magazine.

Keywords

Native American, Spiritual Meanings, Family Life, Holidays and Celebrations

Age Range:

All ages

Author: Jake Swamp

ISBN# 1880000547 *Date Published:* 1997 *Price:* $ 5.95
Publisher: Lee & Low Books *Pages:* 24

GO DOWN MOSES

A celebration of the African American spiritual.

An illustrated celebration of the African American spiritual — a tradition born in slavery that gave rise to some of the most powerful poetry ever composed in America — *Go Down Moses* includes the lyrics to 200 songs, along with the music to 25 of the most popular ones. Preface by Cornel West. A very attractive book that belongs in the home library of all Americans.

Keywords

African American, Music and Dance, Racial/Ethnic Identity, Self-Esteem, Black Identity

Age Range:

All ages

Author: Richard Newman

ISBN# 609600311 *Date Published:* 98 *Price:* $ 30.00
Publisher: Clarkson Potter *Pages:* 224

Rating

HOW IT FEELS TO BE ADOPTED

How does it feel to be adopted? Read this book for ideas from the experts.

This classic is still the best book we've found on a child's view of how it feels to be adopted. 19 kids from diverse backgrounds confide their feelings. Required reading for Pact parents.

Keywords

Adoption, Core Issues (Feelings), Required for Pact Families

Age Range:

All ages

Author-Photographer: Jill Krementz

ISBN# 394758536 *Date Published:* *Price:* $ 15.00

Publisher: Knopf *Pages:* 128

Rating

I HAVE A DREAM

A great book for every family!

On August 28, 1963, Dr. King delivered a speech that moved and inspired America. This beautiful, collectible book is the perfect way to remind everyone — young and old — that the dream must be kept alive. Full color. Illustrated by 15 illustrators who have received the Coretta Scott King Award and the Honor Book award for illustration, including Leo and Diane Dillon, Jerry Pinckney, and Floyd Cooper.

Keywords

African American, Biography, Role Models, Self-Esteem, Black Identity, Cultural History

Age Range:

All ages

Author: Martin Luther King, Jr.

ISBN# 590205161 *Date Published:* *Price:* $ 16.95

Publisher: Scholastic *Pages:* 40

IN THE BEGINNING

Creation stories from around the world.

Selected from the vast treasure of myths from around the world, these 25 narratives, each based on the theme of origin, reflect the diverse cultures which created them while sharing a feeling for the wonder and glory of the universe. 42 full-color illustrations. Newbery Honor Book.

Keywords

Multiracial, Multicultural, Folk tales and Legends, Spiritual Meanings, Diversity

Age Range:

All ages

Author: Virginia Hamilton

ISBN# 152387420 *Date Published:* 1988 *Price:* $ 15.00

Publisher: Harcourt Brace *Pages:* 161

JUMP UP AND SAY

A collection of Black storytelling.

A collection of irresistible stories celebrating the African American storytelling tradition: folk tales, funny stories, family stories, scary stories, everyday life stories and recipes. Includes tales rich in humor, along with raps and rhymes, memoirs and commentaries, and songs, stories and poems about freedom and protest. The stories project positive images children will identify with. African American children will see that this book is specific to them, and all children will be able to appreciate the affirming values of the culture.

Keywords

African American, Folk tales and Legends, Family Life, Poetry, Black Identity, Cultural History

Age Range:

All ages

Author: Linda Goss

Author: Clay Goss

Linda Goss is the author of *The Frog Who Wanted To Be A Star* and *Jump Up and Say.*

ISBN# 684810018 *Date Published:* 1995 *Price:* $ 13.00

Publisher: Simon & Schuster *Pages:*

Rating

LIFE DOESN'T FRIGHTEN ME

A powerful poem and haunting paintings tackle one of life's great challenges: addressing fear.

Basquiat died a troubled young man, but his art remains, powerful and compelling and offering an opportunity for one of Maya Angelou's most direct and unadorned poems: "Shadows on the wall/Noises down the hall/Life doesn't frighten me at all." This is not a sugarcoated book about the success of conquering fear; rather, it's a somewhat sober if moving demonstration of the constancy of the challenge, of the sometimes unrelenting and implacable aspects of life's terrors. Basquiat's paintings are not reassuring — nor were they meant to be — so this is perhaps a book best-suited for careful selection and lots of conversation.

Keywords

African American, Core Issues (Feelings), Poetry, Black Identity

Age Range:

All ages

Author: Maya Angelou

Illustrator: Jean-Michel Basquiat

Maya Angelou is a world-famous author. Her works include *Kofi and His Magic; My Painted House, My Friendly Chicken and Me;* and *Life Doesn't Frighten Me.*

ISBN# 1-55670-288-4 Date Published: 1993 Price: $ 18.95

Publisher: Stewart, Tabori and Chang Pages: 32

Rating

LOVE YOU FOREVER

This superbly touching book is an affirmation of unconditional love.

Love You Forever is a gem of a book that most parents cannot read aloud without tears springing into their eyes. Tracing the circle of love from young mother with infant son to grown man with aged mother, this is a story about the enduring quality of family love that adults and children will enjoy over and over and over. Among the best, and a Pact bestseller.

Keywords

Family Life, Core Issues (Feelings), Intergenerational

Age Range:

All ages

Author: Robert Munsch

ISBN# 0-920668-37-2 Date Published: Price: $ 4.95

Publisher: Firefly Pages:

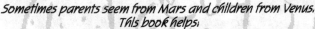

MA, YOU'RE DRIVING ME CRAZY

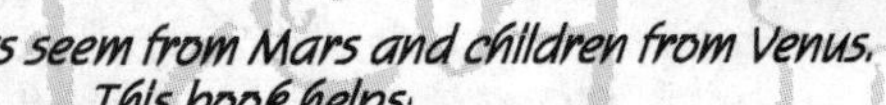

Sometimes parents seem from Mars and children from Venus. This book helps!

We can't keep this book in stock, the demand is so great. A very funny, poignant, cartoon-like picture-book format (more for adults than kids) about the things moms do that drive kids crazy. Everybody loves this book.

Keywords

Parenting, Family Life, Mothers

Age Range:

All ages

Author: Toni Goffe

ISBN# 0-85953-401-4 Date Published: Price: $ 6.99

Publisher: child's play Pages:

MARTIN LUTHER KING

A biography of Dr. Martin Luther King illustrated by powerful folk art paintings.

Powerful paintings and an accessible, fact-filled text add up to a vivid portrait of Martin Luther King, Jr., and his courageous fight for human rights. Here is a biography that is inspiring both to read and to look at. This story projects a clear and positive perspective for young people in general and a role model that African American children will identity with and others will find most interesting. King is portrayed as a well-rounded character willing to make every sacrifice to help the community.

Keywords

Biography, African American, Role Models, Black Identity, Skill Mastery, Self-Esteem

Age Range:

All ages

Author: Rosemary Bray

ISBN# 0-688-152198 Date Published: 1995 Price: $ 5.95

Publisher: Greenwillow Pages: 48

MISSING PIECE, THE

Rating

A circle has difficulty finding its missing piece, but has fun looking for it.

What the circle finds on its search for the missing piece is told in a fable that gently probes the nature of quest and fulfillment. "Few artists have put so much verve and meaning into simple lines and circles as Shel Silverstein," praises Publishers Weekly. Like a person searching for his soul mate, the Circle is happy in life but feels incomplete, longing for the day when it will finally find what it has been missing. Whatever it takes, the Circle doesn't give up. It rolls along, talking to a worm, or smelling a flower, and singing its song. Though humans may not have a good fit with everyone we meet, if we just roll along...

Keywords

Family Life, Core Issues (Feelings)

Age Range:

All ages

Author-Illustrator: Shel Silverstein

ISBN# 60256710 Date Published: 1976 Price: $ 14.95

Publisher: HarperCollins Pages: 105

NEIGHBORHOOD ODES

Rating

Twenty-one poems from Gary Soto about growing up as a Latino.

A snow cone, a first dog, a neighbor's forbidden pomegranate tree, and a sprinkler on a hot summer's day — these poems about life in a Latino neighborhood will strike a chord in everyone as Soto celebrates the moments that define childhood.

Keywords

Core Issues (Feelings), Latino/a, Poetry, Family Life

Age Range:

All ages

Author: Gary Soto

Gary Soto is an acclaimed poet and fiction writer. He is the author of *Living Up The Street; Jesse; Nerdlandia, Chato's Kitchen* and *Baseball in April.*

ISBN# 590473352 Date Published: 1994 Price: $ 3.99

Publisher: Mass Market Paperback Pages:

OF MANY COLORS

Illuminating photographs and interviews documenting the joys and challenges of life in a multiracial family.

In this moving and intimate look at multiracial family life, the compelling photograph of each family is accompanied by the revealing text culled from interviews with the family members — children as well as adults — who describe in their own voices and words some of the joys and challenges of life in a multiracial family. Because the text reflects conversations with the children as well as the adults involved, this book offers the valuable reminder that different members of the same family may have differing points of view about life in a multicultural family. The families include transracial, interracial, same-race blended, adoptive, single-parent, and two-parent families, both heterosexual and homosexual.

Keywords

Multiracial, Multicultural, Transracial Adoption, International Adoption, Family Life, Gay and/or Lesbian

Age Range:

All ages

Author: Peggy R. Gillespie

Illustrator: Gigi Kaeser

ISBN# 1558491015 Date Published: 1997 Price: $ 19.95

Publisher: University of Massachusetts Press Pages: 146

ONE MORE RIVER TO CROSS

African Americans whose defiant rejection of inequality and subjugation put their own lives at risk.

One More River to Cross is essentially a photographic history of Black America. Walter Dean Myers, a celebrated writer of young adult books, writes that he wanted to show Black Americans in ways that often go unrepresented. There are photographs of former slaves, Black soldiers in the Civil War, Black cowboys, baseball players, sailors, aviators, farmers, field hands, and just plain folks. Myers' text is minimal, leaving the emphasis on the photographs; sometimes haunting, sometimes inspiring, they always moving. Black Studies Editors' Recommended Book, Winner of the Golden Kite Award from the Society of Children's Book Writers and Illustrators.

Keywords

African American, US History, Self-Esteem, Race Relations, Black Identity, Racism

Age Range:

All ages

Author: Walter Dean Myers

Walter Dean Myers is the author of *One More River To Cross; Brown Angels; Me, Mop,* and *The Moondance Kid s, Slam, Malcolm X, Hoops,* and many more.

ISBN# 015100191X Date Published: 1995 Price: $ 40.00

Publisher: Harcourt Brace Pages:

Rating

OUR ONE BIG FAMILY COOKBOOK

Celebrating diversity, great food, and learning to cook.

Features 400 recipe greats from families touched by adoption, to enable very young children to cook foods of their heritage as independently as possible.

Keywords

Family Life, Diversity, Skill Mastery, Cultural History, Food

Age Range.

All ages

Editor: Pact Staff

ISBN# NA | Date Published. 1995 | Price. $ 10.00
Publisher. Pact Press | Pages.

Rating

PALM OF MY HEART, THE

Little-heard and often overlooked poetry by African American children.

These twenty terrific poems, created in Adedjouma's "Writing Between the Lines" workshops for inner-city children, stay with you like haiku, with the power to wake you up. George Christie won the Coretta Scott King Illustrator Honor Award for this book, which uses elongated proud strong human figures with long necks standing in front of blocks of color. Exciting!

Keywords

Poetry, African American, Core Issues (Feelings)

Age Range.

All ages

Author: Davida Adedjouma

Author: George Christie

ISBN# 1880000768 | Date Published. 1996 | Price. $ 6.95
Publisher. Lee & Low Books | Pages. 32

PASS IT ON

African American poems for kids.

An inspiring collection of African American poetry for children. Works have been selected to capture the experiences of African American children, from the joy of eating chocolate to the pain of becoming the target of someone's hatred.

Keywords

Poetry, Core Issues (Feelings), African American, Racial/Ethnic Identity, Race Relations, Black Identity

Age Range.

All ages

Author: Wade Hudson

ISBN# 0-590-45770-5 | Date Published. | Price. $ 14.95
Publisher. Scholastic | Pages.

PEOPLE

Nobody should be without this book.

In a humorous, ingenious way, Spier takes us around the world, exploring the idea that each of us is unique together. Illustrations are sure to evoke curiosity and discussion. Look at Noses: small noses, round noses, flat noses, immense noses, pointy noses, etc.

Keywords

Diversity, Race Relations, Racial/Ethnic Identity, Self-Esteem, Multicultural

Age Range.

All ages

Author: Peter Spier

ISBN# 0-385-24469-X | Date Published. | Price. $ 10.95
Publisher. Zephyr | Pages.

Rating

PETE'S A PIZZA

Pete's parents cheer him up by pretending he's a pizza – and it works!

Pete's in a bad mood; Dad makes a pizza out of him. The recipe: knead him, stretch him, twirl him in the air. Add oil (water), flour (talcum powder), tomatoes (checkers!), and cheese (paper). The expressions on the characters' faces are terrific. What a treat to see such playful, loving parents. A fast-paced, easy read filled with terrific visual images and humor from the play on words of the title to the end. A great reminder that bad moods don't last forever. Kirkus Reviews says, "What leaps from the page is warmth and imagination wrapped in an act of kindness and tuned-in parenting." Read it!

Keywords

Family Life, Core Issues (Feelings), Parenting

Age Range:

All ages

Author-Illustrator: William Steig

William Steig has written and illustrated 27 books for children, including *Sylvester and the Magic Pebble; Pete's A Pizza;* and *Pebble and Toby, Where Are You?*

ISBN# 62051571 Date Published: 1999 Price: $ 13.95
Publisher: HarperCollins Pages: 32

Rating

PLAITED GLORY

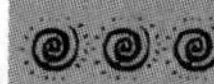

For colored girls who've considered braids, locks, and twists.

From the uptown micro braid to the simple cornrow, braids, locks and twists have come into their own. Learn the basics of maintaining locks, twists and braids while you get the lowdown on everything from choosing braiding salons to tips for parents with style-hungry daughters. Learn how to care for your braided natural, textured, or chemically-relaxed hair.

Keywords

Hair, African American, Black Identity, Skill Mastery

Age Range:

All ages

Author: Lonice Bonner

Lonice Bonner is the author of *Plaited Glory* and *Good Hair.*

ISBN# 517884984 Date Published: 1996 Price: $ 12.00
Publisher: Crown Pages:

POEMS BY LANGSTON HUGHES

With a distinctive voice, this twentieth-century African American poet presents powerful, inspiring images.

Poems that touch your heart from a great poet. Don't hesitate.

Keywords

African American, Poetry, Black Identity, Cultural History

Age Range:

All ages

Author: Langston Hughes

ISBN# 0-679-84421-X Date Published: 1994 Price: $ 12.00
Publisher: Knopf Pages: 83

SERPENT'S TONGUE, THE

Prose, poetry, and art of more than 500 years of Pueblo culture.

Sampling the work of important Native American artists and writers: Simon J. Ortiz, N. Scott Momaday, Leslie Marmon Silko, Paula Gunn Allen, Helen Hardin, and Pablita Velarde. An authentic introduction to the cultural legacy of the ancient peoples of the Southwest.

Keywords

Native American, History, Poetry, Fiction

Age Range:

All ages

Editor: Nancy Wood

ISBN# 525455140 Date Published: 1997 Price: $ 35.00
Publisher: Dutton Pages: 256

Rating

SHAKE IT TO THE ONE YOU LOVE THE BEST

A must-have collection for every music lover – young and old!

These play songs and lullabies from Black musical traditions, performed by top artists including Taj Mahal, make you wanna dance. Piano music, guitar chords and great illustrations.

Keywords

African American, Cultural History, Music and Dance, Cassette, Black Identity

Age Range:

All ages

Author: Cheryl Warren Mattox

Illustrator: Brenda Joysmith

Illustrator: Varnette P. Honeywood

Cheryl Warren Mattox is the editor of *Let's Get the Rhythm of the Band* and *Shake it to the One You Love The Best.*

ISBN# 0-9623381-0-9 Date Published: 1990 Price: $ 6.95
Publisher: Warren-Mattox Pages:

Rating

STORY OF LITTLE BABAJI, THE

A culturally-sensitive retelling of the story originally written in 1899 as "Little Black Sambo."

"Little Black Sambo," though a familiar tale in popular culture, has fallen out of favor due to its offensive racial and cultural depictions. But as Marcellino mentions in a quiet endnote, when Bannerman wrote the story it was free of caricature; she had lived in India for thirty years and the story is clearly Indian in its original setting. In this new version, Marcellino has salvaged the pleasures of the tale of a small boy outsmarting a vain tiger (and generating pancakes in the process); the human characters have been given authentic Indian names and are portrayed with warmth and appreciation in the lovely illustrations. With its small size and beautiful format, this is a lovely gift book.

Keywords

India, Folk tales and Legends

Age Range:

All ages

Author: Helen Bannerman

Illustrator-Adapter: Fred Marcellino

ISBN# 0-06-205064-8 Date Published: 1996 Price: $ 14.95
Publisher: HarperCollins Pages:

STRAIGHT TO THE HEART

Photos of kids being kids around the world will make you feel glad.

A collection of photographs and short descriptions of spirited children from many different cultures.

Keywords

Multicultural, Diversity, Multiracial

Age Range:

All ages

Author: Ethan Hubbard

ISBN# 0-9694992-1-0 Date Published: 1992 Price: $ 10.95
Publisher: Craftsbury Pages: 60

TALKING WALLS

A great look at uses and abuses of walls as means of cultural expression.

Talking Walls introduces young readers to different cultures by exploring the stories of walls around the world and examining how they can separate communities or hold them together. The stories feature walls such as the Western Wall, the wall murals of Diego Rivera, the Great Wall of China, the Berlin Wall and more. Gorgeous illustrations!! An American Bookseller's "Pick of the Lists." Also available is a teacher's activity guide (grades 3-8): $9.95

Keywords

Multicultural, Race Relations, Diversity, Educational Issues

Age Range:

All ages

Author: Margy Burns Knight

Illustrator: Anne Sibley O'Brien

Margy Burns Knight also wrote *Welcoming Babies* and *Talking Walls*, illustrated by Anne Sibley O'Brien.

ISBN# 0-88448-154-9 Date Published: 1995 Price: $ 8.95
Publisher: Tilbury Pages: 40

Rating

THERE IS A RAINBOW BEHIND EVERY DARK CLOUD

A book written by children facing terminal illnesses.

Incredibly popular multicultural book about overcoming fear, written and drawn by eleven children, each facing life-threatening illnesses, and edited by Gerald G. Jampolsky, MD, of the Center for Attitudinal Healing in Tiburon, CA, an author loved by millions of people. Covers "What we experienced" and "Choices you have in helping yourself."

Keywords

Grief and Loss, Core Issues (Feelings), Self-Esteem, Health

Age Range:

All ages

Editor: Gerald G. Jampolsky, M.D.

ISBN# 0-89087-253-8-Q *Date Published:* 1978 *Price:* $ 8.95

Publisher: Celestial Arts *Pages:* 96

Rating

TO EVERY THING THERE IS A SEASON

Leo and Diane Dillon's beautiful rendition of the Book of Ecclesiastes.

"In this elegant picture book, the timeless beauty and truth of the passages from the Book of Ecclesiastes are matched with illustrations that represent the artistic styles of cultures from all over the globe in many periods of history. Thumbnail reproductions of the glorious two-page spreads are included at the end of the book with notes on the artistic traditions represented, as well as brief interpretations of the lines quoted in those scenes. The universality of the scriptural reference and of the ongoing need for humans to express themselves in art and poetry is documented in this work that may entice children to explore the various traditions more deeply." — Book Links

Keywords

Spiritual Meanings, Religion, Multicultural

Age Range:

All ages

Illustrator: Leo Dillon

Illustrator: Diane Dillon

ISBN# 590478877 *Date Published:* 1999 *Price:* $ 15.95

Publisher: Scholastic *Pages:* 40

TOBY, WHERE ARE YOU?

"A note of caution: be prepared to play real hide-and-seek whenever you read this story."

Toby loves hiding from his parents — upstairs, downstairs, just about anywhere. But when Toby begins to think that his parents will never find him, he just can't stand it. "Here I am!" he cries. Another simple book about how it feels to be separated from one's parents, if only for a short time — a topic of considerable interest for most children who have been adopted or are in foster care. Kirkus Reviews says, "It's a charmer."

Keywords

Family Life, Games and Activities

Age Range:

All ages

Author: William Steig

Illustrator: Teryl Euvremer

William Steig has written and illustrated 27 books for children, including *Sylvester and the Magic Pebble; Pete's A Pizza;* and *Pebble and Toby, Where Are You?*

ISBN# 62059297 *Date Published:* 1999 *Price:* $ 4.95

Publisher: HarperCollins *Pages:* 32

VELVETEEN RABBIT

The original version of an enduring favorite gently depicts the power of real love.

Becoming "real" to one another through the power of connection is what adoption is all about. This classic story is perfect for any adoptive family and has stood the test of time.

Keywords

Core Issues (Feelings), Family Life, Self-Esteem

Age Range:

Adult

Author: Margery Williams

ISBN# 0-385-07725-4 *Date Published:* 1958 *Price:* $ 2.99

Publisher: Doubleday *Pages:* 44

Rating

VOICES OF THE HEART

Ed Young does it again. Don't miss this beautiful book.

An exploration of twenty-six Chinese characters describing emotions, each of which includes the symbol for the heart in its representation. A feast for the eyes as well as the heart, this is a children's book not just for children and will make a wonderful wedding, Valentine's Day, Mother's Day, Father's Day, or birthday gift.

Keywords

Asian American, Asian, Chinese American, Language, Cultural History, Racial/Ethnic Identity

Age Range.

All ages

Author: Ed Young

Ed Young is the author/illustrator of *Chinese Mother Goose Rhymes; Lon po po; Mouse Match;* and *Voices of the Heart.*

ISBN# 590501992 Date Published. 1997 Price. $ 17.95
Publisher. Scholastic Pages. 32

Rating

WE ARE ALL RELATED

Art and text by First Nations students.

We Are All Related was created by 28 experts/teachers, aged 8-12, who created collages using photos of their elders and themselves along with a variety of cultural symbols to explore and express ideas about their own history, values and heritage. The results are imaginative, creative, and touching. We hope this book inspires all readers to create their own family heritage collage.

Keywords

Native American, Multicultural, Multiracial, Cultural History, Family Life

Age Range.

All ages

Author: George T Cunningham

ISBN# 968047904 Date Published. 1996 Price. $ 18.00
Publisher. Polester Books Pages. 60

WHAT A WONDERFUL WORLD

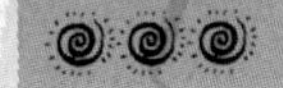

Bright, light-filled drawings jump off the page and warm you up. A feel good book.

Ashley Bryan has taken the words of this familiar and much-loved song, inspired by the genius of Louis Armstrong, and created a picture book that represents all races and demonstrates the wonderful beauty of diversity in the world.

Keywords

African American, Music and Dance, Multicultural, Self-Esteem, Black Identity, Role Models

Age Range.

All ages

Author: George David Weiss

Author: Bryan Thiele

Illustrator: Ashley Bryan

Ashley Bryan is an award winning author and illustrator. He lives in Maine.

ISBN# 1568013698 Date Published. 1997 Price. $ 7.95
Publisher. Athenaeum Pages. 32

WISDOM OF THE ELDERS, THE

Wise thoughts from African Americans.

Robert Fleming has collected more than 150 life-affirming quotations from African American luminaries including Sojourner Truth, W.E.B. DuBois, Martin Luther King, Jr., Elijah Muhammad, Lorraine Hansberry, Thurgood Marshall, Zora Neale Hurston, Adam Clayton Powell, Jr., Barbara Jordan, Paul Robeson and more. An attractive and inspiring volume.

Keywords

African American, Core Issues (Feelings), Proverbs, Race Relations, Black Identity, Spiritual Meanings

Age Range.

All ages

Editor: Robert Fleming

ISBN# 345409752 Date Published. 1997 Price. $ 11.00
Publisher. Ballantine Pages. 368

A

B

C

D

E

F

G

H

I

J

K

L

M

N

O

P

Q

R

S

T

UV

W

XYZ

Pact An Adoption Alliance

About Pact

What is Pact?

Pact, An Adoption Alliance, provides the highest quality adoption services to children of color. Our primary client is the child. To serve the child, we address the needs of all the child's parents, by advising families facing a crisis pregnancy and by offering lifelong education to adoptive and birth families on matters of race and adoption. Our goal is for every child to feel wanted, honored and loved, a cherished member of a strong family with proud connections to the rich cultural heritage that is his or her birthright. Pact was incorporated in 1991 as a non-profit 501(c)(3) charitable organization.

ADOPTION SERVICES

Pact helps find permanent adoptive families for African American, Latino, Asian and multiracial children born in the US whose birth families are seeking to make adoption plans. We believe every child deserves to grow up in a permanent, nurturing home. We work with families from all over the country, and we are always seeking potential adoptive families, whether same-race adoptive parents or potential transracial adoptive parents who are willing to make special strides to help provide their children with positive racial identity.

PACT PROGRAMS FOR CHILDREN AND FAMILIES OF COLOR

Pact is the nation's largest national organization serving adoptive parents, birth parents, adopted people, foster parents, adoption professionals and friends devoted to better understanding of and support for adopted children of color. The following programs are currently available: Pact's Website (http://www.pactadopt.org), the largest website in the nation addressing issues for adopted children of color, offering articles, profiles of triad members and families, links to Internet resources and opportunities to ask questions about adoption; Pact's Multiracial Resource Guide, a yellow-pages-format guide to professionals in all walks of life who have been referred because they offer culturally competent and adoption-sensitive services to families of color; and Pact Press, a quarterly magazine addressing issues of race and adoption. Recently, we have decided to upgrade Pact Press and change the format; the process is taking some time but the result should be well worth it, and you can expect a lively, honest magazine focusing on the issues of children of color touched by adoption. We expect to see publication in its new form early in the year 2000, and to compensate for the issues that went unpublished during the magazine's hiatus, we have extended all memberships for an additional year of Pact Press.

As a result of increased federal interest in transracial adoption, Pact was the only organization in the United States to have been awarded a Federal Grant in 1998 to support transracial adoptive families. Over the next three years, we will launch 13 new programs, each one designed to help build or strengthen connections between transracial adoptive families and people who share the racial heritage of the children in these families. And at the same time that we strive to provide exemplary services for children in transracial adoptive families, we retain a primary commitment to provide support and education for same-race adoptive families; we believe all Pact families will benefit from these new programs. In 1999, we were awarded an additional Federal Grant to support research to determine the predictable developmental milestones of adopted children of color. We look forward to providing new information for all who are concerned about the issues of race and adoption.

Current programs include Good Times, a series of multicultural child-focused entertainment events; My Friend, a program linking transracially-adopted kids to same-race mentors; Hand in Hand, a cross-cultural program to build enduring friendships through family-to-family social interaction programs; Multicultural Mini-Grants we award to groups to strengthen their services to transracial adoptive families; and TAPS 800 (Transracial Adoptive Parent Support), a toll-free telephone line to provide referrals and support, at 1-888 488-8277.

Additional programs to be launched in the years 2000 and 2001 are now under development: Multicultural reading groups focused on racial issues; Camp Just Like Us, a multiracial day camp to strengthen cultural identity; Virtual Village, Internet access to experts, peers and mentors; Moving a Mountain, projects which interrupt racism; and Interracial Families, Interwoven Cultures Conference, a national conference for transracial adoptive families.